D1154258

PRINCIPLES OF POLYMERIZATION

PRINCIPLES OF POLYMERIZATION

GEORGE ODIAN
Associate Professor of Chemistry
Richmond College
The City University of New York
Staten Island, New York

McGRAW-HILL BOOK COMPANY New York St. Louis
San Francisco London Sydney Toronto Mexico Panama

PRINCIPLES OF POLYMERIZATION

 Library of Congress Catalog Card Number 78-78958

47585

1234567890 MAMM 7543210

PREFACE

This book is concerned with the physical and organic chemistry of the reactions by which polymer molecules are synthesized. The sequence I have followed is to introduce the reader to the characteristics which distinguish polymers from their much smaller-sized homologs (Chap. 1) and then to proceed to a detailed consideration of the three types of polymerization reactions–step, chain, and ring-opening polymerizations (Chaps. 2–5, 7). Polymerization reactions are characterized as to their kinetic and thermodynamic features, their scope and utility for the synthesis of different types of polymer structures, and the process conditions which can be used to carry them out. To a large extent, polymer chemistry has advanced to the point where it is essentially possible to tailor-make a variety of different types of polymers with specified molecular weights and structures. Emphasis is placed throughout the text on understanding the reaction parameters which are important in controlling polymerization rates, polymer molecular weight, and structural features such as branching and cross-linking. It has been my intention to give the reader an appreciation of the versatility which is inherent in polymerization processes and which is available to the synthetic polymer chemist.

The versatility of polymerization resides not only in the different types of reactants which can be polymerized but also in the variations allowed by copolymerization and stereospecific polymerization. Chain copolymerization is the most important kind of copolymerization process and is considered separately in Chap. 6. Other copolymerizations are discussed in the appropriate chapters. Chapter 8 describes the stereochemistry of polymerization with emphasis on the synthesis of polymers with stereoregular structures by the appropriate choice of polymerization conditions. In the last chapter, there is a brief discussion of the reactions of polymers which are useful for modifying or synthesizing new polymer structures. The literature has been relatively thoroughly covered through 1968; a less thorough coverage of most subjects has been made up to approximately June, 1969.

The study of polymers has been largely ignored in our colleges and universities—both at the undergraduate and graduate levels—in spite of the fact that polymer chemistry is the largest single field in chemistry. Thus, approximately 30 percent of all chemists and over 50 percent of graduate chemists in the United States are engaged directly in the polymer field.* Most workers entering the field have only a fragmentary educational background in polymer chemistry and are forced to educate themselves in its basic principles. It is hoped that this book will be useful to those chemists as a self-educating introductory text. Additionally, it is intended that the book will serve as a classroom text for the first half of a one-year course in polymer chemistry. This book is an outgrowth of polymer courses taught by the author at Columbia University. With the appropriate addition or deletion of some materials, it could be used at either the graduate or advanced undergraduate levels. Each chapter contains a selection of problems which should be of use in guiding the study of the student. (A solutions manual for the problems is available directly from the author.)

I would like to take this opportunity to thank the many publishers who cooperated by allowing the generous use of various data and illustrations from their publications. I am also thankful to my publisher and editor for their cooperation and guidance throughout the course of these writings.

This book is dedicated to my wife, parents, and family. I am grateful to my wife Beverly for her great patience, understanding, and moral support. I am grateful to my parents without whose hard work and encouragement I would never have reached the point of being able to undertake the writing of this book.

George Odian

Staten Island,
New York 10301

*"Polymer Chemistry in the Undergraduate Curriculum," Symposium in *J. Chem. Educ.*, **45**(8):498 (1968).

CONTENTS

Preface v

1 INTRODUCTION 1

1-1 Types of Polymers and Polymerizations 1
1-1a Polymer Composition and Structure 2
1-1b Polymerization Mechanism. 9
1-2 Nomenclature of Polymers. 12
1-2a Nomenclature Based on Source 12
1-2b Nomenclature Based on Structure 14
1-2c Trade and Non-Names 15
1-3 Structural Shape of Polymer Molecules 16
1-4 Molecular Weight 19
1-5 Physical State 24
1-5a Crystalline and Amorphous Behavior 24
1-5b Determinant of Polymer Crystallinity 26
1-5c Thermal Transitions 28
1-6 Applications of Polymers 33
1-6a Mechanical Properties 33
1-6b Elastomers, Fibers, Plastics 36

2 STEP POLYMERIZATION 40

2-1 Reactivity of Functional Groups 41
2-1a Basis for Analysis of Polymerization Kinetics. . . 41
2-1b Experimental Evidence 43
2-1c Theoretical Considerations. 45
2-1d Equivalence of Groups in Bifunctional Reactants . 46
2-2 Kinetics of Step Polymerization 47
2-2a Self-Catalyzed Polymerization 49
2-2a-1 Experimental Observations 50
2-2a-2 Reasons for Nonlinearity in Third Order Plots . 53
2-2a-3 Molecular Weight of Polymer 56
2-2b External Catalysis of Polymerization 57
2-2c Step Polymerizations Other Than Polyesterification 60
2-2d Non-Equivalence of Functional Groups in Polyfunctional Reagents 60
2-3 Cyclization versus Linear Polymerization 63
2-3a Possible Cyclization Reactions 63
2-3b Thermodynamic and Kinetic Considerations . . . 64
2-3c Other Considerations 68
2-4 Molecular Weight Control in Linear Polymerization . . . 69
2-4a Need for Stoichiometric Control 69
2-4b Quantitative Aspects. 71
2-5 Molecular Weight Distribution in Linear Polymerization . . 75
2-5a Derivation of Size Distribution 76
2-5b Breadth of Molecular Weight Distribution 78
2-5c Interchange Reactions 80
2-5d Experimental Verification 80
2-6 Process Conditions 82
2-6a Physical Nature of Polymerization Systems . . . 82
2-6b Different Reactant Systems 83
2-6b-1 Polyesters 84
2-6b-2 Polyamides 88
2-6b-3 Polyurethanes 89
2-6b-4 Polysiloxanes 90
2-6c Interfacial Polymerization 91
2-6c-1 Description of Process 91
2-6c-2 Utility 93
2-7 Multi-Chain Polymerization 94
2-7a Branching 94
2-7b Molecular Weight Distribution 95
2-8 Crosslinking 96
2-8a Carothers Equation 99
2-8a-1 Equivalent Amounts of Reactants 99

2-8a-2 Extension to Non-Equivalent Reactant Mixtures 100
2-8b Statistical Approach to Gelation 102
2-8c Experimental Gel Points 105
2-9 Molecular Weight Distributions in Nonlinear Polymerizations 107
2-10 Crosslinking Technology 110
2-10a Random Prepolymers 112
2-10a-1 Polyesters 112
2-10a-2 Phenol-Formaldehyde Polymers 113
2-10a-3 Urea-Formaldehyde Polymers. 118
2-10b Structoset Prepolymers 119
2-10b-1 Diol Prepolymers 120
2-10b-2 Epoxy Prepolymers 121
2-10b-3 Unsaturated Polyesters 122
2-10b-4 Phenol-Formaldehyde Polymers 123
2-11 Step Copolymerization 124
2-11a Types of Copolymers 125
2-11b Methods of Synthesizing Copolymers 126
2-11c Utility of Copolymerization 129
2-12 Newer Types of Step Polymerizations 131
2-12a Presently Available Polymers 132
2-12a-1 Polycarbonates 132
2-12a-2 Polyamides 133
2-12a-3 Aromatic Polyethers 134
2-12a-4 Poly(*p*-xylylene) 137
2-12a-5 Aromatic Polyimides 139
2-12a-6 Polybenzimidazoles 141
2-12b Research Polymers 143
2-12b-1 Polyimidazopyrrolones 145
2-12b-2 Polybenzoxazoles and Polybenzothiazoles. . . 145
2-12b-3 Polyquinoxalines 146
2-12b-4 Polyoxadiazoles and Polytriazoles 146
2-12b-5 Polymerization via Diels-Alder Reaction . . . 147
2-12b-6 Polymerization by 1,3-Dipolar Addition . . . 147
2-12b-7 Spiro Structures 148
2-12b-8 Copolymers 149
2-12b-9 Inorganic and Semi-Inorganic Polymers . . . 149

3 RADICAL CHAIN POLYMERIZATION 161

3-1 Nature of Radical Chain Polymerization 162
3-1a Comparison of Chain and Step Polymerization . . 162

3-1b Radical versus Ionic Chain Polymerization . . . 163
3-1b-1 General Considerations of Polymerizability . . 163
3-1b-2 Effects of Substituents 164
3-2 Structural Arrangement of Monomer Units 167
3-2a Possible Modes of Propagation 167
3-2b Experimental Evidence 168
3-3 Overall Kinetics of Chain Polymerization 170
3-3a Sequence of Events 170
3-3b Rate Expression 172
3-4 Initiation 175
3-4a Thermal Decomposition of Initiators 175
3-4a-1 Types of Initiators 175
3-4a-2 Kinetics of Initiation and Polymerization . . . 177
3-4a-3 Dependence of Polymerization Rate on Initiator 178
3-4a-4 Dependence of Polymerization Rate on Monomer 179
3-4b Photochemical Initiation 181
3-4b-1 Pure Monomer. 181
3-4b-2 Photolytic Dissociation of Initiators. 184
3-4b-3 Photosensitizers 185
3-4b-4 General Observations 186
3-4c Initiation by Ionizing Radiations. 186
3-4d Pure Thermal Initiation 188
3-4e Redox Initiation 189
3-4f Initiator Efficiency 192
3-4f-1 Definition of f 192
3-4f-2 Mechanism of $f < 1$ 193
3-4f-3 Experimental Determination of f 196
3-5 Molecular Weight 201
3-5a Kinetic Chain Length 201
3-5b Mode of Termination 202
3-6 Chain Transfer. 203
3-6a Effect of Chain Transfer 203
3-6b Transfer to Monomer and Initiator 205
3-6b-1 Determination of C_M and C_I 205
3-6b-2 Monomer Transfer Constants 207
3-6b-3 Initiator Transfer Constants 210
3-6c Transfer to Chain Transfer Agent 211
3-6c-1 Determination of C_S. 211
3-6c-2 Structure and Reactivity 212
3-6c-3 Applications of Chain Transfer Agents 216
3-6d Chain Transfer to Polymer 217

3-7 Inhibition and Retardation 221
3-7a Types of Inhibitors and Retarders 221
3-7b Kinetics of Inhibition or Retardation 225
3-7c Autoinhibition of Allylic Monomers 230
3-8 Determination of Absolute Rate Constants 231
3-8a Non-Steady-State Kinetics 231
3-8b Rotating Sector Method 235
3-8c Typical Values of Reaction Parameters. 239
3-9 Energetic Characteristics 240
3-9a Activation Energy and Frequency Factor 240
3-9a-1 Rate of Polymerization 241
3-9a-2 Degree of Polymerization 244
3-9b Thermodynamics of Polymerization 245
3-9b-1 Significance of ΔG, ΔH and ΔS 245
3-9b-2 Effect of Monomer Structure 248
3-9b-3 Polymerization of 1,2-Disubstituted Ethylenes . 250
3-9c Polymerization-Depolymerization Equilibria; Ceiling Temperature 251
3-10 Autoacceleration 255
3-10a Course of Polymerization 255
3-10b Diffusion-Controlled Termination 257
3-10c Effects of Reaction Conditions 258
3-10d Dependence of Polymerization Rate on Initiator . 259
3-11 Molecular Weight Distribution 260
3-11a Low Conversion Polymerization 260
3-11b High Conversion Polymerization 263
3-12 Effect of Pressure. 264
3-12a Volume of Activation 265
3-12b Rate of Polymerization 266
3-12c Degree of Polymerization 266
3-13 Process Conditions 268
3-13a Bulk (Mass) Polymerization 268
3-13b Solution Polymerization 269
3-13c Suspension Polymerization 270
3-13d Solid-State Polymerization 270
3-14 Polymerization of Dienes 271

4 **EMULSION POLYMERIZATION** 279

4-1 Description of Process 279
4-1a Utility 279
4-1b Qualitative Picture 280
4-1b-1 Components and Their Locations 280

4-1b-2 Site and Progress of Polymerization 282
4-2 Kinetics 284
4-2a Rate of Polymerization 284
4-2b Degree of Polymerization 287
4-3 Number of Polymer Particles 289
4-4 Other Characteristics of Emulsion Polymerization 290
4-4a Initiation 290
4-4b Emulsifiers 291
4-4c Propagation and Termination 292
4-4d Energetics 292
4-4e Inverse Emulsion Systems 293
4-5 Deviations from Smith-Ewart Behavior 294
4-5a Value of $\bar{n}$ 294
4-5b Medvedev-Sheinker Theory 295
4-5c Effect of Water Solubility 296
4-5d Inhibition of Emulsifier 297
4-5e Molecular Weight Distribution 298

5 IONIC CHAIN POLYMERIZATION 301

5-1 Comparison of Radical and Ionic Polymerizations 302
5-2 Cationic Polymerization of Alkenes 303
5-2a Initiation 303
5-2a-1 Protonic Acids 303
5-2a-2 Lewis Acids 304
5-2a-3 Other Catalysts 306
5-2b Propagation 307
5-2c Termination 308
5-2c-1 Non-Termination of Kinetic Chain 308
5-2c-2 Termination of Kinetic Chain 309
5-2d Kinetics 312
5-2d-1 Different Kinetic Situations 312
5-2d-2 Validity of the Steady-State Assumption . . . 314
5-2e Absolute Rate Constants 315
5-2e-1 Experimental Methods 315
5-2e-2 Comparison of Cationic and Radical Polymerization Rates 316
5-2e-3 C_M and C_S Values 317
5-2f Effect of Reaction Media 319
5-2f-1 Solvent Effects 320
5-2f-2 Effect of Gegen-Ion 321
5-2f-3 Pseudocationic Polymerization 322
5-2g Energetics 323

5-3 Anionic Polymerization of Alkenes 325
5-3a Initiation by Metal Amides 327
5-3b Polymerization without Termination 329
5-3b-1 Initiation by Electron Transfer 330
5-3b-2 Initiation by Metal Alkyls 333
5-3b-3 Polymerization Rate 334
5-3b-4 Effects of Reaction Media 335
5-3b-5 Degree of Polymerization 338
5-3b-6 Association Phenomena 341
5-3b-7 Energetics 342
5-4 Distinguishing between Radical, Cationic, and Anionic Polymerizations 344
5-5 Carbonyl Polymerization 345
5-5a Anionic Polymerization 346
5-5a-1 Formaldehyde 347
5-5a-2 Other Carbonyl Monomers 348
5-5b Cationic Polymerization 349
5-5c Radical Polymerization 351
5-5d Step Polymerization 352
5-5e End-Capping 352
5-6 Miscellaneous Monomers 353
5-6a Monomers with Two Different Polymerizable Groups 353
5-6a-1 Dimethylketene 353
5-6a-2 Acrolein 354
5-6b Acrylamide 355
5-6c Isocyanates 356
5-6d Diazoalkanes 357
5-6e Triple Bonded Monomers 358

6 CHAIN COPOLYMERIZATION 363

6-1 General Considerations 364
6-1a Importance of Chain Polymerization 364
6-1b Types of Copolymers 365
6-2 Copolymer Composition 366
6-2a Copolymerization Equation; Monomer Reactivity Ratios 366
6-2b Range of Applicability of Copolymerization Equation 370
6-2c Types of Copolymerization Behavior 372
6-2c-1 Ideal Copolymerization: $r_1 r_2 = 1$ 372
6-2c-2 Alternating Copolymerization: $r_1 = r_2 = 0$ . . 374

6-2c-3 Block Copolymerization: $r_1 > 1$, $r_2 > 1$ . . 376
6-2d Variation of Copolymer Composition with Conversion 376
6-2e Experimental Evaluation of Monomer Reactivity Ratios 381
6-2f Microstructure of Copolymers 383
6-2g Multi-Component Copolymerization 385
6-3 Radical Copolymerization 390
6-3a Effect of Reaction Conditions 391
6-3b Reactivity 392
6-3b-1 Resonance Effects 395
6-3b-2 Steric Effects 400
6-3b-3 Alternation; Polar Effects 402
6-3b-4 *Q-e* Scheme. 405
6-3b-5 Product Probability Approach to Reactivity . . 409
6-3c Rate of Copolymerization 411
6-3c-1 Chemical-Controlled Termination 411
6-3c-2 Diffusion-Controlled Termination 415
6-4 Ionic Copolymerization 417
6-4a Cationic Copolymerization 418
6-4a-1 Monomer Reactivity 418
6-4a-2 Effect of Solvent and Gegen-Ion 420
6-4a-3 Effect of Temperature 422
6-4b Anionic Copolymerization 422
6-4b-1 Reactivity 422
6-4b-2 Effects of Solvent and Gegen-Ion 423
6-5 Deviations from Copolymer Composition Equation . . . 425
6-5a Kinetic Penultimate Effect. 425
6-5b Depropagation during Copolymerization 429
6-6 Copolymerizations of Dienes 432
6-6a Crosslinking 432
6-6b Alternating Intra-Intermolecular Polymerization . 436
6-7 Other Copolymerizations 441
6-7a Miscellaneous Copolymerizations of Alkenes. . . 441
6-7b Copolymerization of Carbonyl Monomers. . . . 442

7 RING-OPENING POLYMERIZATION 450

7-1 General Characteristics 451
7-1a Scope 451
7-1b Polymerization Mechanism and Kinetics 452
7-2 Cyclic Ethers 453
7-2a Anionic Polymerization of Epoxides 454

7-2a-1 Reaction Characteristics 454
7-2a-2 Exchange Reactions 456
7-2a-3 Chain Transfer to Monomer 458
7-2b Cationic Polymerization 459
7-2b-1 Initiation 460
7-2b-2 Termination 465
7-2b-3 Kinetics 467
7-2b-4 Cyclic Acetals 471
7-2b-5 Energetic Characteristics 475
7-3 Cyclic Amides 479
7-3a Anionic Polymerization. 479
7-3a-1 Use of Strong Bases Alone 479
7-3a-2 Use of Acylating Agents 482
7-3b Cationic Polymerization 486
7-3b-1 Polymerization by Protonic Acids 486
7-3b-2 Polymerization by Amines. 487
7-3c Catalysis by Water 489
7-3c-1 Reaction Mechanism. 489
7-3c-2 Degree of Polymerization 490
7-3d Reactivity 492
7-4 Cyclosiloxanes 495
7-4a Anionic Polymerization 495
7-4b Cationic Polymerization 496
7-5 Other Cyclic Monomers 497
7-5a Cyclic Esters 497
7-5b Cyclic Amines 499
7-5c Cyclic Sulfides. 500
7-5d *N*-Carboxy-α-Amino Acid Anhydrides 501
7-5e Miscellaneous Polymerizations 503
7-6 Polymerization of Inorganic or Semi-Inorganic Monomers . 503
7-6a Polyphosphazenes 504
7-6b Other Polymerizations 506
7-7 Copolymerization 507
7-7a Monomers Containing the Same Functional Group. 507
7-7b Monomers Containing Different Functional Groups 511

8 STEREOCHEMISTRY OF POLYMERIZATION 518

8-1 Types of Stereoisomerism in Polymers 520
8-1a Monosubstituted Ethylenes 520
8-1a-1 Site of Steric Isomerism 520
8-1a-2 Tacticity 522
8-1b Disubstituted Ethylenes 523

8-1b-1 1,1-Disubstituted Ethylenes 523
8-1b-2 1,2-Disubstituted Ethylenes 524
8-1c Carbonyl and Ring-Opening Polymerizations . . . 526
8-1d 1,3-Butadiene and 2-Substituted 1,3-Butadienes . 528
8-1d-1 1,2- and 3,4-Polymerizations 528
8-1d-2 1,4-Polymerization 529
8-1e 1-Substituted and 1,4 Disubstituted 1,3-Butadienes 530
8-1e-1 1,2- and 3,4-Polymerizations 530
8-1e-2 1,4-Polymerization 532
8-1f Cyclopolymers 534
8-2 Properties of Stereoregular Polymers 534
8-2a Significance of Stereoregularity in Polymers . . . 534
8-2a-1 *Isotactic, Syndiotactic,* and *Atactic* Polypropylenes 534
8-2a-2 *Cis*- and *Trans*-1,4-Poly-1,3-Dienes 536
8-2a-3 Cellulose and Amylose 537
8-2b Analysis of Stereoregularity 538
8-2b-1 Experimental Methods 538
8-2b-2 Definition of Tacticity 539
8-3 Forces of Stereoregulation in Alkene Polymerizations . . . 541
8-3a Radical Polymerization 542
8-3a-1 Energetics of Syndiotactic and Isotactic Placements 542
8-3a-2 Distribution of Stereoregular Sequence Lengths. 545
8-3b Ionic and Coordination Polymerization 547
8-3b-1 Effect of Coordination 547
8-3b-2 Mechanism of Stereospecific Placement . . . 549
8-4 Ziegler-Natta Polymerization of Non-Polar Alkenes . . . 552
8-4a Mechanism of Ziegler-Natta Polymerization . . . 553
8-4a-1 Chemical Nature of Propagating Species . . . 554
8-4a-2 Propagation at Carbon-Transition Metal Bond . 556
8-4a-3 Bimetallic versus Monometallic Mechanisms . . 557
8-4a-4 Physical Nature of Catalyst 560
8-4a-5 Direction of Double Bond Opening 569
8-4b Effect of Components of Ziegler-Natta Catalyst . . 569
8-4b-1 Transition Metal Component 570
8-4b-2 Group I-III Metal Component. 571
8-4b-3 Third Component. 573
8-4c Kinetics 574
8-4c-1 Reaction Scheme 574
8-4c-2 Rate Expressions 576
8-4c-3 Observed Kinetic Behavior 577
8-4c-4 Values of Kinetic Parameters 578

8-4d Scope of the Ziegler-Natta Catalyst 579
8-4d-1 Cycloalkenes 580
8-4d-2 Copolymerization 582
8-4e Supported Metal Oxide Catalysts 583
8-5 Stereospecific Polymerization of Polar Alkenes 584
8-5a Methyl Methacrylate 585
8-5b Vinyl Ethers 588
8-5c Styrene 588
8-6 Stereospecific Polymerization of 1,3-Dienes 588
8-6a Radical Polymerization 588
8-6b Anionic and Coordination Polymerizations . . . 590
8-6c Cationic Polymerization 596
8-7 Other Stereospecific Polymerizations 598
8-7a Epoxides 598
8-7b Carbonyl Monomers 599
8-8 Optical Activity in Polymers 599
8-8a Polymerization with Optically Active Catalysts . . 600
8-8b Polymerization of Optically Active Monomers . . 601

9 SYNTHETIC REACTIONS OF POLYMERS 611

9-1 Polymer Reactivity 611
9-2 Crosslinking 614
9-2a Unsaturated Polyesters 614
9-2a-1 Copolymerization 614
9-2a-2 Oxygen 616
9-2b Elastomers Based on 1,3-Dienes 617
9-2b-1 Sulfur 618
9-2b-2 Accelerated Sulfur Vulcanization 619
9-2c Polyolefins and Polysiloxanes 621
9-2d Other Crosslinking Processes 622
9-3 Reactions of Cellulose 623
9-3a Solution of Cellulose 624
9-3b Esterification 625
9-3c Etherification 626
9-4 Reactions of Poly(vinyl acetate) 626
9-5 Halogenation 627
9-5a Natural Rubber 627
9-5b Saturated Hydrocarbon Polymers 628
9-6 Aromatic Substitution 629
9-7 Cyclization 630
9-8 Graft and Block Copolymers 632
9-8a Graft Copolymers 632

9-8a-1 Chain Transfer 632
9-8a-2 Ultraviolet and Ionizing Radiation 633
9-8a-3 Redox 635
9-8a-4 Other Grafting Systems 635
9-8b Block Copolymers 636
9-8b-1 Mechanical Bond Scission 636
9-8b-2 Other Methods 637

INDEX 641

1
INTRODUCTION

Polymers are macromolecules built up by the linking together of large numbers of much smaller molecules. The small molecules which combine with each other to form polymer molecules are termed *monomers* and the reactions by which they combine are termed *polymerizations.* There may be hundreds, thousands, tens of thousands, or more monomer molecules linked together in a polymer molecule. When one speaks of polymers, one is concerned with materials whose molecular weights may reach into the millions. Most of the polymers, however, that one usually encounters either in the laboratory or in practical applications will usually fall into the 5,000–200,000 molecular weight range.

1-1 TYPES OF POLYMERS AND POLYMERIZATIONS

There has been and still is considerable confusion concerning the classification of polymers. This is especially the case for the beginning student. During the development of polymer science, two classifications of polymers have come into use. One classification divides polymers into *condensation* and *addition* polymers and the other divides them into *step* and *chain* polymers. Confusion and error arise because the two classifications are usually used interchangeably without careful thought. The terms condensation and step are usually used synonymously as are the terms addition and chain. Although these terms can often be used synonymously as noted, this is not always the case because the two classifications arise from two different bases of classification. The condensation-addition classification is primarily applicable to the composition or structure of polymers. The step-chain classification is based on the mechanism of the polymerization reactions.

1-1a Polymer Composition and Structure

Polymers were originally classified by Carothers [1] in 1929 into condensation and addition polymers on the basis of the compositional difference between the polymer and the monomer(s) from which it was synthesized. Condensation polymers were those polymers that were formed from polyfunctional monomers by the various condensation reactions of organic chemistry with the elimination of some small molecule such as water. An example of such a condensation polymer is the polyamides formed from diamines and diacids with the elimination of water according to

$$n\ H_2N{-}R{-}NH_2 + n\ HO_2C{-}R'{-}CO_2H \longrightarrow$$

$$H{\left(}NH{-}R{-}NHCO{-}R'{-}CO{\right)}_n OH + (2n-1)\ H_2O \qquad (1\text{-}1)$$

where R and R′ are aliphatic or aromatic groupings. The unit in parentheses in the polyamide formula repeats itself many times in the polymer chain and is termed the *repeating unit* or *base unit* [2]. The composition of the repeating unit differs from that of the two monomers by the elements of water. The polyamide synthesized from hexamethylene diamine, $R = (CH_2)_6$, and adipic acid, $R' = (CH_2)_4$, is the extensively used fiber and plastic known commonly as nylon-6,6 or poly(hexamethylene adipamide). Other examples of condensation polymers are the polyesters formed from diacids and diols with the elimination of water

$$n\ HO{-}R{-}OH + n\ HO_2C{-}R'{-}CO_2H \longrightarrow$$

$$HO{\left(}R{-}OCO{-}R'{-}COO{\right)}_n H + (2n-1)\ H_2O \qquad (1\text{-}2)$$

and the polycarbonates from the reaction of an aromatic dihydroxy reactant and phosgene with the elimination of hydrogen chloride

$$n\ \text{HO}-\text{C}_6\text{H}_4-\text{R}-\text{C}_6\text{H}_4-\text{OH} + n\ \text{Cl}-\text{CO}-\text{Cl} \longrightarrow$$

$$\text{H}\!\left[\text{O}-\text{C}_6\text{H}_4-\text{R}-\text{C}_6\text{H}_4-\text{O}-\text{CO}\right]_n\!\text{Cl} + (2n-1)\ \text{HCl} \qquad (1\text{-}3)$$

The common condensation polymers and the reactions by which they are formed are shown in Table 1-1. It should be noted from Table 1-1 that for many of the condensation polymers, there are different combinations of reactants which can be employed for their synthesis. Thus, polyamides can be synthesized by the reactions of diamines with diacids or diacyl chlorides and by the self-condensation of amino acids. Similarly, polyesters can be synthesized from diols by esterification with diacids or ester interchange with diesters.

Some naturally occurring polymers such as cellulose, starch, wool, and silk are classified as condensation polymers since one can postulate their synthesis from certain hypothetical reactants by the elimination of water. Thus, cellulose can be thought of as the polyether formed by the dehydration of glucose. Carothers included such polymers by defining condensation polymers as those in which the formula of the repeating unit lacks certain atoms which are present in the monomer(s) from which it is formed or to which it may be degraded. In this sense, cellulose is considered a condensation polymer since its hydrolysis yields glucose which contains the repeating unit of cellulose plus the elements of water

$$\text{H}\!\left[\text{O}-\text{CH}\underset{\text{CH(OH)}-\text{CH(OH)}}{\overset{\text{CH}(\text{CH}_2\text{OH})-\text{O}}{\diagdown\diagup}}\text{CH}\right]_n\!\text{OH} + (n-1)\ \text{H}_2\text{O} \longrightarrow n\ \text{HO}-\text{CH}\underset{\text{CH(OH)}-\text{CH(OH)}}{\overset{\text{CH}(\text{CH}_2\text{OH})-\text{O}}{\diagdown\diagup}}\text{CH}-\text{OH} \qquad (1\text{-}4)$$

Cellulose Glucose

Table 1-1 Typical Condensation Polymers

Type	Characteristic linkage	Polymerization reaction
Polyamide	—CO—NH—	$H_2N{-}R{-}NH_2 + HO_2C{-}R'{-}CO_2H \longrightarrow H{+}NH{-}R{-}NHCO{-}R'{-}CO{+}_n OH + H_2O$ $H_2N{-}R{-}NH_2 + ClCO{-}R'{-}COCl \longrightarrow H{+}NH{-}R{-}NHCO{-}R'{-}CO{+}_n Cl + HCl$ $H_2N{-}R{-}CO_2H \longrightarrow H{+}NH{-}R{-}CO{+}_n OH + H_2O$
Protein, wool, silk	—CO—NH—	Naturally occurring polypeptide polymers; degradable to mixtures of different amino acids. $H{+}NH{-}R{-}NHCO{-}R'{-}CO{+}_n OH + H_2O \longrightarrow H_2N{-}R{-}CO_2H + H_2N{-}R'{-}CO_2H$
Polyester	—CO—O—	$HO{-}R{-}OH + HO_2C{-}R'{-}CO_2H \longrightarrow HO{+}R{-}OCO{-}R'{-}COO{+}_n H + H_2O$ $HO{-}R{-}OH + R''O_2C{-}R'{-}CO_2R'' \longrightarrow HO{+}R{-}OCO{-}R'{-}COO{+}_n R'' + R''OH$ $HO{-}R{-}CO_2H \longrightarrow HO{+}R{-}COO{+}_n H + H_2O$
Polyurethane	—O—CO—NH—	$HO{-}R{-}OH + OCN{-}R'{-}NCO \longrightarrow {+}O{-}R{-}OCO{-}NH{-}R'{-}NH{-}CO{+}_n$
Polysiloxane	—Si—O—	$Cl{-}SiR_2{-}Cl \xrightarrow[-HCl]{H_2O} HO{-}SiR_2{-}OH \longrightarrow HO{+}SiR_2{-}O{+}_n H + H_2O$
Phenol-formaldehyde	—Ar—CH_2—	$C_6H_5OH + CH_2O \longrightarrow [\,C_6H_3(OH){-}CH_2\,]_n + H_2O$

Urea-formaldehyde	$-NH-CH_2-$	$H_2N-CO-NH_2 + CH_2O \longrightarrow \text{+}HN-CO-NH-CH_2\text{+}_n + H_2O$
Melamine-formaldehyde	$-NH-CH_2-$	$H_2N-C_3N_3(NH_2)-NH_2 + CH_2O \longrightarrow \left[HN-C_3N_3(NH_2)-NH-CH_2 \right]_n$ (melamine: triazine ring C=N with NH_2 groups)
Cellulose	$-O-C-$	Naturally occurring; degradable to glucose $\text{+}C_6H_{12}O_4\text{+}_n + H_2O \longrightarrow C_6H_{12}O_6$
Polysulfide	$-S_m-$	$Cl-R-Cl + Na_2S_m \longrightarrow \text{+}R-S_m\text{+}_n + NaCl$
Polyacetal	$-O-CH(R)-O-$	$R-CHO + HO-R'-OH \longrightarrow \text{+}O-R'-OCHR\text{+}_n + H_2O$

Addition polymers were classified by Carothers as those formed from monomers without the loss of a small molecule. Unlike condensation polymers, the repeating unit of an addition polymer has the same composition as the monomer. The major addition polymers are those formed from vinyl monomers. These monomers are caused to react with themselves to form polymers by conversion of their double bonds into saturated linkages according to

$$n\ CH_2{=}CHY \longrightarrow \left(CH_2{-}CHY\right)_n \tag{1-5}$$

where Y can be any substituent group such as hydrogen, alkyl, aryl, nitrile, ester, acid, ketone, ether, and halogen. Aldehyde monomers are another class of compounds which undergo addition polymerization. Table 1-2 shows many of the common addition polymers and the monomers from which they are produced.

Table 1-2 Typical Addition Polymers

Polymer	Monomer	Repeating unit
Polyethylene	$CH_2{=}CH_2$	$-CH_2-CH_2-$
Polyisobutylene	$CH_2{=}C(CH_3)_2$	$-CH_2-C(CH_3)_2-$
Polyacrylonitrile	$CH_2{=}CH-CN$	$-CH_2-CH(CN)-$
Poly(vinyl chloride)	$CH_2{=}CH-Cl$	$-CH_2-CH(Cl)-$
Polystyrene	$CH_2{=}CH-\phi$	$-CH_2-CH(\phi)-$
Poly(methyl methacrylate)	$CH_2{=}C(CH_3)(CO_2CH_3)$	$-CH_2-C(CH_3)(CO_2CH_3)-$

Table 1-2 Typical Addition Polymers *(Continued)*

Polymer	Monomer	Repeating unit
Poly(vinyl acetate)	$CH_2{=}CH{-}OCOCH_3$	$-CH_2-CH(OCOCH_3)-$
Poly(vinylidene chloride)	$CH_2{=}CCl_2$	$-CH_2-CCl_2-$
Polytetrafluoroethylene	$CF_2{=}CF_2$	$-CF_2-CF_2-$
Polyformaldehyde	$CH_2{=}O$	$-CH_2-O-$
Polyacetaldehyde	$CH_3CH{=}O$	$-CH(CH_3)-O-$
Polyisoprene (Natural rubber)	$CH_2{=}C(CH_3){-}CH{=}CH_2$	$-CH_2-C(CH_3){=}CH-CH_2-$

The development of polymer science with the study of new polymerization processes and polymers showed that the original classification by Carothers was not entirely adequate and left much to be desired. Thus, for example, consider the polyurethanes which are formed by the reaction of diols with diisocyanates without the elimination of any small molecule

$$n\ HO-R-OH + n\ OCN-R'-NCO \longrightarrow$$

$$HO\!\left(R-OCONH-R'-NHCO-O\right)_{(n-1)}R-OCONH-R'-NCO \qquad (1\text{-}6)$$

Using Carothers' original classification, one would classify the polyurethanes as addition polymers since the polymer has the same net composition as the monomer. However, the polyurethanes are structurally much more similar to the condensation polymers than to the addition polymers.

To avoid the obviously incorrect classification of polyurethanes as well as of some other polymers as addition polymers, polymers have also been classified from a consideration of the chemical structure of the groups present in the polymer chains [3]. Condensation polymers have been defined as those polymers whose repeating units are joined together by functional units of one kind or another such as the ester, amide, urethane, sulfide, and ether linkages. Thus, the structure of condensation polymers has been defined by

$$—R—Z—R—Z—R—Z—R—Z—R—Z— \quad \text{I}$$

where R is an aliphatic or aromatic grouping and Z is a functional unit such as —OCO—, —NHCO—, —S—, —OCONH—, —O—, —OCOO—, and —SO_2—. Addition polymers, on the other hand, do not contain such functional groups as part of the polymer chain. Such groups may, however, be present in addition polymers as pendant substituents hanging off the polymer chain. According to this classification, the polyurethanes are readily and more correctly classified as condensation polymers.

It should not be taken for granted that all polymers which are defined as condensation polymers by Carothers' classification will also be so defined by a consideration of the polymer chain structure. Some condensation polymers do not contain functional groups in the polymer chain. An example is the phenol-formaldehyde polymers produced by the reaction of phenol (or substituted phenols) with formaldehyde

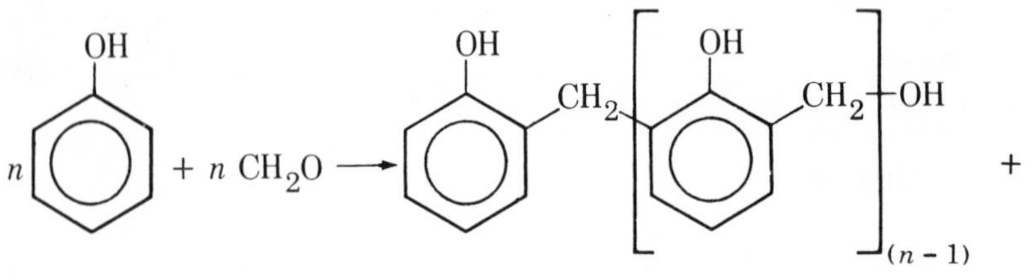

$$n\, C_6H_5OH + n\, CH_2O \longrightarrow HOC_6H_4CH_2\!\left[C_6H_3(OH)CH_2\right]_{(n-1)}\!OH + (n-1)\, H_2O \tag{1-7}$$

These polymers do not contain a functional group within the polymer chain but are classified as condensation polymers since water is split out during the polymerization process. Another example is poly(*p*-xylylene) which is produced by the oxidative coupling (dehydrogenation) of *p*-xylene

$$n\,CH_3-C_6H_4-CH_3 \longrightarrow H\!\left[CH_2-C_6H_4-CH_2\right]_n\!H + (n-1)\,H_2 \qquad (1\text{-}8)$$

In summary, a polymer is classified as a condensation polymer if its synthesis involves the elimination of small molecules, or it contains functional groups as part of the polymer chain, or its repeating unit lacks certain atoms which are present in the (hypothetical) monomer to which it can be degraded. If a polymer does not fulfill any of these requirements, it is classified as an addition polymer.

1-1b Polymerization Mechanism

In addition to the structural and compositional differences between polymers, Flory [3] stressed the very significant difference in the mechanism by which polymer molecules are built up. Polymerizations are classified into step and chain polymerizations based on the polymerization mechanism. Step polymers are, then, those produced by step polymerization and chain polymers, those produced by chain polymerization. The characteristics of the two polymerizations are considerably different. The two reactions differ basically in terms of the time-scale of various reaction events. More specifically, step and chain polymerizations differ in the length of time required for the complete growth of full-sized polymer molecules.

Step polymerizations proceed by the stepwise reaction between the functional groups of reactants as in reactions such as those described by Eqs. 1-1 through 1-3 and Eqs. 1-6 through 1-8. The size of the polymer molecules increases at a relatively slow rate in such polymerizations. One proceeds slowly from monomer to dimer, trimer, tetramer, pentamer, and so on until eventually large polymer molecules containing large numbers of monomer molecules have been formed. The situation is quite different in chain polymerizations where full-sized polymer molecules are produced almost immediately after the start of the reaction.

Chain polymerizations require a catalyst from which is produced an initiator species R* with a reactive center. The reactive center may be either a free radical, cation, or anion. Polymerization occurs by the propagation of the reactive species by the successive additions of large numbers of monomer molecules in a chain reaction happening, in a matter of a second or so at most, and usually in much shorter times. By far, the most common example of chain polymerization is that of vinyl monomers. The process can be depicted as

$$\mathrm{R^*} \xrightarrow{\mathrm{CH_2{=}CHY}} \mathrm{R{-}CH_2{-}\overset{\displaystyle H}{\underset{\displaystyle Y}{\overset{|}{\underset{|}{C}}}}{}^*} \xrightarrow{\mathrm{CH_2{=}CHY}} \mathrm{R{-}CH_2{-}\overset{\displaystyle H}{\underset{\displaystyle Y}{\overset{|}{\underset{|}{C}}}}{-}CH_2{-}\overset{\displaystyle H}{\underset{\displaystyle Y}{\overset{|}{\underset{|}{C}}}}{}^*} \overset{\mathrm{CH_2{=}CHY}}{\dashrightarrow}$$

$$\mathrm{R}\left[\mathrm{CH_2{-}\overset{\displaystyle H}{\underset{\displaystyle Y}{\overset{|}{\underset{|}{C}}}}}\right]_n \mathrm{CH_2{-}\overset{\displaystyle H}{\underset{\displaystyle Y}{\overset{|}{\underset{|}{C}}}}{}^*} \qquad (1\text{-}9)$$

The growth of the polymer chain ceases when the reactive center is destroyed by one of a number of possible termination reactions.

One should not infer from the above discussion that chain polymerizations are faster than step polymerizations. The net rate at which monomer molecules disappear (i.e., the rate of polymerization) in step polymerization can be as great or greater than that in chain polymerization. The difference between the two processes lies simply in the time required for the growth of each polymer molecule. Thus, if we start out a chain polymerization and a step polymerization side-by-side, we may observe a variety of situations with regard to their relative rates of polymerization. However, the molecular weights of the polymers produced at any time after the start of the reactions will always be very characteristically different for the two polymerizations. If the two polymerizations are stopped at 0.1% conversion, 1% conversion, 10% conversion, 40% conversion, 90% conversion, and so on, one will always observe the same behavior. The chain polymerization will show the presence of high molecular weight polymer molecules at all percents of conversion. There are no intermediate sized molecules in the reaction mixture—only monomer and high polymer. The only change that occurs with reaction time is the increase in the number of polymer molecules. Polymer size is independent of percent conversion, although the amount of polymer certainly depends on it. On the other hand, high molecular weight polymer is obtained in step polymerizations only near the very end of the reaction (> 98% conversion). Thus, both polymer size and the amount of polymer are dependent on the reaction time in step polymerization.

The classification of polymers according to polymerization mechanism, like that by structure and composition, is not without its ambiguities. The *ring-opening* polymerizations of cyclic monomers such as propylene oxide

$$n\ CH_3-\overset{\overset{O}{\diagup\ \diagdown}}{CH-CH_2} \longrightarrow \left[CH_2-\underset{\underset{CH_3}{|}}{CH}-O \right]_n \tag{1-10}$$

or ε-caprolactam

$$n \begin{array}{c} CH_2-CH_2-CO \\ | \qquad\qquad\quad | \\ CH_2-CH_2-CH_2-NH \end{array} \longrightarrow -\!\!\left(NHCH_2CH_2CH_2CH_2CH_2CO \right)\!\!-_n \tag{1-11}$$

can proceed both by step and chain mechanisms depending on the reaction conditions and catalyst employed. The polymer obtained is the same regardless of the polymerization mechanism. Such polymerizations point out very clearly that one must distinguish between the classification of the polymerization mechanism and that of the polymer structure. The two classifications cannot always be used interchangeably. Polymers such as the polyethers and polyamides produced in Eqs. 1-10 and 1-11, as well as those from other cyclic monomers, must be separately classified as to polymerization mechanism and polymer structure. These polymers are structurally classified as condensation polymers since they contain functional groups (e.g., ether, amide) in the polymer chain. They, like the polyurethanes, are not classified as addition polymers by the use of

Carothers' original classification. The situation is even more complicated for a polymer such as that obtained from ϵ-caprolactam. The exact same polymer can be obtained by the step polymerization of the linear monomer ϵ-aminocaproic acid. It should suffice at this point to summarize the situation by stressing that the terms condensation and step polymer or polymerization are not synonymous nor are the terms addition and chain polymer or polymerization.

1-2 NOMENCLATURE OF POLYMERS

Polymer nomenclature in general leaves much to be desired. A standard nomenclature system based on chemical structure as is used for organic compounds would be most desirable. Unfortunately, the naming of polymers has not proceeded in such a systematic manner. Polymer nomenclature has been largely a matter of custom without any one system being universally accepted. It is not at all unusual for a polymer to have several different commonly used names due to different nomenclature systems. The nomenclature systems that are used are based either on the structure of the polymer or the source of the polymer (i.e., the monomer(s) used in its synthesis) or trade names [2–5]. Not only are there several different nomenclature systems but none of the presently used ones are applied rigorously. Attempts are increasingly being made to standardize polymer nomenclature.

1-2a Nomenclature Based on Source

The most simple and commonly used nomenclature system is probably that based on the source of the polymer. This system is applicable primarily to polymers synthesized from a single monomer as in addition and ring-opening polymerizations. Such polymers are named by adding the name of the monomer onto the prefix "poly" without a space or hyphen. Thus, the polymers from ethylene and acetaldehyde are named polyethylene and polyacetaldehyde, respectively. When the monomer has a substituted parent name or a multi-worded name or an abnormally long name, parentheses are placed around its name following the prefix poly. The polymers from 3-methyl-1-pentene, vinyl chloride, propylene oxide, chlorotrifluoroethylene, and ϵ-caprolactam are named poly(3-methyl-1-pentene), poly(vinyl chloride), poly(propylene oxide), poly(chlorotrifluoroethylene), and poly(ϵ-caprolactam), respectively. Other examples are listed in Table 1-2. The parenthesis is frequently omitted in common usage when naming polymers. Although this will usually not present a problem, in some cases the omission can lead to uncertainty as to the structure of the polymer named [4]. Thus, the use of polyethylene oxide instead of poly(ethylene oxide) can be ambiguous in denoting one of the following possible structures

$$\text{-}\!\!\left(CH_2CH_2\right)\!_n\!O\!\left(CH_2CH_2\right)\!_n \qquad \text{II}$$

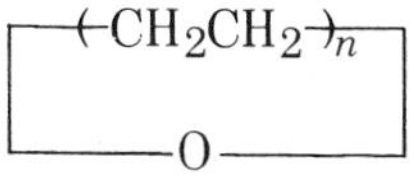

$$\overbrace{\left(CH_2CH_2\right)_n\ \ \underbrace{\qquad O \qquad}}\qquad \text{III}$$

instead of the polymer, $\left(CH_2CH_2-O\right)_n$, from ethylene oxide.

Some polymers are named as being derived from hypothetical monomers. Thus, poly(vinyl alcohol) is actually produced by the hydrolysis of poly(vinyl acetate)

$$\left[\begin{array}{c} \quad CH_3COO \\ \quad | \\ CH_2-CH \end{array}\right]_n + n\,H_2O \longrightarrow \left[\begin{array}{c} \quad HO \\ \quad | \\ CH_2-CH \end{array}\right]_n + n\,CH_3COOH \qquad (1\text{-}12)$$

It is, however, named as a product of the hypothetical monomer vinyl alcohol (which in reality is simply the enol form of acetaldehyde).

Condensation polymers synthesized from single reactants are named in a similar manner. Examples are the polyamides and polyesters produced from amino acids and hydroxy acids, respectively. Thus, the polymer from 6-aminocaproic acid is named poly(6-aminocaproic acid)

$$n\,H_2N-CH_2CH_2CH_2CH_2CH_2-COOH \longrightarrow$$

6-Aminocaproic acid

$$\left(HN-CH_2CH_2CH_2CH_2CH_2-CO\right)_n \qquad (1\text{-}13)$$

Poly(6-aminocaproic acid)

It should be noted that there is an ambiguity here in that poly(6-aminocaproic acid) and poly(ϵ-caprolactam) are one and the same polymer. The same polymer is produced from two different monomers–a not uncommonly encountered situation.

1-2b Nomenclature Based on Structure

Condensation polymers synthesized from two (or more) monomers are usually named according to the chemical structure of their repeating units. The name is obtained by following the prefix without a space or hyphen with parentheses enclosing the name of the structural grouping attached to the parent compound. The parent compound is the particular member of the class of the polymer—the particular ester, amide, urethane, etc. Thus, the polymer from hexamethylene diamine and sebacic acid is considered as the substituted amide derivative of the parent compound sebacic acid, $HO_2C(CH_2)_8CO_2H$, and is named poly(hexamethylene sebacamide). Poly(ethylene terephthalate) is the polymer from ethylene glycol and terephthalic acid, p-$HO_2C\phi CO_2H$. The polymer from trimethylene glycol and ethylene diisocyanate is poly(trimethylene ethylene-urethane)

$$\left[HN{-}(CH_2)_6{-}NHCO{-}(CH_2)_8{-}CO \right]_n$$

Poly(hexamethylene sebacamide)

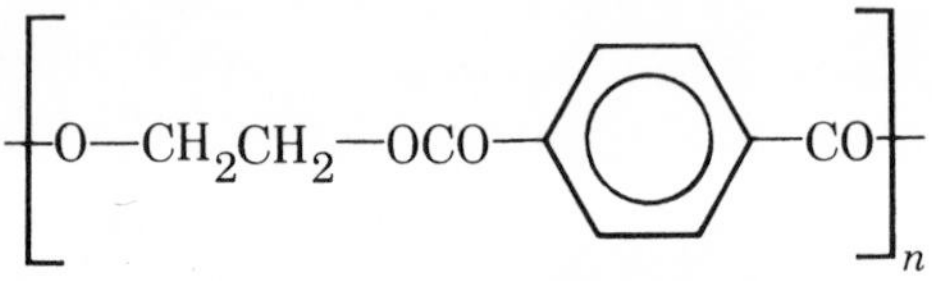

$$\left[O{-}CH_2CH_2{-}OCO{-}C_6H_4{-}CO \right]_n$$

Poly(ethylene terephthalate)

$$\left[O{-}CH_2CH_2CH_2{-}OCONH{-}CH_2CH_2{-}NHCO \right]_n$$

Poly(trimethylene ethylene-urethane)

It has also been suggested [4, 5] that such condensation polymers might more appropriately be named according to the monomers by following the prefix "poly" with parenthesis enclosing the two reactants. The names of the reactants would be separated by the term *-co-*. Thus, the above three polymers could be named poly(hexamethylene diamine-*co*-sebacic acid), poly(ethylene glycol-*co*-terephthalic acid), and poly(trimethylene glycol-*co*-ethylene diisocyanate), respectively. This suggestion has not gained general acceptance and further serves to indicate the vexed state of polymer nomenclature.

Nomenclature based on structure is not common for addition polymers since most of them are named according to their sources. Exceptions to this generalization are polymers such as poly(1,4-phenylene), polymethylene, and poly(p-xylylene)

$$\left[-C_6H_4- \right]_n \qquad -\!\!(CH_2)\!\!-_n \qquad \left[-CH_2-C_6H_4-CH_2- \right]_n$$

Poly(1,4-phenylene) Polymethylene Poly(*p*-xylylene)

Further, some of the addition polymers such as polyethylene and polypropylene are simultaneously named on the basis of both source and structure. In these cases, the names of the monomers and the repeating structural units are exactly the same.

1-2c Trade and Non-Names

Special terminology based on trade names has been employed for some polymers. Although trade names should be avoided, one must be familiar with those that are firmly established and commonly used. An outstanding example of trade name nomenclature is the use of the name nylon for the polyamides from unsubstituted, non-branched aliphatic monomers. Two numbers are added onto the word "nylon" with the first number indicating the number of methylene groups in the diamine portion of the polyamide and the second number the number of carbon atoms in the diacyl portion. Thus, poly(hexamethylene adipamide) and poly(hexamethylene sebacamide) are nylon-6,6 and nylon-6,10, respectively. Unfortunately, variants of these names are all too frequently employed. The literature contains such variations of nylon-6,6 as nylon-66, 66-nylon, nylon 6/6, 6,6-nylon, and 6-6-nylon. Polyamides from single monomers are denoted by a single number to denote the number of carbon atoms in the repeating unit. Poly(ϵ-caprolactam) or poly(6-aminocaproic acid) is nylon-6.

In far too many instances, trade name polymer nomenclature conveys very little meaning regarding the structure of a polymer. Many condensation polymers, in fact, seem not to have names. Thus, the polymer obtained by the step polymerization of formaldehyde and phenol is variously referred to as phenol-formaldehyde polymer, phenol-formaldehyde resin, phenolic, phenolic resin, and phenoplast. Polymers of formaldehyde or other aldehydes with urea or melamine are generally referred to as amino resins or aminoplasts without any more specific names. It is often extremely difficult to determine which aldehyde and which amino monomers have been used to synthesize a particular polymer being referred to as an amino resin.

More specific nomenclature, if it can be called that, is afforded by indicating the two reactants as in names such as urea-formaldehyde resin or melamine-formaldehyde resin.

A similar situation exists with the naming of many other polymers. Thus, the polymer

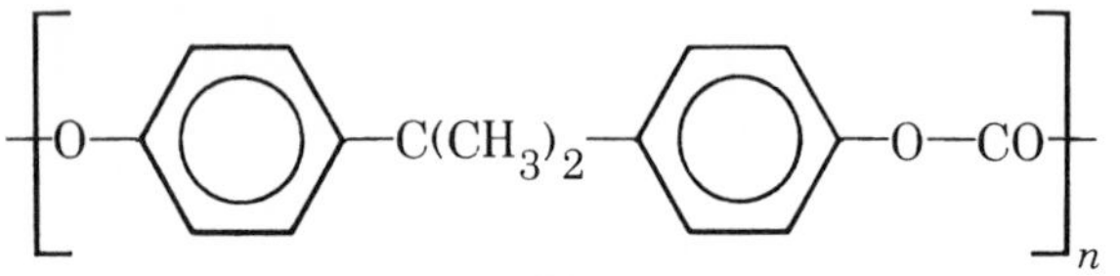

$$\left[O-C_6H_4-C(CH_3)_2-C_6H_4-O-CO \right]_n$$

IV

is usually referred to as "the polycarbonate from bisphenol A" (R = $-C(CH_3)_2-$ in Eq. 1-3). This polymer could much more systematically be named as poly(4,4′-isopropylidenediphenylene carbonate) on the basis of its chemical structure.

1-3 STRUCTURAL SHAPE OF POLYMER MOLECULES

There are three main structural shapes in which polymer molecules are produced. Polymers can be classified as *linear, branched,* or *crosslinked* polymers depending on the structural shape of the polymer molecules. In the previous discussion on the different types of polymers and polymerizations, we have considered only those polymers in which the monomer molecules have been linked together in one continuous length to form the polymer molecule. Such polymers are termed *linear polymers.* Under certain reaction conditions or with certain kinds of monomers, the polymers produced can be quite different in shape.

Branched polymers are often obtained in both step and chain polymerizations, although for reasons which are usually quite different in the two cases. Branched polymer molecules are those in which there are side branches of linked monomer molecules protruding from various central branch points along the main polymer chain. The difference between the shapes of linear and branched polymer molecules can be seen from the structural representations in Fig. 1-1. The branch points are indicated by heavy dots. The illustrations show that there are several different kinds of branched polymers. The branched polymer can be comb-like in structure with either long (A) or short (B) branches [6]. When there is extensive branching, the polymer can have a dendritic structure in which there are branches

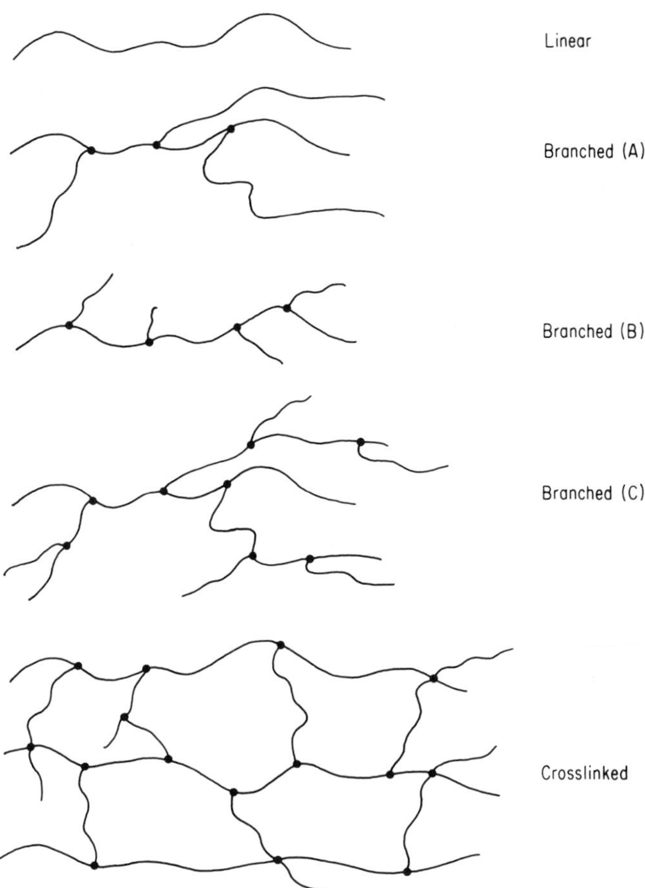

FIG. 1-1 *Structure of linear, branched, and crosslinked polymers.*

protruding from other branches, i.e., branched branches (C). The presence of branching in a polymer usually has a large effect on many important polymer properties. The most significant property change brought about by branching is the decrease in crystallinity. Branched polymers do not pack as easily into a crystal lattice as do linear polymers.

It is important to point out that the term "branched polymer" does not refer to linear polymers containing side groups which are part of the monomer structure. Only those polymers which contain side branches composed of complete monomer units are termed "branched polymers." Thus, polystyrene (V)

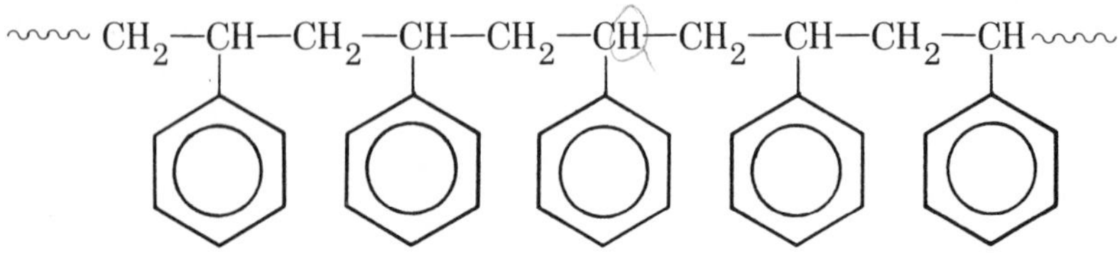

$$\sim\sim CH_2-\underset{C_6H_5}{CH}-CH_2-\underset{C_6H_5}{CH}-CH_2-\underset{C_6H_5}{CH}-CH_2-\underset{C_6H_5}{CH}-CH_2-\underset{C_6H_5}{CH}\sim\sim$$

V

is classified as a linear polymer, and not as a branched polymer, for the reason that the phenyl groups are part of the monomer unit and are not considered as branches. Branched polystyrene would be the polymer VI in which one has one or more polystyrene branches protruding from the main linear polystyrene chain

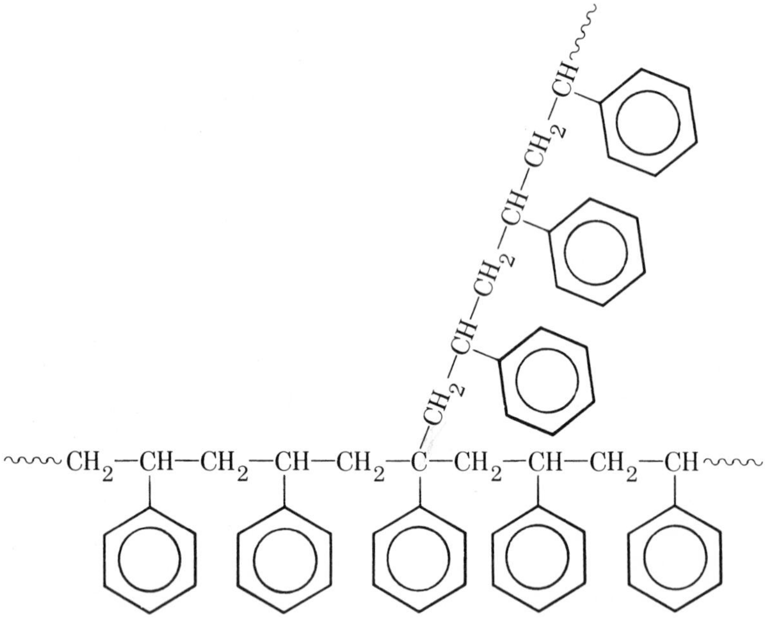

$$\sim\sim CH_2-\underset{C_6H_5}{CH}-CH_2-\underset{C_6H_5}{CH}-CH_2-\underset{C_6H_5}{\overset{CH_2-CH(C_6H_5)-CH_2-CH(C_6H_5)-CH_2-CH(C_6H_5)\sim\sim}{C}}-CH_2-\underset{C_6H_5}{CH}-CH_2-\underset{C_6H_5}{CH}\sim\sim$$

VI

When polymers are produced in which the polymer molecules are linked to each other at points other than their ends, the polymers are said to be crosslinked (Fig. 1-1). Crosslinking can be made to occur during the polymerization process by the use of appropriate monomers. It can also be brought about after the polymerization by various chemical reactions. The crosslinks between polymer chains can be of different lengths depending on the crosslinking method and the specific conditions employed. One can also vary the number of crosslinks so as to obtain lightly or highly crosslinked polymers. When the number of crosslinks is sufficiently high, a *three-dimensional* or *space network* polymer is produced in which all the polymer chains in a sample have been linked together to form one giant molecule. Light crosslinking is used to impart good recovery (elastic) properties to polymers to be used as rubbers. High degrees of crosslinking are used to impart high rigidity and dimensional stability (under conditions of heat and stress) to polymers such as the phenol-formaldehyde and urea-formaldehyde polymers.

1-4 MOLECULAR WEIGHT

The molecular weight of a polymer is of prime importance in its synthesis and application. The interesting and useful mechanical properties which are uniquely associated with polymeric materials are a consequence of their high molecular weight. Most important mechanical properties depend on and vary considerably with molecular weight. Thus, strength does not begin to develop in polymers until a minimum molecular weight of about 5,000–10,000 is achieved. Above that size, there is a rapid increase in the mechanical performance of polymers as their molecular weight increases; the effect levels off at still higher molecular weights. In most instances, there is some molecular weight range for which a given polymer property will be optimum for a particular application. One should bear this in mind throughout the text as different polymerization processes are discussed. The utility of a polymerization is greatly reduced unless the process can be carried out to yield polymer of a sufficiently high and specified molecular weight. The control of molecular weight is essential for the practical application of a polymerization process.

When one speaks of the molecular weight of a polymer, one means something quite different from that which applies to small-sized compounds. Polymers differ from the small-sized compounds in that they are polydisperse or heterogeneous in molecular weight. Even if a polymer is synthesized free from contaminants and impurities, it is still not a pure substance in the usually accepted sense. Polymers, in their purest form, are mixtures of molecules of different molecular weight. The reason for the polydispersity of polymers lies in the statistical variations present in the polymerization processes. When one discusses the molecular weight of a polymer, one is actually involved with its average molecular weight. Both the average molecular weight and the exact distribution of different molecular weights within a polymer are required in order to fully characterize it. The control of molecular weight and molecular weight distribution (MWD) is often used to obtain and improve certain desired physical properties in a polymer product.

Various methods are available for the experimental measurement of the average molecular weight of a polymer sample. These include methods based on colligative properties, light scattering, viscosity, ultracentrifugation, and sedimentation [6–8]. The various methods do not yield the same average molecular weight. Different average molecular weights are obtained because the properties being measured are biased differently toward the different sized polymer molecules in a polymer sample. Some methods are biased toward the larger sized polymer molecules while other methods are biased toward the smaller sized molecules. The result is that the average molecular weights obtained are correspondingly biased toward the larger or smaller sized molecules. The most important average molecular weights which are determined are:

1) The *number-average molecular weight* $\overline{M}_n$ is determined by the measurement of colligative properties such as freezing point depression (cryoscopy), boiling point elevation (ebulliometry), osmotic pressure, and vapor pressure lowering. $\overline{M}_n$ is defined as the total weight w of all the molecules in a polymer sample divided by the total number of molecules present. Thus, the number-average molecular weight is defined by

$$\overline{M}_n = \frac{w}{\sum N_x} = \frac{\sum N_x M_x}{\sum N_x} \qquad (1\text{-}14)$$

where the summations are over all the different sizes of polymer molecules from $x = 1$ to $x = \infty$ and N_x is the number of molecules whose weight is M_x. Equation 1-14 can also be written as

$$\overline{M}_n = \sum \underline{N}_x M_x \qquad (1\text{-}15)$$

where N_x is the mole-fraction (or the number-fraction) of molecules of size M_x.

2) The *weight-average molecular weight* $\overline{M}_w$ is obtained from light scattering measurements and is defined as

$$\overline{M}_w = \sum w_x M_x \tag{1-16}$$

where w_x is the weight-fraction of molecules whose weight is M_x. $\overline{M}_w$ can also be defined as

$$\overline{M}_w = \frac{\sum c_x M_x}{\sum c_x} = \frac{\sum c_x M_x}{c} = \frac{\sum N_x M_x^2}{\sum N_x M_x} \tag{1-17}$$

where c_x is the weight concentration of M_x molecules, c is the total weight concentration of all the polymer molecules, and the following relationships hold

$$w_x = \frac{c_x}{c} \tag{1-18}$$

$$c_x = N_x M_x \tag{1-19}$$

$$c = \sum c_x = \sum N_x M_x \tag{1-20}$$

3) The *viscosity-average molecular weight* $\overline{M}_v$ is obtained from viscosity measurements and is defined by

$$\overline{M}_v = \left[\sum w_x M_x^a\right]^{1/a} = \left[\frac{\sum N_x M_x^{a+1}}{\sum N_x M_x}\right]^{1/a} \tag{1-21}$$

where a is a constant. The viscosity- and weight-average molecular weights are equal when a is unity. However, $\overline{M}_v$ is almost always less than $\overline{M}_w$ since a is usually in the range of 0.5–0.9.

More than one average molecular weight is required to reasonably characterize a polymer sample. There is no such need for a monodisperse product (i.e., one which is composed of molecules whose molecular weights are all the same) for which all three average molecular weights are the same. The situation is very much different for a polydisperse polymer where all three molecular weights are different if the constant a in Eq. 1-21 is less than unity as is the usual case. A careful consideration of Eqs. 1-14 through 1-21 shows that the number-, viscosity-, and weight-average molecular weights, in that order, are increasingly biased toward the higher molecular weight fractions in a polymer sample. For a polydisperse polymer

$$\overline{M}_w > \overline{M}_v > \overline{M}_n$$

with the differences between the various average molecular weights increasing as the molecular weight distribution broadens. A typical polymer sample will have the molecular weight distribution shown in Fig. 1-2. The approximate positions of the different average molecular weights are indicated on this distribution curve.

For most practical purposes, one usually characterizes the molecular weight of a polymer sample by measuring $\overline{M}_n$ and either $\overline{M}_w$ or $\overline{M}_v$. The $\overline{M}_v$ is commonly used as a close approximation of $\overline{M}_w$ since the two are usually quite close (within 10–20 percent). Thus, in most instances, one is concerned with the $\overline{M}_n$ and $\overline{M}_w$ of a polymer

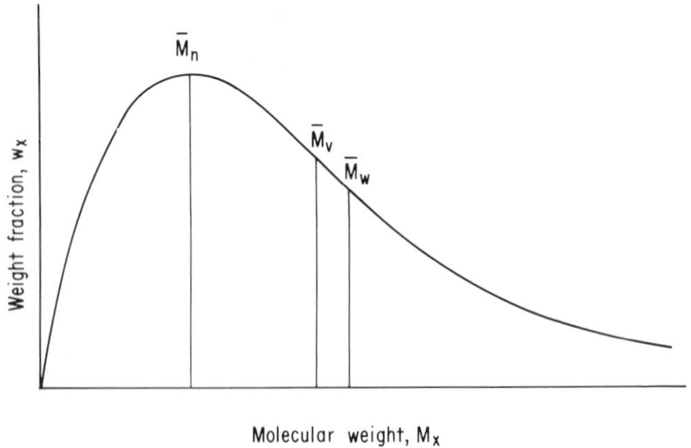

FIG. 1-2 *Distribution of molecular weights in a typical polymer sample.*

sample. The former is biased toward the lower molecular weight fractions while the latter is biased toward the higher molecular weight fractions. The ratio of the two average molecular weights $\overline{M}_w/\overline{M}_n$ depends on the breadth of the distribution curve (Fig. 1-2) and is often useful as a measure of the polydispersity in a polymer. The value of $\overline{M}_w/\overline{M}_n$ would be unity for a perfectly monodisperse polymer. The ratio is greater than unity for all actual polymers and increases with increasing polydispersity.

The characterization of a polymer by $\overline{M}_n$ alone, without regard to the polydispersity, can be extremely misleading since most polymer properties such as strength and melt viscosity are determined primarily by the size of the molecules which make up the bulk of the sample by weight. Polymer properties are much more dependent on the larger sized molecules in a sample than on the smaller ones. Thus, for example, consider a hypothetical mixture containing 95 percent by weight of molecules of molecular weight 10,000, and 5 percent of molecules of molecular weight 100. (The low molecular weight fraction might be monomer, a low molecular weight polymer, or simply some impurity.) The $\overline{M}_n$ and $\overline{M}_w$ are calculated from Eqs. 1-14 and 1-16 as 1,680 and 9,505, respectively. The use of the $\overline{M}_n$ value of 1,680 gives an inaccurate indication of the properties of this polymer. The properties of the polymer are determined primarily by the 10,000 molecular weight molecules which comprise 95 percent of the weight of the mixture. The weight-average molecular weight is a much better indicator of the properties to be expected in a polymer. The utility of $\overline{M}_n$ resides primarily in its use to obtain an indication of polydispersity in a sample by measuring the ratio $\overline{M}_w/\overline{M}_n$.

In addition to the different average molecular weights of a polymer sample, it is frequently desirable and necessary to know the exact distribution of molecular weights. As indicated previously, there is usually a molecular weight range for which any given polymer property will be optimum for a particular application. The polymer sample containing the greatest percentage of polymer molecules of that size is the one which will have the optimum value of the desired property. Since samples with the same average molecular weight may possess different molecular weight distributions, information regarding the distribution allows the proper choice of a polymer for optimum performance. A variety of different fractionation methods are used to determine the molecular weight distribution of a polymer sample [9]. These are based on fractionation of a polymer sample using properties, such as solubility and permeability, which vary with molecular weight.

1-5 PHYSICAL STATE

1-5a Crystalline and Amorphous Behavior

Solid polymers differ from ordinary, low molecular weight compounds in the nature of their physical state or morphology. Most polymers simultaneously show the characteristics of both crystalline solids and highly viscous liquids [10, 11]. X-ray and electron diffraction patterns often show the sharp features typical of three-dimensionally ordered, crystalline materials as well as the diffuse features characteristic of liquids. The terms *crystalline* and *amorphous* are usually used to indicate the ordered and unordered polymer regions, respectively. Different polymers show different degrees of crystalline behavior. Although a few polymers may be completely amorphous and a few completely crystalline, most polymers are partially or *semi-crystalline* in character.

The exact nature of polymer crystallinity has been the subject of considerable controversy. The *fringed-micelle* theory, developed in the 1930's, considers polymers to consist of small-sized, ordered crystalline regions—termed *crystallites*—imbedded in an unordered, amorphous polymer matrix. Polymer molecules are considered to pass through several different crystalline regions with crystallites being formed when segments from different polymer chains are precisely aligned together and undergo crystallization. Each polymer chain can contribute ordered segments to several crystallites. The segments of the chain in between the crystallites make up the unordered amorphous matrix. This concept of polymer crystallinity is shown in Fig. 1-3.

The *folded-chain lamella* theory arose in the late 1950's when polymer single crystals in the form of thin platelets termed *lamella* were grown from polymer solutions. The diffraction patterns of these single crystals indicate that the polymer molecules fold back and forth on themselves like in an accordion in the process of crystallization (Fig. 1-4). The theory of chain-folding applies generally to most polymers—not only for solution-grown single crystals, but also for polymers crystallized from the melt. Semi-crystalline polymers are considered by advocates of the folded-chain theory to be

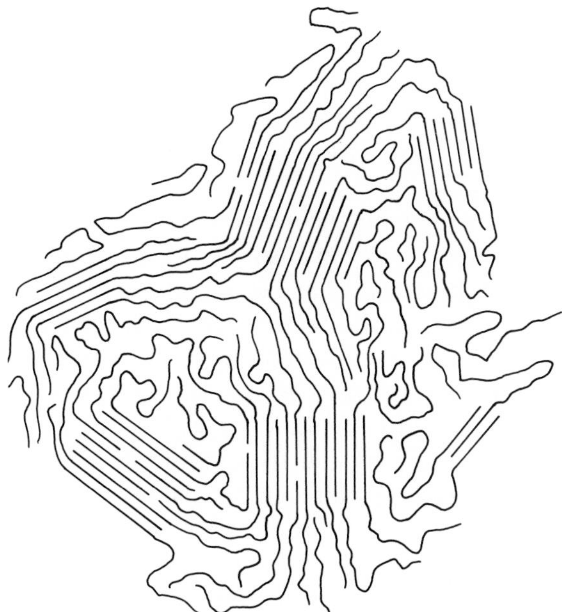

FIG. 1-3 *Fringed-micelle picture of polymer crystallinity.*

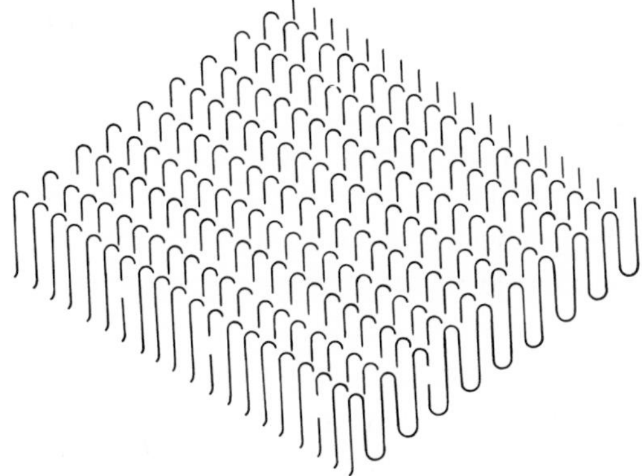

FIG. 1-4 *Folded-chain picture of polymer crystallinity.*

chain-folded crystals with varying amounts of defects. The crystallinity of polymers is pictured as being completely similar to that of low molecular weight compounds. The defects in the chain folded crystals may be imperfect folds, irregularities in packing, chain entanglements, loose chain ends, dislocations, occluded impurities, or numerous other imperfections.

The fringed-micelle and folded-chain theories of polymer crystallinity are often considered to be mutually exclusive but they need not be so considered. It is usually practical to adopt a working model of polymer crystallinity which employs the features of both concepts. The folded-chain theory is especially well suited for highly crystalline polymers where one can consider them to be one phase crystalline systems with defects. Polymers with medium to low crystallinity can often be advantageously treated by the fringed-micelle concept as two-phase systems composed of crystallites imbedded in uncrystallized, amorphous polymer. The structure of the crystallites in such polymers may be that of the folded-chain lamella. The extent and type of crystallinity in a polymer is experimentally determined by methods such as density, x-ray and electron diffraction, infrared spectroscopy, and nuclear magnetic resonance. The results are often interpreted in a simplified manner as a weight or volume percent crystallinity by comparison with measurements on completely crystalline and completely amorphous polymer samples.

1-5b Determinants of Polymer Crystallinity

Regardless of the precise picture of order and disorder in polymers, the prime consideration that should be emphasized is that polymers have a tendency to crystallize. The extent of this crystallization tendency plays a most significant role in the practical ways in which polymers are used. This is a consequence of the large effect of crystallinity on the thermal, mechanical, and other important properties of polymers. Different polymers have different properties and are synthesized and used differently because of varying degrees of crystallinity. It is useful to indicate the factors that lead to differences in crystallinity between various polymers. The extent to which a polymer crystallizes depends on whether its structure is conducive to packing into the crystalline state and on the magnitude of the secondary forces of the polymer chains. Packing is facilitated for polymer chains which have structural regularity, compactness, streamlining, and some degree of flexibility. The stronger the secondary forces, the greater will be the driving force for the ordering and crystallization of polymer chains.

Some polymers are highly crystalline primarily because their structure is conducive to packing, while others are crystalline primarily because of strong secondary forces. For still other polymers, both factors may be favorable for crystallization. Polyethylene, for example, has essentially the best structure in terms of its ability to pack into the crystalline state. Its very simple and perfectly regular structure allows chains to pack tightly and without any restrictions as to which segment of one chain need line up next to which other segment of the same chain or of another chain. The flexibility of the polyethylene chains is also conducive to crystallization in that the comformations required for packing can be easily achieved. Even though its secondary forces are small, polyethylene crystallizes easily and to a high degree because of its simple and regular structure.

Polymers other than polyethylene have less simple and regular chains. Poly(ϵ-caprolactam) can be considered as a modified polyethylene chain containing the amide group in between every five methylenes. Poly(ϵ-caprolactam) and other polyamides are highly crystalline polymers. The amide group is a polar one and leads to much larger secondary forces in polyamides (due to hydrogen bonding) compared to polyethylene; this is most favorable for crystallization. However, the polyamide chains are not as simple as those of polyethylene and packing requires that chain segments be brought together so that the amide groups are aligned. This restriction leads to a somewhat lessened degree of crystallization in polyamides than expected, based only on a consideration of the high secondary forces. Crystallinity in a polymer such as a polyamide can be significantly increased by mechanically stretching it to facilitate the ordering and alignment of polymer chains.

Polymers such as polystyrene, poly(vinyl chloride), and poly(methyl methacrylate) usually show very poor crystallization tendencies. Loss of structural regularity results in a very marked decrease in the tendency toward crystallization. The substituents hanging off the main polymer chains stiffen the chains and lead to difficulties in packing of the polymer chains, even though their dipoles result in higher secondary forces than in polyethylene. Polymers with rigid, cyclic structures in the polymer chain, as in cellulose and poly(ethylene terephthalate), are similarly difficult to crystallize. Excessive rigidity in polymers due to extensive crosslinking, as in phenol-formaldehyde and urea-formaldehyde polymers, also leads to an inability to crystallize.

Chain flexibility also affects the ability of a polymer to crystallize. Excessive flexibility in a polymer chain as in polysiloxanes and natural rubber leads to an inability of the chains to pack. The chain conformations required for packing cannot be maintained due to the high flexibility of the chains. The flexibility in the cases of the polysiloxanes and natural rubber is due to the bulky Si-O and cis-olefin groups, respectively. Such polymers remain as almost completely amorphous materials which, however, show the important property of elastic behavior.

1-5c Thermal Transitions

Polymeric materials are characterized by two major types of transition temperatures—the *crystalline melting temperature* T_m and the *glass transition temperature* T_g. The crystalline melting temperature is the melting temperature of the crystalline domains of a polymer sample. The glass transition temperature is the temperature at which the amorphous domains of a polymer take on the characteristic properties of the glassy state—brittleness, stiffness, and rigidity. The difference between the two thermal transitions can be understood more clearly by considering the changes which occur in a liquid polymer as it is cooled. The translational, rotational, and vibrational energies of the polymer molecules decrease on cooling. When the total energies of the molecules have fallen to the point where the translational and rotational energies are essentially zero, crystallization is possible. If certain symmetry requirements are met, the molecules are able to pack into an ordered, lattice arrangement and crystallization occurs. The temperature at which this occurs is T_m. However, not all polymers meet the necessary symmetry requirements for crystallization. If the symmetry requirements are not met, crystallization does not take place, but the energies of the molecules continue to decrease as the temperature decreases. A temperature is finally reached—the T_g—at which the wriggling (segmental) motions of the polymer chains stop due to the cessation of bond rotations.

Whether a polymer specimen exhibits both thermal transitions or only one depends on its morphology. Completely amorphous polymers show only a T_g and completely crystalline polymers only a T_m. Most polymers undergo only partial crystallization at T_m; these semicrystalline polymers exhibit both the crystalline melting and glass transition temperature. The two thermal transitions are conveniently measured by changes in properties such as specific volume and heat capacity. Figure 1-5 shows the changes in specific volume with temperature for completely amorphous and completely crystalline polymers (the solid lined plots). The crystalline melting temperature is a first-order transition with a discontinuous change in the specific volume at the transition temperature; the glass transition temperature is a second-order transition involving only a change in the temperature coefficient of the specific volume. The corresponding plot for a semi-crystalline polymer consists of the plot for the crystalline polymer plus the dotted portion corresponding to the glass transition.

The values of the crystalline melting and glass transition temperatures of a polymer affect its mechanical properties at any particular temperature and determine the temperature range in which that polymer can be employed. The T_g and T_m values for some of the common polymers are shown [12] in Table 1-3. Consider briefly the manner in which T_g and T_m vary from one polymer to another. One can discuss the two transitions simultaneously since, in general, both are similarly affected by considerations of polymer structure.

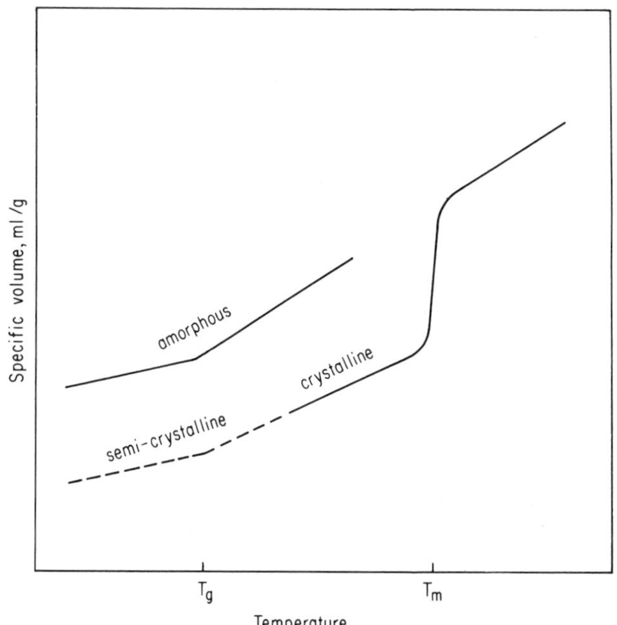

FIG. 1-5 *Determination of glass transition and crystalline melting temperatures by changes in specific volume.*

Table 1-3 Thermal Transitions of Polymers[a]

Polymer	Repeating unit	T_g (°C)	T_m (°C)
Polydimethylsiloxane	$—OSi(CH_3)_2—$	−123	−85 to −65
Polyethylene	$—CH_2CH_2—$	−115	137
Polyoxymethylene	$—CH_2O—$	− 85	181
Natural rubber	$—CH_2C(CH_3){=}CHCH_2—$	− 73	14
Polyisobutylene	$—CH_2C(CH_3)_2—$	− 73	44
Poly(ethylene oxide)	$—CH_2CH_2O—$	− 67	66
Polypropylene	$—CH_2CH(CH_3)—$	− 20	176
Poly(vinyl fluoride)	$—CH_2CHF—$	− 20	200
Poly(vinylidene chloride)	$—CH_2CCl_2—$	− 19	190
Poly(vinyl acetate)	$—CH_2CH(OCOCH_3)—$	28	
Poly(chlorotrifluoroethylene)	$—CF_2CFCl—$	45	220
Poly(ϵ-caprolactam)	$—(CH_2)_5CONH—$	50	223
Poly(hexamethylene adipamide)	$—NH(CH_2)_6NHCO(CH_2)_4CO—$	53	265
Poly(ethylene terephthalate)	$—OCH_2CH_2OCO—C_6H_4—CO—$	69	265
Poly(vinyl chloride)	$—CH_2CHCl—$	81	212
Polystyrene	$—CH_2CH\phi—$	100	240

Poly(methyl methacrylate)	$—CH_2C(CH_3)(CO_2CH_3)—$	105	200
Cellulose triacetate	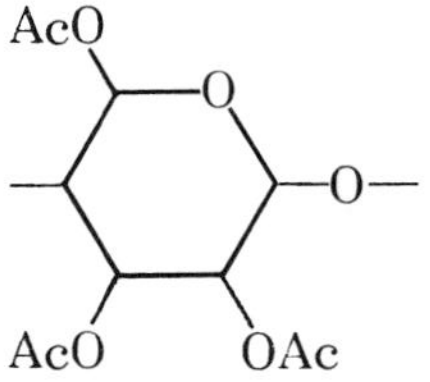 (ring structure: AcO, O, —O—, AcO, OAc)	105	306
Polytetrafluoroethylene	$—CF_2CF_2—$	127	327

[a]Data from [12].

Polymers with low T_g values usually have low T_m values; high T_g and high T_m values are usually found together. Polymer chains which do not easily undergo bond rotations so as to pass through the glass transition would also be expected to melt with difficulty. This is reasonable, since similar considerations of polymer structure are operating in both instances. The two thermal transitions are generally affected in the same manner by the molecular symmetry, structural rigidity, and secondary forces of polymer chains [10, 11]. High secondary forces (due to high polarity or hydrogen-bonding) lead to strong crystalline forces requiring high temperatures for melting. High secondary forces also decrease the mobility of the amorphous polymer chains leading to high T_g values. Decreased mobility of polymer chains, increased chain rigidity, and high T_g values are found where the chains are substituted with several substituents as in polyisobutylene and polytetrafluoroethylene or with bulky substituents as in polystyrene. The T_m values of crystalline polymers produced from such rigid chains would also be high. The rigidity of polymer chains is especially high when there are cyclic structures in the main polymer chains. Polymers such as cellulose acetate have high T_g and T_m values. On the other hand, the highly flexible polysiloxane chain leads to very low values of T_g and T_m.

Molecular symmetry of polymer chains also plays an important role in determining T_g and T_m. Asymmetrically structured polymers such as poly(vinyl chloride) and polypropylene have higher T_g and T_m values than their symmetrical counterparts poly(vinylidene chloride) and polyisobutylene. The asymmetric chains are more polar and can pack more tightly, leading to greater secondary forces. Although T_g and T_m depend similarly on the molecular structure of the polymer chains, the variations in the two transition temperatures do not always quantitatively parallel each other. Table 1-3 shows the various polymers listed in order of their increasing T_g values. The T_m values are seen to generally increase in the same order but there are many polymers whose T_m values do not follow in the same exact order. Molecular symmetry, chain rigidity, and secondary forces do not affect T_g and T_m in the same quantitative manner. Thus polyethylene and polyoxymethylene have low T_g values due to their highly flexible chains; however, their simple and regular structures yield tightly packed crystals with high T_m values.

It should be evident that some of the factors which decrease the crystallization tendency of a polymer also lead to increased values of T_m (and also of T_g). The reason for this is that the extent of crystallinity developed in a polymer is both kinetically and thermodynamically controlled while the melting temperature is only thermodynamically controlled. Polymers with rigid chains are difficult or slow to crystallize, but the portions which do crystallize will have high melting temperatures. (The extent of crystallinity can be greatly increased in such polymers by mechanical stretching to align and crystallize the polymer chains.) Thus, compare the differences between polyethylene and poly(hexamethylene adipamide). Polyethylene tends to crystallize easier and faster than the polyamide due to its simple and highly regular structure and is therefore usually obtained in higher degrees of crystallinity (about 80 percent versus 50 percent). On the other hand, the T_m of the polyamide is much higher (by about 130°C) than that of polyethylene because of the much greater secondary forces.

1-6 APPLICATIONS OF POLYMERS

1-6a Mechanical Properties

Many polymer properties such as gas permeability, solvent and chemical resistance, and electrical resistance are significant in determining the use of a specific polymer in a specific application. However, the prime consideration in determining the general utility of a polymer is its mechanical behavior, i.e., its deformation and flow characteristics under stress. The mechanical behavior of a polymer can be characterized by its *stress-strain* properties [13]. This involves observing the behavior of a polymer as one applies tension stress to it in order to elongate (strain) it to the point where it ruptures (pulls apart). The results are usually shown as a plot of the stress versus the elongation (strain). The stress is usually expressed in psi and the elongation as the fractional increase in the length of the polymer sample (i.e., $\Delta L/L$ where L is the original, unstretched sample length). (The elongation can also be expressed as the percent elongation, defined by $\Delta L/L \times 100$ percent.) Several such plots, referred to as stress-strain plots, are shown in Fig. 1-6. Four important quantities characterize the stress-strain behavior of a polymer:

1) *Modulus*—the resistance to deformation as measured by the initial stress divided by $\Delta L/L$

2) *Ultimate strength* or *tensile strength*—the stress required to rupture the sample

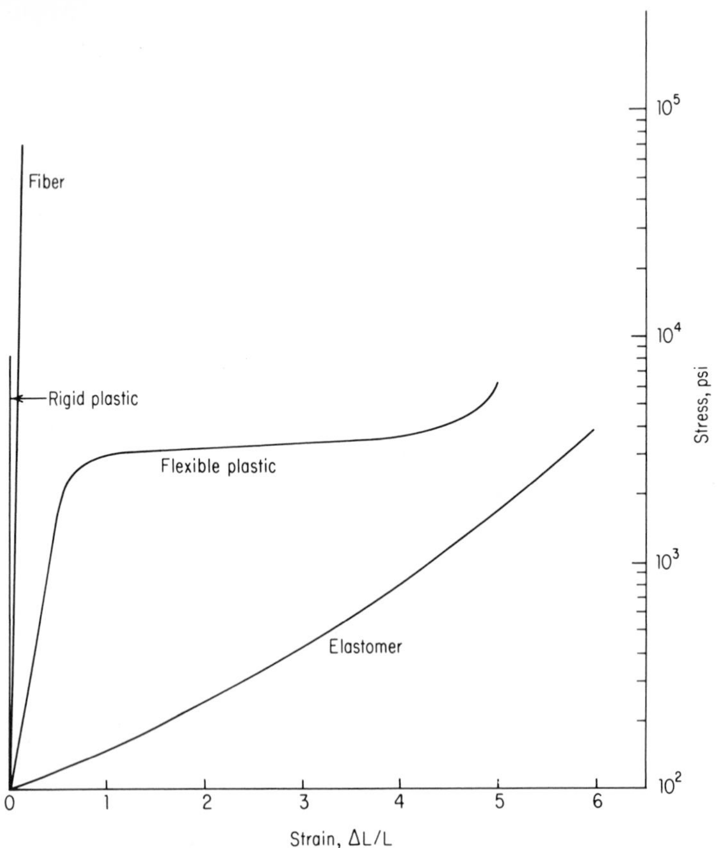

FIG. 1-6 *Stress-strain plots for a typical elastomer, flexible plastic, rigid plastic, and fiber.*

3) *Ultimate elongation*—the extent of elongation at the point where the sample ruptures

4) *Elastic elongation*—the elasticity as measured by the extent of reversible elongation

Polymers vary widely in their mechanical behavior depending on the degree of crystallinity, the degree of crosslinking, and the values of T_g and T_m. High strength and low extensibility are obtained in polymers by having high degrees of crystallinity or crosslinking, or a high glass transition temperature. High extensibility and low strength in polymers are synonymous with low degrees of crystallinity and crosslinking and low T_g values. The temperature limits of utility of a polymer are governed by its crystalline melting and/or glass transition temperatures; strength is lost above T_g for an amorphous polymer and above T_m for a crystalline polymer.

There is an almost infinite variety of polymeric materials that can be produced. The polymer scientist must have an awareness of the properties desired in the final polymer in order to make a decision about the polymer to be synthesized. Different polymers are synthesized to yield various mechanical behaviors by the appropriate combinations of crystallinity, crosslinking, T_g, and T_m. Depending on the particular combination, a specific polymer will be used as a *fiber, flexible plastic, rigid plastic,* or *elastomer (rubber)* [14–16]. Commonly encountered articles which typify these uses of polymers are clothing (fiber), packaging films (flexible plastic), contact lenses (rigid plastic), and rubber bands (elastomer). Table 1-4 shows the uses of many of the common polymers. Some polymers are used in more than one category because certain mechanical properties can be altered by appropriate chemical or physical methods—usually by affecting the degree of crystallinity. Some polymers are used as both plastics and fibers; others as both elastomers and plastics.

Table 1-4 Uses of Polymers

<table>
<tr><th>Elastomers</th><th>Plastics</th><th>Fibers</th></tr>
<tr><td>Polyisoprene
Polyisobutylene</td><td>Polyethylene
Polytetrafluoroethylene
Poly(methyl methacrylate)
Phenol-formaldehyde
Urea-formaldehyde
Melamine-formaldehyde</td><td></td></tr>
<tr><td colspan="2">←Polystyrene→</td><td></td></tr>
<tr><td colspan="2">←Poly(vinyl chloride)→</td><td></td></tr>
<tr><td colspan="2">←Polyurethane→</td><td></td></tr>
<tr><td colspan="2">←Polysiloxane→</td><td></td></tr>
<tr><td></td><td colspan="2">←Polyamide→</td></tr>
<tr><td></td><td colspan="2">←Polyester→</td></tr>
<tr><td></td><td colspan="2">←Cellulosics→</td></tr>
<tr><td></td><td colspan="2">←Polypropylene→</td></tr>
<tr><td></td><td></td><td>Polyacrylonitrile</td></tr>
</table>

1-6b Elastomers, Fibers, Plastics

The differences between fibers, plastics, and elastomers can be seen in the typical stress-strain plots in Fig. 1-6. The modulus of a polymer is the initial slope of such a plot; the tensile strength and ultimate elongation are the highest stress and elongation values, respectively. Elastomers are the group of polymers which can easily undergo very large, reversible elongations (up to 500–1,000 percent) at relatively low stresses. This requires that the polymer be completely amorphous with a low glass transition temperature and low secondary forces so as to obtain high mobility of the polymer chains. Some degree of crosslinking is needed so that the deformation is rapidly reversible (elastic). The initial modulus of an elastomer should be very small ($<$ 150 psi) but this should increase fairly rapidly with increasing elongation, i.e., it should develop a progressively increasing resistance to elongation; otherwise it will have no overall strength. Many elastomers obtain such strength by undergoing partial crystallization during the elongation. However, the T_m of the crystalline regions must be below the use temperature of the elastomer in order that the crystals melt and deformation be reversible when the stress on the elastomer is removed. If the polymer does not undergo crystallization during stretching, strength can be imparted by the use of crosslinking and the incorporation of inorganic reinforcing fillers. Polyisoprene (natural rubber) is a typical elastomer–it is amorphous, easily crosslinked, has a low T_g (−73°C), crystallizes on stretching, and has a low T_m (14°C). The crosslinked rubber has a modulus which is initially less than 100 psi; however, its strength increases to about 2,000 psi at 400 percent elongation and about 3,000 psi at 500 percent elongation. Its elongation is reversible over the whole range of elongation, i.e., just prior to the rupture point.

Fibers are polymers which have very high resistance to deformation–they undergo only low elongations ($<$ 10–50 percent) and have very high moduli ($>$ 50,000 psi) and tensile strengths ($>$ 50,000 psi). A polymer must be very highly crystalline and contain polar chains with strong secondary forces in order to be useful as a fiber. Mechanical stretching is used to impart very high crystallinity to a fiber. The crystalline melting temperature of a fiber must be above 200°C so that it will maintain its physical integrity during the use temperatures encountered in cleaning and ironing. However, T_m should not be excessively high–not higher than 300°C–otherwise, fabrication of the fiber by melt spinning may not be possible. The polymer should be soluble in solvents used for solution spinning of the fiber but not in dry cleaning solvents. The glass transition temperature should have an intermediate value; too high a T_g interferes with the stretching operation as well as with ironing, while too low a T_g would not allow crease retention in fabrics. Poly(hexamethylene adipamide) is a typical fiber. It is stretched to high crystallinity and its amide groups yield very strong secondary forces due to hydrogen bonding; the result is very high tensile strength (100,000 psi) and modulus (700,000 psi), and low elongation (< 20 percent). The T_m and T_g have optimal values of 265°C and 53°C, respectively.

Plastics comprise a large group of polymers which have a wide range of mechanical behaviors in between those of the elastomers and fibers. There are two types of plastics–flexible plastics and rigid plastics. The flexible plastics possess moderate-to-high degrees of crystallinity and a wide range of T_m and T_g values. They have moderate-to-high moduli (20,000–500,000 psi), tensile strengths (2,000–10,000 psi), and ultimate elongations (20–800 percent). The more typical members of this sub-group have moduli and tensile strengths in the low ends of the indicated ranges with elongations in the high end. Thus, polyethylene is a typical flexible plastic with a tensile strength of 3,500 psi, a modulus of 30,000 psi, and an ultimate elongation of 500 percent. Other flexible plastics include polypropylene and poly(hexamethylene adipamide). Poly(hexamethylene adipamide) is used as both a fiber and a flexible plastic. It is a plastic when it has moderate crystallinity, while stretching converts it into a fiber. Many flexible plastics undergo large ultimate elongations–some as large as those of elastomers. However, they differ from elastomers in that only a small portion (approximately < 20 percent) of the ultimate elongation is reversible. The elongation of a plastic past the reversible region results in its permanent deformation, i.e., the plastic will retain its elongated shape when the stress is removed.

The rigid plastics are quite different from the flexible plastics. The rigid plastics are characterized by high rigidity and high resistance to deformation. They have high moduli (100,000–500,000 psi), and moderate-to-high tensile strengths (5,000–12,000 psi), but more significantly, they undergo very small elongations ($<$ 0.5–3 percent) before rupturing. The polymers in this category are amorphous polymers with very rigid chains. The high chain rigidity is achieved in some cases by extensive crosslinking, e.g., phenol-formaldehyde, urea-formaldehyde, and melamine-formaldehyde polymers. In other polymers, the high rigidity is due to bulky side groups on the polymer chains resulting in high T_g values, e.g., polystyrene ($T_g = 100°C$) and poly(methyl methacrylate) ($T_g = 105°C$).

REFERENCES

1. W. H. Carothers, *J. Am. Chem. Soc.,* **51**:2548 (1929).
2. M. L. Huggins, P. Corradini, V. Desreux, O. Kratsky, and H. Mark, *J. Polymer Sci.,* **B6**:257 (1968).
3. P. J. Flory, "Principles of Polymer Chemistry," chap. II, Cornell University Press, Ithaca, New York, 1953.
4. R. B. Fox, R. Beaman, N. M. Bikales, B. P. Block, W. E. Cohn, H. K. Livingston, K. L. Loening, A. Mercurio, and A. M. Schiller, *Macromolecules,* **1**:193 (1968); *Polymer Preprints,* **8(1)**, e(1967).
5. J. Brandup and E. H. Immergut (eds.), "Polymer Handbook," chap. I, Interscience Publishers, John Wiley & Sons, Inc., New York, 1966.
6. M. L. Miller, "The Structure of Polymers," chaps. 1-3, 7, Reinhold Book Corp., New York, 1966.
7. F. W. Billmeyer, Jr., *J. Polymer Sci.,* **C8**:161 (1965).
8. H. Morawetz, "Macromolecules in Solution," chap. IV–VI, Interscience Publishers, John Wiley & Sons, Inc., New York, 1965.
9. M. J. R. Cantow (ed.), "Polymer Fractionation," Academic Press, Inc., New York, 1967.
10. M. Gordon, "High Polymers," chaps. 3-7, Addison-Wesley Publishing Co., Inc., Reading, Mass., 1963.
11. A. Sharples, "Introduction to Polymer Crystallization," chaps. 1–3, 9–10, St. Martin's Press, New York, 1966.
12. J. Brandup and E. H. Immergut (eds.), "Polymer Handbook," pp. III-32–92, Interscience Publishers, John Wiley & Sons, Inc., New York, 1966.
13. L. E. Nielsen, "Mechanical Properties of Polymers," Reinhold Book Corp., New York, 1962.
14. W. Cooper and N. S. Grace, *J. Polymer Sci.,* **C12**:133 (1966).
15. E. A. Tippetts and J. Zimmerman, *J. Appl. Polymer Sci.,* 8:2465 (1964).
16. F. W. Billmeyer, Jr., "Textbook of Polymer Science," chaps. 20–22, Interscience Publishers, John Wiley & Sons, Inc., New York, 1962.

PROBLEMS

1-1. Show by equations the overall chemical reactions involved in the synthesis of polymers from *a.* $CH_2{=}CH{-}CO_2H$

b. $\underline{CH_2CH_2CH_2O}$ (ring: the first CH_2 is bonded to O)

c. $H_2N{-}(CH_2)_5{-}NH_2 + ClCO{-}(CH_2)_5{-}COCl$

d. $HO{-}(CH_2)_5{-}CO_2H$

e. $CH_3{-}C_6H_3(NCO){-}NCO + HO{-}CH_2CH_2{-}OH$ (benzene ring bearing CH_3, NCO, and a second NCO on the ring)

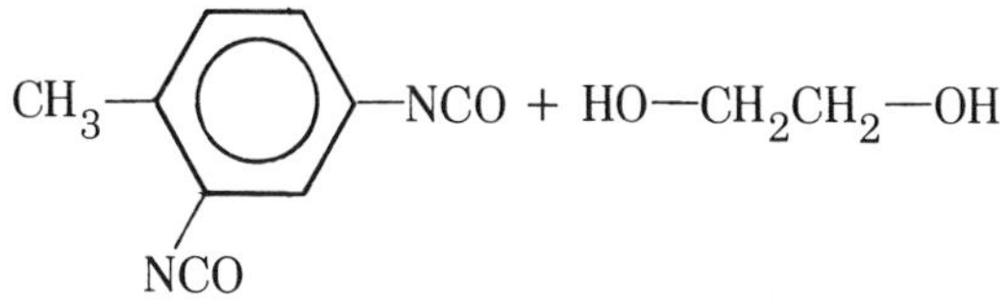

f. $CH_2{=}CH{-}F$

1-2. What is the structure of the repeating unit in each of the polymers in Question 1-1? Can any other monomer(s) be used to obtain the same polymer structure?

1-3. Name each of the polymers in Question 1-1. Indicate alternate names where applicable.

1-4. Classify the polymers as to whether they are condensation or addition polymers. Classify the polymerizations as to whether they are step, chain, or ring-opening polymerizations.

1-5. How would you experimentally determine whether the polymerization of an unknown monomer X was proceeding by a step or a chain mechanism?

1-6. A sample of polystyrene is composed of a series of fractions of different-sized molecules:

Fraction	Weight fraction	Molecular weight
A	0.10	12,000
B	0.19	21,000
C	0.24	35,000
D	0.18	49,000
E	0.11	73,000
F	0.08	102,000
G	0.06	122,000
H	0.04	146,000

Calculate the number-average and weight-average molecular weights of this polymer sample. Draw a molecular weight distribution curve analogous to Fig. 1-2.

2

STEP POLYMERIZATION

Most of the common condensation polymers are listed in Table 1-1. In all instances the polymerization reactions shown are those proceeding by the step polymerization mechanism. This chapter will consider the characteristics of step polymerization in detail. The synthesis of condensation polymers by ring-opening polymerization will be subsequently treated in Chap. 7. Many different chemical reactions may be used to synthesize polymeric materials by step polymerization. These include esterification, amidation, the formation of urethanes, aromatic substitution, and others as noted in Chap. 1. Polymerization proceeds by the reactions between two different functional groups, e.g., hydroxyl and carboxyl groups, or isocyanate and hydroxyl groups.

All step polymerizations fall into two groups depending on the type of monomer(s) employed. The first involves two different polyfunctional monomers in which each monomer possesses only one type of functional group. (A *polyfunctional monomer* is one with two or more functional groups per molecule.) The second involves a single monomer containing both types of functional groups. The synthesis of polyamides illustrates both groups of polymerization reactions. Thus, polyamides can be obtained from the reaction of diamines with diacids

$$n\ H_2N{-}R{-}NH_2 + n\ HO_2C{-}R'{-}CO_2H \longrightarrow$$

$$H{+}NH{-}R{-}NHCO{-}R'{-}CO{+}_nOH + (2n-1)\ H_2O \qquad (1\text{-}1)$$

or from the reaction of amino acids with themselves

$$n\ H_2N{-}R{-}CO_2H \longrightarrow H{+}NH{-}R{-}CO{+}_nOH + (n-1)\ H_2O \qquad (2\text{-}1)$$

The two groups of reactions can be represented in a general manner by the equations

$$n\ A{-}A + n\ B{-}B \longrightarrow {+}A{-}AB{-}B{+}_n \qquad (2\text{-}2)$$

$$n\ A{-}B \longrightarrow {+}A{-}B{+}_n \qquad (2\text{-}3)$$

where A and B are the two different types of functional groups. The characteristics of these two polymerization reactions are very similar. The successful synthesis of high polymers (i.e., polymer of sufficiently high molecular weight to be useful from the practical viewpoint) requires the same kinds of stringent precautions and controls.

2-1 REACTIVITY OF FUNCTIONAL GROUPS

2-1a Basis for Analysis of Polymerization Kinetics

The kinetics of polymerization are of prime interest from two viewpoints. The practical synthesis of high polymers requires a knowledge of the kinetics of the polymerization reaction. From the theoretical viewpoint, the significant differences between step and chain polymerizations reside in large part in their respective kinetic features.

Step polymerization proceeds by a slow increase in the molecular weight of the polymer. Consider the synthesis of a polyester from a diol and a diacid. The first step is the reaction of the diol and diacid monomers to form dimer

$$\text{HO—R—OH} + \text{HO}_2\text{C—R}'\text{—CO}_2\text{H} \longrightarrow$$

$$\text{HO—R—OCO—R}'\text{—CO}_2\text{H} + \text{H}_2\text{O} \tag{2-4}$$

The dimer then reacts with itself to form tetramer

$$2\ \text{HO—R—OCO—R}'\text{—CO}_2\text{H} \longrightarrow$$

$$\text{HO—R—OCO—R}'\text{—CO}_2\text{—R—OCO—R}'\text{—CO}_2\text{H} + \text{H}_2\text{O} \tag{2-5}$$

or with unreacted monomer to yield trimer

$$\text{HO—R—OCO—R}'\text{—CO}_2\text{H} + \text{HO—R—OH} \longrightarrow$$

$$\text{HO—R—OCO—R}'\text{—CO}_2\text{R—OH} + \text{H}_2\text{O} \tag{2-6}$$

The tetramer and trimer proceed to react with themselves, with each other, and with monomer and dimer. The polymerization proceeds in this stepwise manner with the molecular weight of the polymer continuously increasing. Step polymerizations are characterized by the disappearance of monomer very early in the reaction far before the production of any polymer of sufficiently high molecular weight (approximately $>$ 5,000–10,000) to be of practical utility. Thus, for most step polymerizations there is less than 1 percent of the original monomer remaining at a point where the average polymer chain contains only approximately 10 monomer units. As will be seen in Chap. 3, the situation is quite different in the case of chain polymerization.

The rate of a step polymerization is, therefore, the sum of the rates of reaction between molecules of various sizes, that is, the sum of the rates for reactions such as

monomer + monomer ⟶ dimer
dimer + monomer ⟶ trimer
dimer + dimer ⟶ tetramer
trimer + dimer ⟶ pentamer
tetramer + monomer ⟶ pentamer
tetramer + dimer ⟶ hexamer
tetramer + trimer ⟶ heptamer
tetramer + tetramer ⟶ octamer

$$\begin{aligned}&\text{pentamer} + \text{trimer} \longrightarrow \text{octamer}\\&\text{pentamer} + \text{tetramer} \longrightarrow \text{nonamer}\\&\text{etc.}\\&\text{etc.}\end{aligned} \tag{2-7a}$$

which can be expressed as the general reaction

$$n\text{-mer} + m\text{-mer} \longrightarrow (n+m)\text{-mer} \tag{2-7b}$$

A characteristic of step polymerization is that any two species in the reaction mixture can react with each other.

The kinetics of such a situation with innumerable separate reactions would normally be difficult to analyze. However, the kinetic analysis is greatly simplified if one assumes that the reactivities of both functional groups of a bifunctional monomer (e.g., both hydroxyls of a diol) are the same, the reactivity of one functional group of a bifunctional reactant is the same irrespective of whether or not the other functional group has reacted, and the reactivity of a functional group is independent of the size of the molecule to which it is attached (i.e., independent of the values of n and m). These simplifying assumptions make the kinetics of step polymerization identical to those for the analogous small molecule reaction. As will be seen shortly, the kinetics of a polyesterification, for example, become essentially the same as that for the esterification of acetic acid with ethanol.

2-1b Experimental Evidence

These simplifying assumptions are justified on the basis that many step polymerizations have reaction rate constants which are independent of the reaction time or polymer molecular weight. It is, however, useful to examine in more detail the experimental and theoretical justifications for these assumptions. Studies of the reactions of certain non-polymeric molecules are especially useful for understanding polymerization kinetics [1]. The independence of the reactivity of a functional group on molecular size can be observed from the reaction rates in a homologous series of compounds differing from each other only in molecular weight. Consider, for example, the rate constant data [2] in the first column in Table 2-1 for the esterification of a series of homologous carboxylic acids

$$H(CH_2)_nCO_2H + C_2H_5OH \xrightarrow{HCl} H(CH_2)_nCO_2C_2H_5 + H_2O \tag{2-8}$$

Table 2-1 Rate Constants for Esterification (25°C) in Homologous Compounds[a,b]

Molecular size (n)	$k \times 10^4$ for $H(CH_2)_nCO_2H$	$k \times 10^4$ for $(CH_2)_n(CO_2H)_2$
1	22.1	
2	15.3	6.0
3	7.5	8.7
4	7.5	8.4
5	7.4	7.8
6		7.3
8	7.5	
9	7.4	
11	7.6	
13	7.5	
15	7.7	
17	7.7	

[a]All rate constants are in units of (moles carboxyl groups/liter)$^{-1}$sec^{-1}.
[b]Data from [2].

It is evident that although there is a decrease in reactivity with increased molecular size, the effect is only significant at a very small size. The reaction rate constant very quickly (at $n = 3$) reaches a limiting value which remains constant and independent of molecular size. Other reactions show similar behavior. Thus, the rate constant for the reaction of a 393 molecular weight poly(ethylene oxide) with hydroxyl end-groups (i.e., hydroxyl groups on both ends of the polymer molecule) with phenyl isocyanate at 30°C in toluene solution

$$HO(CH_2CH_2O)_{17}H + \phi\text{—}NCO \longrightarrow$$

$$\phi\text{—}NH\text{—}COO\text{—}(CH_2CH_2O)_{17}H \tag{2-9}$$

is 1.5×10^{-3} liter/mole-sec compared to a value of 1.7×10^{-3} liter/mole-sec for the corresponding reaction of 1-butanol with phenyl isocyanate [3]

$$CH_3CH_2CH_2CH_2OH + \phi\text{—}NCO \longrightarrow$$

$$\phi\text{—}NH\text{—}COO\text{—}CH_2CH_2CH_2CH_3 \tag{2-10}$$

The independence of functional group reactivity of molecular size is contrary to the general impression that was widely held in the early years of polymer science. There was a general misconception of decreased reactivity with increased molecular size. This was due in large part to the fact that reactions with the larger sized species were often attempted without adjusting concentrations so as to have equivalent concentrations of the reacting functional groups. In many instances, the low or difficult solubility of the higher molecular weight reactants in a homologous series was responsible for the observed, apparent low reactivity. These effects are still pitfalls to be avoided by beginning students.

2-1c Theoretical Considerations

There is ample theoretical justification for the independence of the reactivity of a functional group of molecular size [4]. The fairly common misconception regarding the alleged low reactivity of groups attached to large molecules comes from the lower diffusion rates of the latter. However, the observed reactivity of a functional group is dependent on the collision frequency of the group, not on the diffusion rate of the whole molecule. The collision frequency is the number of collisions one functional group makes with other functional groups per unit of time. A terminal functional group attached to a growing polymer has a much greater mobility than would be expected from the mobility of the polymer molecule as a whole. The functional group has appreciable mobility due to the rearrangements which occur in nearby segments of the polymer chain. The collision rate of such a functional group with neighboring groups will be about the same as for small molecules.

The lowered mobility of the polymer molecule as a whole alters the time distribution of collisions. A lower diffusion rate means that any two functional groups will undergo more total collisions before diffusing apart. Thus, in any particular time interval (which is long compared to the interval required for diffusion of a group from one collision partner to the next) the number of partners with which a functional group undergoes collisions is less for a group attached to a polymer chain than for one attached to a small molecule. But, most significantly, their overall collision frequencies are the same in the two cases. If the diffusion of a functional group from one collision partner to the next were too slow to maintain the concentration of the reactive pairs of functional groups at equilibrium, one would observe decreased reactivity for the functional group. The opposite is the case since reaction between two functional groups in a step polymerization occurs only about once in every 10^{13} collisions [1]. During the time interval required for this many collisions, sufficient diffusion of the molecule and of the functional group occurs to maintain the equilibrium concentration of collision pairs of functional groups. The net result of these considerations is that the reactivity of a functional group will be independent of the size of the molecule to which it is attached. Exceptions to this occur when the reactivities of the groups are very high and/or the molecular weights of the polymer are very high. The polymerization becomes diffusion controlled in these cases because mobility is too low to allow maintenance of the equilibrium concentration of reactive pairs and of their collision frequencies.

2-1d Equivalence of Groups in Bifunctional Reactants

The equivalence of the reactivities of the two functional groups in bifunctional reactants has also been demonstrated in many systems. The second column in Table 2-1 shows data for the esterification of a homologous series of dibasic acids

$$\mathrm{HO_2C{-}(CH_2)_n{-}CO_2H + 2\,C_2H_5OH \longrightarrow}$$

$$\mathrm{C_2H_5O_2C{-}(CH_2)_n{-}CO_2C_2H_5 + 2\,H_2O} \tag{2-11}$$

The rate constants tabulated are the averages of those for the two carboxyl groups in each dibasic acid. The rate constants for the two carboxyls were the same within experimental error. Further, a very important observation is that the reactivity of one of the functional groups is not dependent on whether the other has reacted. As in the case of the monocarboxylic acids, the reactivity of the carboxyl group quickly reaches a limiting value.

It should not be concluded that the reactivity of a functional group is not altered by the presence of a second group. The data show that at small values of n up to 4 or 5, there is an effect of the second group. In most instances the effect disappears fairly rapidly with increasing molecular size as the two functional groups become isolated from each other. Thus, the rate constant for the esterification of the dibasic acid with $n = 6$ is the same as that for the monobasic acids. It might appear at first glance that polymerizations involving bifunctional reagents with low n values would present a problem. However, the difference in reactivities of the functional groups of a bifunctional reagent compared to the functional group in a monofunctional reagent is not an important consideration in handling the kinetics of step polymerization. The most significant considerations are that the reactivity of a functional group in a bifunctional monomer is not altered by the reaction of the other group, and that the reactivities of the two functional groups are the same and do not change during the course of the polymerization.

2-2 KINETICS OF STEP POLYMERIZATION

Consider the polyesterification of a diacid and a diol to illustrate the general form of the kinetics of a typical step polymerization. Simple esterification is a well-known acid catalyzed reaction and polyesterification, no doubt, follows the same course [5]. The reaction involves protonation of the carboxylic acid

$$\sim\!\!\sim\!\!\sim \overset{\displaystyle O}{\overset{\|}{C}}\text{—OH} + \text{HA} \underset{k_2}{\overset{k_1}{\rightleftharpoons}} \sim\!\!\sim\!\!\sim \underset{\underset{\displaystyle \text{I}}{+}}{\overset{\overset{\displaystyle \text{OH}}{|}}{C}}\text{—OH} + \text{A}^- \tag{2-12}$$

followed by reaction of the protonated species with the alcohol to yield the ester

$$\sim\!\!\sim\!\!\sim \underset{+}{\overset{\overset{\displaystyle \text{OH}}{|}}{C}}\text{—OH} + \sim\!\!\sim \text{OH} \underset{k_4}{\overset{k_3}{\rightleftharpoons}} \sim\!\!\sim\!\!\sim \underset{\underset{\underset{\displaystyle \text{II}}{\overset{\sim\sim\text{OH}}{+}}}{|}}{\overset{\overset{\displaystyle \text{OH}}{|}}{C}}\text{—OH} \tag{2-13}$$

$$\sim\!\!\sim\!\!\sim \underset{\underset{\overset{\sim\sim\text{OH}}{+}}{|}}{\overset{\overset{\displaystyle \text{OH}}{|}}{C}}\text{—OH} \overset{k_5}{\rightleftharpoons} \sim\!\!\sim\!\!\sim \overset{\displaystyle O}{\overset{\|}{C}}\text{—O}\sim\!\!\sim + H_2O + H^+ \tag{2-14}$$

In the above equations $\sim\!\sim\!\sim$ and $\sim\!\sim$ are used to indicate all acid or alcohol species in the reaction mixture (i.e., monomer, dimer, trimer, . . . , n-mer). Polyesterifications, like many other step polymerizations, are equilibrium reactions. However, from the practical viewpoint of obtaining high yields of high molecular weight product, such polymerizations are run in a manner so as to continuously shift the equilibrium in the direction of the polymer. In the case of a polyesterification, this is easily accomplished by removal of the water which is a product of the reaction of species II (Eq. 2-14). Under these conditions, the kinetics of the polymerization can be handled by considering the reactions in Eqs. 2-13 and 2-14 to be irreversible. (A brief consideration of the kinetics of a reversible step polymerization is given in Sec. 2-6b-1-b.)

The rate of a step polymerization is usually most conveniently expressed in terms of the concentrations of the reacting functional groups. Thus, the polyesterification can be experimentally followed by titrating for the unreacted carboxyl groups with a base. The *rate of polymerization* R_p can then be expressed as the *rate of disappearance of carboxyl groups*, $-d[CO_2H]/dt$. For the usual polyesterification, the polymerization rate is synonymous with the rate of formation of species II, i.e., k_4 is non-existent (since the reaction is run under non-equilibrium conditions), and k_1, k_2, and k_5 are large compared to k_3. An expression for the reaction rate can be obtained following the general procedures [6] for handling a reaction scheme with the characteristics described. The rate of polyesterification is given by

$$R_p = \frac{-d[\mathrm{COOH}]}{dt} = k_3[\overset{+}{\mathrm{C}}(\mathrm{OH})_2][\mathrm{OH}] \tag{2-15}$$

where [COOH], [OH], and $[\overset{+}{\mathrm{C}}(\mathrm{OH})_2]$ represent the concentrations of carboxyl, hydroxyl, and protonated carboxyl groups, respectively. The concentration terms are in units of moles of the particular functional group per liter of solution.

Equation 2-15 is inconvenient in that the concentration of protonated carboxyl groups is not easily determined experimentally. One can obtain a more convenient expression for the polymerization rate by substituting for $[\overset{+}{\mathrm{C}}(\mathrm{OH})_2]$ from the equilibrium expression

$$K = \frac{k_1}{k_2} = \frac{[\overset{+}{\mathrm{C}}(\mathrm{OH})_2][\mathrm{A}^-]}{[\mathrm{COOH}][\mathrm{HA}]} \tag{2-16}$$

for the protonation reaction (Eq. 2-12). Combination of Eqs. 2-15 and 2-16 yields

$$\frac{-d[\mathrm{COOH}]}{dt} = \frac{k_1 k_3 [\mathrm{COOH}][\mathrm{OH}][\mathrm{HA}]}{k_2 [\mathrm{A}^-]} \tag{2-17a}$$

This equation can also be written in the form

$$\frac{-d[\mathrm{COOH}]}{dt} = \frac{k_1 k_3 [\mathrm{COOH}][\mathrm{OH}][\mathrm{H}^+]}{k_2 K_{\mathrm{HA}}} \tag{2-17b}$$

where K_{HA} is the acid dissociation constant for HA. Two quite distinct kinetic situations arise from Eq. 2-17 depending on the identity of HA, i.e., on whether or not a strong acid such as sulfuric acid is added as an external catalyst.

2-2a Self-Catalyzed Polymerization

In the absence of an externally added strong acid, the diacid monomer acts as its own catalyst for the esterification reaction. For this case [HA] is replaced by [COOH] and Eq. 2-17a can be written in the usual form [1, 7]

$$\frac{-d[\mathrm{COOH}]}{dt} = k[\mathrm{COOH}]^2[\mathrm{OH}] \tag{2-18}$$

where the three rate constants k_1, k_2, k_3 and the concentration term $[\mathrm{A}^-]$ have been collected into the experimentally determined rate constant k. Equation 2-18 shows the important characteristic of the self-catalyzed polymerization—the reaction is third order overall with a second order dependence on the carboxyl concentration. The second order dependence on the carboxyl concentration is comprised of two first order dependencies—one for the carboxyl as the reactant and one as the catalyst.

For most polymerizations, the concentrations of the two functional groups are very nearly stoichiometric and Eq. 2-18 can be written as

$$\frac{-d[\mathrm{M}]}{dt} = k[\mathrm{M}]^3 \tag{2-19a}$$

or

$$\frac{-d[\mathrm{M}]}{[\mathrm{M}]^3} = k\,dt \tag{2-19b}$$

where [M] is the concentration of hydroxyl groups or carboxyl groups. Integration of Eq. 2-19b yields

$$2kt = \frac{1}{[\mathrm{M}]^2} - \text{constant} \tag{2-20}$$

The constant in Eq. 2-20 is $1/[\mathrm{M}]_0^2$ where $[\mathrm{M}]_0$ is the initial (at $t = 0$) concentration of hydroxyl or carboxyl groups. It is convenient at this point to write Eq. 2-20 in terms of the *extent of reaction* p defined as the fraction of the hydroxyl or carboxyl functional groups that has reacted at time t. (The value of p is calculated from the determination of the unreacted carboxyl concentration.) The concentration [M] at time t of either hydroxyl or carboxyl groups is then given by

$$[\mathrm{M}] = [\mathrm{M}]_0 - [\mathrm{M}]_0\, p = [\mathrm{M}]_0(1-p) \tag{2-21}$$

Combination of Eqs. 2-20 and 2-21 yields

$$2[\mathrm{M}]_0^2 kt = \frac{1}{(1-p)^2} - \text{constant} \tag{2-22}$$

2-2a-1 Experimental Observations. Equation 2-22 indicates that a plot of $1/(1-p)^2$ versus t should be linear. This behavior has been generally observed in polyesterifications. Figure 2-1 shows the results for the polymerization of diethylene glycol, $(HOCH_2CH_2)_2O$, and adipic acid [8, 9]. The results are typical of the behavior generally observed for polyesterifications. At first glance, the plot does not appear to exactly follow the relationship. The experimental points deviate from the third order plot in the initial region below 80% conversion and in the later stages above 93% conversion. These deviations have led various workers to suggest alternate kinetic expressions [9, 10] based on either first or three-halves order

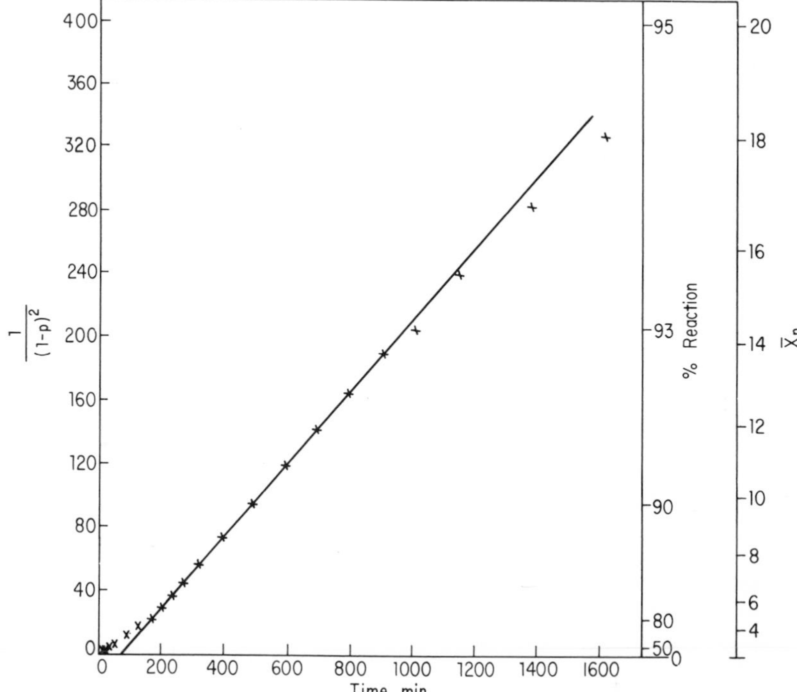

FIG. 2-1 *Third order plot of the self-catalyzed polyesterification of adipic acid with diethylene glycol at 166°C. After [9] (by permission of Marcel Dekker, Inc., New York) from the data of [8] (by permission of American Chemical Society, Washington).*

dependencies of the reaction rate on the carboxyl concentration, i.e., second order and two and one-half order overall dependencies according to

$$\frac{-d\,[\mathrm{COOH}]}{dt} = k\,[\mathrm{COOH}][\mathrm{OH}] \tag{2-23a}$$

and

$$\frac{-d\,[\mathrm{COOH}]}{dt} = k\,[\mathrm{COOH}]^{3/2}\,[\mathrm{OH}] \tag{2-23b}$$

However, a critical evaluation shows that both kinetic possibilities leave much to be desired [9]. A plot (Fig. 2-2) of the experimental

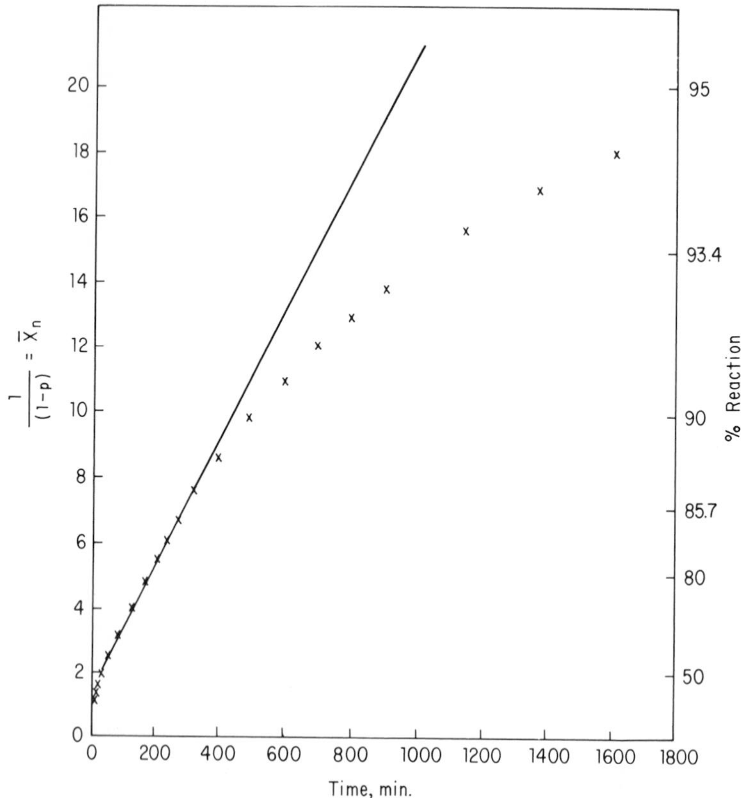

FIG. 2-2 *Second order plot of the self-catalyzed polyesterification of adipic acid with diethylene glycol at 166°C. After [9] (by permission of Marcel Dekker, Inc., New York) from the data of [8] (by permission of American Chemical Society, Washington).*

rate data according to Eq. 2-23a fits the experimental data well only in the region between 50% and 86% conversion with an excessively poor fit above 86% conversion. On the other hand, a plot (Fig. 2-3) according to Eq. 2-23b fits reasonably well up to about 69% conversion but deviates badly above that point. Neither of the two alternate kinetic plots comes close to being as useful as the third order plot in Fig. 2-1. The third order plot fits the experimental data much better than does either of the others at the higher conversions. The fit of the data to the third order plot is reasonably good over a much greater range of the higher conversion region. The region of high conversion is of prime importance since, as will be

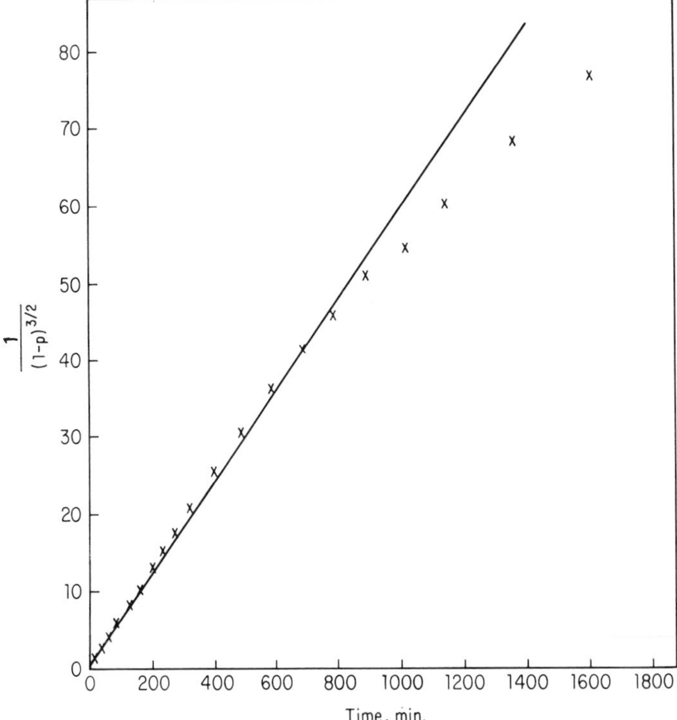

FIG. 2-3 *Two and one-half order plot of the self-catalyzed polyesterification of adipic acid with diethylene glycol at 166°C. After [9] (by permission of Marcel Dekker, Inc., New York) from the data of [8] (by permission of American Chemical Society, Washington).*

shown in Sec. 2-2a-2, high molecular weight polymer is only obtained at high conversions. From the practical viewpoint, the low conversion region of the kinetic plot is of little significance.

2-2a-2 Reasons for Nonlinearity in Third Order Plot

2-2a-2-a Low Conversion Region. The two nonlinear regions of the third order plot in Fig. 2-1 can be explained reasonably well. Consider first the initial stages of reaction. The nonlinearity observed in this region is not a characteristic of the polymerization reaction. The deviation from the third order plot is characteristic of esterifications in general. Thus, Flory [8] observed the very same behavior for the esterifications between

1) $CH_3(CH_2)_4CO_2H$ and $HOCH_2CH_2OCH_2CH_2OH$
Caproic acid — Diethylene glycol

2) $CH_3(CH_2)_{10}CO_2H$ and $CH_3(CH_2)_{10}CH_2OH$
Lauric acid — Lauryl alcohol

3) $HO_2C(CH_2)_4CO_2H$ and $CH_3(CH_2)_{10}CH_2OH$
Adipic acid — Lauryl alcohol

and ascribed the deviation from linearity to the large changes which take place in the reaction medium. At the point of 50% conversion, there is a 50 percent decrease in the concentration of carboxyl groups (although, as will be shown below, the average polymer molecular weight is extremely low). Thus, there is a definite and large change in the polarity of the reaction mixture as the polar carboxylic acid groups are converted to the less polar ester linkages. However, the exact manner in which this polarity change affects the rate of esterification is not too clear.

One possibility is that the ability of the reaction system to donate a proton to the carboxyl group (Eq. 2-12) is not correctly accounted for in the kinetic expression (Eq. 2-18) by the carboxyl concentration. It is often found that [HA] or $[H^+]$ is not an accurate measure of the acidity of a non-aqueous system or a system containing high concentrations of an acid. In such systems, the *acidity function* h_o may be the more applicable indicator of the acidity of the reaction system. The h_o function for a system is defined [11] by

$$h_o = \frac{a_{H^+}\gamma_B}{\gamma_{BH^+}} = \frac{\gamma_{H^+}[H^+]\gamma_B}{\gamma_{BH^+}} \tag{2-24}$$

where a_{H^+} and γ_{H^+} are the activity and activity coefficient, respectively, of H^+ in the system, and γ_B/γ_{BH^+} is the ratio of the activity coefficients of a base B and its conjugate acid BH^+. For the esterification reaction, the carboxyl group and its protonated form would be considered as B and BH^+, respectively.

The h_o function has been found to be the applicable measure of acidity in many reaction systems which are highly concentrated or non-aqueous solutions. It should be useful in polyesterifications as well as in other acid catalyzed polymerization reactions which typically are carried out in highly concentrated, non-aqueous solutions. The use of the h_o function would involve the substitution of the appropriate expression from Eq. 2-24 for $[H^+]$ in Eq. 2-17b to yield

$$\frac{-d[\mathrm{COOH}]}{dt} = \frac{k_1 k_3 [\mathrm{COOH}][\mathrm{OH}] h_o \gamma_{\overset{+}{\mathrm{C}}(\mathrm{OH})_2}}{k_2 K_{\mathrm{HA}} \gamma_{\mathrm{H}^+} \gamma_{\mathrm{COOH}}} \tag{2-25}$$

Unfortunately, the necessary values of h_o and the activity coefficients are not readily available except in a few instances. Interestingly, the h_o function has been successfully used in the kinetic analysis of the acid catalyzed polymerization reaction of formaldehyde with phenol and other aromatic compounds [12].

2-2a-2-b High Conversion Region. The nonlinearity observed in the third order plot in the final stages of the polyesterification (Fig. 2-1) is probably not due to failure to employ the h_o function. In this region, the acid concentration is appreciably less than in the earlier stages. Further, it would be difficult to conjecture the necessity for using the h_o function for the final stages of reaction when it is not required in the intermediate region between 80% and 93% conversion. It is more likely that several other factors are responsible for the nonlinear region above 93% conversion.

Under the reaction conditions of moderate-to-high temperature and partial vacuum which are frequently employed in the polymerization, small amounts of one or the other or both reactants may be lost by degradation or volatilization. In the case of polyesterification, small degradative losses might arise from dehydration of the diol, decarboxylation of the diacid, or other side reactions (Sec. 2-6b-1). Although such losses may not be important initially, they can become very significant during the later stages of reaction. Thus, a loss of only 0.3 percent of one reactant can lead to an error of almost 5 percent in the concentration of that reactant at 93% conversion. Detailed studies in some polymerization systems have shown that losses of this magnitude can readily occur.

Another possible reason for the observed nonlinearity is an increase in the rate of the reverse reaction. The polyesterification reaction (as well as many other step polymerizations) is an equilibrium reaction. It often becomes progressively more difficult to displace the equilibrium to the right (towards the polymer) as the conversion increases. This is due in large part to the greatly increased viscosity of the reaction medium at high conversions. The viscosity in the adipic acid-diethylene glycol polymerization increases from 0.015 poise to 0.30 poise during the course of the reaction [8]. This large viscosity increase decreases the efficiency of water removal and may lead to the observed decrease in the reaction rate with increasing conversion.

2-2a-3 Molecular Weight of Polymer. The molecular weight of a polymer is of prime concern from the practical viewpoint, for unless a polymer is of sufficiently high molecular weight (approximately $>$ 5,000–10,000) it will not have the desirable strength characteristics. It is therefore important to consider the change in polymer molecular weight with reaction time. For the case at hand of stoichiometric amounts of diol and diacid, the number of unreacted carboxyl groups N is equal to the total number of molecules present in the system at some time t. This is so because each molecule larger than a monomer will have a hydroxyl at one end and a carboxyl at the other end, while each diacid monomer molecule contains two carboxyls and each diol monomer contains no carboxyls.

The residue from each diol and each diacid (separately, not together) in the polymer chain is termed a *structural unit* (or a *monomer unit*). The *repeating unit* of the chain consists of two structural units, one each of the diol and diacid. The total number of structural units in any particular system equals the total number of bifunctional monomers initially present. The *number-average degree of polymerization* $\overline{X}_n$ is defined as the average number of structural units per polymer chain. (The symbols $\overline{P}$ and $\overline{DP}$ are also employed to signify the number-average degree of polymerization.) $\overline{X}_n$ is simply given as the total number of monomer molecules initially present divided by the total number of molecules present at time t

$$\overline{X}_n = \frac{N_0}{N} = \frac{[\mathrm{M}]_0}{[\mathrm{M}]} \tag{2-26}$$

Combining Eqs. 2-21 and 2-26, one obtains

$$\overline{X}_n = \frac{1}{(1-p)} \tag{2-27}$$

This equation relating the degree of polymerization to the extent of reaction was originally set forth by Carothers [13] and is sometimes referred to as the *Carothers equation.*

The *number-average molecular weight* $\overline{M}_n$, defined as the total weight of a polymer sample divided by the total number of molecules in it (Eqs. 1-13 and 1-14), is given by

$$\overline{M}_n = M_o \overline{X}_n = \frac{M_o}{(1-p)} \tag{2-28}$$

where M_o is the mean of the molecular weights of the two structural units. For the polyesterification of adipic acid, $HO_2C(CH_2)_4CO_2H$, and ethylene glycol, $HOCH_2CH_2OH$, the repeating unit is

$$\text{—}OCH_2CH_2OCO(CH_2)_4CO\text{—}$$

III

and one-half of its weight or 86 is the value of M_o.

Combination of Eqs. 2-22 and 2-27 yields

$$2[\mathrm{M}]_0^2 kt = \overline{X}_n^2 - \text{constant} \tag{2-29}$$

Since the reaction time and degree of polymerization appear as the first and second powers, respectively, the polymer molecular weight will increase only slowly with reaction time except in the early stages of the reaction. This means that very long reaction times are needed to obtain a high molecular weight polymer product. The right hand ordinate of Fig. 2-1 shows the variation of $\overline{X}_n$ with t. The slow increase of the molecular weight of the polymer with time is clearly apparent. The rate of increase of $\overline{X}_n$ with time decreases as the reaction proceeds. The production of high polymers requires reaction times that are too long from the practical viewpoint.

2-2b External Catalysis of Polymerization

This slow increase in molecular weight was mistakenly thought originally to be due to the low reactivity of functional groups attached to large molecules. It is, however, simply a consequence of the third order kinetics of the direct polyesterification reaction. The realization of this kinetic situation led to the achievement of high molecular weight products in reasonable reaction times by employing small amounts of externally added strong acids (such as sulfuric acid) as catalysts. Under these conditions, [HA] in Eq. 2-17a (or $[H^+]$ in Eq. 2-17b) is the concentration of the catalyst. Since this remains constant throughout the course of the polymerization, Eq. 2-17b can be written as

$$\frac{-d[M]}{dt} = k'[M]^2 \tag{2-30}$$

where the various constant terms in Eq. 2-17 have been collected into the experimentally determinable rate constant k'. Equation 2-30 applies to reactions between stoichiometric concentrations of the diol and diacid.

Integration of Eq. 2-30 and combination of the result with Eq. 2-21 yields

$$[M]_0 k' t = \frac{1}{(1-p)} - \text{constant} \tag{2-31a}$$

or

$$[M]_0 k' t = \overline{X}_n - \text{constant} \tag{2-31b}$$

Data for the polymerization of diethylene glycol with adipic acid catalyzed by p-toluenesulfonic acid are shown in Fig. 2-4. The plot follows Eq. 2-31 with the degree of polymerization increasing linearly with reaction time. The much greater rate of increase of $\overline{X}_n$ with reaction time in the catalyzed polyesterification (Fig. 2-4) relative to the uncatalyzed reaction (Fig. 2-1) is a general and most significant phenomenon. The polyesterification becomes a much more economically feasible reaction when it is catalyzed by an external acid. The self-catalyzed polymerization is not a useful reaction from the practical viewpoint of producing high polymer in reasonable reaction times.

The nonlinearity in the initial region of Fig. 2-4 is, like that in Fig. 2-1, a characteristic of esterifications in general and not of the polymerization reaction. As indicated in Sec. 2-2a-2-b, the nonlinearity may be due to failure to employ the h_o function in place of the acid concentration in the rate expression. The general linearity of the plot in the higher conversion region is a strong confirmation of the concept of functional group reactivity independent of molecular size. Figure 2-4 shows that the polyesterification continues its

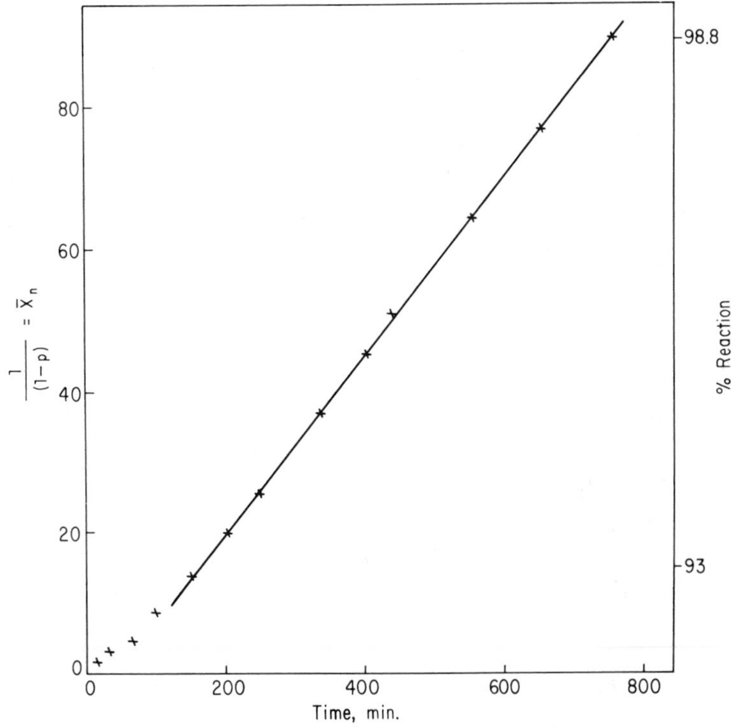

FIG. 2-4 *Polyesterification of adipic acid with diethylene glycol at 109°C catalyzed by 0.4 mole percent p-toluenesulfonic acid. After [9] (by permission of Marcel Dekker, Inc., New York) from the data of [8] (by permission of American Chemical Society, Washington).*

second order behavior at least up to a degree of polymerization of 90 corresponding to a molecular weight of approximately 10,000. There is no change in the reactivities of the hydroxyl and carboxyl groups in spite of the large increase in molecular size (and the accompanying large viscosity increase of the medium). Similar results have been observed in many other polymerizations. Data on the degradation of polymers also show the same effect. Thus, in the acid hydrolysis of cellulose [1] there is no effect of molecular size on hydrolytic reactivity up to a degree of polymerization of 1,500 (molecular weight 250,000). The concept of functional group reactivity independent of molecular size has been highly successful in allowing the kinetic analysis of a wide range of polymerizations and reactions of polymers. Its validity, however, may not always be quite rigorous at very low or very high conversions. Step polymerizations have been reported in which the reactivity of monomer was appreciably different from the other species although all other species from the dimer on up had the same reactivity [14, 15].

2-2c Step Polymerizations Other Than Polyesterification

The kinetics of step polymerizations other than polyesterification follow easily from those considered for the latter. The number of different general kinetic schemes encountered in actual polymerization situations is rather small. Polymerizations by reactions between the A and B functional groups of appropriate monomers proceed by one of the following situations:

1) Some polymerizations, such as the formation of polyamides, proceed at reasonable rates as uncatalyzed reactions.

2) Other polymerizations such as those of urea, melamine, or phenol with formaldehyde (see Table 1-1) require an externally added acid or base catalyst to achieve the desired rates of reaction.

3) A few polymerizations can be reasonably employed either in a catalyzed or an uncatalyzed process. Polyurethane formation is an example of this type of behavior. The reaction between diols and diisocyanates is subject to base catalysis. However, the polymerization is often carried out as an uncatalyzed reaction to avoid various undesirable side reactions.

Regardless of the situation into which a particular polymerization falls, the observed overall kinetic features will be the same. The polymerization rates will be first order in both the A and B groups. For the usual case where one has stoichiometric amounts of the two functional groups, the kinetics will be governed by Eqs. 2-30 and 2-31. The observed kinetics will also be the same whether the polymerization is carried by the reaction of A—A and B—B monomers or by the self-reaction of an A—B monomer.

2-2d Non-Equivalence of Functional Groups in Polyfunctional Reagents

Before proceeding, it is useful to point out that there are instances where the first two assumptions made in Sec. 2-1a are not valid. The assumption of equal reactivities of all functional groups in a polyfunctional monomer may often be incorrect. The same is true for the assumption that the reactivity of a functional group is independent of whether or not the other functional groups in the monomer have reacted. Neither of these assumptions is valid [16] for 2,4-tolylene diisocyanate (IV)

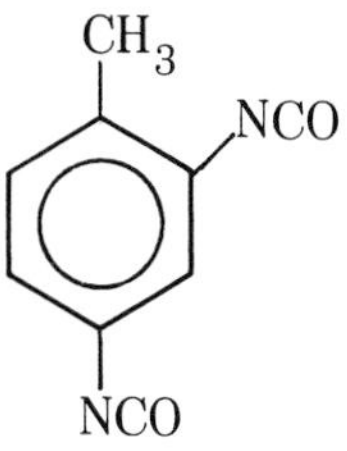

$$\text{IV: } 1\text{-}CH_3\text{-}2,4\text{-}(NCO)_2C_6H_3$$

IV

which is the diisocyanate monomer most commonly employed in the synthesis of polyurethanes.

Urethane formation can be depicted as occurring by the sequence

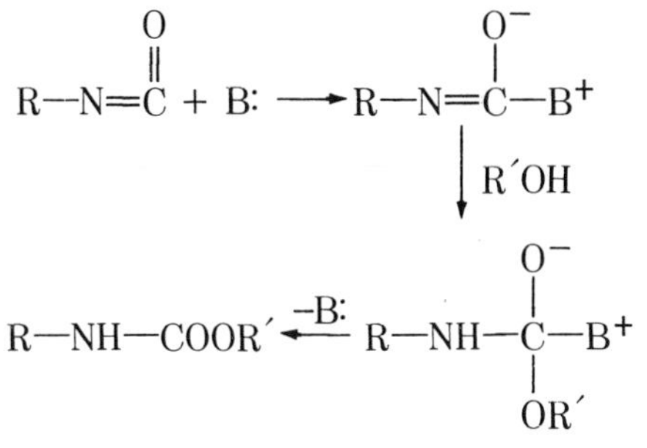

$$R{-}N{=}\overset{O}{\overset{\|}{C}} + B\colon \longrightarrow R{-}N{=}\overset{O^-}{\overset{|}{C}}{-}B^+$$

$$\downarrow R'OH$$

$$R{-}NH{-}COOR' \xleftarrow{-B\colon} R{-}NH{-}\underset{OR'}{\underset{|}{\overset{O^-}{\overset{|}{C}}}}{-}B^+ \tag{2-32}$$

where B: is a base catalyst (e.g., a tertiary amine). The reaction involves a rate determining nucleophilic attack by the alcohol on the electrophilic carbon-nitrogen linkage of the isocyanate. This is substantiated by the observation that the reactivity of the isocyanate group increases with the electron-pulling ability of the substituent attached to it [17].

In 2,4-tolylene diisocyanate, several factors cause the reactivities of the two functional groups to differ. These can be discussed by considering the data in Table 2-2 on the reactivities of various isocyanate groups compared to that in phenyl isocyanate toward reaction with *n*-butanol at 40°C with triethylamine as the catalyst [10]. It is clear that a methyl substituent deactivates the isocyanate group by increasing its electronegativity; the effect is greater when the substituent is at the nearby ortho position. One isocyanate group activates

Table 2-2 Reactivity of Isocyanate Group with n-C_4H_9OH[a]

Isocyanate reactant	Rate constants[b]	
	$k_1 \times 10^2$	k_1/k_2
Monoisocyanate		
Phenyl isocyanate	0.53	
p-Tolyl isocyanate	0.26	
o-Tolyl isocyanate	0.076	
Diisocyanates		
m-Phenylene diisocyanate	7.2	8.4
p-Phenylene diisocyanate	5.3	9.2
2,6-Tolylene diisocyanate	1.5	6.1
2,4-Tolylene diisocyanate	3.3	11.9

[a]Data from [18].
[b] k_1 and k_2 are in units of liter/mole-sec.

the other by electron-withdrawal as shown by the increased reactivity in the diisocyanates relative to the monoisocyanates. Further, once the first isocyanate group has reacted, the reactivity of the second group decreases by almost an order of magnitude; the urethane group is a much weaker electron-pulling substituent than the isocyanate group. Thus, for 2,6-tolylene diisocyanate, the para isocyanate group shows high reactivity compared to the ortho isocyanate group by an order of magnitude. This makes kinetic analysis of the polymerization extremely difficult if not impossible; indeed, definitive kinetic studies of polyurethane formation from 2,4-tolylene diisocyanate are not to be found in the literature. (It is to be expected that the application of computer techniques to the mathematics of such a problem will prove fruitful in the future.)

Trifunctional monomers constitute an important class of monomers. One often encounters such reactants in which the various functional groups have different reactivities. Thus, the polyesterification of glycerol (V)

```
CH2—OH
|
CH—OH
|
CH2—OH
  V
```

with phthalic anhydride proceeds with incomplete utilization of the hydroxyl groups [19]. This has been attributed to the lowered reactivity of the secondary hydroxyl group compared to the two primary hydroxyls. However, there is a question as to whether this explanation is valid. Systems containing trifunctional reagents often reach a point in the reaction at which they cease being homogeneous solutions. Some systems have been found to contain dispersed polymer particles 0.05 to 1 micron in diameter [1, 20]. These particles have been termed *microgel particles* and are the result of crosslinking reactions (Sec. 2-8). Functional group reactivity in trifunctional monomers is considered further in Sec. 2-10a-2.

2-3 CYCLIZATION VERSUS LINEAR POLYMERIZATION

2-3a Possible Cyclization Reactions

The production of linear polymers by the step polymerization of polyfunctional monomers is sometimes complicated by the competitive occurrence of *cyclization reactions.* Ring formation is a possibility in the polymerizations of both the A—B and A—A plus B—B types. Reactants of the A—B type such as amino or hydroxy acids may form cyclic amide and ester structures (called lactams and lactones, respectively) either by cyclic dimerization

$$2\,H_2N\text{—}R\text{—}CO_2H \longrightarrow \begin{array}{c} R\text{—}NH \\ CO \qquad\quad CO \\ NH\text{—}R \end{array} + 2\,H_2O \qquad (2\text{-}33)$$

$$2\,HO\text{—}R\text{—}CO_2H \longrightarrow \begin{array}{c} R\text{—}O \\ CO \qquad\quad CO \\ O\text{—}R \end{array} + 2\,H_2O \qquad (2\text{-}34)$$

or by direct intramolecular cyclization of the monomer

$$H_2N\text{—}R\text{—}CO_2H \longrightarrow \underbrace{HN\text{—}R\text{—}CO}_{} + H_2O \qquad (2\text{-}35)$$

$$HO\text{—}R\text{—}CO_2H \longrightarrow \underbrace{O\text{—}R\text{—}CO}_{} + H_2O \qquad (2\text{-}36)$$

Reactants of the A—A type such as diacids may undergo similar cyclization reactions

$$HO_2C{-}R{-}CO_2H \longrightarrow \underbrace{OCO{-}R{-}CO}_{\text{ring}} + H_2O \tag{2-37}$$

$$2\,HO_2C{-}R{-}CO_2H \longrightarrow \underbrace{OCO{-}R{-}COO{-}R{-}CO}_{\text{ring}} \tag{2-38}$$

Many A—A reactants, however, possess functional groups which are incapable of reacting with each other under the conditions of step polymerization. Thus, there is usually no possibility of cyclization reactions between the hydroxyl groups of diols or between the amine groups of diamines.

Reactions between A—A and B—B monomers can also lead to ring formation via cyclic dimerization between the two reactants. Thus, the reaction between diols and acetaldehyde may yield either linear polyacetal or cyclic acetal

$$HO{-}R{-}OH + CH_3CHO \longrightarrow \left(O{-}R{-}O\underset{\substack{|\\CH_3}}{CH}\right)_n \tag{2-39}$$

$$HO{-}R{-}OH + CH_3CHO \longrightarrow \underbrace{O{-}R{-}O{-}CH}_{\text{ring}}{-}CH_3 \tag{2-40}$$

2-3b Thermodynamic and Kinetic Considerations

Whether cyclization is competitive with linear polymerization for a particular reactant or pair of reactants depends on thermodynamic and kinetic considerations of the size of the ring structure which may be formed. An understanding of the relative ease of cyclization or linear polymerization comes from a variety of sources. These include direct studies [1, 21] with various bifunctional monomers in cyclization reactions (such as those in Eqs. 2-33 through 2-40) as well as ring-opening polymerization studies (Chap. 7) and data such as the heats of combustion of cyclic compounds [22]. Consider first the thermodynamic stability of different sized ring structures. Some of

Table 2-3 Heats of Combustion and Strains of Cycloalkanes per Methylene Group[a]

$\overline{(CH_2)_n}$ n	Heat of combustion per methylene group (kcal/mole)	Strain per methylene group[b] (kcal/mole)
3	166.6	9.2
4	164.0	6.6
5	158.7	1.3
6	157.4	0.0
7	158.3	0.9
8	158.6	1.2
9	158.8	1.4
10	158.6	1.2
11	158.4	1.0
12	157.7	0.3
13	157.8	0.4
14	157.4	0.0
15	157.5	0.1
16	157.5	0.1
17	157.2	−0.2
n-alkane	157.4	0.0

[a] Data from [22].
[b] Calculated as the heat of combustion per methylene group minus the value (157.4) for the *n*-alkane methylene group.

the most useful data on the effect of ring size on thermodynamic stability is that on the heats of combustion of cycloalkanes (Table 2-3). A comparison of the heats of combustion per methylene group in these ring compounds with that in an open chain alkane yields a general measure of the thermodynamic stabilities of different sized rings [22]. More precisely, thermodynamic stability decreases with increasing strain in the ring structure as measured by the differences in the heats of combustion per methylene group of the cycloalkane and the *n*-alkane. The strain in cyclic structures is very high for the 3- and 4-membered rings, decreases sharply for 5-,6-, and 7-membered rings, increases for 8- to 11-membered rings, and then decreases again for larger rings.

The strain in ring structures is of two types—*angle strain* and *crowding repulsions.* Ring structures of less than five atoms are highly strained due to the high degree of angle strain, i.e., the large distortion of their bond angles from the normal tetrahedral angle. Bond angle distortion is essentially absent in rings of 5 or more members since such rings are puckered to varying degrees. The 5-membered ring is strain-free with virtually no bond distortions. For rings larger than five atoms, the strain due to bond angle distortions would be excessive for planar rings. For this reason, rings larger than five atoms exist in more stable, non-planar (puckered) forms. Rings of six and seven atoms are stable with 6-membered rings being appreciably more favored than 7-membered rings. Although rings of eight to twelve atoms are relatively free of strain due to bond angle distortion, they are still thermodynamically unstable. Hydrogen (or other) substituents are forced to crowd positions inside the ring where there are substantial crowding repulsions of one substituent with another. A consideration of rings of more than twelve atoms shows them to be very stable as there no longer are any crowding repulsions.

The general order of thermodynamic stability of different sized ring structures is, thus, given by

$$3,4,8 \text{ to } 11 < 7,12 \text{ and larger} < 5 < 6$$

This same order of stability is generally observed for a variety of ring structures including those containing atoms or groups other than methylene. Although data are not as extensive for ring structures such as ethers, lactones, or lactams, the general expectation is borne out. The substitution of an oxygen, carbonyl, nitrogen, or other group for methylene does not appreciably alter the bond angles in the ring structure. Replacement of a methylene group by a less bulky oxygen atom or carbonyl group may, however, slightly increase the stability of the ring structure by a decrease in the ring strain due to crowding repulsions. It has also been observed that substituents, other than hydrogen, on the ring structure generally increase its stability, although the reasons for this are not well understood.

In addition to thermodynamic stability, kinetic feasibility is important in determining the competitive position of cyclization relative to linear polymerization. Kinetic feasibility for the cyclization reaction depends on the probability of having the functional group ends of the reactant molecules approach each other. As the potential ring size increases, the monomers which would give rise to ring structures have many configurations, very few of which involve the two ends being adjacent [23]. The probability of ring formation decreases as the probability of the two functional groups encountering each other decreases. The effect is reflected in an increasingly unfavorable entropy of activation.

The overall ease of cyclization is thus dependent on the interplay of two factors: (1) the continuous decrease in kinetic feasibility with ring size, and (2) the thermodynamic stability which increases as the ring size increases to the 6-membered ring, then decreases as the ring size increases up to the 9- to 11-membered ring and then increases again for larger rings. The net result of the two factors is that one usually observes the ease of ring formation to be low for the 3-membered ring and very low for the 4-membered ring. The 3-membered ring is formed easier than the 4-membered ring due to the more favorable kinetic factor. There is a sharp increase for the 5-membered ring because of a highly favorable thermodynamic factor. The 6-membered ring is slightly less easily formed than the 5-membered because the slightly more favorable thermodynamic factor is negated by a decrease in the kinetic factor. There is a sharper drop for the 7-membered ring and then another drop for the 8-membered ring as both the kinetic and thermodynamic factors become less favorable. At this point, the kinetic factor has almost levelled off and cyclization is determined primarily by thermodynamic feasibility. The ease of ring formation is low for 9- and 10-membered rings, increases slightly for 11- and 12-membered rings and levels off for larger sized ring structures.

One can summarize these conclusions in a qualitative manner by a plot such as that in Fig. 2-5. The ease of cyclization is high for 5- and 6-membered rings, appreciable for 7-membered rings, low for 3-membered rings and those of greater than 12 members, and negligible for all other sized rings. From the practical viewpoint of obtaining linear polymerization, it turns out that ring formation is generally only a problem when the monomer(s) can form 5-, 6-, or 7-membered rings. For cyclization via Eqs. 2-33, 2-34, and 2-38, this corresponds to reactants in which the R group contributes only one atom to the ring. For cyclization via Eqs. 2-35 and 2-36, cyclization is possible when R contributes 3–5 atoms to the ring. Cyclization via Eqs. 2-37 and 2-40 requires that R contribute only 2–4 atoms to the ring. The formation of 3-membered rings is not encountered since the usually used monomers would not yield such ring structures. The formation of the very large sized rings (>12 members) is only very

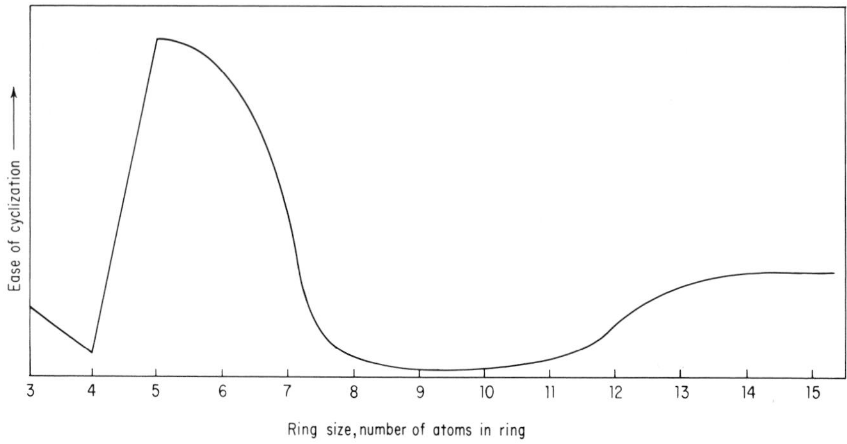

FIG. 2-5 *Dependence of the ease of cyclization on the size of the ring.*

rarely encountered in step polymerization, and then only to an exceedingly low extent. (The situation is quite different in chain polymerization—see Sec. 6-6b.)

2-3c Other Considerations

Step polymerizations are almost always carried out using high concentrations of the reactant(s). This is highly favorable for linear polymerization. Cyclization is a unimolecular (intramolecular) reaction, while linear polymerization is a bimolecular (intermolecular) reaction. The rate of the latter increases much faster than that of the former as the reactant concentration is increased. Thus, this factor of reactant concentration is superimposed on the previous thermodynamic and kinetic considerations. The concentration factor increases the overall competitive position of linear polymerization relative to cyclization. This is the reason why cyclization is not a problem for rings of greater than 12 members. Further, it explains the lack of appreciable cyclization in many step polymerizations in which 6- or 7-membered rings can be formed. Another factor which often can be employed to shift the competitive balance between linear polymerization and cyclization toward the former is the interconvertibility of the linear and cyclic structures under appropriate reaction conditions. In these cases, it is possible to shift the equilibrium between the two structures in the direction of the linear polymer.

It is interesting to note that when reactants can form 5-membered rings, cyclization occurs to almost the total exclusion of linear polymerization. Further, such cyclizations generally occur at faster rates than the linear polymerizations of other reactants in which cyclization is not competitive. The reasons for this behavior are not understood [1]. (Five-membered ring structures, although previously thought to be completely inert, have been polymerized by the ring-opening mechanism in some instances—see Chap. 7.)

The discussion above has been concerned primarily with rings containing carbon, carbon and oxygen, or carbon and nitrogen atoms. The situation as regards the competition between cyclization and linear polymerization as a function of ring size may be altered when other atoms make up the ring structure. Thus, in the case of silicones where the ring structure VI would be made up of alternating oxygen and silicone atoms, for example,

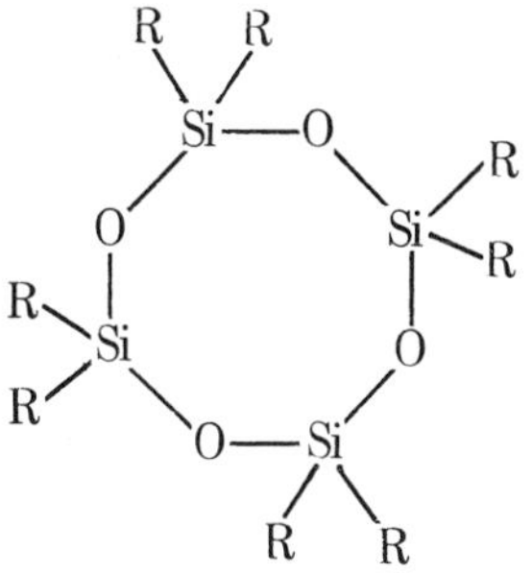

VI

rings of less than eight atoms are quite strained due to the large size of the silicon atom, the greater length of the Si—O bond, and the large Si—O—Si bond angle. The optimum ring size is the eight membered one, although the preference is not overwhelming due to the kinetic factor [24, 25]. The larger sized rings are also not favored—for the same reasons discussed previously.

2-4 MOLECULAR WEIGHT CONTROL IN LINEAR POLYMERIZATION

2-4a Need for Stoichiometric Control

There are two important aspects with regard to the control of molecular weight in polymerizations. In the synthesis of polymers, one is usually interested in obtaining a product of very specific molecular weight, since the properties of the polymer will usually be highly dependent on molecular weight. Molecular weights higher or lower than the desired weight are equally undesirable. Since the degree of polymerization is a function of reaction time, the desired molecular weight can be obtained by quenching the reaction (e.g., by cooling) at the appropriate time. However, the polymer obtained in this manner is unstable in that subsequent heating leads to changes in molecular weight because the ends of the polymer molecules contain functional groups (referred to as *end-groups*) which can react further with each other.

This situation is avoided by adjusting the concentrations of the two monomers (e.g., diol and diacid) so that they are slightly non-stoichiometric. One of the reactants is present in slight excess. The polymerization then proceeds to a point at which one reactant is completely used up and all the chain ends possess the same functional group–the group which is in excess. Further polymerization is not possible and the polymer is stable to subsequent molecular weight changes. Thus, the use of excess diamine in the polymerization of a diamine with a diacid (Reaction 1-1) yields a polyamide (VII) with amine end-groups

$$\text{H}\!\left(\!\text{NH—R—NHCO—R}'\text{—CO}\!\right)_{n}\!\text{NH—R—NH}_2$$

VII

in the absence of any diacid for further polymerization. The use of excess diacid accomplishes the same result; the polyamide (VIII) in this case has carboxyl end-groups

$$\text{HO}\!\left(\!\text{CO—R}'\text{—CONH—R—NH}\!\right)_{n}\!\text{CO—R}'\text{—COOH}$$

VIII

which are incapable of further reaction since the diamine has been completely reacted.

Another method of achieving the desired molecular weight is by the addition of a small amount of a *monofunctional monomer*. Acetic acid or lauric acid, for example, are often used to achieve molecular weight stabilization of polyamides. The monofunctional monomer controls and limits the polymerization of bifunctional monomers because its reaction with the growing polymer yields chain ends devoid of a functional group and therefore incapable of further reaction. Thus, the use of benzoic acid in Reaction 1-1 yields a polyamide (IX) with phenyl end-groups

$$\phi\text{—CO}\!\left(\text{NH—R—NHCO—R}'\text{—CO}\right)_n\!\text{OCO}\phi$$

IX

which are unreactive toward polymerization.

2-4b Quantitative Aspects

In order to properly control the polymer molecular weight, one must precisely adjust the stoichiometric imbalance of the bifunctional monomers or of the monofunctional monomer. If the non-stoichiometry is too large, the polymer molecular weight will be too low. It is therefore important to understand the quantitative effect of the stoichiometric imbalance of reactants on the molecular weight. This is also necessary in order to know the quantitative effect of any reactive impurities which may be present in the reaction mixture either initially or which are formed by undesirable side reactions. Impurities with A or B functional groups may drastically lower the polymer molecular weight unless one can quantitatively take their presence into account. Consider now the various different reactant systems which are employed in step polymerizations:

Type 1: For the polymerization of the bifunctional monomers A—A and B—B (e.g., diol and diacid or diamine and diacid) where B—B is present in excess, the numbers of A and B functional groups are given by N_A and N_B, respectively. N_A and N_B are equal to twice the number of A—A and B—B molecules, respectively, which are present. The *stoichiometric imbalance* r of the two functional groups is given by $r = N_A/N_B$. (The ratio r is always defined so as to have a value equal to or less than unity but never greater than unity, i.e., the B groups are those in excess.) The total number of monomer molecules is given by $(N_A + N_B)/2$ or $N_A(1 + 1/r)/2$.

The extent of reaction p is introduced here and defined as the fraction of A groups which have reacted at a particular time. The fraction of B groups which have reacted is given by rp. The fractions of unreacted A and B groups are $(1-p)$ and $(1-rp)$, respectively. The total numbers of unreacted A and B groups are $N_A(1-p)$ and $N_B(1-rp)$, respectively. The total number of polymer chain ends is given by the sum of the total number of unreacted A and B groups. Since each polymer chain has two chain ends, the total number of polymer molecules is one-half the total number of chain ends or $[N_A(1-p) + N_B(1-rp)]/2$.

The number-average degree of polymerization $\overline{X}_n$ is the total number of A—A and B—B molecules initially present divided by the total number of polymer molecules

$$\overline{X}_n = \frac{N_A(1 + 1/r)/2}{[N_A(1-p) + N_B(1-rp)]/2} = \frac{1 + r}{1 + r - 2rp} \tag{2-41}$$

Equation 2-41 shows the variation of $\overline{X}_n$ with the stoichiometric imbalance r and the extent of reaction p. There are two interesting limiting forms of this relationship. When the two bifunctional monomers are present in stoichiometric amounts (that is, $r = 1.000$), Eq. 2-41 reduces to the previously discussed Eq. 2-27

$$\overline{X}_n = \frac{1}{(1-p)} \tag{2-27}$$

On the other hand, when the polymerization is 100 percent complete (that is, $p = 1.000$), Eq. 2-41 becomes

$$\overline{X}_n = \frac{(1+r)}{(1-r)} \tag{2-42}$$

In actual practice, p may approach but never becomes equal to unity.

Figure 2-6 shows plots of $\overline{X}_n$ versus the stoichiometric imbalance for several values of p in accordance with Eq. 2-41. The stoichiometric imbalance is expressed both as the ratio r and also as the mole-percent excess of the B—B reactant over the A—A reactant. The various plots show how r and p must be controlled so as to obtain a particular degree of polymerization. However, one does not usually have complete freedom of choice of the r and p values in a polymerization. Complete control of the stoichiometric ratio is not always possible since reasons of economy and difficulties in the purification of reactants may prevent one from obtaining r values very close to 1.000. Similarly, many polymerizations are carried out to less than 100 percent completion (i.e., to $p < 1.000$) for reasons of time and economy. The time required to achieve each of the last few percent of reaction is close to that required for the first 97–98 or so

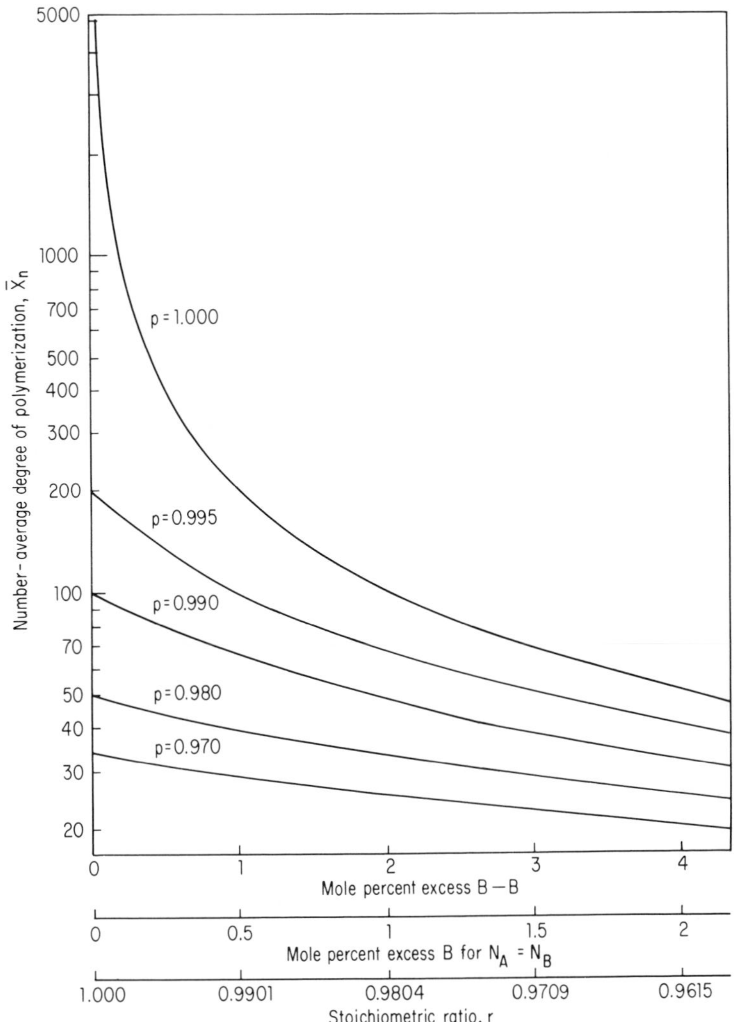

FIG. 2-6 *Dependence of the number-average degree of polymerization* $\overline{X}_n$ *on the stoichiometric ratio r for different extents of reaction p in the polymerization of A–A with B–B.*

percent of reaction. Thus, a detailed consideration of Fig. 2-4 shows that the time required to go from $p = 0.97$ ($\overline{X}_n = 33.3$) to $p = 0.98$ ($\overline{X}_n = 50$) is approximately the same as that to reach $p = 0.97$ from the start of reaction.

Consider a few examples to illustrate the use of Eq. 2-41 and Fig. 2-6. For stoichiometric imbalances of 0.1 and 1 mole-percent (r

values of 1,000/1,001 and 100/101, respectively) at 100 percent reaction, the values of $\overline{X}_n$ are 2,001 and 201, respectively. The degrees of polymerization decrease to 96 and 66, respectively, at 99 percent reaction and to 49 and 40 at 98 percent reaction. It is clear that step polymerizations will almost always be carried out to at least 98 percent reaction since a degree of polymerization of at least approximately 50–100 is usually required for a useful polymer. Higher conversions and the appropriate stoichiometric ratio are required to obtain higher degrees of polymerization. The exact combination of p and r values necessary to obtain any particular degree of polymerization is obtained from Fig. 2-6 and Eq. 2-41. One can also calculate the effect of losses of one reactant or both during the polymerization through volatilization, or side reactions. The precision required in the control of the stoichiometric ratio in a polymerization is easily found from Eq. 2-41. An error in the experimentally employed r value yields a corresponding error in $\overline{X}_n$. The shape of the plots in Fig. 2-6 shows that the effect of an error in r, however, is progressively greater at higher degrees of polymerization. Progressively greater control is required to synthesize the higher molecular weight polymer.

Type 2: The control of the degree of polymerization in an A—A plus B—B polymerization by the addition of small amounts of a monofunctional reactant, for example, B, has been described above. The same equations that apply to a Type 1 polymerization also are applicable here except that r must be redefined as

$$r = \frac{N_A}{N_B + 2N_{B'}} \tag{2-43}$$

where $N_{B'}$ is the number of B molecules present and N_A and N_B have the same meaning as before. The coefficient 2 in front of $N_{B'}$ is required since one B molecule has the same quantitative effect as one excess B—B molecule on limiting the growth of a polymer chain.

Type 3: Polymerizations of A—B type monomers such as hydroxy and amino acids automatically take place with internally supplied stoichiometry. For such a polymerization, Eqs. 2-41 and 2-42 apply with r equal to one. This leads to a polymer product which is subsequently unstable toward molecular weight changes because the end-groups of the polymer molecules can react with each other. Molecular weight stabilization is usually accomplished by using a monofunctional B reactant. In this latter case, the same equations apply with r redefined as

$$r = \frac{N_A}{N_B + 2N_{B'}} \tag{2-44}$$

where $2N_{B'}$ has the same meaning as in a Type 2 polymerization and $N_A = N_B$ = the number of A—B molecules. (Bifunctional A—A or B—B monomers cannot be employed to control molecular weight in this polymerization.)

The plots in Fig. 2-6 apply equally well to polymerizations of Types 1, 2, and 3 although the scale of the x-axis may be different. When the x-axis is expressed as the stoichiometric ratio r, the scale is exactly the same for all three types of polymerization. Different scales will be applicable when the x-axis is expressed in terms of the mole-percent excess of the molecular weight controlling reactant. Thus, the x-axis is shown as the mole-percent excess of the B—B reactant for Type 1 polymerizations. For polymerizations of Type 2 when $N_A = N_B$ and those of Type 3, the x-axis is shown as the mole-percent excess of B molecules. The two x-axes differ by a factor of two because two B—B molecules are needed to give the same effect as one B molecule. The relationship between the degree of polymerization and the stoichiometric ratio (Eq. 2-41 and Fig. 2-6) has been verified in a large number of step polymerizations. Its verification and use for molecular weight control has recently been extensively reviewed in several polymer systems including polyamides, polyesters, and polybenzimidazoles [26]. The effect of excess A—A or B—B reactants as well as A or B molecules follows the expected behavior.

2-5 MOLECULAR WEIGHT DISTRIBUTION IN LINEAR POLYMERIZATION

The product of a polymerization is a mixture of polymer molecules of different molecular weights. For theoretical and practical reasons it is of interest to discuss the distribution of molecular weights in a polymerization. The *molecular weight distribution* (MWD) has been derived by Flory by a statistical approach based on the concept of functional group reactivity independent of molecular size [27, 28]. The derivation which follows is essentially that of Flory and applies equally to A—B and stoichiometric A—A plus B—B types of step polymerizations.

2-5a Derivation of Size Distributions

Consider the probability of finding a polymer molecule containing x structural units. This is synonymous with the probability of finding a molecule with $(x-1)$ A groups reacted and one A group unreacted. The probability that an A group has reacted at time t is defined as the extent of reaction p. The probability that $(x-1)$ A groups have reacted is the product of $(x-1)$ separate probabilities or p^{x-1}. Since the probability of an A group being unreacted is $(1-p)$, the probability $\underline{N}_x$ of finding the molecule in question, with x structural units, is given by

$$\underline{N}_x = p^{x-1}(1-p) \tag{2-45}$$

Since $\underline{N}_x$ is synonymous with the *mole* or *number fraction* of molecules in the polymer mixture which are x-mers (i.e., which contain x structural units), then

$$N_x = Np^{x-1}(1-p) \tag{2-46}$$

where N is the total number of polymer molecules and N_x is the number which are x-mers. If the total number of structural units present initially is N_0, then $N = N_0(1-p)$ and Eq. 2-46 becomes

$$N_x = N_0(1-p)^2 p^{x-1} \tag{2-47}$$

Neglecting the weights of the end-groups, the *weight fraction* w_x of x-mers (i.e., the weight fraction of the molecules which contains x structural units) is given by $w_x = xN_x/N_0$ and Eq. 2-47 becomes

$$w_x = x(1-p)^2 p^{x-1} \tag{2-48}$$

Equations 2-46 and 2-48 give the *number-* and *weight-distribution functions*, respectively, for linear step polymerizations at the extent of reaction p. These distributions are usually referred to as the *most probable* or *Flory distributions*. Plots of the two distribution functions for several values of p are shown in Figs. 2-7 and 2-8. It is seen that on a number basis there are more monomer molecules than

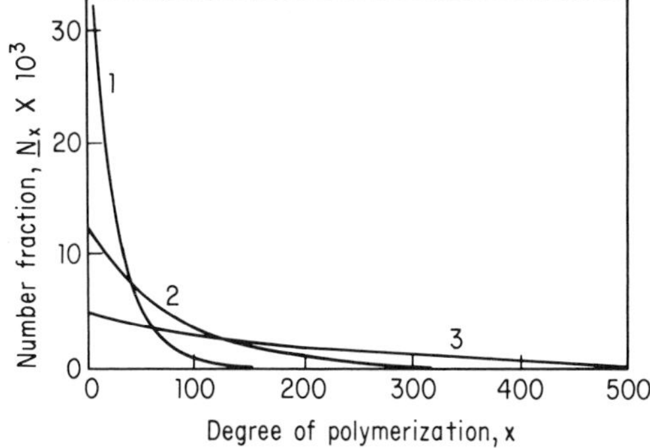

FIG. 2-7 *Number fraction distribution curve for linear polymerization. Curve 1: p = 0.9600; Curve 2: p = 0.9875; Curve 3: p = 0.9950. After [28] (by permission of Iliffe Books, Ltd., London).*

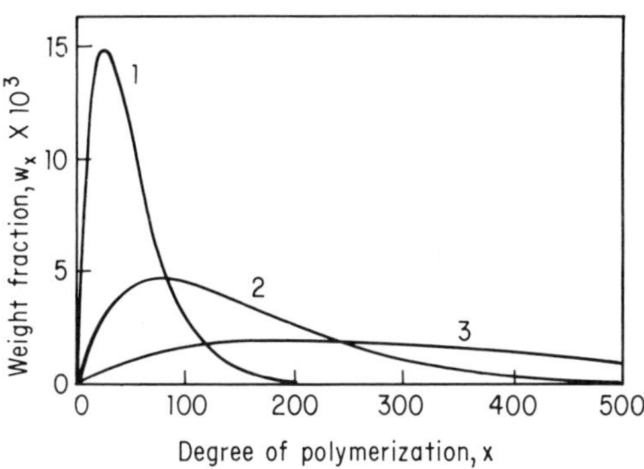

FIG. 2-8 *Weight fraction distribution curve for linear polymerization. Curve 1: p = 0.9600; Curve 2: p = 0.9875; Curve 3: p = 0.9950. After [28] (by permission of Iliffe Books, Ltd., London).*

any polymer species regardless of the extent of reaction. Although the number of monomer molecules decreases as the extent of reaction increases, they are still the most plentiful species. The situation is quite different for the weight distribution of molecular weights. On a weight basis, the proportion of low molecular weight species is very small and decreases as the extent of reaction increases. The maxima in Fig. 2-8 occur at $x = -(1/\ln p)$ which is very near the number-average degree of polymerization given by Eq. 2-27.

Experimental determinations of molecular weight distribution are frequently obtained in an integral form in which the *combined* or *cumulative weight fraction* I_x of all polymer molecules having degrees of polymerization up to and including x are plotted against x. For this reason, it is useful to express the Flory distribution function in terms of I_x. This is done by integrating Eq. 2-48 to yield

$$I_x = 1 - [1 + (1-p)x]p^x \tag{2-49}$$

The integral weight-distribution function is graphically illustrated in Fig. 2-9.

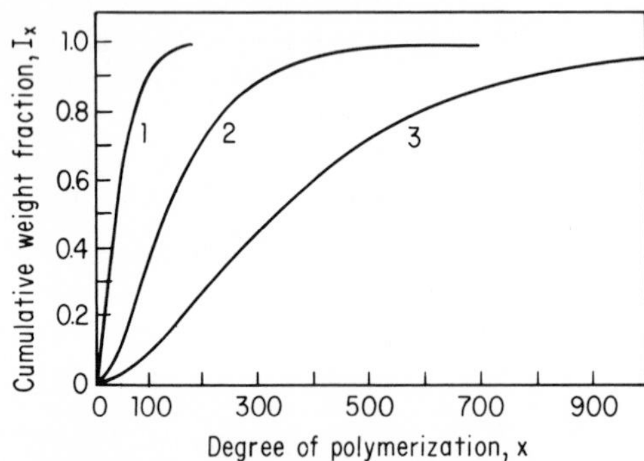

FIG. 2-9 *Integral distribution curve for linear polymerization. Curve 1: p = 0.9600; Curve 2: p = 0.9875; Curve 3: p = 0.9950. After [28] (by permission of Iliffe Books, Ltd., London).*

2-5b Breadth of Molecular Weight Distribution

The number- and weight-average degree of polymerization $\overline{X}_n$ and $\overline{X}_w$ can be derived from the number- and weight-distribution functions, respectively. The number- and weight-average molecular weights have been defined by Eqs. 1-14 and 1-16. Dividing Eq. 1-14 by the weight M_o of a structural unit yields the number-average degree of polymerization as

$$\overline{X}_n = \frac{\sum xN_x}{\sum N_x} = \sum x\underline{N}_x \tag{2-50}$$

where the summations are over all values of x. Combination of Eqs. 2-45 and 2-50 gives

$$\overline{X}_n = \sum xp^{x-1}(1-p) \tag{2-51}$$

Evaluation of this summation yields

$$\bar{X}_n = \frac{1}{(1-p)} \tag{2-27}$$

which is the same result obtained earlier. Dividing Eq. 1-16 by M_o yields

$$\bar{X}_w = \sum x w_x \tag{2-52}$$

Combination of Eqs. 2-48 and 2-52 gives

$$\bar{X}_w = \sum x^2 p^{x-1}(1-p)^2 \tag{2-53}$$

which is evaluated as

$$\bar{X}_w = \frac{(1+p)}{(1-p)} \tag{2-54}$$

The *breadth of the molecular weight distribution curve* is then given by

$$\frac{\bar{X}_w}{\bar{X}_n} = (1+p) \tag{2-55}$$

The ratio $\bar{X}_w/\bar{X}_n$ is synonymous with the ratio $\bar{M}_w/\bar{M}_n$ discussed in Sec. 1-4. It is a measure of the polydispersity of a polymer sample. The value of $\bar{X}_w/\bar{X}_n$ increases with the extent of reaction and approaches 2 in the limit of large extents of reaction.

The above equations (Eqs. 2-45 through 2-55) are also applicable with minor modifications to polymerizations where a monofunctional monomer or an excess of bifunctional monomer is employed to stabilize the polymer [27]. For the former case, the extent of reaction p must be replaced by the probability that a given functional group has reacted with a bifunctional monomer. In both cases, the equations are applicable as a very close approximation when p is replaced by $pr^{1/2}$. The number- and weight-distribution functions in such non-stoichiometric polymerizations are essentially the same as for the stoichiometric polymerizations.

2-5c Interchange Reactions

Some polymers (polyesters, polyamides, polysulfides, and others) may undergo *interchange reactions* under appropriate conditions. Interchange involves reaction between the terminal functional group of one polymer molecule with the interunit repeating linkage of another polymer molecule, for example, between the terminal $—NH_2$ and interunit —CONH— groups of polyamide molecules. Two polymer chains may react to yield one shorter and one longer chain

$$\text{H}\!\left(\text{NH—R—CO}\right)_n\text{OH} + \text{H}\!\left(\text{NH—R—CO}\right)_m\text{OH} \longrightarrow$$

$$\text{H}\!\left(\text{NH—R—CO}\right)_w\text{OH} + \text{H}\!\left(\text{NH—R—CO}\right)_z\text{OH} \qquad (2\text{-}56)$$

If free interchange occurs, the molecular weight distribution will be the Flory distribution described by Eqs. 2-47 and 2-48 [27, 28]. Free interchange corresponds to all interunit linkages in all polymer molecules having equal probabilities of interchange. This is analogous to the concept of functional group reactivity independent of molecular size as applied to the interchange reaction. It is apparent that the presence of interchange during a polymerization will not affect the size distribution from that expected for the random polymerization. The Flory or most probable distribution is also that expected for the random scission of the interunit linkages of polymer chains, e.g., in the hydrolysis of cellulose.

2-5d Experimental Verification

The most probable distribution of Flory is generally well established although its experimental verification is somewhat limited. Direct evidence for the Flory distribution requires the careful and detailed fractionation of polymer samples to allow the construction of experimental curves of $\underline{N}_x$, w_x, or I_x versus x for comparison with the theoretical curves. The experimental difficulties involved in polymer fractionation have limited the number of different types of polymers which have been extensively studied. The recent availability of automatic instrumentation and newly developed techniques [29] such as gel permeation chromatography should greatly increase the available data on molecular weight

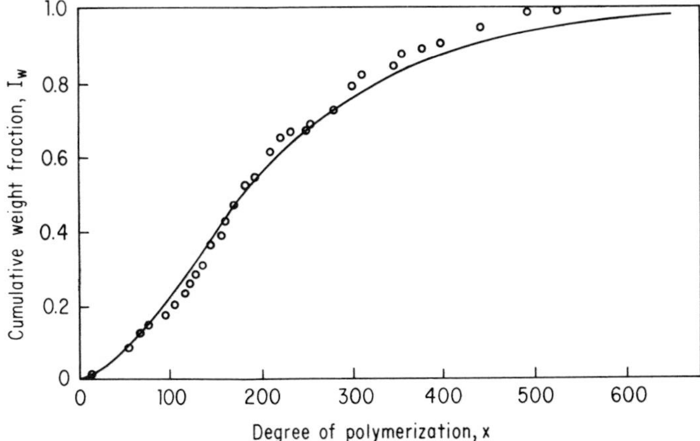

FIG. 2-10 *Integral distribution curve for poly(hexamethylene adipate). The curve shown is that for the theoretical distribution (p = 0.9909) and the circles are the experimental values. After [30] (by permission of Interscience Publishers, John Wiley & Sons, Inc., New York).*

distributions of polymers. (MWD data on chain polymerizations are becoming quite extensive for this reason, but those for step polymerization are still lagging.)

The major amount of work on size distributions has been on polyesters and polyamides. Poly(hexamethylene adipamide) has probably been studied more extensively than any other polymer. Figure 2-10 shows the integral size distribution for this polymer compared to the Flory distribution curve [30]. The agreement of the data with the theoretical curve is very good within the limits of experimental error. Similar data for poly(hexamethylene adipamide) by several other workers further confirm the Flory distribution [28]. Indirect verification of the most probable distribution has been made in many instances by determining the ratio $\overline{X}_w/\overline{X}_n$. For many different step polymerizations, this ratio has been found to be close to 2 as required by Eq. 2-55. Molecular weight distributions differing from the Flory distribution have been postulated. The evidence in favor of these is generally based on experimental studies which involve insufficient fractionation. The situation has been reviewed [28] and it is apparent that the best experimental evidence supports the Flory distribution.

Although the statistical approach to size distribution in polymerization has proved to be highly useful, there are limitations to the method. The computation of the size distributions in chemical reactors other than batch reactors, e.g., continuous flow stirred tank reactors (CFSTR) and plug flow reactors with recycle (PFRR), by the statistical approach proceeds in a relatively unwieldy fashion. These systems have been recently handled by kinetic formulation of the infinite set of rate equations describing the production of each individual sized polymer species [31, 32]. The results indicate that the molecular weight distributions obtained in reactors other than batch reactors can be appreciably different from the Flory distribution under certain conditions.

2-6 PROCESS CONDITIONS

2-6a Physical Nature of Polymerization Systems

Several considerations are common to all processes for step polymerization. A prime requisite for step polymerization is the need for high purity reactants in stoichiometric amounts in order to obtain high molecular weight products. The molecular weight is controlled by the presence of controlled amounts of monofunctional reagents or an excess of one of the bifunctional reagents. A second consideration is that of reaction temperature. Most step polymerizations proceed at relatively slow rates at ordinary temperatures. High temperatures in the range of 150–200°C and higher are frequently used in order to obtain rapid polymerization rates. Equilibrium considerations are also of prime importance. Since many step polymerizations are equilibrium reactions, appropriate means must be employed to displace the equilibrium in the direction of the polymer product. Distillation of water or other small molecule products from the reaction mixture by suitable reaction temperatures and vacuums are often employed for this purpose.

Bulk or *mass polymerization* is the simplest process for step polymerizations since it involves only the reactants and whatever catalyst, if any, which is required. There is a minimum of potentialities for contamination, and product separation is simple. Bulk polymerization is particularly well suited for step polymerization because high molecular weight polymer is not produced until the very last stages of reaction. This means that the viscosity is relatively low throughout most of the course of the polymerization and mixing of the reaction mixture is easily accomplished. Furthermore, although step polymerizations have reasonably high activation energies, e.g., about 20 kcal/mole for poly(ethylene terephthalate) and poly(hexamethylene adipamide) [14, 33], thermal control is relatively easy since most reactions are not highly exothermic. The exact opposite is the case for chain polymerizations which are generally highly exothermic with high activation energies and where the viscosity increases much more rapidly. Thermal control and mixing present much greater problems in chain polymerizations.

Bulk polymerization is widely used for step polymerizations. Many polymerizations, however, are carried out in *solution* with a solvent present to solubilize the reactants, or to allow higher reaction temperatures to be employed, or as a convenience in moderating the reaction and acting as a carrier. *Dispersed* systems are used in a few instances, e.g., the synthesis of polysulfides from alkyl dihalides and an inorganic sulfide is often carried out in an aqueous dispersion.

2-6b Different Reactant Systems

For many step polymerizations, there are different combinations of reactants which can be employed to produce the same type of polymer (Table 1-1). Further, it is apparent that there are different reactant systems which can yield the exact same polymer. The organic chemical aspects of the synthesis of various different polymers by different step polymerization processes have been reviewed [33, 34]. Whether one particular reaction or another is employed to produce a specific polymer depends on several factors. These include the availability, ease of purification, and properties (both chemical and physical) of the different reactants.

The ability to obtain high molecular weight polymer from a reaction depends on whether or not the equilibrium is favorable. If the equilibrium is unfavorable as it is in many instances, success depends on the ease with which the polymerization can be driven close to completion. The need for and the ease of obtaining and maintaining stoichiometry in a polymerization is an important consideration. The various requirements for producing a high polymer may be resolved in quite different ways for different polymers. One must completely understand each type of polymerization reaction so as to appropriately meet the stringent requirements for the synthesis of high molecular weight polymer. Consider some of the different step polymerizations to illustrate how the reaction characteristics are controlled so as to obtain high polymer.

2-6b-1 Polyesters. Polyesters can be produced by direct esterification of a diacid with a diol

$$n\ \mathrm{HO{-}R{-}OH} + n\ \mathrm{HO_2C{-}R'{-}CO_2H} \longrightarrow$$

$$\mathrm{HO{+}R{-}OCO{-}R'{-}COO{+}_{n}H} + (2n-1)\ \mathrm{H_2O} \qquad (1\text{-}2)$$

Since polyesterification, like many step polymerizations, is an equilibrium reaction, water must be continuously removed to achieve high conversions and high molecular weights. Control of the polymerization temperature is important to prevent undesirable side reactions such as dehydration of the diol (yielding an unsaturated alkene double bond or an ether) and ester pyrolysis [33], for example,

$$\mathrm{HOCH_2CH_2OH} \longrightarrow \mathrm{H_2O} + \mathrm{CH_3CHO} \qquad (2\text{-}57)$$

$$2\ \mathrm{HO{+}R{-}OCO{-}R'{-}COO{+}_{n}H} \longrightarrow \mathrm{H_2O} +$$

$$\mathrm{H{+}OCO{-}R'{-}COO{-}R{+}_{n}O{+}R{-}OCO{-}R'{-}COO{+}_{n}H} \qquad (2\text{-}58)$$

$$\sim\!\sim \mathrm{R'{-}COOCH_2CH_2{-}OCO{-}R'} \sim\!\sim \longrightarrow$$

$$\sim\!\sim \mathrm{R'{-}COOH} + \mathrm{CH_2{=}CH{-}OCO{-}R'} \sim\!\sim \qquad (2\text{-}59)$$

$$\mathrm{HOOC(CH_2)_4COOH} \longrightarrow \mathrm{CO_2} + \mathrm{H_2O} + \text{cyclopentanone} \qquad (2\text{-}60)$$

The polymerization is catalyzed by protonic or Lewis acids although a wide variety of basic catalysts such as calcium acetate, antimony trioxide, and titanium tetralkoxides can also be used [35]. Basic catalysts are useful for polymerizations carried out at high temperatures to minimize the undesirable side reactions.

Polyesters can also be produced by the Schotten-Baumann reaction of diacyl chlorides and diols, e.g., Eq. 1-3. The use of the Shotten-Baumann reaction in interfacial polymerization and in the synthesis of polycarbonates is discussed in Secs. 2-6c and 2-11b-1, respectively. A few polyesters are made by the esterification of cyclic anhydrides such as phthalic anhydride and maleic anhydride with polyols (see Sec. 2-10).

2-6b-1-a Poly(ethylene terephthalate). Ester interchange is often the most practical reaction for polyester synthesis. The ester interchange reaction is usually a faster reaction than direct esterification of a diacid and can be used when the diacid has poor solubility characteristics or is not easily purified. Methyl esters are often used and the polymerization is driven to completion by the removal of the alcohol by distillation from the reaction mixture. Various weak bases [35] are used to catalyze the polymerization. Poly(ethylene terephthalate) is synthesized from dimethyl terephthalate and ethylene glycol by a two-step ester interchange process. (This polymer may be familiar to many students by the trade names *Mylar* and *Dacron*.) The first step involves an ester interchange reaction to produce primarily bis(2-hydroxyethyl) terephthalate

$$CH_3OCO-C_6H_4-COOCH_3 + 2\ HOCH_2CH_2OH \longrightarrow$$

$$HOCH_2CH_2OCO-C_6H_4-COOCH_2CH_2OH + 2\ CH_3OH \qquad (2\text{-}61)$$

along with small amounts of dimer, trimer, and tetramer. The reaction is run at 105–200°C and the methanol is continuously distilled off.

In the second step, the temperature is raised to about 260°C and polymerization proceeds

$$n\ HOCH_2CH_2OCO-C_6H_4-COOCH_2CH_2OH \longrightarrow$$

$$HOCH_2CH_2O\!\left[CO-C_6H_4-COO-CH_2CH_2O\right]_n\!H +$$

$$(n-1)\ HOCH_2CH_2OH \qquad (2\text{-}62)$$

with the removal of ethylene glycol being facilitated by using a partial vacuum or forcing an inert gas through the reaction mixture.

The production of high molecular weight polymer requires the complete removal of ethylene glycol because of the unfavorable equilibrium which would otherwise exist. If ethylene glycol were not removed, equilibrium would be established at too low an extent of reaction (approximately $p < 0.7$) and the product would be of very low molecular weight (Fig. 2-6). A unique feature of the ester interchange process is the absence of the need for stoichiometric balance of the two functional groups at the start of the polymerization. Stoichiometric balance is inherently achieved in the last stages of the second step of the process.

2-6b-1-b Kinetics of Reversible Polymerization. Although reversible polymerizations such as the above ester interchange would almost always be carried out in an irreversible manner, it is interesting to consider the kinetics of polymerization for the case in which the reaction was allowed to proceed in a reversible manner. (The kinetics of reversible or equilibrium ring-opening polymerizations are discussed in Chap. 7.) The kinetics of the reversible ester interchange polymerization of bis(2-hydroxyethyl) terephthalate have been studied in considerable detail [14, 36]. The reaction (Eq. 2-62) can be depicted as

$$2 \sim\!\!\sim \phi COOCH_2CH_2OH \underset{k_2}{\overset{k_1}{\rightleftharpoons}}$$

X

$$\sim\!\!\sim \phi COOCH_2CH_2OOC\phi \sim\!\!\sim + HOCH_2CH_2OH \tag{2-63}$$

XI

The rate of polymerization, denoted by the net rate of ethylene glycol formation $d[G]/dt$, is given by the difference in the rates of the forward and back reactions

$$R_p = \frac{d[G]}{dt} = k_1[M]^2 - 4k_2[P][G] \tag{2-64}$$

where [M], [P], and [G] refer to the concentrations of the 2-hydroxyethyl ester end-group (X), the ethylene diester group (XI), and ethylene glycol, respectively. The factor of 4 in Eq. 2-64 takes into account the statistical favoring of the reverse action. Reaction between any bifunctional ethylene diester group and any bifunctional glycol molecule can proceed in four equivalent ways; the forward reaction between any hydroxyl group and any ester linkage belonging to different 2-hydroxyethyl ester end-groups can only go in one way.

The concentrations of the various species can be conveniently expressed in terms of the extent of reaction p at time t in the reaction by

$$[\mathrm{M}] = 2(1-p)[\mathrm{R}]_0 \tag{2-65}$$

$$[\mathrm{P}] = p[\mathrm{R}]_0 \tag{2-66}$$

$$[\mathrm{G}] = (q+p-p_0)[\mathrm{R}]_0 \tag{2-67}$$

where $[\mathrm{R}]_0$ is the initial concentration of the repeating unit XII

$$-\mathrm{CH_2OOC}-\phi-\mathrm{COOCH_2}-$$

XII

and

$$q = \frac{[\mathrm{G}]_0}{[\mathrm{R}]_0} \tag{2-68}$$

$$p = \frac{2[\mathrm{R}]_0 - [\mathrm{M}]}{2[\mathrm{R}]_0} \tag{2-69}$$

where $[\mathrm{G}]_0$ is the initial ethylene glycol concentration. One should note that the various terms have been defined so that the kinetic treatment applies equally to polyesterification systems containing any initial combination of the three species X, XI, and glycol. For the case in which only bis(2-hydroxyethyl) terephthalate is initially present, one has $[\mathrm{P}]_0 = [\mathrm{G}]_0 = 0$, $[\mathrm{M}]_0 = 2[\mathrm{R}]_0$, $p_0 = 0$, and $q = 0$.

Combination of Eqs. 2-64 through 2-67 gives the rate expression

$$\frac{dp}{dt} = 4[\mathrm{R}]_0 \left\{ k_1(1-p)^2 - k_2 p(q+p-p_0) \right\} \tag{2-70}$$

which can be integrated between $t = 0\,(p = 0)$ and $t = t\,(p = p)$ to yield

$$k_1 t = \frac{K}{4B[\mathrm{R}]_0} \ln \left\{ \frac{(p_0 - p_e)[(1-K)(p-p_e) + B]}{(p-p_e)[(1-K)(p_0-p_e) + B]} \right\} \tag{2-71}$$

where p_e is the extent of reaction at equilibrium, $K = k_1/k_2$, and

$$B = [(2K + q - p_0)^2 - 4K(K-1)]^{1/2} \tag{2-72}$$

Equation 2-71 is used to describe the polymerization rate in terms of the extent of reaction as a function of time once the equilibrium quantities K and p_e are known for a system [14, 36].

2-6b-2 Polyamides. The synthesis of polyamides follows a different route from that of polyesters. Although several different polymerization reactions are possible, polyamides are usually produced either by direct amidation of a diacid with a diamine or the self-amidation of an amino acid. Ring-opening polymerization of lactams is also employed to synthesize polyamides (Sec. 7-3). Poly(hexamethylene adipamide) is the most important member of the polyamide family and is synthesized from hexamethylene diamine and adipic acid. A stoichiometric balance of amine and carboxyl groups is readily obtained by the preliminary formation of a 1:1 ammonium salt. The salt is often referred to as a *nylon salt*. The polymerization is carried out by heating an aqueous slurry of approximately 60–80% of the salt at about 200°C in a closed autoclave under a pressure of about 15 atmospheres.

$$n\,\mathrm{H_2N(CH_2)_6NH_2} + n\,\mathrm{HO_2C(CH_2)_4CO_2H} \longrightarrow n \begin{bmatrix} {}^{-}\mathrm{O_2C(CH_2)_4CO_2^{-}} \\ {}^{+}\mathrm{H_3N(CH_2)_6NH_3^{+}} \end{bmatrix} \longrightarrow$$

$$\mathrm{H{+}NH{-}(CH_2)_6{-}NHCO{-}(CH_2)_4{-}CO{+}_n OH} + (2n-1)\,\mathrm{H_2O} \tag{2-73}$$

Unlike polyester synthesis, polyamidation does not require a catalyst. Further, the equilibrium for the amidation reaction is very favorable—much more favorable than that for the ester interchange polymerization. For this reason, the amidation is carried out without concern for shifting the equilibrium until the last stages of reaction. The polymerization proceeds to approximately 80–90% conversion in a closed autoclave without removal of the by-product water. The temperature is then raised to 270–300°C, and the steam continuously driven off to drive the polymerization to completion. The earlier stages of the polymerization involve a solution reaction. The later stages constitute a *melt polymerization* since the reaction temperature is above the melting point of the polyamide.

2-6b-3 Polyurethanes. The synthesis of polyurethanes (or polycarbamates, as they are also referred to)

$$n \text{ HO—R—OH} + n \text{ OCN—R'—NCO} \longrightarrow$$

$$\text{HO}\!\left(\text{R—OCONH—R'—NHCO—O}\right)_{(n-1)}\text{R—OCONH—R'—NCO} \qquad (1\text{-}6)$$

presents several special requirements. The polymerization is subject to many side reactions [33, 34] due to the reactivity of the isocyanate group towards a variety of reagents including water, amines, phenols, and carboxylic acids. Thus, water reacts with isocyanates to yield carbon dioxide and an amine

$$\text{R—NCO} + \text{H}_2\text{O} \longrightarrow \text{RNH}_2 + \text{CO}_2 \qquad (2\text{-}74)$$

Dimerization to carbodiimides

$$2\ \text{R—NCO} \longrightarrow \text{R—N=C=N—R} + \text{CO}_2 \qquad (2\text{-}75)$$

and trimerization

$$3\ \text{R—NCO} \longrightarrow \text{(cyclic trimer: six-membered ring of alternating N(R) and C=O)} \qquad (2\text{-}76)$$

as well as several other types of side reactions may also be encountered.

The various side reactions make it difficult to obtain a stoichiometric balance of the diisocyanate and diol reactants. In fact, a slight excess of the diisocyanate is usually needed to overcome the effect of the side reactions and to produce high molecular weight polyurethanes [37]. These side reactions also play a decisive role in determining many of the other process variables. Relatively low temperatures of up to 100–120°C are usually employed. Further, although the polymerization is subject to catalysis by bases such as tertiary amines and metal salts, it is often run without the addition of catalysts so as to limit the extent of side reactions. The reactions are carried out as solution polymerizations. Melt polymerization is not employed since the reaction temperatures are appreciably lower than the melting temperatures of most polyurethanes. High reaction temperatures are also avoided because urethane polymers undergo several different types of degradation reactions such as

$$\text{R—NH—COO—CH}_2\text{CH}_2\text{—R}' \longrightarrow \text{R—NH}_2 + \text{CO}_2 + \text{CH}_2\text{=CH—R}' \tag{2-77}$$

$$\text{R—NH—COO—CH}_2\text{CH}_2\text{—R}' \longrightarrow \text{CO}_2 + \text{R—NH—CH}_2\text{CH}_2\text{—R}' \tag{2-78}$$

as well as decomposition back to the alcohol and isocyanate components.

2-6b-4 Polysiloxanes. Polysiloxanes (or silicones, as they are alternately referred to) are synthesized from chlorosilanes such as dichlorodimethylsilane. The chlorosilane is hydrolyzed to the corresponding silanol which then undergoes polymerization by dehydration

$$\text{Cl—}\underset{\text{CH}_3}{\overset{\text{CH}_3}{\text{Si}}}\text{—Cl} \xrightarrow[-\text{HCl}]{\text{H}_2\text{O}} \text{HO—}\underset{\text{CH}_3}{\overset{\text{CH}_3}{\text{Si}}}\text{—OH} \xrightarrow{-\text{H}_2\text{O}} \left[\text{O—}\underset{\text{CH}_3}{\overset{\text{CH}_3}{\text{Si}}}\right]_n \tag{2-79}$$

The silanol is not isolated under the conditions of the reaction. Polymerization occurs rapidly upon hydrolysis of the chlorosilane.

The product obtained by this reaction is usually a relatively low molecular weight fluid polymer used in such applications as lubricating oils. The product consists of a mixture of cyclic and linear polymers of different sizes. The composition of the product varies considerably depending on the reaction conditions [38]. Hydrolysis of the chlorosilane under basic conditions favors the production of higher molecular weight linear polymers. Strongly acidic conditions favor cyclic siloxanes or low molecular weight linear polymers. Higher temperatures tend to yield higher molecular weight products. However, the synthesis of polysiloxanes of sufficiently high degrees of polymerization to be solids usually is accomplished by the ring-opening polymerization of cyclic polysiloxanes by ionic initiators (Sec. 7-4). Solid polysiloxanes find utility as elastomers.

2-6c Interfacial Polymerization

Many of the polymers that are commercially produced by the usual high temperature reactions described above could be produced at low temperatures by using the faster Schotten-Baumann reactions of acid chlorides. Thus, polyesters and polyamides could be produced by replacing the diacid or diester reactant by the corresponding diacyl chloride

$$n\ \mathrm{ClCO{-}R{-}COCl} + n\ \mathrm{HO{-}R'{-}OH} \longrightarrow$$

$$\mathrm{\left(CO{-}R{-}CO_2{-}R'{-}O\right)_{\mathit{n}}} + 2n\ \mathrm{HCl} \tag{2-80}$$

$$n\ \mathrm{ClCO{-}R{-}COCl} + n\ \mathrm{H_2N{-}R'{-}NH_2} \longrightarrow$$

$$\mathrm{\left(CO{-}R{-}CONH{-}R'{-}NH\right)_{\mathit{n}}} + 2n\ \mathrm{HCl} \tag{2-81}$$

2-6c-1 Description of Process. The rate constants for these reactions are orders of magnitude greater than those for the corresponding reactions of the diacid or diester reactants. In recent years, the use of such reactants in a novel low temperature polymerization technique called *interfacial polymerization* has been extensively studied [39, 40]. Polymerization of two reactants is carried out at the interface between two liquid phases, each containing one of the reactants (Fig. 2-11). Polyamidation is performed at room temperature by placing an aqueous solution of the diamine on top of an organic phase containing the acid chloride. The reactants diffuse to and undergo polymerization at the interface. The polymer product precipitates and is continuously withdrawn in the form of a continuous film or filament. The polymerization rate is governed by the rates of diffusion of the two reactants to the interface. Interfacial polymerization is mechanistically different from the usual step polymerization in that the monomers diffusing to the interface will react only with polymer chain ends. The reaction rates are so high that diacid chloride and diamine monomer molecules will react with the growing polymer chain ends before they can penetrate through

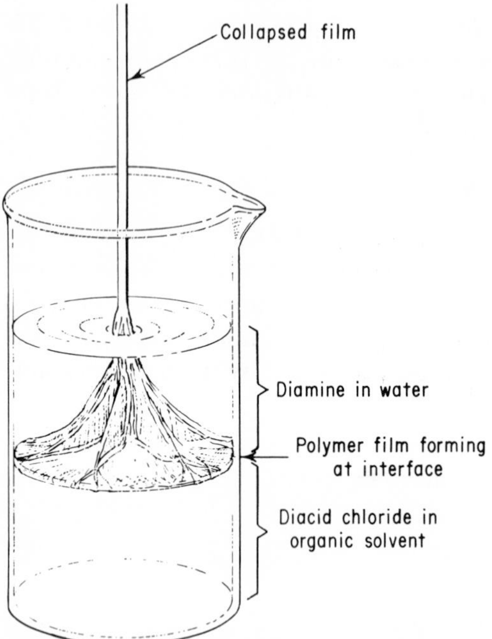

FIG. 2-11 *Interfacial polymerization; removal of polymer film from the interface. From [39] (by permission of Division of Chemical Education, American Chemical Society, Washington and Interscience Publishers, John Wiley & Sons, Inc., New York); an original photograph, from which this figure was drawn, was kindly supplied by Dr. P. W. Morgan.*

the polymer film to start the growth of new chains. There is, thus, a tendency to produce higher molecular weight polymer in the interfacial process compared to the usual processes.

Several reaction parameters must be controlled in order for interfacial polymerization to proceed successfully. An inorganic base must be present in the aqueous phase to neutralize the by-product hydrogen chloride. If it were not neutralized, the hydrogen chloride would tie up the diamine as its unreactive amine hydrochloride salt leading to lowered reaction rates. The acid chloride may undergo hydrolysis to the unreactive acid at high concentrations of the inorganic base or at low rates of polymerizations. However, under the usual reaction conditions, the acid chloride has too low a water solubility and polymerization rates are too high to allow diffusion of the acid chloride through the interface and into the water layer.

The choice of the organic solvent is very important in controlling the polymer molecular weight since it appears that the polymerization actually occurs on the organic side of the interface. An organic solvent which precipitates the high molecular weight polymer but not the low molecular weight fractions is desirable. Premature precipitation of the polymer will prevent the production of the desired high molecular weight product. Thus, for example, xylene and carbon tetrachloride are precipitants for all molecular weights of poly(hexamethylene sebacate), while chloroform is a precipitant only for the high molecular weight polymer. Interfacial polymerization with the former organic solvents would yield only low molecular weight polymer. The molecular weight distributions observed in interfacial polymerizations are usually quite different from the Flory distribution [26, 40]. Both broader and narrower distributions than the most probable distribution have been found. The differences are probably caused by the occurrence of fractionation during the precipitation of the polymer. The effect would be expected to be highly dependent on the organic solvent employed and the solubility characteristics of the polymer.

2-6c-2 Utility. The interfacial technique has several advantageous characteristics. The purity of the reactants is not as important as in the high temperature polymerization since side reactions due to impurities will not be as important at the lower temperatures. Interfacial polymerization does not require overall bulk stoichiometry of the reactants in the two phases. Stoichiometry automatically exists at the interface where polymerization proceeds. There is always a supply of both reactants at the interface due to diffusion from the organic and aqueous phase. Furthermore, high molecular weight polymer is formed at the interface regardless of the overall percent conversion based on the bulk amounts of the two reactants. The overall percent conversion can be increased by employing a stirred system as a means of increasing the total area of reacting interface.

The interfacial technique has been extended to many different polymerizations including the formation of polyamides, polyesters, polyurethanes, polysulfonamides, polycarbonates, polyureas, polyphosphonamides, and many others. In addition to the advantages cited, it has the advantage that its low temperatures allow the synthesis of polymers which are unstable at the high temperatures required in the usual step polymerization. It might also allow the direct polymerization of reactants to final products in the form of films, coatings, fibers, and fibrous particles. However, there are disadvantages to the process which have limited the commercial use of interfacial polymerization. These include the high cost of acid chloride reactants, the large amounts of solvents which must be employed and recovered, and other considerations.

2-7 MULTI-CHAIN POLYMERIZATION

2-7a Branching

The discussions until this point have been concerned with the polymerization of bifunctional monomers to form *linear polymers.* When one or more monomers with more than two functional groups per molecule are present, the resulting polymer will be *branched* instead of linear. With certain monomers, crosslinking will also take place with the formation of *network structures* in which a branch or branches from one polymer molecule become attached to other molecules. The structures of linear, branched, and crosslinked polymers are compared in Fig. 1-1.

Consider the polymerization of an A—B reactant in the presence of a small amount of a monomer A_f containing f functional groups per molecule. The value of f is termed the *functionality of the monomer.* The product of this polymerization will be a branched

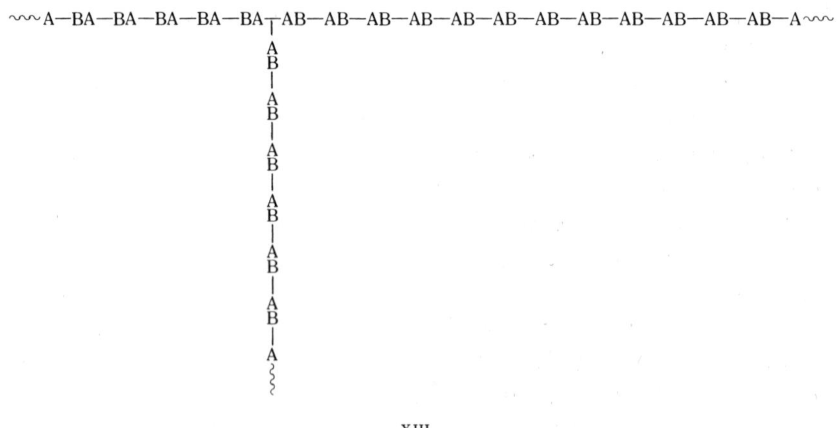

XIII

polymer in which f chains are attached to a central branch point (i.e., an A_f species). For the specific case of $f = 3$, polymerization of

A—B in the presence of $\text{A}\underset{\text{A}}{\top}\text{A}$ leads to the structure XIII. A careful consideration of this structure shows that there can be only one A_f reactant molecule incorporated into each polymer molecule. Further, crosslinked species will not be formed. Reactions between two polymer molecules of the above type cannot occur since all growing branches possess A functional groups at their ends. Branch chains from one molecule cannot react with those from another. (This would not be true if A groups were capable of reacting with each other. However, that is not the usual situation.)

2-7b Molecular Weight Distribution

The molecular weight distribution in this type of non-linear polymerization will be much narrower than for a linear polymerization. Molecules of sizes very much different from the average are less likely than in linear polymerization since this would require having the statistically determined f branches making up a molecule all very long or all very short. The distribution functions for this polymerization have been derived statistically [41] and the results are given as

$$\bar{X}_n = \frac{(fp+1-p)}{(1-p)} \tag{2-82}$$

$$\bar{X}_w = \frac{(f-1)^2p^2 + (3f-2)p + 1}{(fp+1-p)(1-p)} \tag{2-83}$$

The breadth of the distribution is characterized by

$$\frac{\bar{X}_w}{\bar{X}_n} = 1 + \frac{fp}{(fp+1-p)^2} \tag{2-84}$$

which becomes

$$\frac{\bar{X}_w}{\bar{X}_n} = 1 + \frac{1}{f} \tag{2-85}$$

in the limit of $p = 1$.

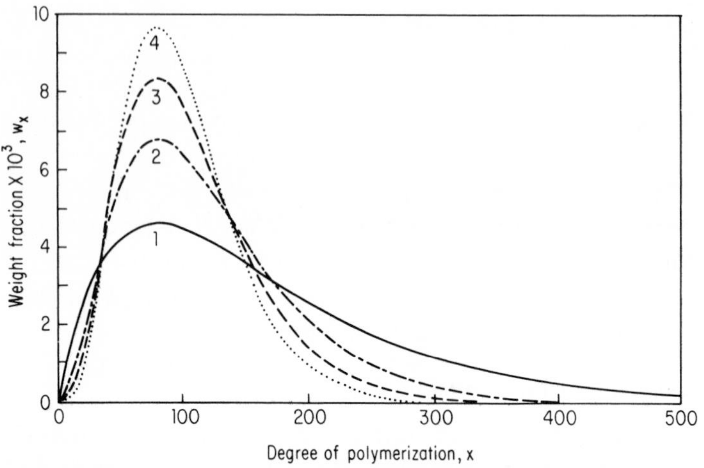

FIG. 2-12 *Weight fraction distribution curve for multi-chain polymerization. Curve 1: f = 1; Curve 2: f = 2; Curve 3: f = 3; Curve 4: f = 4. After [28] (by permission of Iliffe Brooks, Ltd., London).*

The weight distribution (Eq. 2-83) is shown in Fig. 2-12 for several values of f. The extents of reaction have been adjusted to maintain a constant number-average degree of polymerization of 80 in all four cases. The size distribution becomes progressively narrower with increasing functionality of A_f. This is also evident from Eq. 2-85 where $\overline{X}_w/\overline{X}_n$ decreases from 2 for $f = 1$ to 1.25 for $f = 4$ (at $p = 1$). Linear polymers are formed for f values of one or two while branched polymers are formed when f is greater than two. The case of $f = 1$ corresponds to the Type 3 polymerization discussed in Sec. 2-4. The distribution is the exact same as the most probable distribution for linear polymerization (Sec. 2-5). Linear polymerization with $f = 2$ is of interest in that the distribution is narrower than that for the usual linear polymerization. The linking of two statistically independent A—B type polymer chains into one polymer molecule via an A—A molecule leads to a significantly narrower distribution than in the usual polymerizations of the A—B or A—A plus B—B types.

2-8 CROSSLINKING

Polymerization of the A—B plus A_f system (with $f > 2$) in the presence of B—B will lead not only to branching but also to a *crosslinked* polymer structure. Branches from one polymer molecule will be capable of reacting with those of another polymer molecule because of the presence of the B—B reactant. Crosslinking can be pictured as leading to the structure XIV in which two polymer chains have been joined together (crosslinked) by a branch. The branch joining the two chains is referred to as a *crosslink.* A crosslink can be formed whenever there are two branches (e.g., those indicated in XIV by the arrows) which have different functional groups at their ends, i.e., one has an A group and the other a B group. Crosslinking

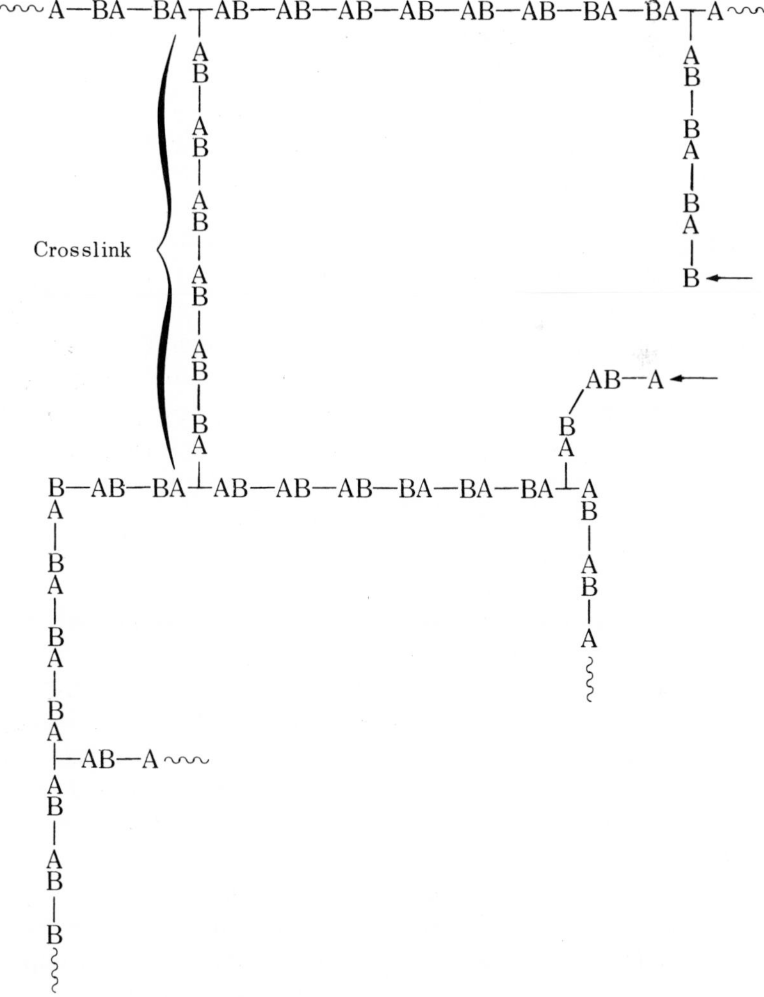

XIV

will also occur in other polymerizations involving reactants with functionalities greater than two. These include the polymerizations

$$A\text{—}A + B_f \longrightarrow$$

$$A\text{—}A + B\text{—}B + B_f \longrightarrow$$

$$A_f + B_f \longrightarrow$$

Crosslinking is distinguished by the occurrence of *gelation* at some point in the polymerization. At this point termed the *gel point,* one first observes the visible formation of a *gel* or *insoluble polymer fraction.* (The gel point is alternately taken as the point at which the system loses fluidity as measured by the failure of an air bubble to rise in it.) The gel is insoluble in all solvents at elevated temperatures under conditions where polymer degradation does not occur. The gel corresponds to the formation of an infinite network in which polymer molecules have been crosslinked to each other to form a macroscopic molecule. The gel is, in fact, considered as one molecule. The non-gel portion of the polymer remains soluble in solvents. As the polymerization and gelation proceed beyond the gel point, the amount of gel increases at the expense of the sol as more and more polymer chains in the sol are crosslinked to the gel. There is a dramatic physical change which occurs during the process of gelation. The reaction mixture is transformed into a polymer of infinite viscosity.

The crosslinking reaction is an extremely important one from the commercial standpoint. Crosslinked plastics are increasingly used as engineering materials because of their excellent stability toward elevated temperatures and physical stress. They are dimensionally stable under a wide variety of conditions due to their rigid network structure. Such polymers will not flow when heated and are termed *thermosetting* polymers or simply *thermosets.* (Plastics which do soften and flow when heated, i.e., uncrosslinked plastics, are called *thermoplastics.* Almost all of the polymers produced by chain polymerization are thermoplastics. There are only a relatively few such polymers which are crosslinked.) The commercial importance of the thermosets is seen from the fact that of the approximately 15 billion pounds of plastics produced in the United States, in 1968, almost 3.5 billion pounds were crosslinked plastics [42].

2-8a Carothers Equation

2-8a-1 Equivalent Amounts of Reactants. In order to control the crosslinking reaction so that it can be used properly, it is important to understand the relationship between gelation and the extent of reaction. Carothers derived a useful relationship between the extent of reaction at the gel point and the *average functionality* f_{avg} of the polymerization system for the case where the two functional groups A and B are present in equivalent amounts [13]. The derivation follows in a manner very close to that for Eq. 2-41. The average functionality of a mixture of monomers is the average number of functional groups per monomer molecule for all types of monomer molecules. It is defined by

$$f_{avg} = \frac{\sum N_i f_i}{\sum N_i} \tag{2-86}$$

where N_i is the number of molecules of monomer i with functionality f_i and the summations are over all the monomers present in the system. Thus, for a system consisting of two moles of glycerol (a triol) and three moles of phthalic acid (a diacid), there is a total of twelve functional groups per five monomer molecules and f_{avg} is 12/5 or 2.4. For a system consisting of equimolar amounts of glycerol, phthalic anhydride, and a monobasic acid, there is a total of six functional groups per three molecules and f_{avg} is 6/3 or 2.

In a system containing equivalent numbers of A and B groups, the number of monomer molecules present initially is N_0 and the corresponding total number of functional groups is $N_0 f_{avg}$. If N is the number of molecules after reaction has occurred, then $2(N_0 - N)$ is the number of functional groups that have reacted. The extent of reaction p is the fraction of functional groups lost

$$p = \frac{2(N_0 - N)}{N_0 f_{avg}} \tag{2-87}$$

while the degree of polymerization is

$$\overline{X}_n = \frac{N_0}{N} \tag{2-88}$$

Combination of Eqs. 2-87 and 2-88 yields

$$\overline{X}_n = \frac{2}{2 - pf_{\text{avg}}} \tag{2-89}$$

which can be rearranged to

$$p = \frac{2}{f_{\text{avg}}} - \frac{2}{\overline{X}_n f_{\text{avg}}} \tag{2-90}$$

Equation 2-90, often referred to as the *Carothers equation,* relates the extent of reaction and degree of polymerization to the average functionality of the system.

An important consequence of Eq. 2-90 is its limiting form at the gel point where the number-average degree of polymerization becomes infinite. The *critical extent of reaction* p_c at the gel point is given by

$$p_c = \frac{2}{f_{\text{avg}}} \tag{2-91}$$

since the second term on the right side of Eq. 2-90 vanishes. Equation 2-91 can be used to calculate the extent of reaction required to reach the onset of gelation in a mixture of reacting monomers from its average functionality. Thus, the glycerol-phthalic acid (2:3 molar ratio) system mentioned above has a calculated critical extent of reaction of 0.833.

2-8a-2 Extension to Non-Equivalent Reactant Mixtures. Equations 2-90 and 2-91 apply only to systems containing stoichiometric numbers of the two different functional groups. For non-equivalent numbers of the functional groups, the average functionality calculated from Eq. 2-86 is too high. Thus, consider the extreme example of a mixture of 1 mole of glycerol and 5 moles of phthalic acid. Using

Eq. 2-86, one calculates a value of 13/6 or 2.17 for f_{avg}. This indicates that high polymer will be obtained. Further, one would predict from Eq. 2-91 that crosslinking will occur at $p_c = 0.922$. Both of these conclusions are grossly in error. It is apparent from previous discussions (Sec. 2-4) that the gross stoichiometric imbalance between the A and B functional groups in this system ($r = 0.3$) precludes the formation of any but extremely low molecular weight species. The polymerization will stop with the large portion of the acid functional groups being unreacted.

The average functionality of non-stoichiometric mixtures has been deduced [43] as being equal to twice the total number of functional groups which are not in excess divided by the total number of all molecules present. This simply takes into account the fact that the extent of polymerization (and crosslinking, if it can occur) depends on the deficient reactant. The excess of the other reactant is not useful; in fact, it results in a lowering of the functionality of the system. For the above non-stoichiometric mixture of 1 mole of glycerol and 5 moles of phthalic acid, the f_{avg} value is correctly calculated as 6/6 or 1.00. This low value of f_{avg} is indicative of the low degree of polymerization which will occur in the system.

In a similar manner, the average functionality of non-stoichiometric mixtures containing more than two monomers has been obtained. Consider a ternary mixture of N_A moles of A_{f_A}, N_C moles of A_{f_C}, and N_B moles of B_{f_B} with functionalities f_A, f_C, and f_B, respectively. In this system, A_{f_A} and A_{f_C} contain the same functional groups (i.e., A groups) and the total number of A functional groups is less than the number of B groups (i.e., B groups are in excess). The average functionality in such a system is given [43] by

$$f_{avg} = \frac{2(N_A f_A + N_C f_C)}{N_A + N_C + N_B} \tag{2-92a}$$

or

$$f_{avg} = \frac{2r f_A f_B f_C}{f_A f_C + r\rho f_A f_B + r(1-\rho) f_B f_C} \tag{2-92b}$$

where

$$r = \frac{N_A f_A + N_C f_C}{N_B f_B} \tag{2-93}$$

$$\rho = \frac{N_C f_C}{N_A f_A + N_C f_C} \tag{2-94}$$

The term r is the ratio of A groups to B groups and has a value equal to or less than unity. r is comparable to the previously discussed stoichiometric imbalance. The term ρ is the fraction of all A functional groups which belong to reactant A_{f_C}.

The special case of $f_C > 2$ and $f_A = f_B = 2$ corresponding to

$$A_{f_C} + \text{A—A} + \text{B—B} \longrightarrow \tag{2-95}$$

is an important one from the technological viewpoint. For this system, Eq. 2-92 becomes

$$f_{avg} = \frac{4rf_C}{f_C + 2r\rho + rf_C(1-\rho)} \tag{2-96}$$

which can be substituted into Eq. 2-91 to yield

$$p_c = \frac{(1-\rho)}{2} + \frac{1}{2r} + \frac{\rho}{f_C} \tag{2-97}$$

It should be kept clearly in mind that the extent of reaction p_c at the gel point refers to the extent of reaction of the A functional groups. The extent of reaction of the B groups at the gel point is rp_c.

2-8b Statistical Approach to Gelation

Flory [27] and also Stockmayer [44] used a statistical approach to derive a useful expression for the prediction of the extent of reaction at the gel point. This approach assumes that the reactivity of all functional groups of the same type is the same and independent of molecular size. It is further assumed that there are no intramolecular reactions between functional groups on the same molecule.

(These assumptions are also inherent in the use of Eqs. 2-89 to 2-97.) For this derivation, the *branching coefficient* α is defined as the probability that a given functional group of a branch unit at the end of a polymer chain segment leads to another branch unit. For the polymerization of A—A with B—B and A_f, this corresponds to obtaining a chain segment of the type

$$\text{A—A} + \text{B—B} + \text{A}_f \longrightarrow$$

$$\text{A}_{(f-1)}\text{—A(B—BA—A)}_n\text{—B—BA—A}_{(f-1)} \tag{2-98}$$

where n may have any value from zero to infinity. The multifunctional monomer A_f is considered a *branch unit,* while the segments between branch units are defined as *chain segments.* The branch units occur on a polymer chain at the branch points (Fig. 1-1). Infinite networks are formed when n number of chains or chain segments give rise to more than n chains through branching of some of them. The criterion for gelation in a system containing a reactant of functionality f is that at least one of the $(f-1)$ chain segments radiating from a branch unit will in turn be connected to another branch unit. The probability for this occurring is simply $1/(f-1)$ and the *critical branching coefficient* α_c for gel formation is

$$\alpha_c = \frac{1}{(f-1)} \tag{2-99}$$

The f in Eq. 2-99 is the functionality of the branch units, i.e., of the monomer with functionality greater than two. It is not the average functionality f_{avg} from the Carothers equation. If more than one type of multifunctional branch unit is present, an average f value of all the monomer molecules with functionality greater than two is used in Eq. 2-99.

When $\alpha(f-1)$ equals one, a chain segment will, on the average, be succeeded by $\alpha(f-1)$ chains. Of these $\alpha(f-1)$ chains, a portion α will each end in a branch point so that $\alpha^2(f-1)^2$ more chains are created. The branching process continues with the number of succeeding chains becoming progressively greater through each succeeding branching reaction. The growth of the polymer is limited only by the boundaries of the reaction vessel. If, on the other hand, $\alpha(f-1)$ is less than one, chain segments will not be likely to end in branch units. For a trifunctional reactant ($f = 3$) the critical value of α is 1/2.

The probability α is now related to the extent of reaction by determining the probability of obtaining a chain segment of the type shown in Eq. 2-98. The extents of reaction of A and B functional groups are p_A and p_B, respectively. The ratio of all A groups, both reacted and unreacted, which are part of branch units, to the total number of all A groups in the mixture is defined by ρ. (This corresponds to the same definition of ρ as in Eq. 2-94.) The probability that a B group has reacted with a branch unit is $p_B \rho$. The probability that a B group has reacted with a non-branch A—A unit is $p_B(1-\rho)$. Therefore, the probability of obtaining a segment of the type in Eq. 2-98 is given by $p_A[p_B(1-\rho)p_A]^n p_B \rho$. Summation of this over all values of n and then evaluation of the summation yields

$$\alpha = \frac{p_A p_B \rho}{1 - p_A p_B(1-\rho)} \tag{2-100}$$

Either p_A or p_B can be eliminated by using the ratio r of all A groups to all B groups (i.e., Eq. 2-93) to substitute $p_B = rp_A$ into Eq. 2-100 to yield

$$\alpha = \frac{rp_A^2 \rho}{1 - rp_A^2(1-\rho)} = \frac{p_B^2 \rho}{r - p_B^2(1-\rho)} \tag{2-101}$$

Equation 2-101 can be combined with Eq. 2-99 to yield a useful expression for the extent of reaction (of the A functional groups) at the gel point

$$p_c = \frac{1}{[r + r\rho(f-2)]^{1/2}} \tag{2-102}$$

Several special cases of Eqs. 2-101 and 2-102 are of interest. When the two functional groups are present in equivalent numbers, $r = 1$ and $p_A = p_B = p$, Eqs. 2-101 and 2-102 become

$$\alpha = \frac{p^2 \rho}{1 - p^2(1-\rho)} \tag{2-103}$$

and

$$p_c = \frac{1}{[1 + \rho(f-2)]^{1/2}} \tag{2-104}$$

When the polymerization is carried out without any A—A molecules ($\rho = 1$) with $r < 1$, the equations reduce to

$$\alpha = rp_A^2 = \frac{p_B^2}{r} \tag{2-105}$$

and

$$p_c = \frac{1}{[r + r(f-2)]^{1/2}} \tag{2-106}$$

If both of the above conditions are present, $r = \rho = 1$, Eqs. 2-101 and 2-102 become

$$\alpha = p^2 \tag{2-107}$$

and

$$p_c = \frac{1}{[1 + (f-2)]^{1/2}} \tag{2-108}$$

For the special case where only monomers with $f > 2$ are present, the probability that a functional group on a branch unit leads to another branch unit is simply the probability that it has reacted, that is, $\alpha = p$, and therefore

$$p_c = \frac{1}{f-1} \tag{2-109}$$

2-8c Experimental Gel Points

The two approaches to the problem of predicting the extent of reaction at the onset of gelation differ appreciably in their predictions of p_c for the same system of reactants. The Carothers equation (Eq. 2-91) and its extension to ternary mixtures (Eq. 2-97) predicts the extent of reaction at which the number-average degree of polymerization becomes infinite. This must, obviously, yield a value of p_c that is too large because polymer molecules larger than $\overline{X}_n$ are present and will reach the gel point earlier than those of size $\overline{X}_n$. The statistical treatment (Eq. 2-92) theoretically overcomes this error since it predicts the extent of reaction at which the polymer size distribution curve first extends into the region of infinite size [43].

The gel point is usually determined experimentally as that point in the reaction at which the reacting mixture loses fluidity as indicated by the failure of bubbles to rise in it. Experimental observations of the gel point in a number of systems have confirmed the general utility of the Carothers and statistical approaches. Thus, in the reactions of glycerol (a triol) with equivalent amounts of several diacids, the gel point was observed [45] at an extent of reaction of 0.765. The predicted values of p_c are 0.709 and 0.833 from Eqs. 2-102 (statistical) and 2-91 (Carothers), respectively. Flory [46] studied several systems composed of diethylene glycol ($f = 2$), 1,2,3-propanetricarboxylic acid ($f = 3$), and either succinic or adipic acid ($f = 2$) with both stoichiometric and non-stoichiometric amounts of hydroxyl and carboxyl groups. Some of the experimentally observed p_c values are shown in Table 2-4 along with the corresponding theoretical values calculated by both the Carothers and statistical equations.

The observed p_c values in Table 2-4 as in many other similar systems fall approximately midway between the two calculated values. The Carothers equation gives a high value of p_c for reasons mentioned

Table 2-4 Gel Point Determinations for Mixtures of 1,2,3-Propanetricarboxylic Acid, Diethylene Glycol, and either Adipic or Succinic Acid[a]

		Extent of reaction at gel point (p_c)		
$r = \frac{[CO_2H]}{[OH]}$	ρ	Calculated from Eq. 2-91 or 2-97	Calculated from Eq. 2-102	Observed[a]
1.000	0.293	0.951	0.879	0.911
1.000	0.194	0.968	0.916	0.939
1.002	0.404	0.933	0.843	0.894
0.800	0.375	1.063	0.955	0.991

[a]Data from [46].

above. The experimental p_c values are close to but always higher than those calculated from Eq. 2-102. This difference is generally attributed to the occurrence of *intramolecular cyclization* reactions between functional groups which are ignored in the theoretical derivations. The intramolecular reactions are wasteful and require the polymerization to be carried out to a greater extent of reaction to reach the gel point. That this is indeed the case was clearly shown by Stockmayer [47] who studied the gelation of pentaerythritol ($f = 4$) with adipic acid as a function of concentration. The results were extrapolated to infinite concentration where intramolecular reactions would be expected to be nil. The experimental p_c value of 0.578 ± 0.005 compared exceptionally well with the theoretical value of 0.577. The value of p_c calculated by the Carothers equation is 0.75 for this system.

The difference between the observed p_c values and those calculated from Eq. 2-102 could also be ascribed in some cases to the failure of the assumption of equal reactivity of all functional groups of the same type. An example is the glycerol-phthalic acid system previously mentioned. The difference between the calculated and observed values of p_c (0.709 versus 0.765) would be decreased, but not eliminated, if the calculation were corrected for the known lower reactivity of the secondary hydroxyl group of glycerol.

Although both the Carothers and statistical approaches are used for the practical prediction of gel points, the statistical approach is the more frequently employed. The statistical method is preferred since it theoretically gives the gel point for the largest sized molecules in a size distribution. Further, the statistical approach offers a greater possibility of adaption to various systems of reactants as well as the inclusion of corrections for the non-applicability of the equal reactivity assumption and the occurrence of intramolecular reactions. Equation 2-102 and its modifications have been used extensively in the technology of crosslinked polymers such as formaldehyde-phenol polymers [48], alkyd resins [49–51], and others.

2-9 MOLECULAR WEIGHT DISTRIBUTIONS IN NONLINEAR POLYMERIZATIONS

The molecular size distribution functions for three dimensional polymers are derived in a manner analogous to those for linear polymers, but with more difficulty. The derivations have been discussed elsewhere [27, 44, 52] and only their results will be considered here. The number N_x, number or mole fraction $\underline{N}_x$, and weight fraction w_x of x-mer molecules in a system containing monomer(s) with $f > 2$ are given, respectively, by

$$N_x = N_0\left[\frac{(fx-x)!\,f}{x!\,(fx-2x+2)!}\right]\alpha^{x-1}(1-\alpha)^{fx-2x+2} \tag{2-110}$$

$$\underline{N}_x = \left[\frac{(fx-x)!\,f}{x!\,(fx-2x+2)!\,(1-\alpha f/2)}\right]\alpha^{x-1}(1-\alpha)^{fx-2x+2} \tag{2-111}$$

$$w_x = \left[\frac{(fx-x)!\,f}{(x-1)!\,(fx-2x+2)!}\right]\alpha^{x-1}(1-\alpha)^{fx-2x+2} \tag{2-112}$$

The number- and weight-average degrees of polymerization are given by

$$\overline{X}_n = \frac{1}{1-(\alpha f/2)} \tag{2-113}$$

$$\overline{X}_w = \frac{(1+\alpha)}{1-(f-1)\alpha} \tag{2-114}$$

$$\frac{\overline{X}_w}{\overline{X}_n} = \frac{(1+\alpha)(1-\alpha f/2)}{1-(f-1)\alpha} \tag{2-115}$$

These equations are general and apply equally for multifunctional reactions such as that of A_f with B_f or that of A_f with A—A and B—B. Depending on which of these reactant combinations is involved, the value of α will be appropriately determined by the parameters r, f, p, and ρ in accordance with Eqs. 2-101 to 2-109. For convenience, the size distributions in the reaction of equivalent amounts of trifunctional reactants alone, i.e., where $\alpha = p$, will be considered. A comparison of Eqs. 2-48 and 2-112 shows that the weight distribution of branched polymers is broader than that of linear polymers at equivalent extents of reaction. Furthermore, the distribution for the branched polymers becomes increasingly broader as the functionality of the multifunctional reactant increases. The distributions

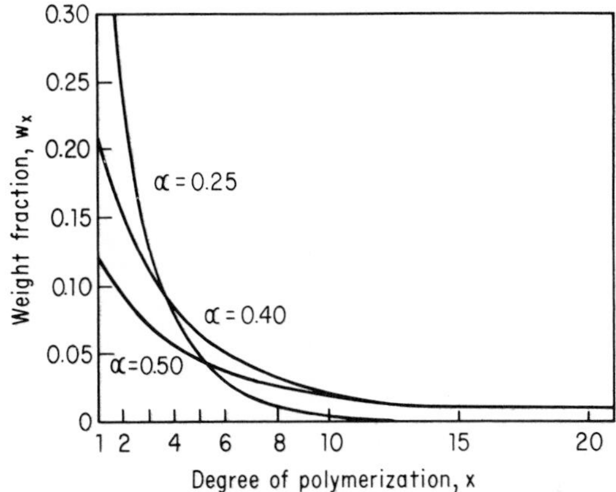

FIG. 2-13 *Molecular weight distribution as a function of the extent of reaction for the polymerization of trifunctional reactants where $\alpha = p$. After [52] (by permission of American Chemical Society, Washington).*

also broaden with increasing values of α. This is seen in Fig. 2-13 which shows the weight fraction of x-mers as a function of α for the polymerization involving only trifunctional reactants.

Figure 2-14 shows a plot of the weight fraction of different x-mers versus α or p for the trifunctional polymerization. The weight fraction w_{gel} of the gel or ∞-mer is also plotted. A comparison of Figs. 2-13 and 2-14 with Fig. 2-8 for linear polymerization shows that the weight fraction of monomer is always greater than that of any one of the other species (up to the point where the curves for w_1 and w_{gel} intersect). As reaction proceeds, larger species are built up at the expense of the smaller ones with a maximum being reached at a value of p less than 1/2. The maximum shifts to higher values of p for the larger species. The distribution broadens and reaches maximum heterogeneity at the gel point (α = 1/2) where the fraction of species which are highly branched is still small. The infinite network polymer is first formed at the gel point and its weight fraction rapidly increases. The species in the sol (comprised of all species other than gel) decrease in average size because the larger, branched species are preferentially tied into the gel. Past the point of intersection for the w_1 and w_{gel} curves, gel is the most abundant species on a weight basis.

The broadening of the distribution with increasing α can also be noted by the $\bar{X}_w/\bar{X}_n$ value. Equations 2-113 to 2-115 show that the

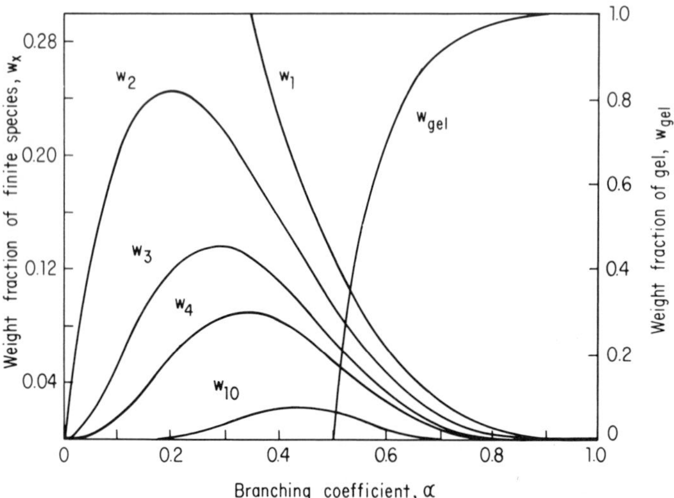

FIG. 2-14 *Weight fractions of various finite species and of gel in a trifunctional polymerization where* $\alpha = p$. *After [52] (by permission of American Chemical Society, Washington).*

difference between the number- and weight-average degrees of polymerization increases very rapidly with increasing extent of reaction. At the gel point the breadth of the distribution $\bar{X}_w/\bar{X}_n$ is enormous since $\bar{X}_w$ is infinite while $\bar{X}_n$ has a finite value of four (Fig. 2-15). Past the gel point, the value of $\bar{X}_w/\bar{X}_n$ for the sol fraction decreases. Finally at $\alpha = p = 1$, the whole system has been converted to gel (i.e., one giant molecule) and $\bar{X}_w/\bar{X}_n$ equals one.

As previously mentioned, the behavior of systems containing bifunctional as well as trifunctional reactants is also governed by the equations developed above. The variation of w_x for the polymerization of bifunctional monomers, where the branching coefficient α is varied by using appropriate amounts of a trifunctional monomer, is similar to that observed for the polymerization of trifunctional reactants alone. The distribution broadens with increasing extent of reaction.

2-10 CROSSLINKING TECHNOLOGY

The theory of the crosslinking process and the parameters which control it has been discussed. Control of the process is extremely important in the commercial processing of thermosetting plastics.

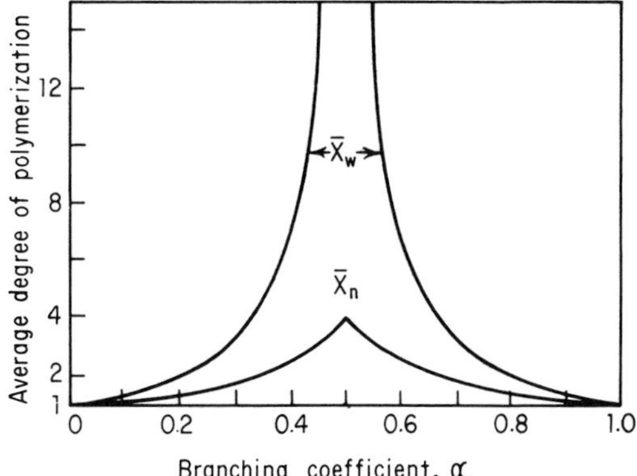

FIG. 2-15 *Number- and weight-average degrees of polymerization as a function of α for a trifunctional polymerization. The portions of the curves after the gel point (α = 1/2) are for the sol fraction only. After [52] (by permission of American Chemical Society, Washington).*

This applies both to the reaction prior to the gel point and that subsequent to it. The period after the gel point is usually referred to as the curing period. Too slow or too rapid crosslinking can be detrimental to the properties of a desired product. Thus, in the production of a thermoset foamed product, the foam structure may collapse if gelation occurs too slowly. On the other hand, for reinforced and laminated products, the bond strength of the components may be low if crosslinking occurs too quickly.

The fabrication techniques for producing objects from thermosetting and thermoplastic polymers are vastly different. In the case of the thermoplastics, the polymerization reaction is completed by the plastics manufacturer. The fabricator takes the polymer and applies heat and pressure in order to produce a flowable material which can be shaped into the desired finished object. The situation is quite different for thermosetting plastics. A completely polymerized thermoset is no longer capable of flow and cannot be processed into an object. Instead, the fabricator receives an incompletely polymerized polymer—termed a *prepolymer*—from the plastics manufacturer and polymerization (and crosslinking) is completed during the fabrication step. For example, a prepolymer can be poured into an appropriate mold and then solidified to form the desired finished object by completing the polymerization. The prepolymers are usually in the molecular weight range 500–5,000 and may be either liquid or solid.

Thermoset polymers are classified as *A*-, *B*-, and *C*-stage polymers according to their extent of reaction p compared to the extent of reaction at gelation p_c. The polymer is an *A-stage* polymer if $p < p_c$, *B-stage* if the system is close to the gel point (p_c), and *C-stage* when it is well past p_c. The *A*-stage polymer is soluble and fusible. The *B*-stage polymer is still fusible but is barely soluble. The *C*-stage polymer is highly crosslinked and both infusible and insoluble. The prepolymer employed by a fabricator is usually a *B*-stage polymer although it may be an *A*-stage one. The subsequent polymerization of the prepolymer takes it through to the *C*-stage.

2-10a Random Prepolymers

Thermoset plastics can generally be grouped into two categories depending on the identity of the prepolymer [53]. The older thermosetting materials involve the random crosslinking of bifunctional monomers with monomers of functionality greater than two. The prepolymer is obtained in this first-stage reaction by stopping the reaction, usually by cooling, at the desired extent of polymerization ($p < p_c$). Such prepolymers are termed *random prepolymers.* Polymerization of the prepolymer is completed during the subsequent second-stage fabrication step usually by simply heating.

2-10a-1 Polyesters. Polyesters formed from phthalic anhydride and glycerol

$$\text{C}_6\text{H}_4(\text{CO})_2\text{O} + \begin{array}{c}\text{CH}_2\text{OH}\\ | \\ \text{CHOH} \\ | \\ \text{CH}_2\text{OH}\end{array} \longrightarrow \sim\!\text{O}-\text{CH}_2-\underset{\substack{|\\ \text{O}\\ \wr}}{\text{CH}}-\text{CH}_2-\text{O}-\overset{\text{O}}{\overset{\|}{\text{C}}}-\text{C}_6\text{H}_4-\overset{\text{O}}{\overset{\|}{\text{C}}}-\text{O}\!\sim \tag{2-116}$$

are an example of the random type of crosslinking polymer.

Diols and even monocarboxylic acids are often used in the polyester system to achieve a more flexible final product by decreasing the density of crosslinking in the network structure. The combination of a monofunctional acid with the trifunctional glycerol and the difunctional phthalic anhydride requires special consideration. Many systems of this type may employ an overall formulation such that the average functionality is 2 or only slightly greater than 2. (For an equimolar mixture of the three reactants, f_{avg} is exactly 2.) The use of the Carothers equation and its modifications (Secs. 2-8a-1 and 2-8a-2) for such formulations are often misleading in that they predict that gelation will not occur. However, many such systems do undergo gelation.

The failure of the Carothers equation and its modifications is due to their assumption that gelation occurs when the number-average molecular weight becomes infinite. Even for systems with an average functionality close to 2, some polymer molecules will be much larger than the number-average size and will undergo gelation as long as there is some trifunctional reactant present in the system. Equations based on the statistical approach to gelation have been developed to predict the gel points in these types of polymerization systems. One of these is the expression

$$p_c = \left[\frac{\epsilon}{2(1-\lambda)}\right]^{1/2} \tag{2-117}$$

with

$$\epsilon = \frac{\text{Total equivalents of OH groups}}{\text{Total equivalents of COOH groups}} \tag{2-118a}$$

$$\lambda = \frac{\text{Equivalents of COOH from mono-acid}}{\text{Total equivalents of COOH groups}} \tag{2-118b}$$

which is especially useful [49–51] in alkyd resin systems (Sec. 2-10b-3).

2-10a-2 Phenol-Formaldehyde Polymers. The base-catalyzed first-stage reaction of phenol (f = 3) and formaldehyde (f = 2) yields mixtures of mononuclear methylolphenols (XV)

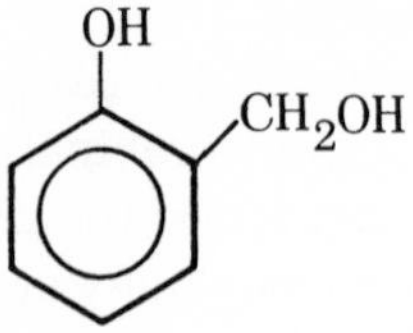

XVa

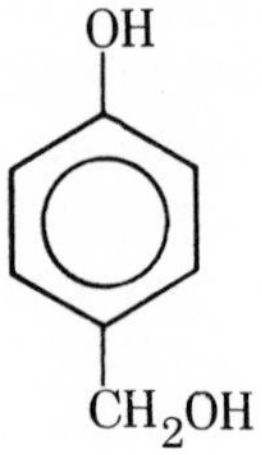

XVb

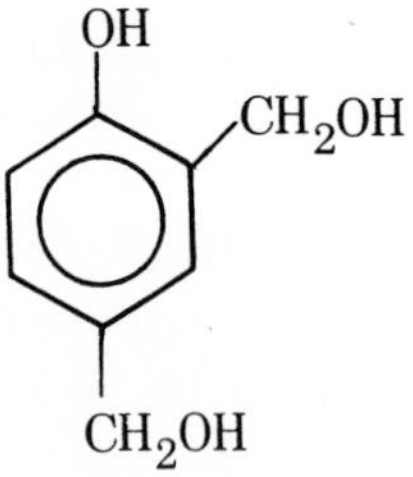

XVc

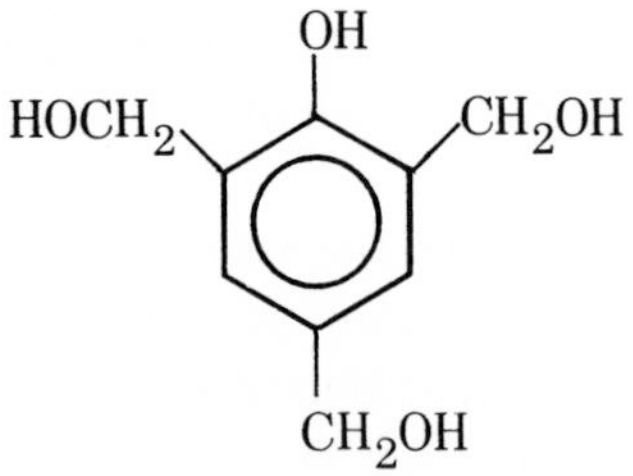

XVd

and the corresponding dinuclear (XVI) and polynuclear compounds (XVII) such as

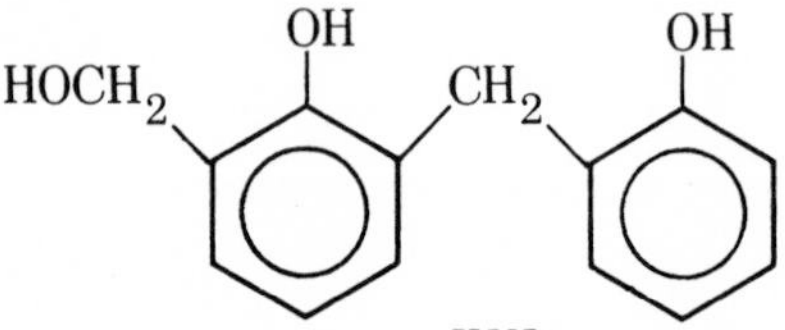

XVIa

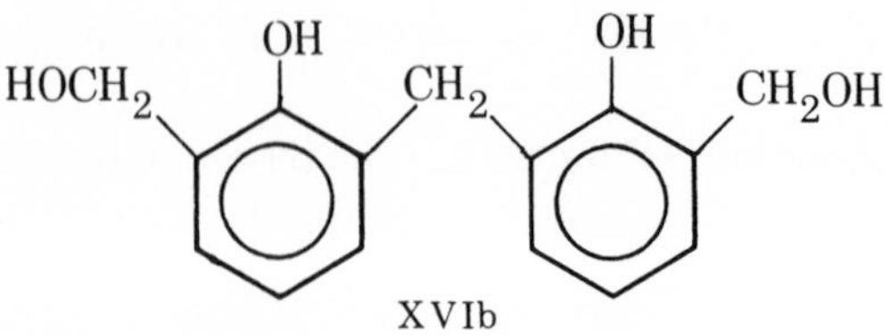

XVIb

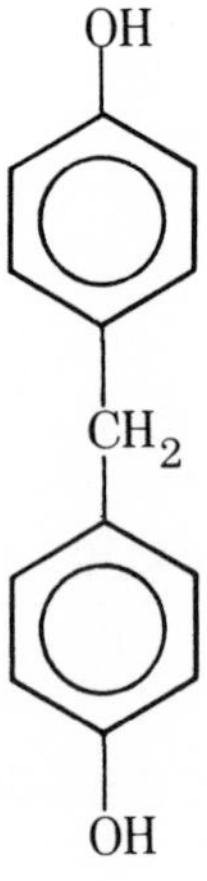

XVIc

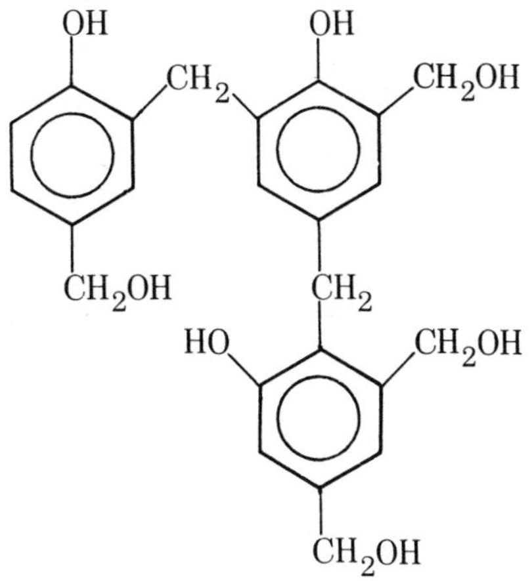

XVII

Such mixtures, whose exact compositions depend on the phenol-to-formaldehyde ratio and the reaction conditions employed are termed "resole prepolymers." The resoles are generally neutralized or made slightly acidic before the second-stage reaction is accomplished by heating. The second-stage polymerization and crosslinking takes place by the formation of methylene and dibenzyl ether linkages between the benzene rings to yield a network structure of the type XVIII

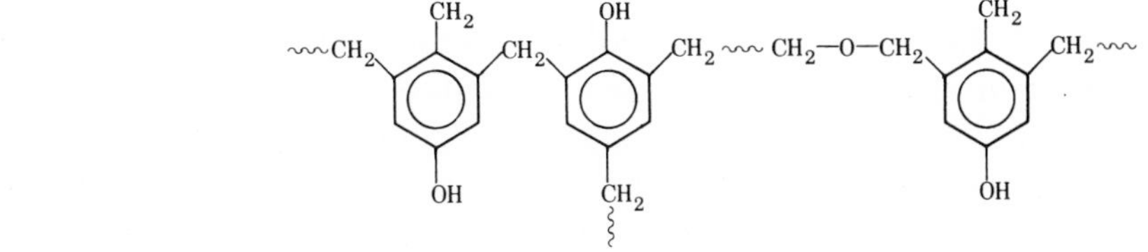

XVIII

The relative importance of the methylene and ether bridges is not well established although both are definitely formed. Higher reaction temperatures favor the formation of the methylene bridges [33, 54].

The polymerization and crosslinking of phenol-formaldehyde is a highly useful industrial process. However, the reactions which take place are quite difficult to handle in a quantitative manner for a number of reasons. The assumption of equal reactivity of all functional groups in a monomer, independent of the other functional groups in the molecule and of whether or not the others are reacted, is dubious in this polymerization. Consider, for example, the routes by which trimethylolphenol (XVd) can be produced in this system

(2-119)

Table 2-5 shows the rate constants for the various reactions [55]. It is apparent that there are significant differences in the reactivities of the different functional groups in phenol (i.e., in the different positions on the ring). The reaction between phenol and formaldehyde involves a nucleophilic attack by the phenolate anion on formaldehyde (Eq. 2-120). The electron-pushing methylol groups generally increase the reactivity of phenol toward further substitution. The effect is large for the dimethylolphenols, especially for the diortho compound. The reason for the low value of k_2'' relative to phenol is unclear.

$$\bar{O}\text{—}C_6H_5 + CH_2{=}O \rightarrow \left[O{=}C_6H_5(H)CH_2\text{—}O^- \right] \rightarrow \bar{O}\text{—}C_6H_4\text{—}CH_2OH \tag{2-120}$$

Not only are the different ring positions on phenol of different reactivity, but one expects that the two functional groups of formaldehyde would also differ. The second functional group of formaldehyde actually corresponds to the methylol group since the reaction of a methylolphenol with a phenol molecule (or with a second methylolphenol) probably proceeds by a sequence such as

$$^-O\text{—}C_6H_4\text{—}CH_2\text{—}OH \xrightarrow{-OH^-} O{=}C_6H_4{=}CH_2 \xrightarrow{\bar{O}\text{—}C_6H_5} \bar{O}\text{—}C_6H_4\text{—}CH_2\text{—}C_6H_4(H){=}O \rightarrow \bar{O}\text{—}C_6H_4\text{—}CH_2\text{—}C_6H_4\text{—}OH \tag{2-121}$$

Direct kinetic measurements are not available to show the reactivity of the methylol group in this reaction compared to the initial reaction of formaldehyde. However, the general observation that the amounts of di- and polynuclear compounds present in resole prepolymers differ widely depending on the reaction condition (temperature, pH, etc.)

Table 2-5 Reaction of Phenol with Formaldehyde Catalyzed by Base[a]

Reaction	Rate constant × 10^6 (liter/mole-sec)
k_1	5.3
k_1'	6.2
k_2	8.7
k_2'	7.3
k_2''	3.8
k_3	42
k_3'	9.1

[a]Data from [55].

indicates that the two functional groups of formaldehyde differ in reactivity.

A further complication in the phenol-formaldehyde polymerization is that it may involve a decrease in functional group reactivity with molecular size. This can easily happen in systems which undergo extensive crosslinking. Such systems may cease to be homogeneous solutions before the experimentally determined gel point. The gel point may be preceded by the formation of microgel particles (Sec. 2-2d) which are too small to be visible to the naked eye. Functional groups in the microgel particles would be relatively unreactive due to their physical unavailability. Similar considerations would apply for the reaction period subsequent to the gel point.

2-10a-3 Urea-Formaldehyde Polymers. The polymerization of urea and formaldehyde under mildly basic conditions yields methylol derivatives such as mono- and dimethylolurea (XIX)

$$\underset{\text{(XIXa)}}{HOCH_2{-}NH{-}CO{-}NH_2} \qquad \underset{\text{(XIXb)}}{HOCH_2{-}NH{-}CO{-}NH{-}CH_2OH}$$

which are then polymerized to network structures under neutral or slightly acid conditions. The nature of the crosslinking reaction is not clear. Crosslinking reactions via both linear (XX)

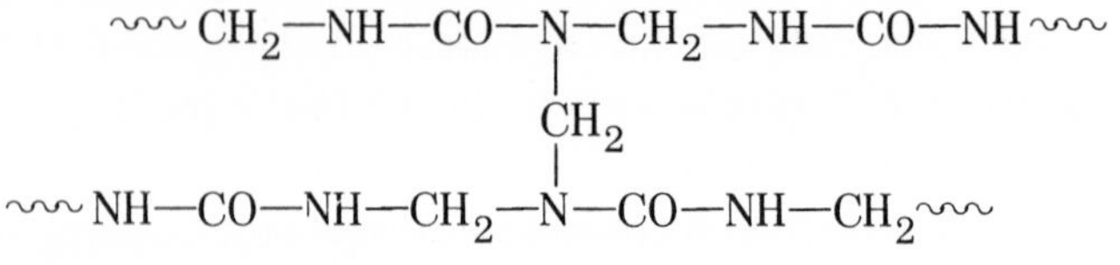

$$\begin{array}{c}\sim CH_2{-}NH{-}CO{-}\underset{|}{N}{-}CH_2{-}NH{-}CO{-}NH\sim \\ CH_2 \\ \sim NH{-}CO{-}NH{-}CH_2{-}\overset{|}{N}{-}CO{-}NH{-}CH_2\sim \\ \text{XX}\end{array}$$

and cyclic (XXI)

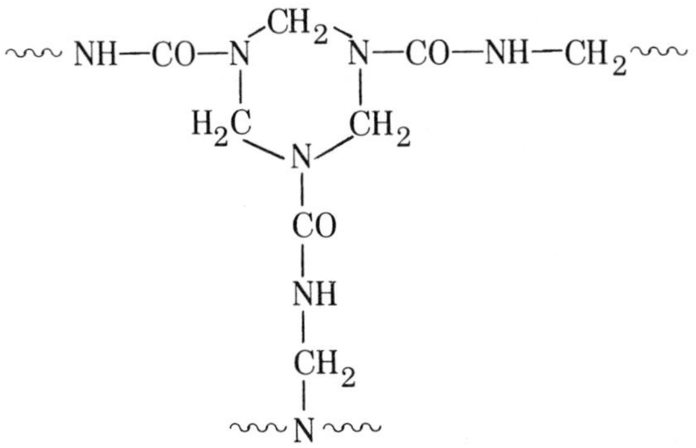

$$
\begin{array}{c}
\sim\sim NH{-}CO{-}N\overset{CH_2}{\frown}N{-}CO{-}NH{-}CH_2\sim\sim \\
H_2C \quad\quad CH_2 \\
N \\
| \\
CO \\
| \\
NH \\
| \\
CH_2 \\
| \\
\sim\sim N \sim\sim
\end{array}
$$

XXI

structures have been proposed [33, 34, 56]. As in the phenol-formaldehyde system, there is considerable evidence that the assumption of constant functional group reactivity is invalid for both urea and formaldehyde [57]. The formation and crosslinking of random prepolymers from melamine (XXII)

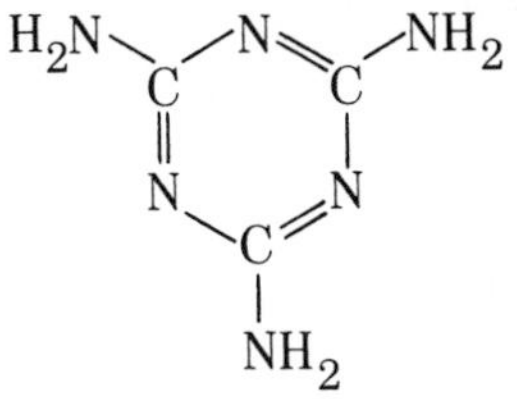

$$
\begin{array}{c}
H_2N \quad N \quad NH_2 \\
C \quad\quad C \\
\| \quad\quad | \\
N \quad\quad N \\
C \\
| \\
NH_2
\end{array}
$$

XXII

and formaldehyde follows in a similar manner.

2-10b Structoset Prepolymers

The newer thermoset polymers involve the use of specially designed prepolymers of more well-defined structure. These prepolymers—termed *structoset prepolymers*—are usually polymerized in the second stage by the addition of a catalyst or other reactant. Further, the second-stage reaction is usually a different one than the first-stage reaction. These polymers are highly advantageous because they generally offer greater control of the polymerization and crosslinking reactions, and very importantly, of the structure of the product. The uses and markets for these newer thermosets are growing more rapidly than those of the older thermosets.

Structoset prepolymers are low molecular weight polymers with various functionalities depending on the particular case. If the functional groups are located at the ends of the prepolymer chains, the prepolymer is termed a *structoterminal* prepolymer. The prepolymer is a *structopendant* prepolymer if the functional groups are located along the polymer chain. The reactions of structoset prepolymers can be treated by the statistical approach to gelation by simply considering the prepolymers as reactants with their appropriate functionalities [58]. Various structoset prepolymers will now be considered briefly.

2-10b-1 Diol Prepolymers. Hydroxyl-terminated structoterminal polyethers, $H{+}OR{+}_nOH$, and polyesters, $H{+}OCOR'COOR{+}_nOH$, are used extensively as prepolymers in polyurethane technology. The polyethers are commonly synthesized from ethylene and propylene oxides (Sec. 7-2), and the polyesters from diacids in the presence of excess diols. These hydroxyl terminated prepolymers are reacted with excess diisocyanates to yield isocyanate terminated polymers, for example,

$$n\,HO\sim\sim OH + (n+1)\,OCN{-}R{-}NCO \longrightarrow$$

$$OCN{+}R{-}NHCOO\sim\sim OOCNH{-}R{+}_nNCO \qquad (2\text{-}122)$$

which can then be crosslinked in a variety of ways [59]. Thus, the

$$2\,OCN\sim\sim NCO + H_2N{-}R{-}NH_2 \longrightarrow$$

$$OCN\sim\sim NHCONHRNHCONH\sim\sim NCO$$

$$\downarrow OCN\sim\sim NCO$$

$$\begin{array}{c} OCN\sim\sim NHCONHRNCONH\sim\sim NCO \\ | \\ CO \\ | \\ NH \\ \wr \\ NH \\ | \\ CO \\ | \\ OCN\sim\sim NHCONHRNCONH\sim\sim NCO \end{array} \qquad (2\text{-}123)$$

addition of a diamine forms urea linkages, by reaction with the isocyanate endgroups, which then crosslink by the formation of biuret linkages (Eq. 2-123).

2-10b-2 Epoxy Prepolymers. Epoxy prepolymers are commonly formed [60] from 2,2′-bis(4-hydroxyphenyl)propane (Bisphenol A) and epichlorohydrin

$$(n+2)\ \overset{O}{\overbrace{CH_2CH}}CH_2Cl + (n+1)\ HO-C_6H_4-C(CH_3)_2-C_6H_4-OH \longrightarrow (n+2)\ HCl +$$
$$\overset{O}{\overbrace{CH_2CH}}CH_2\left[O-C_6H_4-C(CH_3)_2-C_6H_4-OCH_2\underset{OH}{\underset{|}{C}H}CH_2\right]_n O-C_6H_4-C(CH_3)_2-C_6H_4-OCH_2\overset{O}{\overbrace{CHCH_2}} \quad (2\text{-}124)$$

These are considered as structoterminal or structopendant prepolymers depending on whether crosslinking occurs through the epoxy endgroups or the hydroxyl groups [61]. Thus, crosslinking

$$\sim O-C_6H_4-C(CH_3)_2-C_6H_4-OCH_2-\underset{OH}{\underset{|}{C}H}-CH_2\sim \ + \ O\left\langle\begin{matrix}CO\\CO\end{matrix}\right\rangle R\left\langle\begin{matrix}CO\\CO\end{matrix}\right\rangle O \longrightarrow \quad (2\text{-}125)$$

$$\begin{matrix}\sim O-C_6H_4-C(CH_3)_2-C_6H_4-OCH_2-CH-CH_2\sim\\ |\\ O\\ |\\ CO\\ |\\ HO_2C-R-CO_2H\\ |\\ CO\\ |\\ O\\ |\\ \sim O-C_6H_4-C(CH_3)_2-C_6H_4-OCH_2-CH-CH_2\sim\end{matrix}$$

occurs primarily through the hydroxyl groups when a polyanhydride is used as the crosslinking agent (Eq. 2-125) and the epoxy prepolymer is considered a structopendant prepolymer. The prepolymer is a structoterminal prepolymer when polyamines are used for crosslinking. Crosslinking in this case involves the base catalyzed opening of the epoxide groups

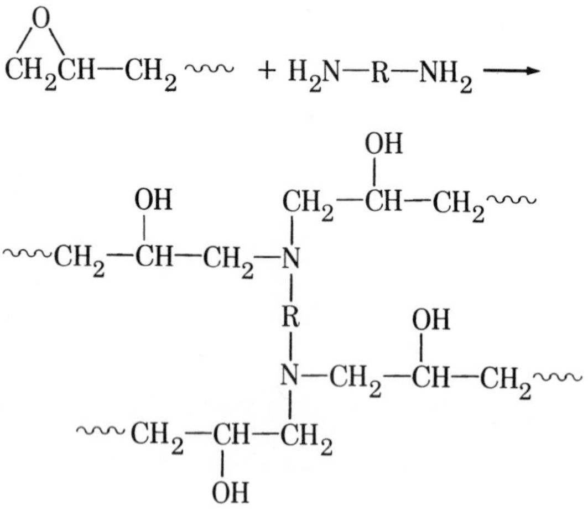

$$\overset{O}{\overbrace{CH_2CH}}-CH_2\sim\sim\sim + H_2N-R-NH_2 \longrightarrow$$

$$\begin{array}{c} \sim\sim CH_2-\underset{}{\overset{OH}{\overset{|}{C}H}}-CH_2-N(-CH_2-\overset{OH}{\overset{|}{C}H}-CH_2\sim\sim)-R-N(-CH_2-\overset{OH}{\overset{|}{C}H}-CH_2\sim\sim)-CH_2-\underset{OH}{\underset{|}{C}H}-CH_2\sim\sim \end{array} \tag{2-126}$$

Crosslinking through the epoxide groups can also be carried out by ring-opening polymerization (Sec. 7-2).

2-10b-3 Unsaturated Polyesters. Unsaturated polyester prepolymers can also be of either the structoterminal or structopendant type

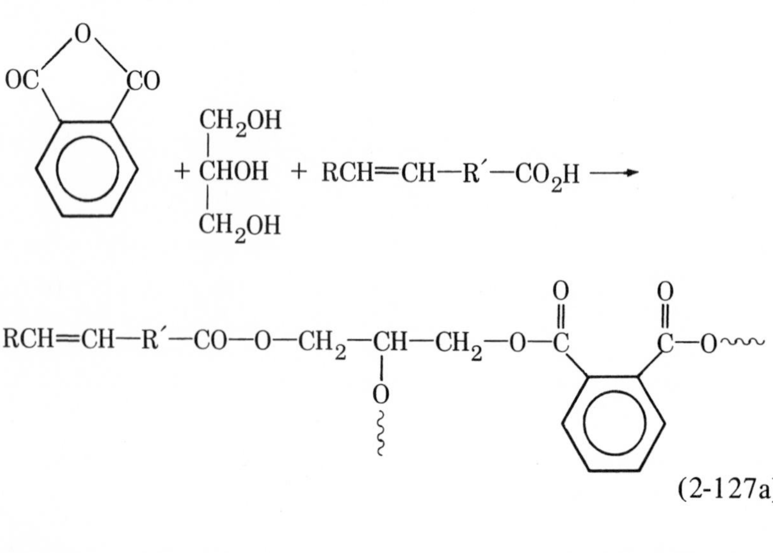

$$C_6H_4(CO)_2O + \begin{array}{c} CH_2OH \\ | \\ CHOH \\ | \\ CH_2OH \end{array} + RCH{=}CH-R'-CO_2H \longrightarrow$$

$$RCH{=}CH-R'-CO-O-CH_2-\underset{\underset{\sim}{O}}{\underset{|}{C}H}-CH_2-O-\overset{O}{\overset{\|}{C}}-C_6H_4-\overset{O}{\overset{\|}{C}}-O\sim\sim \tag{2-127a}$$

depending on the location of the unsaturated linkages. A typical structoterminal polyester is that obtained by reacting phthalic anhydride and glycerol with an unsaturated monocarboxylic acid. The unsaturated acid used is often a fatty acid. The resulting prepolymer has terminal carbon-carbon double bonds (Eq. 2-127a) which can be crosslinked by reaction with oxygen (Sec. 9-2). This type of polyester is usually referred to as an alkyd resin if a fatty acid is employed as the unsaturated monocarboxylic acid [62]; if some other monocarboxylic acid is employed, the polyester is referred to as an unsaturated polyester [63].

Structopendant unsaturated polyesters, containing double bonds within the polymer chain, can be produced by polymerization of a diol with either maleic or fumaric acids (or maleic anhydride)

$$\mathrm{HOCH_2CH_2OH + HOOC{-}CH{=}CH{-}CO_2H \longrightarrow}$$

$$\mathrm{\left(OCH_2CH_2OOC{-}CH{=}CH{-}CO\right)_n} \qquad (2\text{-}127b)$$

Crosslinking of this prepolymer is accomplished by copolymerization with alkene monomers (Sec. 9-2).

2-10b-4 Phenol-Formaldehyde Polymers. Structopendant phenol-formaldehyde prepolymers–termed *Novolacs* (XXIII)–

$$\left[\mathrm{C_6H_3(OH){-}CH_2}\right]_n$$

XXIII

are made by the acid-catalyzed reaction of phenol and formaldehyde [33, 34]. In order to prevent crosslinking from occurring prematurely, a phenol-to-formaldehyde ratio slightly greater than unity is employed. The second-stage crosslinking reaction is carried out by using hexamethylenetetramine, $(CH_2)_6N_4$, as the crosslinking agent. The hexamethylenetetramine acts essentially as the equivalent of a source of formaldehyde in this reaction. Crosslinking takes place primarily through methylene bridging with the simultaneous formation of ammonia as a by-product. However, there are also appreciable degrees of benzylamine crosslinking bridges. The crosslinked network (XXIV) can be pictured as

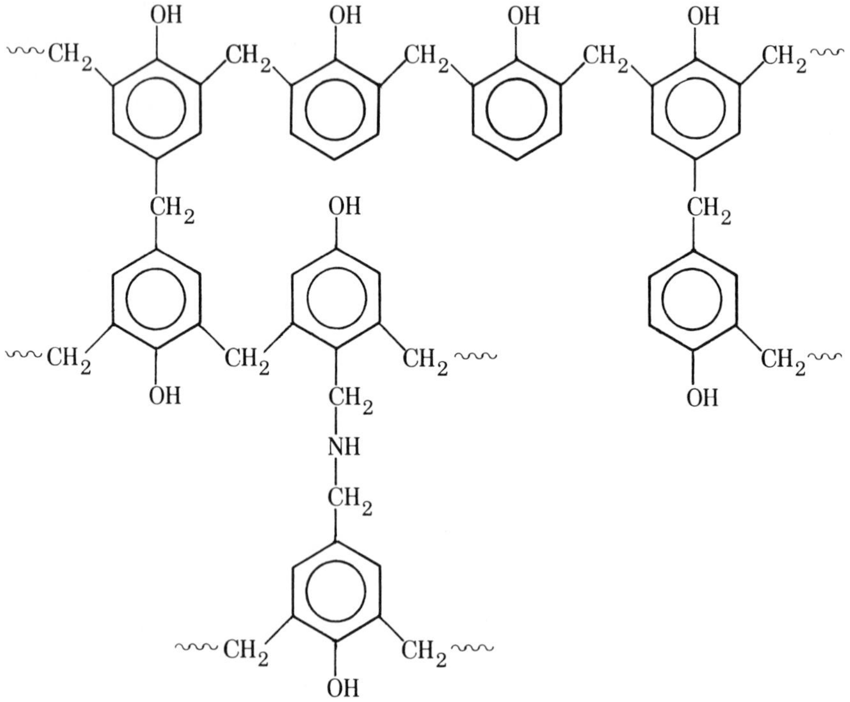

XXIV

2-11 STEP COPOLYMERIZATION

It should be apparent that step polymerization is a versatile means of synthesizing a host of different polymers. The chemical structure of a polymer can be varied over a wide range in order to obtain a product with a particular combination of desirable properties. One can vary the functional group to produce a polyester, polyamide, or some other class of polymer as desired. Further, for any specific class of polymer, there is a considerable choice in the range of structures which can be produced. Consider, for example, the structure of polyamides. Polyamides with either of the general structures

—CO—R—CONH—R′—NH— XXV   —NH—R—CO— XXVI

can be synthesized depending on whether one uses the reaction of a diamine with a diacid or the self-reaction of an amino acid. A range of different polyamides can be obtained by varying the choice of the R and R′ groups in structure XXV and the R group in structure XXVI. Thus, for example, one can produce nylon-6,6 and nylon-6,10 by the reactions of hexamethylenediamine with adipic and sebacic acids, respectively. The nylon-6,10 is a somewhat more flexible fiber than nylon-6,6 due to the longer hydrocarbon segment derived from the sebacic acid.

2-11a Types of Copolymers

Further variation is possible in the polymer structure by using mixtures of the appropriate reactants such that the polymer chain can have different R groups and different R′ groups. Thus, polyamide structures of the types

$$\text{—CO—R—CONH—R}'\text{—NHCO—R}''\text{—CONH—R}'''\text{—NH—}$$

XXVII

$$\text{—NH—R—CO—NH—R}''\text{—CO—}$$

XXVIII

are possible as variations on structures XXV and XXVI, respectively. A polymer with either of structures XXVII or XXVIII is termed a *copolymer*; the process by which either would be synthesized is termed a *copolymerization.* Polymers with structures XXV or XXVI can be termed *homopolymers* to distinguish them from copolymers.

Different types of copolymers are possible depending on the specific method of synthesis that is employed. Thus, a copolymer of the composition indicated by XXVII could have the repeating *alternating copolymer* structure shown in XXVII in which the R, R′, R″, and R‴ groups alternate in a regular fashion along the polymer chain, or a *block copolymer* structure such as XXIX

$$\text{+CO—R—CONH—R}'\text{—NH}\text{+}_m\text{+CO—R}''\text{—CONH—R}'''\text{—NH}\text{+}_p$$

XXIX

in which blocks of one type of homopolymer structure are attached to blocks of another type of homopolymer structure, or a *random copolymer* structure in which the R and R″ groups are randomly distributed along the copolymer chain as are the R′ and R‴ groups. Similarly, one can have alternating, block, and random structures for the copolymer of composition XXVIII.

The alternating, random, and block copolymer structures can be symbolized as

$$\sim\!\sim\!\sim \text{ABABABABABABABABABABABAB} \sim\!\sim\!\sim$$

Alternating copolymer

$$\sim\!\sim\!\sim \text{AABABBBABAABAAABBABBBAAB} \sim\!\sim\!\sim$$

Random copolymer

$$\sim\!\sim\!\sim \text{AAAAAABBBBBBAAAAAABBBBBB} \sim\!\sim\!\sim$$

Block copolymer

where A and B represent two different repeating units. In addition to the different types of copolymers which can be synthesized, there is a fair amount of versatility possible in the synthesis of any one type of copolymer. The relative amounts of the two repeating units A and B in a copolymer can be varied over a considerable range.

2-11b Methods of Synthesizing Copolymers

There are various synthetic routes used to produce copolymer structures. These have been applied to polyamides [64, 65], polyesters [66], polycarbonates [67, 68], polyurethanes [37, 69], and other polymers. Consider the synthesis of copolyamides of composition XXVII. The alternating copolymer of this composition cannot be synthesized. However, it is possible to synthesize an alternating copolymer structure in which $R'' = R$ by using a two-stage process. In the first-stage, a diacid is reacted with a diamine in the molar ratio of 2:1

$$2n\ \mathrm{HO_2C{-}R{-}CO_2H} + n\ \mathrm{H_2N{-}R'{-}NH_2} \longrightarrow$$

$$n\ \mathrm{HO_2C{-}R{-}CONH{-}R'{-}NHCO{-}R{-}CO_2H} \qquad (2\text{-}128)$$

The trimer is then reacted with an equimolar amount of a second diamine in the second-stage

$$n\ HO_2C{-}R{-}CONH{-}R'{-}NHCO{-}R{-}CO_2H\ +$$

$$n\ H_2N{-}R'''{-}NH_2 \longrightarrow$$

$$HO{+}CO{-}R{-}CONH{-}R'{-}NHCO{-}R{-}CONH{-}R'''{-}NH{+}_nH\ +$$

$$(2n-1)\ H_2O \tag{2-129}$$

Block copolyamides can be easily produced by linking together appropriately synthesized low molecular weight homopolymers by reactions of their respective endgroups either with each other or with some reagent. Thus, one can react two prepolymers with each other if one contains amino groups at both ends and the other carboxyl groups at both ends

$$n\ HO_2C{-}R{-}CO{+}NH{-}R'{-}NHCO{-}R{-}CO{+}_mOH\ +$$

$$n\ H_2N{-}R'''{-}NH{+}CO{-}R''CONH{-}R'''{-}NH{+}_pH \longrightarrow$$

$$HO{+}CO{-}R{-}CO{+}NH{-}R'{-}NHCO{-}R{-}CO{+}_mNH{-}R'''{-}NH{+}CO{-}R''{-}CONH{-}R'''{-}NH{+}_p{+}_nH\ +$$

$$(2n-1)\ H_2O \tag{2-130}$$

or

$$n\ HO_2C{\sim\sim}A_m{\sim\sim}CO_2H\ +\ n\ H_2N{\sim\sim}B_p{\sim\sim}NH_2 \longrightarrow$$

$${+}CO{\sim\sim}A_m{\sim\sim}CONH{\sim\sim}B_p{\sim\sim}NH{+}_n \tag{2-131}$$

In typical cases, the prepolymers have molecular weights of 500–2,000 with values of 1–10 for m and p.

Block copolyamides can also be synthesized from two prepolymers both of which are amino-ended. Two such prepolymers can be polymerized by reaction with a diacid chloride

$$n\ H_2N{\sim\sim}A_m{\sim\sim}NH_2\ +\ 2n\ ClCO{-}R{-}COCl\ +$$

$$n\ H_2N{\sim\sim}B_p{\sim\sim}NH_2 \longrightarrow$$

$${+}{\sim\sim}A_m{\sim\sim}NHCO{-}R{-}CONH{\sim\sim}B_p{\sim\sim}NHCO{-}R{-}CONH{+}_n \tag{2-132}$$

One could also use two carboxyl-ended prepolymers and link them together with a diamine. The use of this type of reaction, in which two large species are coupled together by a small reagent, was previously encountered in the discussion on structoset prepolymers (Eqs. 2-122, 2-125, and 2-126 in Sec. 2-10b).

Still another route to block copolymers is by interchange reactions between two homopolymers (Sec. 2-5c). Thus, a block copolyamide can be obtained by heating a mixture of two homopolyamides

$$\sim\sim A_m \sim\sim + \sim\sim B_p \sim\sim \longrightarrow \sim\sim A_w B_x \sim\sim + \sim\sim A_y B_z \sim\sim \tag{2-133}$$

where $m = w + y$ and $p = x + z$.

Random copolymers can be synthesized by polymerizing an equimolar mixture of four monomers

$$\left.\begin{array}{l} HO_2C{-}R{-}CO_2H \\ HO_2C{-}R''{-}CO_2H \\ H_2N{-}R'{-}NH_2 \\ H_2N{-}R'''{-}NH_2 \end{array}\right\} \longrightarrow \text{Random copolymer of XXVII} \tag{2-134}$$

The use of only one diacid or only one diamine would produce a variation on the random copolymer structure in that the product would have structure XXVII in which either $R = R''$ or $R' = R'''$.

The discussions thus far have implied that one is primarily concerned with copolymers in which both of the two repeating units contain the same interunit repeating linkage. This is not necessarily the case although much of the work on step copolymerization has dealt with systems of only one type of interunit repeating linkage. Thus, the amino-ended prepolymers in Eq. 2-132 could be polymerized by using a diisocyanate instead of a diacid chloride to yield the block copolymer structure XXX

$$\left(\sim\sim A_m \sim\sim NHCONH{-}R{-}NHCONH \sim\sim B_p \sim\sim NHCONH{-}R{-}NHCONH\right)_n$$

XXX

in which individual polyamide segments are joined together by urea linkages.

Polyesteramides have been synthesized from preformed bisesteramides by ester interchange with a glycol

$$C_2H_5O_2C\text{—}R\text{—}CONH\text{—}R'\text{—}NHCO\text{—}R\text{—}CO_2C_2H_5 +$$

$$HO\text{—}R''\text{—}OH \longrightarrow$$

$$\text{+}O_2C\text{—}R\text{—}CONH\text{—}R'\text{—}NHCO\text{—}R\text{—}CO_2\text{—}R''\text{+}_n \qquad (2\text{-}135)$$

2-11c Utility of Copolymerization

Almost all of the interest in step copolymerization has been on the block and random copolymer structures. The alternating copolymers have received much less attention because of difficulties involved in their synthesis. Further, the alternating copolymer does not appear to offer any significantly desirable properties which are not obtainable in the corresponding block and random copolymers. A number of studies have demonstrated the differences in the properties of block and random copolymers relative to each other and to the corresponding homopolymers [65, 70]. A block copolymer usually has properties which are close to the average of the properties of the two homopolymers (more accurately, the average weighted in proportion to the relative amounts of the two different repeating units contained in the copolymer). The properties of the corresponding random copolymer, on the other hand, can be quite different from the weighted average of the two homopolymers.

When copolymerization is used to change polymer properties, it is often used to vary such prime properties as crystallinity, flexibility, T_g, and T_m. Thus, copolymerization generally decreases crystallinity, increases flexibility, and decreases both the melting and glass transition temperatures. However, the magnitude of the effect can be quite different for block and random copolymerization. The melting temperature of a block copolymer is usually only slightly less than that of the weighted average of the two homopolymers. The T_m of a random copolymer, on the other hand, is usually much less than that of the block copolymer due to the greater disorder of the random copolymer structure.

The practical utility of copolymerization is not nearly as extensive in step polymerization as it is in chain polymerization (Chap. 6). When step copolymerization is used, block copolymerization is often the desired choice over random copolymerization. The former is much more predictable in terms of the properties to be expected in the product. The recently developed *spandex* elastomeric fibers [70] are an outstanding example of the practical application of step block copolymerization. The synthesis of these materials has been partly discussed in Sec. 2-10b-1. A hydroxyl-terminated prepolymer XXXI or XXXII

$$\underset{\text{XXXI}}{HO{+}RCH_2{-}O{+}_nRCH_2OH} \qquad \underset{\text{XXXII}}{HO{+}R'{-}O_2C{-}R{-}CO_2{+}_nR'{-}OH}$$

is synthesized by the ring-opening polymerization of a cyclic ether (Sec. 7-2) or the reaction of a diacid with an excess of a diol, respectively.

The hydroxyl-terminated prepolymer is reacted with an excess of a diisocyanate

$$HO{\sim\sim}A_m{\sim\sim}OH + 2\ OCN{-}R'''{-}NCO \longrightarrow$$

$$\underset{\text{XXXIII}}{OCN{-}R'''{-}NHCO_2{\sim\sim}A_m{\sim\sim}O_2CNH{-}R'''{-}NCO} \tag{2-136}$$

to yield an isocyanate-terminated prepolymer XXXIII which is then reacted with a low molecular weight diol

$$\underset{\text{XXXIII}}{OCN{-}R'''{-}NHCO_2{\sim\sim}A_m{\sim\sim}O_2CNH{-}R'''{-}NCO} +$$

$$HO{-}R''''{-}OH \longrightarrow \tag{2-137}$$

$$\underset{\text{XXXIV}}{{+}O_2CNH{-}R'''{-}NHCO_2{\sim\sim}A_m{\sim\sim}O_2CNH{-}R'''{-}NHCO_2{-}R''''{+}_n}$$

or with a diamine

$$\underset{\text{XXXIII}}{OCN{-}R'''{-}NHCO_2{\sim\sim}A_m{\sim\sim}O_2CNH{-}R'''{-}NCO} +$$

$$H_2N{-}R''''{-}NH_2 \longrightarrow \tag{2-138}$$

$$\underset{\text{XXXV}}{{+}NHCONH{-}R'''{-}NHCO_2{\sim\sim}A_m{\sim\sim}O_2CNH{-}R'''{-}NHCONH{-}R''''{+}_n}$$

The final product contains polyether or polyester segments (the A_m segments) separated by urethane (XXXIV) or urethane-urea (XXXV) segments depending on the particular reagents used in the various steps of the process. The product has both elastomer and fiber properties. Fiber properties arise from the urethane or urethane-urea segments while elastomer properties arise from the ether or ester segments.

2-12 NEWER TYPES OF STEP POLYMERIZATIONS

There has been a rapidly increasing effort in the last ten to fifteen years toward the synthesis of new polymers with markedly higher temperature resistance than those previously available. Polymers possessing high strength, rigidity, solvent and chemical resistance, and serviceability at high temperatures (approximately $>$300–500°C) would find a variety of uses. These include new specialty applications such as in the aerospace area as well as their use as new structural materials of construction. The synthetic routes studied have involved inorganic and semi-inorganic as well as organic polymer systems. A large range of inorganic and organic reactions have been explored in the process of attempting to synthesize new polymer systems. The efforts to date have been fruitful almost exclusively in the organic polymer systems.

A general problem encountered in many of the polymerization systems has been a difficulty in obtaining polymers of sufficiently high enough molecular weight (at least about 10,000) to have reasonable strength properties. The cause of this difficulty has been due in large part to the general insolubility of the polymers. Low molecular weight polymers often precipitate from the reaction mixture and prevent the achievement of high molecular weights. In addition, the general lack of understanding of the reaction mechanisms involved in many of the systems prevents the appropriate variation of reaction parameters so as to control the polymer yield and molecular weight.

There are three general synthetic approaches that have been used to produce polymers with increased thermal stability. High crystallinity, extensive crosslinking, and the use of inflexible polymer chains lead to higher physical strength and thermal stability in polymers [71]. These can be employed singly or in combination with each other as a particular polymer system dictates. Crystallinity and crosslinking have been extensively utilized previously to achieve higher temperature limits for polymers. The bulk of the more recent effort has been based on synthesizing inflexible polymer chains that would resist deformation and thermal softening.

2-12a Presently Available Polymers

The incorporation of ring structures into organic polymer chains has been extensively used for the purpose of chain stiffening. Aromatic rings have been used in particular because of their known thermal stability. This general approach has in recent years resulted in a number of new commercially available polymers with improved high temperature properties [72].

2-12a-1 Polycarbonates. Polycarbonates are the polyesters of carbonic acid. The most common polycarbonate—that based on Bisphenol A—can be synthesized [73] by the reaction of the dihydroxy reactant with phosgene or by ester interchange with diphenyl carbonate

$$HO-C_6H_4-C(CH_3)_2-C_6H_4-OH \xrightarrow[-\,HCl]{+\,Cl-CO-Cl} \text{ or } \xrightarrow[-\,\phi OH]{+\,\phi O-CO-O\phi}$$

$$\left[O-C_6H_4-C(CH_3)_2-C_6H_4-COO \right]_n \qquad (2\text{-}139)$$

Chain stiffening is accomplished in this case by the combination of the benzene rings and the bulky tetra-substituted carbon atoms in the polymer chain.

Polymerization by the ester interchange route is carried out as a melt polymerization in a two-stage process very similar to that previously described in Sec. 2-6b-1 for the synthesis of poly(ethylene terephthalate). In the first stage, the reaction is carried out at a temperature of 180–200°C and a vacuum of 20–30 mm to a conversion of 80–90 percent. The temperature is then gradually raised to 290–300°C and the vacuum increased to below 1 mm to complete the polymerization. Polymerization using the phosgene reaction is carried out in basic solution. Organic solvents such as pyridine or triethylamine or mixtures of these with hydrocarbons such as benzene, chlorobenzene, and chloroform are most useful for this reaction. Polymerization can also be carried out using a stirred interfacial process. The Bisphenol A is dissolved in aqueous alkali, an organic solvent added followed by the phosgene. The organic solvent prevents the loss of phosgene by hydrolysis and the precipitation of the polymer before it has reached the desired molecular weight.

2-12a-2 Polyamides. Polyamides containing aliphatic or aromatic cyclic structures in the polymer chain are superior to the acyclic polyamides. The alicyclic polyamides (often referred to as polycycloamides) such as poly(1,4-cyclohexylenedimethylene suberamide) (XXXVI)

$$\left[-NHCH_2-\langle C_6H_{10} \rangle-CH_2NHCO(CH_2)_6CO- \right]_n$$

XXXVI

are produced from the appropriate diamine and diacid in the same manner as described in Sec. 2-6b-2 for poly(hexamethylene adipamide). The synthesis of aromatic polyamides cannot be carried out by the same reaction due to the lower reactivity of aromatic amines compared to aliphatic amines [74]. The aromatic ring decreases the electron density on the amine nitrogens and therefore decreases their nucleophilicity toward carboxyl groups.

The aromatic polyamides are produced by using the faster reaction of the diamine with the diacid chloride instead of with the diacid; for example, for the commercial polymer poly(*m*-phenylene isophthalamide)

$$ClCO-C_6H_4-COCl + H_2N-C_6H_4-NH_2 \xrightarrow{-HCl} \left[-CO-C_6H_4-CONH-C_6H_4-NH- \right]_n \qquad (2\text{-}140)$$

A variety of other aromatic polyamides have been investigated. These include those based on reactants containing naphthalene rings as well as heterocyclic rings such as the oxadiazole and thiazole structures [74, 75].

2-12a-3 Aromatic Polyethers. Although a number of different synthetic routes have been studied, nucleophilic aromatic substitution and oxidative coupling have been the most successful for the synthesis of aromatic polyethers [76]. Aromatic nucleophilic substitution has resulted in the commercially useful polymer from Bisphenol *A* and 4,4′-dichlorodiphenyl sulfone [77]. The reaction is carried out with the alkali metal salts of Bisphenol *A*

$$n\ \mathrm{NaO{-}C_6H_4{-}C(CH_3)_2{-}C_6H_4{-}ONa} + n\ \mathrm{Cl{-}C_6H_4{-}SO_2{-}C_6H_4{-}Cl} \xrightarrow{-\mathrm{NaCl}} \left[\mathrm{O{-}C_6H_4{-}SO_2{-}C_6H_4{-}O{-}C_6H_4{-}C(CH_3)_2{-}C_6H_4}\right]_n \tag{2-141}$$

This polymer is generally referred to by its trade name, *polysulfone.* A more logical name, based on chemical structure [78], would be poly(oxy-1,4-phenylenesulfonyl-1,4-phenyleneoxy-1,4-phenyleneisopropylidene-1,4-phenylene).

The phenolate salt is made in situ by the simultaneous addition of Bisphenol A and the alkali metal hydroxide. The polymerization is carried out in aprotic polar solvents such as *N,N*-dimethylformamide, dimethyl sulfoxide, or dimethyl sulfone at moderately high temperatures (approximately 150°C). Aromatic halogens are typically not reactive toward this type of nucleophilic substitution reaction. However, polymerization is rather facile in this system because the ring chlorines are activated to nucleophilic substitution by the electron-pulling sulfone group.

The oxidative coupling polymerization of many 2,6-disubstituted phenols to form aromatic polyethers

$$n\,\text{R}_2\text{C}_6\text{H}_3\text{–OH} + \frac{n}{2}\,O_2 \xrightarrow[\text{Amine}]{Cu^+} \left[\text{–C}_6\text{H}_2\text{R}_2\text{–O–}\right]_n + n\,H_2O \qquad (2\text{-}142)$$

is accomplished by bubbling oxygen through a solution of the phenol in an organic solvent containing a catalytic complex of a cuprous salt and a tertiary amine [78]. The polymer from 2,6-dimethylphenol is the commercial polymer incorrectly referred to as "polyphenylene oxide;" a proper name would be poly(2,6-dimethylphenylene oxide) or poly(oxy-2,6-dimethyl-1,4-phenylene).

For phenols containing small substituents, the polymerization proceeds rapidly under mild conditions. Thus, 2,6-dimethylphenol polymerizes at room temperature while a reaction temperature of 60°C is required for 2-chloro-6-methylphenol. Phenols with bulky substituents, e.g., isopropyl or *t*-butyl, undergo dimerization to diphenoquinones

$$2\,\text{R}_2\text{C}_6\text{H}_3\text{–OH} \longrightarrow \text{O}{=}\text{C}_6\text{H}_2\text{R}_2{=}\text{C}_6\text{H}_2\text{R}_2{=}\text{O} \qquad (2\text{-}143)$$

instead of linear polymerization.

Only a few of the mechanistic details of oxidative coupling polymerization are known [76, 79]. The reaction can be pictured in the reaction sequence in Eqs. 2-144 through 2-148, although the experimental evidence is somewhat lacking. The copper-amine complex functions as a catalyst for the oxidation by oxygen of the phenol to the monomeric phenoxy radical XXXVII. The phenoxy radical then undergoes carbon-to-oxygen coupling to yield the dimer (Eq. 2-144). Polymerization proceeds by oxidation of the dimer to the corresponding phenoxy radical (Eq. 2-145) followed by carbon-to-oxygen

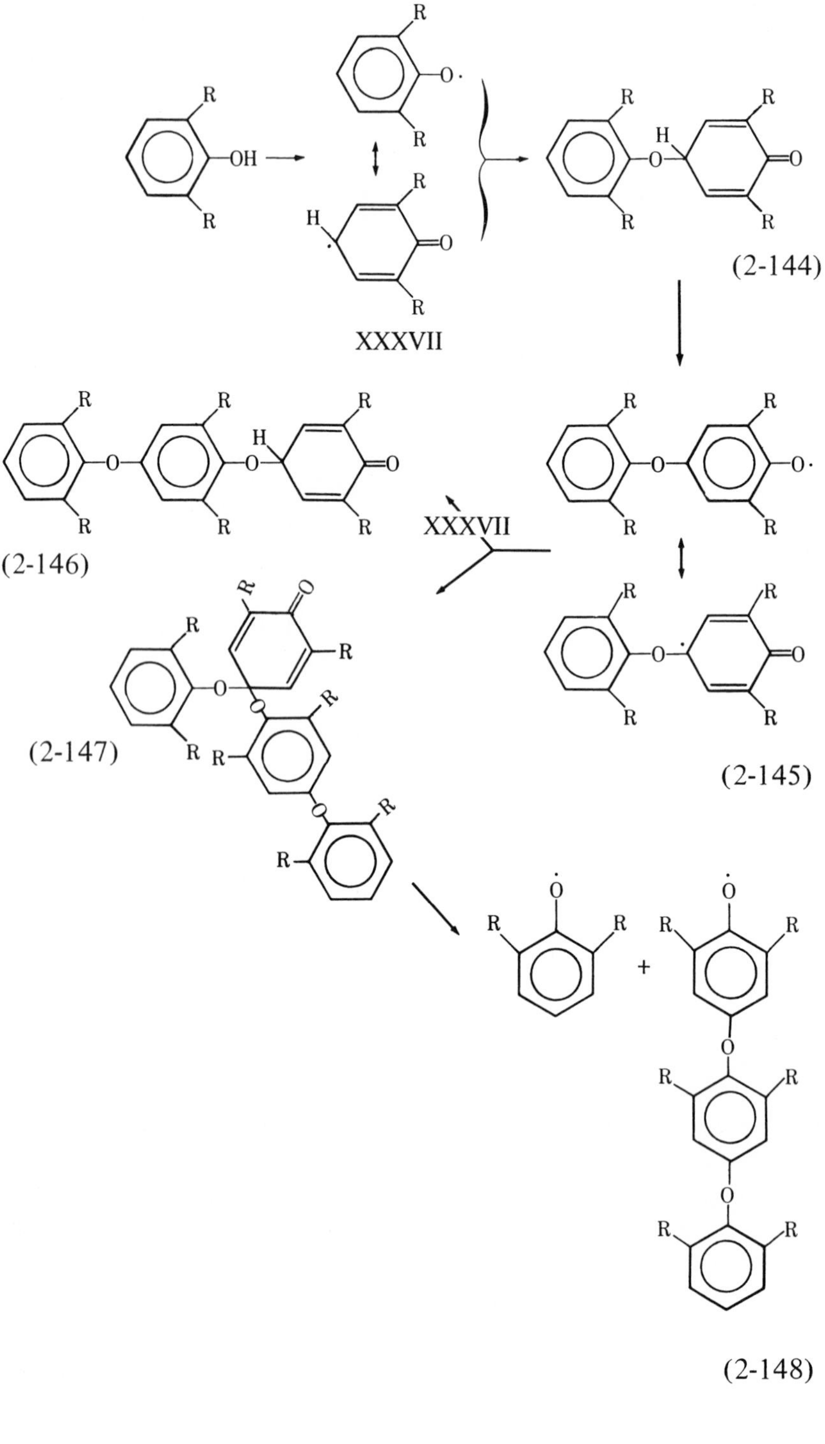

XXXVII

(2-144)

(2-146)

XXXVII

(2-147)

(2-145)

(2-148)

coupling reactions with monomeric phenoxy radical (Eq. 2-146) or with itself (Eq. 2-147). The trimer continues its growth by repeating the oxidation-coupling sequence; the tetramer continues its growth by decomposing (Eq. 2-148) to yield two phenoxy radicals (a monomer and a trimer) which can undergo coupling reactions.

2-12a-4 Poly(*p*-xylylene). Pyrolytic oxidative coupling [72, 80, 81] is used to produce poly(*p*-xylylene) from *p*-xylene

$$H_3C-C_6H_4-CH_3 \xrightarrow{-H_2} \left[CH_2-C_6H_4-CH_2 \right]_n \quad (2\text{-}149)$$

as well as the corresponding polymers from mono- and dichloroxylenes. The reaction is carried out by pyrolyzing *p*-xylene at temperatures of up to 950°C to yield di-*p*-xylylene (XXXVIII). After appropriate separation and purification, di-*p*-xylylene is vacuum pyrolyzed at 550–600°C to yield *p*-xylylene (XXXIX)

$$CH_3-C_6H_4-CH_3 \xrightarrow{-H_2} \underset{\text{XXXVIII}}{\begin{matrix} CH_2-C_6H_4-CH_2 \\ | \qquad\qquad | \\ CH_2-C_6H_4-CH_2 \end{matrix}} \longrightarrow$$

$$2\ \underset{\text{XXXIX}}{CH_2{=}C_6H_4{=}CH_2} \quad (2\text{-}150)$$

which spontaneously polymerizes when it is condensed on surfaces kept at temperatures below 30°C at vacuums of less than 1 mm. Polymerization does not take place if the condensation temperatures are above 30°C. The synthetic procedure is commercially useful in that it lends itself to the vacuum coating of objects and articles. The overall reaction is extremely fast; quantitative conversion of di-*p*-xylylene to poly(*p*-xylylene) takes place in a fraction of a second.

The polymerization is initiated by the coupling of two *p*-xylylene molecules to form a diradical (XL) which then grows by the addition of p-xylylene molecules at both of its ends

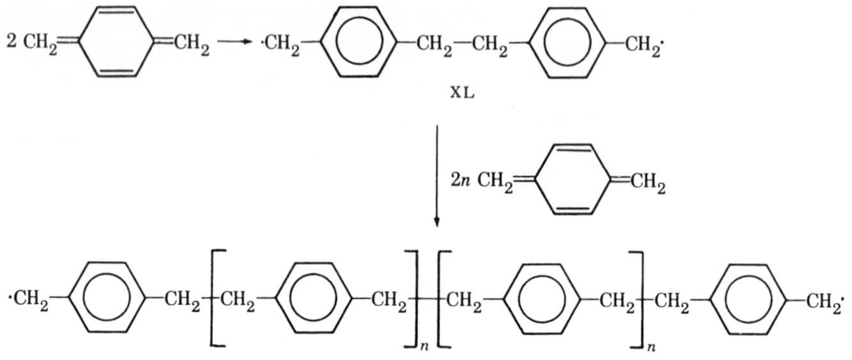

$$2\ CH_2{=}C_6H_4{=}CH_2 \longrightarrow \cdot CH_2{-}C_6H_4{-}CH_2{-}CH_2{-}C_6H_4{-}CH_2\cdot \quad (XL)$$

$$\xrightarrow{2n\ CH_2{=}C_6H_4{=}CH_2} \cdot CH_2{-}C_6H_4{-}CH_2{+}CH_2{-}C_6H_4{-}CH_2{+}_n{+}CH_2{-}C_6H_4{-}CH_2{+}_n CH_2{-}C_6H_4{-}CH_2\cdot$$

(2-151)

Growth continues until the radical ends of a polymer chain encounter and couple with those from other chains, or until they become buried in the polymer mass and physically inaccessible to further addition of p-xylylene. Radical burial is noted by the detection of high concentrations (approximately 5–10 $\times 10^{-4}$ mole per mole of p-xylylene) of radicals in the final polymer product. Whether or not the polymerization of p-xylylene should be included in this chapter on step polymerization is unclear. Detailed experimental data are not available to indicate the classification of this reaction. It may well be that the addition of monomer to the diradical proceeds by a chain reaction with the propagation step consisting of the 1,6-addition of a radical to p-xylylene

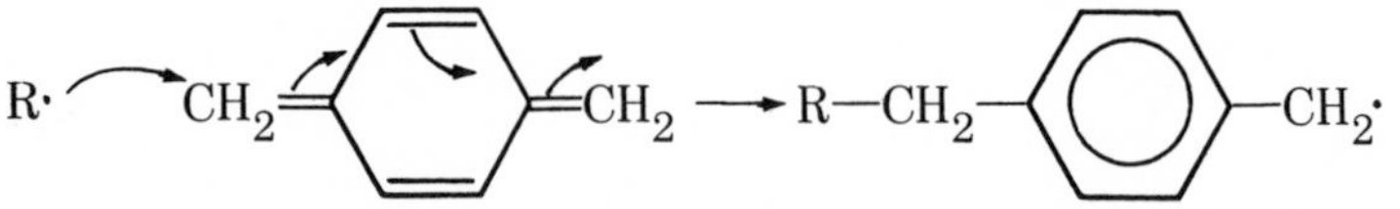

$$R\cdot + CH_2{=}C_6H_4{=}CH_2 \longrightarrow R{-}CH_2{-}C_6H_4{-}CH_2\cdot \qquad (2\text{-}152)$$

An alternate mode of initiation involving the formation of the diradical XL directly from di-p-xylylene by breakage of a single bond

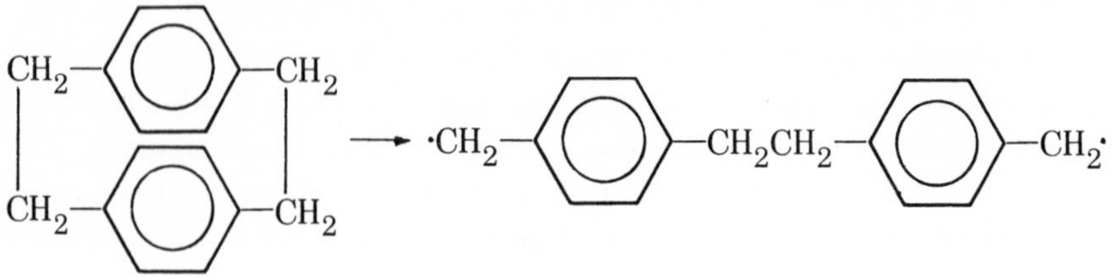

$$\text{di-}p\text{-xylylene} \longrightarrow \cdot CH_2{-}C_6H_4{-}CH_2CH_2{-}C_6H_4{-}CH_2\cdot$$

(2-153)

has been suggested. However, polymerization experiments with monosubstituted di-*p*-xylylenes confirm the initiation mechanism shown in Eqs. 2-150 and 2-151. When acetyl-di-*p*-xylylene is pyrolyzed and the pyrolysis vapor led through successive condensation surfaces at temperatures of 90°C and 25°C, respectively, the result is the formation of two different polymers neither of which is poly(acetyl-di-*p*-xylylene). Pyrolysis yields acetyl-*p*-xylylene and *p*-xylylene

$$\text{acetyl-di-}p\text{-xylylene (}COCH_3\text{ on upper ring; } CH_2\text{—}CH_2 \text{ bridges)} \longrightarrow$$

$$CH_2{=}C_6H_3(COCH_3){=}CH_2 + CH_2{=}C_6H_4{=}CH_2 \qquad (2\text{-}154)$$

which undergo separate polymerizations at different condensation temperatures. Poly(acetyl-*p*-xylylene) is produced at the 90°C surface and poly(*p*-xylylene) at the 25°C surface.

2-12a-5 Aromatic Polyimides. Aromatic polyimides are synthesized [72, 82, 83] by the reactions of dianhydrides with diamines,

$$n\ \text{O}(CO)_2C_6H_2(CO)_2\text{O} + n\ H_2N\text{—}C_6H_4\text{—}NH_2 \xrightarrow{-H_2O}$$

$$\left[\text{—N}(CO)_2C_6H_2(CO)_2\text{N—}C_6H_4\text{—} \right]_n \qquad (2\text{-}155)$$

e.g., the polymerization of pyromellitic dianhydride and *p*-aminoaniline (Eq. 2-155) to form poly(1,4-phenylenepyromellitimide).

The direct production of high molecular weight aromatic polyimides in a one-stage polymerization cannot be accomplished because the polyimides are insoluble and infusible. The polymer chains precipitate from the reaction media (whether solution or melt) before high molecular weights are obtained. Polyimides are, therefore, synthesized by a two-stage process. The first stage involves an amidation reaction carried out in a polar solvent (e.g., *N,N*-dimethylacetamide, *N,N*-dimethylformamide, dimethyl sulfoxide, or *N*-methyl-2-pyrrolidone) to produce a high molecular weight poly(amic acid) XLI

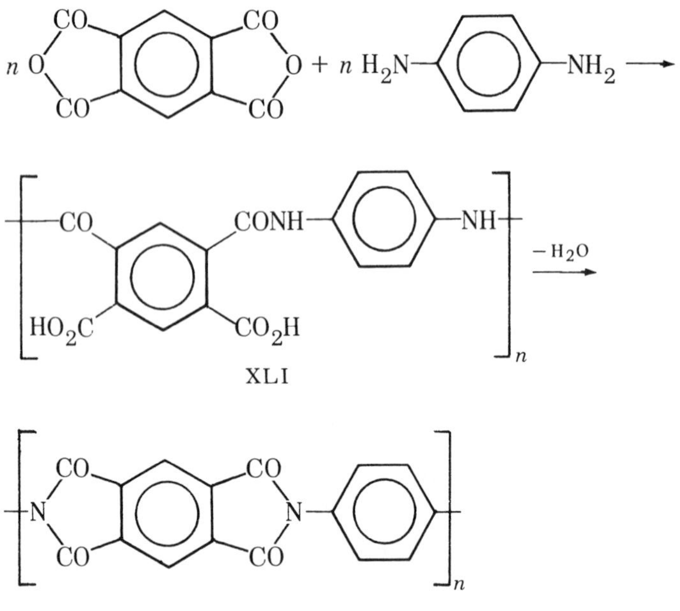

$$n\ \text{O(CO)}_2\text{C}_6\text{H}_2\text{(CO)}_2\text{O} + n\ \text{H}_2\text{N}-\text{C}_6\text{H}_4-\text{NH}_2 \longrightarrow$$

$$\left[\text{CO}-\text{C}_6\text{H}_2(\text{CO}_2\text{H})(\text{HO}_2\text{C})-\text{CONH}-\text{C}_6\text{H}_4-\text{NH}\right]_n \xrightarrow{-\text{H}_2\text{O}}$$

XLI

$$\left[\text{N(CO)}_2\text{C}_6\text{H}_2\text{(CO)}_2\text{N}-\text{C}_6\text{H}_4\right]_n \qquad (2\text{-}156)$$

Processing of the polymer can only be accomplished after the first stage at which point it is still soluble and fusible. It is insoluble and infusible after the second stage of the process. The poly(amic acid) is formed into the desired physical form of the final polymer product (e.g., film, fiber, laminate, coating, etc.) and then the second stage of the reaction carried out. The poly(amic acid) is cyclized in the solid-state to the polyimide by heating at moderately high temperatures above 150°C. The polymer is kept in solution during the amidation reaction by using mild conditions (temperatures of 70°C or below) so as to keep the amount of cyclization to a minimum. The first stage polymer has relatively poor storage stability unless the by-product water is removed. The water can cause partial reversal of the amidation reaction. Temperatures as high as 300°C are employed for the solid-state cyclization reaction although the use of vacuum or dehydrating agents such as acetic anhydride-pyridine lower the cyclization temperature.

2-12a-6 Polybenzimidazoles. Polyimides are obtained from amine and carboxyl reactants when the ratio of amine-to-acid functional groups is 1:2. If reactants with the reverse ratio of functional groups are employed, polybenzimidazoles

$$(H_2N)_2C_6H_3-C_6H_3(NH_2)_2 + \phi O_2C-C_6H_4-CO_2\phi \xrightarrow[-\phi OH]{-H_2O} \left[\text{benzimidazole}-\text{benzimidazole}-C_6H_4 \right]_n \quad (2\text{-}157)$$

can be synthesized [72, 84, 85]. The reaction is usually carried out as a two-stage melt polymerization by initially heating at about 250°C and finally at 350–400°C. The polymerization yields high molecular weight polymer in high conversion only when the diphenyl ester of the dibasic acid is employed. The use of the dibasic acid itself or the dimethyl ester does not yield high molecular polymer due to side reactions (decarboxylation and amine methylation, respectively) which lead to an imbalance of the reacting functional groups. The diacid chloride is also not used due to its high reactivity. Adjacent amine groups would tend to be converted to amide groups and cyclization would be more difficult.

The polymerization probably proceeds by an Aldol-type condensation in the first stage to form a Schiff base-type of polymer structure which cyclizes in the second stage solid-state reaction with the evolution of phenol

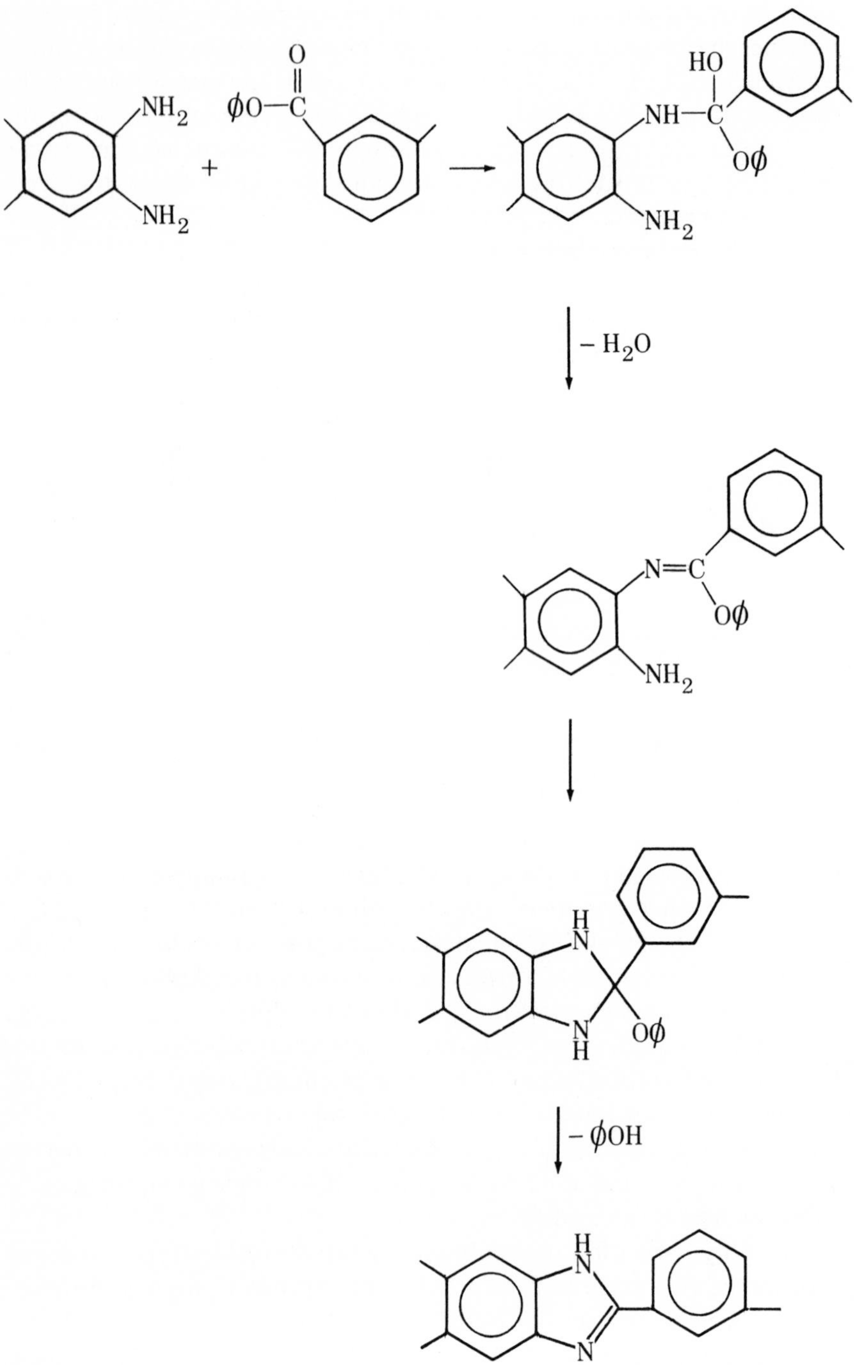

(2-158)

Processing can be carried out using the non-cyclized polymer in a manner similar to that described for the polyimides. The processing of polybenzimidazoles is, however, somewhat more varied than for the polyimides since the former are soluble in a few solvents such as dimethylacetamide and dimethyl sulfoxide. Solution casting of films and spinning of fibers has been accomplished.

2-12b Research Polymers

Of the polymers discussed in the previous section, only the polyimides and polybenzimidazoles have reached far into the desired high temperature range (approximately > 300–500°C). Many of the polymers are far from possessing completely inflexible polymer chains because of the presence of varying numbers of single bonds. Further, some of them contain aliphatic groupings which are relatively "weak links in the chain." Aside from the commercially available polymers, many other promising polymer systems are being studied in the effort to obtain high temperature polymers with serviceability in the 300–500°C range and above [34, 71, 86, 87]. The general approach of building polymer chains composed of ring structures, usually aromatic rings, results in polymer structures which can be classified as *ladder* or *semi-ladder* polymers. A ladder (or *two-strand*) structure is one which has an uninterrupted sequence of rings joined one to another at two connecting atoms. A semi-ladder structure is one in which there are single bonds interconnecting some of the rings.

The semi-ladder structures have usually been not as desirable as the ladder structures from the viewpoint of obtaining stiff polymer chains with maximum resistance to deformation and thermal softening. Thus, considerable effort has been made to obtain and employ the necessary monomers so as to obtain ladder structures. However, other factors such as differences in the stabilities of various ring systems also are important in determining the stability of the final polymer chain. Further, the desire to obtain high temperature polymers which can be readily processed often necessitates a sacrifice in the stiffness of the polymer chains. Needless to say, the various polymer structures which have and are being studied represent a range of different compromises of structure based on the types of monomers which are available and combinations of thermal stability, physical properties, and processability. Many of the polymer systems could potentially solve the problem of processability in the same manner as the polyimides and polybenzimidazoles since their syntheses involve a polymerization reaction followed by a cyclization. Processing could be carried out prior to the cyclization step since most of the polymers are soluble and fusible at that point. Consider now some of the polymer systems which have been studied. It is only a slight

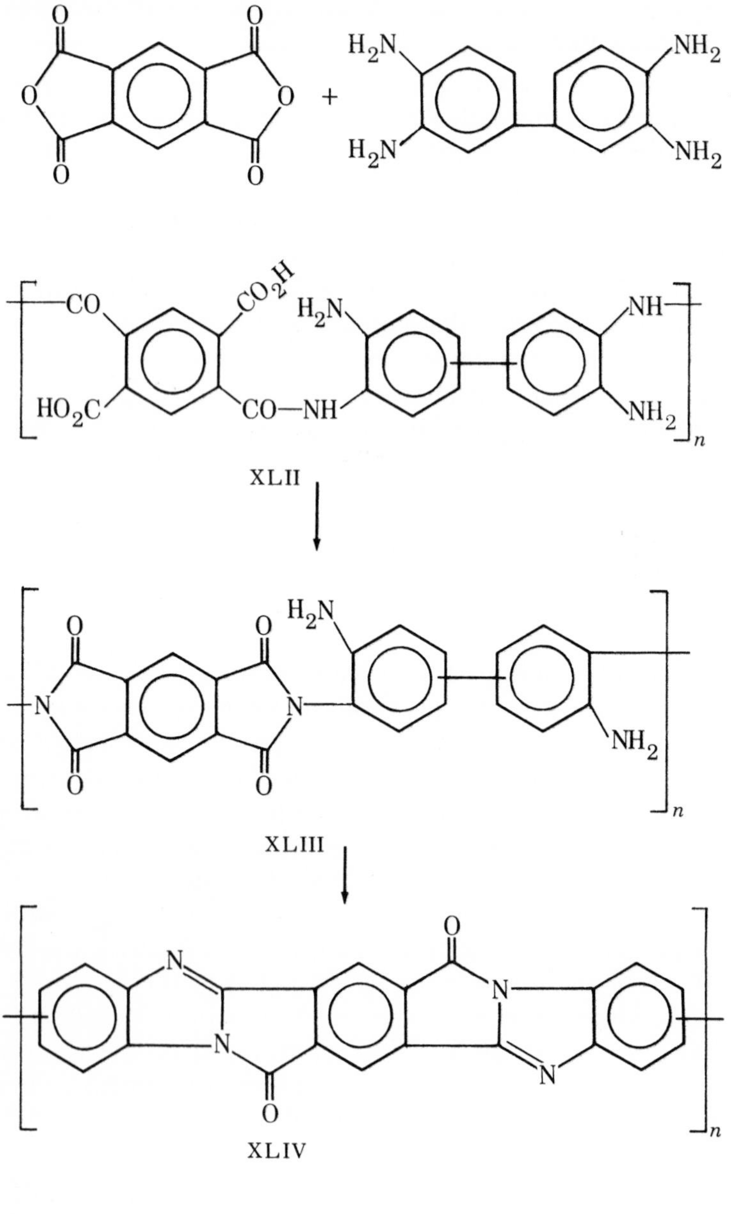

XLII

XLIII

XLIV

(2-159)

exaggeration to state that attempts have been made to build polymer chains based on almost every type of known carbocyclic and heterocyclic structure.

2-12b-1 Polyimidazopyrrolones. Polyimidazopyrrolones, or pyrrones, are synthesized [88] from tetraamine and tetracarboxyl monomers (Eq. 2-159). The initial reaction to form the amide structure XLII is carried out in polar solvents at slightly above room temperature (35–50°C). The subsequent reaction to the imidazopyrrolone (XLIV) via the imide intermediate (XLIII) is carried out as a solid-state reaction at about 300°C. The imidazopyrrolone polymer is a ladder structure in comparison to all of the previously discussed polymers which are semi-ladder structures.

2-12b-2 Polybenzoxazoles and Polybenzothiazoles. Polybenzoxazoles (XLV) and polybenzothiazoles (XLVI) are synthesized [89]

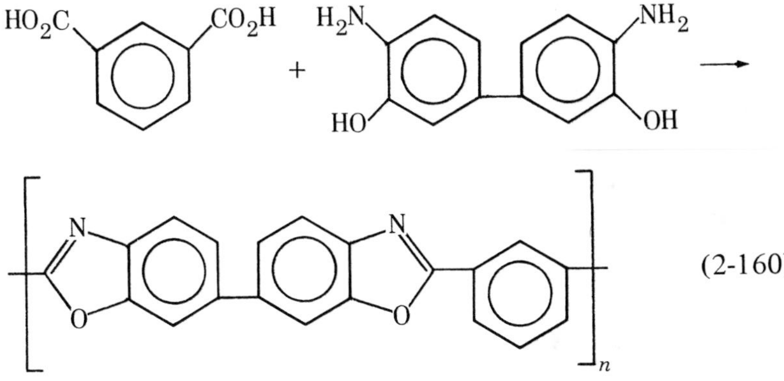

HO_2C CO_2H + H_2N NH_2 HO OH →

N N O O n (2-160)

XLV

HO_2C CO_2H + H_2N NH_2 HS SH →

N N S S n (2-161)

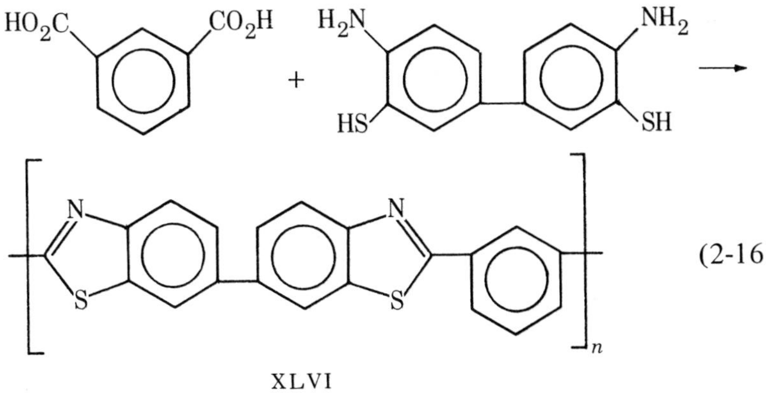

XLVI

from the reaction of a dicarboxyl monomer with bisorthoaminophenols and bisorthoaminothiophenols (Eqs. 2-160 and 2-161).

2-12b-3 Polyquinoxalines. Both semi-ladder (Eq. 2-162) and ladder (Eq. 2-163) polyquinoxalines have been synthesized [90] from the reaction of appropriate ortho-diamine and di-1,2-carbonyl reactants

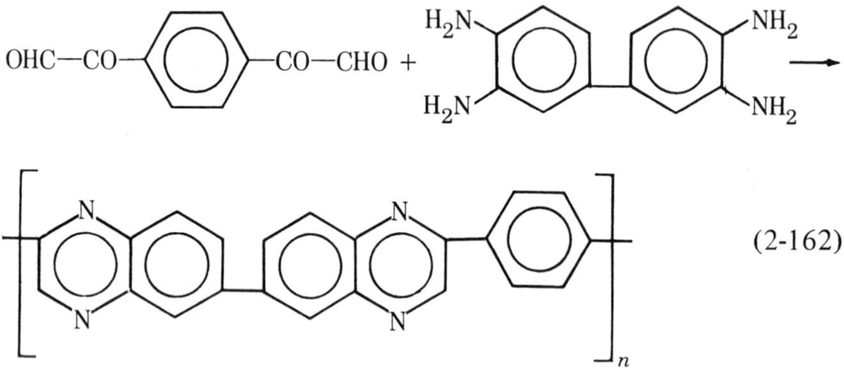

OHC—CO—C_6H_4—CO—CHO + $(H_2N)_2C_6H_3$—$C_6H_3(NH_2)_2$ →

(2-162)

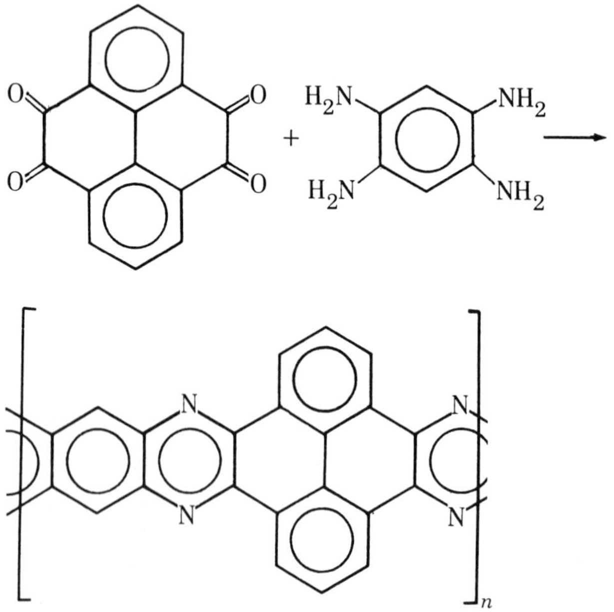

(2-163)

2-12b-4 Polyoxadiazoles and Polytriazoles. Polyoxadiazoles (XLVII) and polytriazoles (XLVIII) have been synthesized [91, 92]

from polyhydrazides

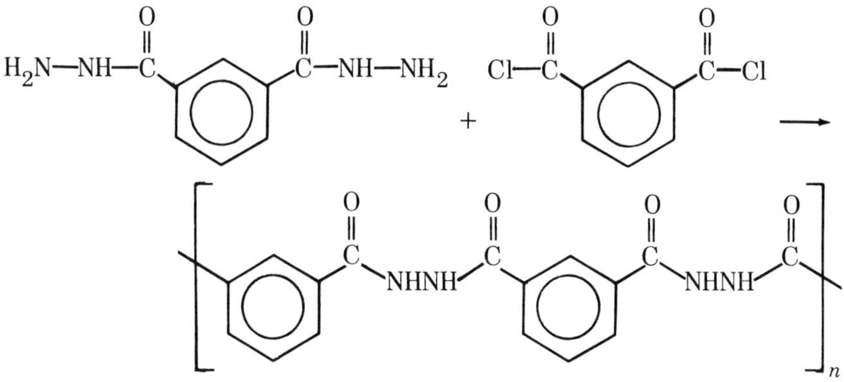

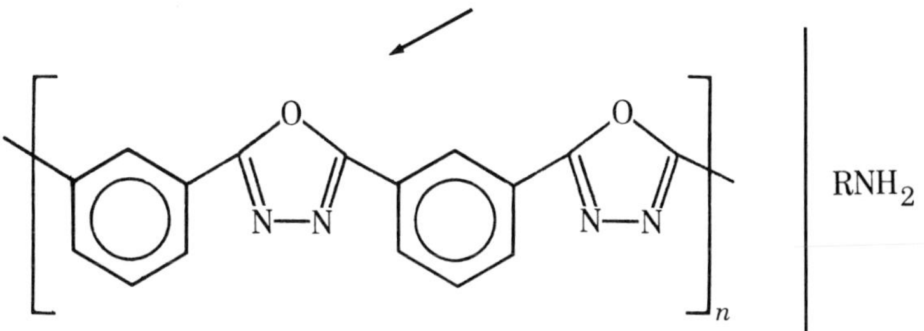

$$H_2N{-}NH{-}\overset{O}{\overset{\|}{C}}{-}C_6H_4{-}\overset{O}{\overset{\|}{C}}{-}NH{-}NH_2 + Cl{-}\overset{O}{\overset{\|}{C}}{-}C_6H_4{-}\overset{O}{\overset{\|}{C}}{-}Cl \longrightarrow \left[{-}C_6H_4{-}\overset{O}{\overset{\|}{C}}{-}NHNH{-}\overset{O}{\overset{\|}{C}}{-}C_6H_4{-}\overset{O}{\overset{\|}{C}}{-}NHNH{-}\overset{O}{\overset{\|}{C}}{-}\right]_n$$

XLVII

(2-164)

$\xrightarrow{RNH_2}$

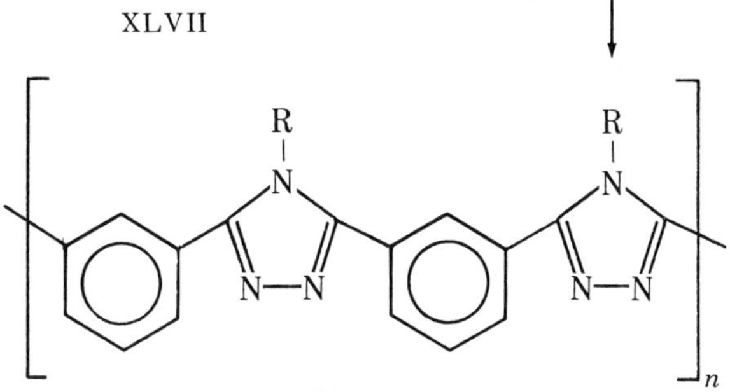

XLVIII

(2-165)

2-12b-5 Polymerization by Diels-Alder Reaction. The Diels-Alder reaction, involving the 1,4-addition of an unsaturated linkage (dienophile) to a 1,3-diene, has been used [93, 94] to synthesize both ladder and semi-ladder polymers (Eqs. 2-166 and 2-167).

2-12b-6 Polymerization by 1,3-Dipolar Addition. A variety of semi-ladder polymers have been synthesized by 1,3-dipolar addition reactions [95–98]. These include the 1,3-addition of the nitrile oxide group to the nitrile group in the reaction of a bisnitrile oxide with itself (Eq. 2-168), or with the nitrile (Eq. 2-169) and

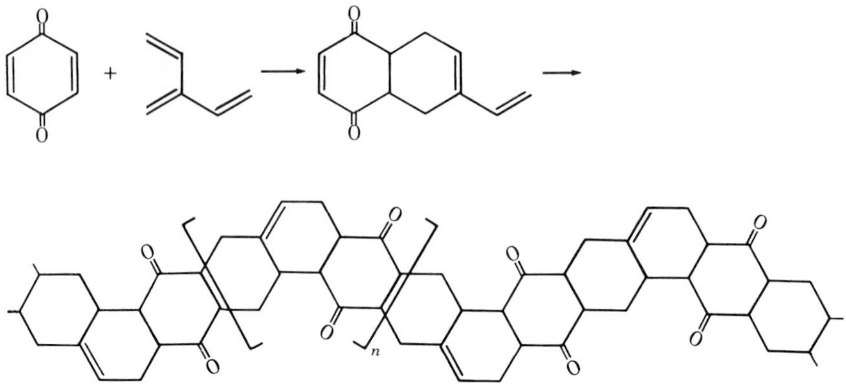

(2-166)

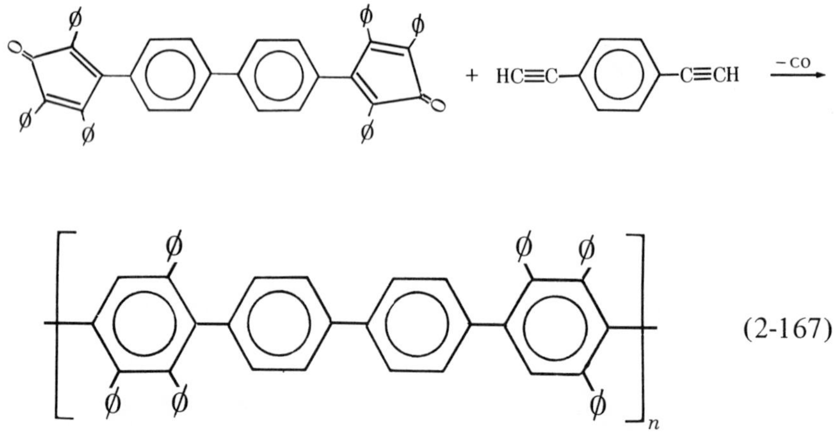

$$\text{HC}\equiv\text{C}-\text{C}_6\text{H}_4-\text{C}\equiv\text{CH} \xrightarrow{-\text{CO}}$$

(2-167)

acetylene (Eq. 2-170) linkages of other reactants as well as the 1,3-addition of the sydnone dipole to the alkene (Eq. 2-171) and acetylene (Eq. 2-172) linkages with simultaneous decarboxylation, and the corresponding 1,3-additions of azides, nitrilimines, and tetrazoles.

2-12b-7 Spiro Structures. Another approach to obtaining rigid polymer chains is by the synthesis of *spiro* polymers—polymers containing ring structures in which there is only one atom common to two rings. Examples of such polymer structures are the polyspiroketal [99] synthesized from 1,4-cyclohexanedione and pentaerythritol (Eq. 2-173) and the spiro polymer from the tetraamine and dianhydride shown in Eq. 2-174 [100].

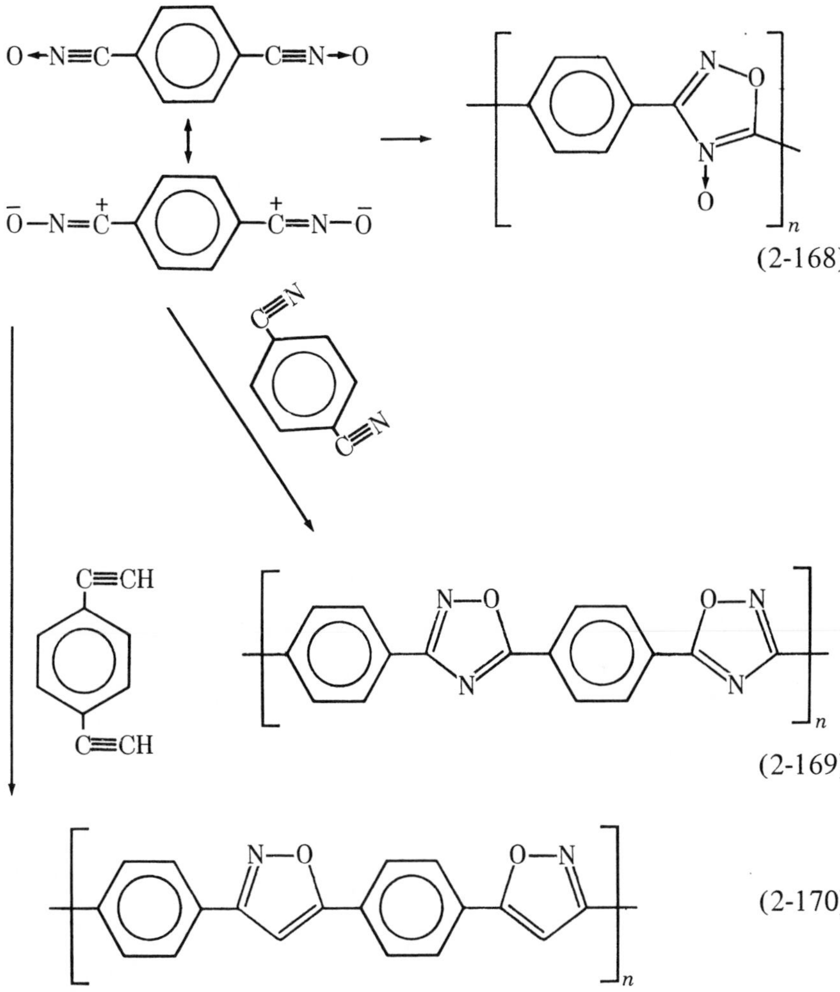

(2-168)

(2-169)

(2-170)

2-12b-8 Copolymers. Some efforts have recently been made to synthesize copolymers containing two different types of ring structures, e.g., the imide-imidazopyrrolones [101] (Eq. 2-175) and the oxadiazole-benzimidazoles [102] (Eq. 2-176).

2-12b-9 Inorganic and Semi-Inorganic Polymers. Bond energy considerations lead one to conclude that polymers based on inorganic elements should be superior to organic polymer in thermal stability. This has led to a large effort in the synthesis of semi-inorganic polymers, containing inorganic elements in the main chain and organic elements as side groups, and wholly inorganic polymers

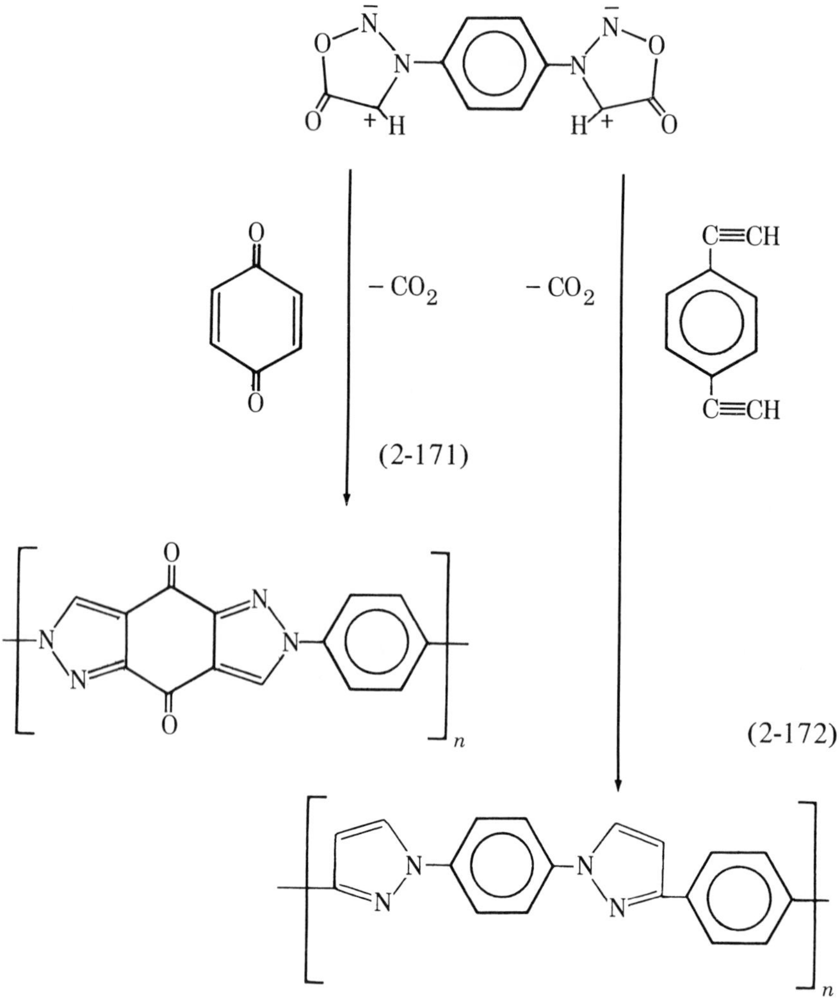

$-CO_2$ $-CO_2$

(2-171)

(2-172)

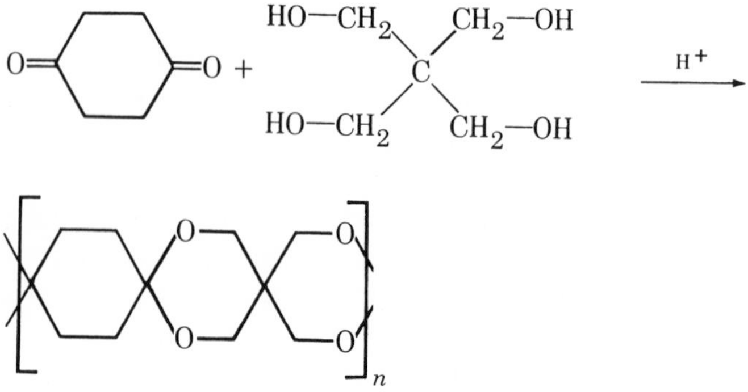

H^+

(2-173)

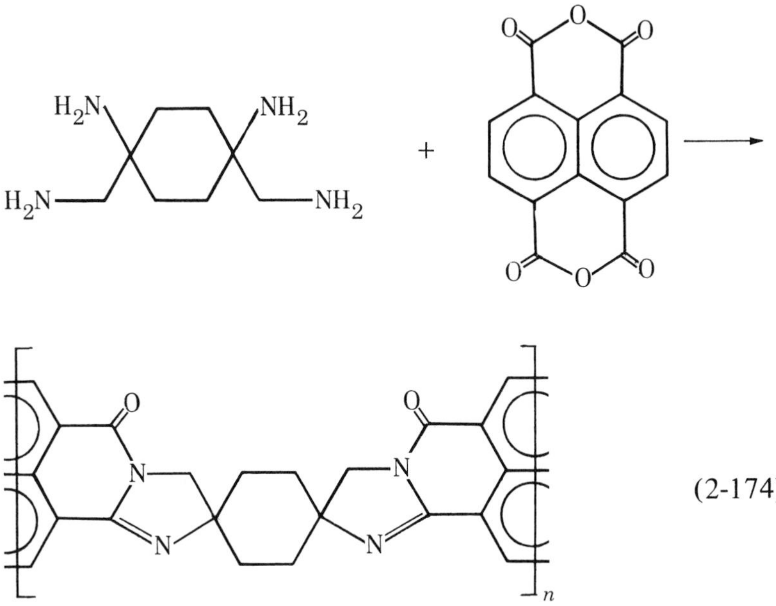

(2-174)

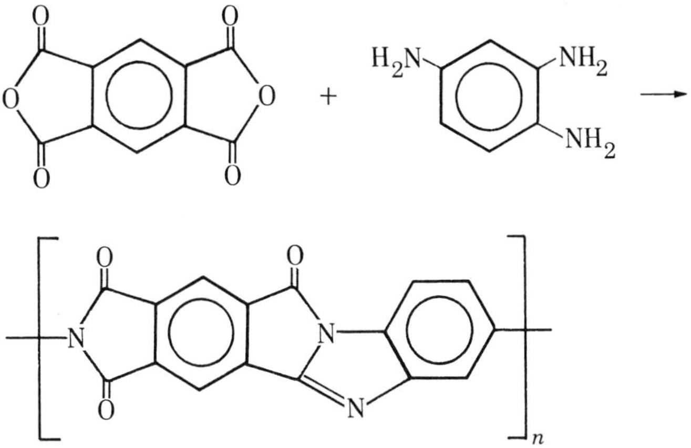

(2-175)

[71, 72, 103, 104]. With a few exceptions, the results of these studies have been very disappointing from the practical viewpoint of obtaining useful polymers. Although the intrinsic thermal stability of many of the polymer systems is good, a variety of difficulties must be overcome before a usable polymer can be obtained. The molecular weights of many of the polymers are too low. Many linear systems undergo thermal rearrangement to cyclic structures of 8, 10, 12, and 14 members with a resulting loss of physical strength. The hydrolytic

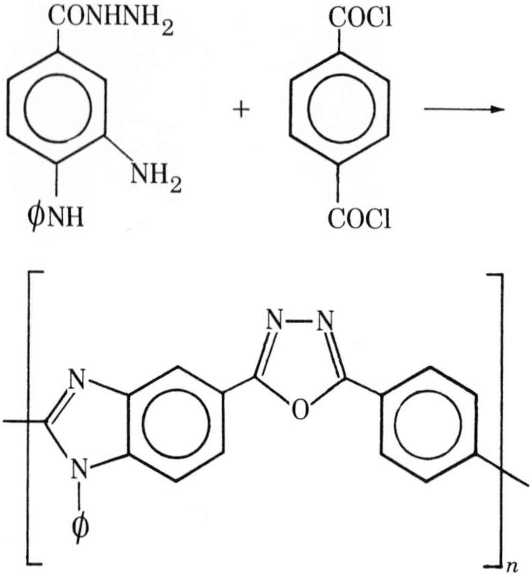

$$\text{(reactants: 3-amino-4-anilinobenzhydrazide (CONHNH}_2\text{, NH}_2\text{, }\phi\text{NH)} + \text{terephthaloyl chloride (COCl, COCl)} \longrightarrow \text{poly[benzimidazole–oxadiazole–phenylene]}_n \qquad (2\text{-}176)$$

stability of many of the polymers is poor; the result is often lower molecular weight species or too extensive a degree of crosslinking. Many of the polymers are intractable to the current methods of polymer processing. The net result of all this is that almost all of the inorganic or semi-inorganic polymer systems are vastly inferior to the organic systems at the present time. One would expect, however, that useful materials will be synthesized as there develops a better understanding of the polymerization mechanisms in inorganic systems.

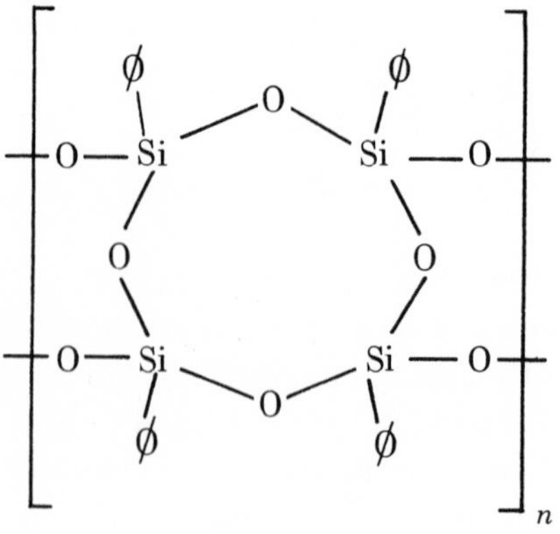

$$\left[\text{ladder siloxane: }-O-Si(\phi)-O-Si(\phi)-O-\text{, cyclic }Si_4O_4\text{ rings}\right]_n$$

IL

The polysiloxanes are the prime exception to the generalizations made above regarding the utility of inorganic and semi-inorganic polymers. The synthesis of polysiloxanes is considered in Secs. 2-6b-4 and 7-4. With a view toward improving the thermal stability of the polysiloxane chain, the phenylated ladder polymer polyphenylsilsesquioxane IL has been synthesized by the basic hydrolysis of phenyltrichlorosilane [105].

Among the various inorganic and semi-inorganic polymer systems studied are various polymetallosiloxane structures [103, 104] such as

$$\begin{array}{ccccccccc}
 & \mathrm{R} & & & & \mathrm{R} & & & \\
 & | & & & & | & & & \\
-\mathrm{O}- & \mathrm{Si} & -\mathrm{O}- & \mathrm{M} & -\mathrm{O}- & \mathrm{Si} & -\mathrm{O}- & \mathrm{M} & - \\
 & | & & | & & | & & | & \\
 & \mathrm{R} & & \mathrm{O} & & \mathrm{R} & & \mathrm{O} & \\
 & & & | & & & & | &
\end{array}$$

L

$$\begin{array}{ccccccccc}
 & \mathrm{R} & & \mathrm{R'} & & \mathrm{R} & & \mathrm{R'} & \\
 & | & & | & & | & & | & \\
-\mathrm{O}- & \mathrm{Si} & -\mathrm{O}- & \mathrm{M'} & -\mathrm{O}- & \mathrm{Si} & -\mathrm{O}- & \mathrm{M'} & - \\
 & | & & | & & | & & | & \\
 & \mathrm{R} & & \mathrm{R'} & & \mathrm{R} & & \mathrm{R'} &
\end{array}$$

LI

$$\begin{array}{ccccccccc}
 & & & | & & & & | & \\
 & \mathrm{R} & & \mathrm{O} & & \mathrm{R} & & \mathrm{O} & \\
 & | & & | & & | & & | & \\
-\mathrm{O}- & \mathrm{Si} & -\mathrm{O}- & \mathrm{M''} & -\mathrm{O}- & \mathrm{Si} & -\mathrm{O}- & \mathrm{M''} & - \\
 & | & & | & & | & & | & \\
 & \mathrm{R} & & \mathrm{O} & & \mathrm{R} & & \mathrm{O} & \\
 & & & | & & & & | &
\end{array}$$

LII

$$\begin{array}{ccccccccc}
 & \mathrm{R} & & \mathrm{O} & & \mathrm{R} & & \mathrm{O} & \\
 & | & & \| & & | & & \| & \\
-\mathrm{O}- & \mathrm{Si} & -\mathrm{O}- & \mathrm{M'''} & -\mathrm{O}- & \mathrm{Si} & -\mathrm{O}- & \mathrm{M'''} & - \\
 & | & & | & & | & & | & \\
 & \mathrm{R} & & \mathrm{O} & & \mathrm{R} & & \mathrm{O} & \\
 & & & | & & & & | &
\end{array}$$

LIII

where M = Al or B, M′ = Sn or Ge, M″ = Ti and M‴ = P or As. A host of other systems have been investigated including polymer chains based on B—N, B—O, B—B, B—P, B—S, B—C, N—P, N—S, P—O linkages as well as other combinations of these [103, 104, 106]. Various other inorganic polymers have also been synthesized by ring-opening polymerizations (Sec. 7-6).

REFERENCES

1. P. J. Flory, "Principles of Polymer Chemistry," chap. II, Cornell University Press, Ithaca, New York, 1953.
2. B. V. Bhide and J. J. Sudborough, *J. Indian Inst. Sci.*, **8A**:89 (1925).
3. L. Rand, B. Thir, S. L. Reegen, and K. C. Frisch, *J. Appl. Polymer Sci.*, **9**:1787 (1965).
4. E. Rabinowitch, *Trans. Faraday Soc.*, **33**:1225 (1937).
5. I. Vancso-Szmercsanyi and E. Makay-Bodi, *Eur. Polym. J.*, **5**:145, 155 (1969).
6. A. A. Frost and R. G. Pearson, "Kinetics and Mechanism," 2d ed., chap. 9, John Wiley & Sons, Inc., New York, 1961.
7. F. W. Billmeyer, Jr., "Textbook of Polymer Science," chap. 8, Interscience Publishers, John Wiley & Sons, Inc., New York, 1962.
8. P. J. Flory, *J. Am. Chem. Soc.*, **61**:3334 (1939).
9. D. H. Solomon, *J. Macromol. Sci.–Revs. Macromol. Chem*, **C1(1)**, 179 (1967).
10. A. Tang and K. Yao, *J. Polymer Sci.*, **35**:219 (1959).
11. J. Hine, "Physical Organic Chemistry," chap. 2, McGraw-Hill Book Company, Inc., New York, 1962.
12. M. Imoto and T. Tanigaki, *J. Chem. Soc., Ind. (Kogyo Kagaku Zasshi)*, **66**:517 (1963).
13. W. H. Carothers, *Trans. Faraday Soc.*, **32**:39 (1936).
14. G. Challa, *Makromol. Chem.*, **38**:105, 123 (1960).
15. R. W. Lenz, C. E. Handlovits, and H. A. Smith, *J. Polymer Sci.*, **58**:351 (1962).
16. E. G. Lovering and K. J. Laidler, *Can. J. Chem.*, **40**:31 (1962).
17. M. Kaplan, *J. Chem. Eng. Data*, **6**:272 (1961).
18. J. W. Burkus and C. F. Eckert, *J. Am. Chem. Soc.*, **80**:5948 (1958).
19. R. H. Kienle, P. A. Van der Meulen, and F. E. Petke, *ibid.*, **61**:2258 (1939).
20. D. H. Solomon and J. J. Hopwood, *J. Appl. Polymer Sci.*, **10**:1431 (1966).
21. W. H. Carothers and J. W. Hill, *J. Am. Chem. Soc.*, **55**:5043 (1933).
22. E. L. Eliel, "Stereochemistry of Carbon Compounds," chap. 7, McGraw-Hill Book Company, Inc., New York, 1962.
23. H. Jacobson and W. H. Stockmayer, *J. Chem. Phys.*, **18**:1600 (1950).
24. D. W. Scott, *ibid.*, **68**:2294 (1946).
25. J. F. Brown and G. M. J. Slusarczuk, *J. Am. Chem. Soc.*, **87**:931 (1965).

26. V. V. Korshak, *Pure and Appl. Chem.,* **12**:101 (1966).
27. P. J. Flory, ref. 1, chaps. 8 and 9.
28. G. J. Howard, The Molecular Weight Distribution of Condensation Polymers, in J. C. Robb and F. W. Peaker (eds.), "Progress in High Polymers," vol. I, pp. 185-231, Iliffe Books, Ltd., London, 1961.
29. M. J. R. Cantow (ed.), "Polymer Fractionation," Academic Press, Inc., New York, 1967.
30. G. J. Howard, *J. Polymer Sci.,* **37**:310 (1959).
31. H. Kilkson, *Ind. Eng. Chem. Fundamentals,* **3**:281 (1964).
32. W. H. Abraham, *Chem. Eng. Sci.,* **21**:327 (1966).
33. R. W. Lenz, "Organic Chemistry of Synthetic High Polymers," chaps. 4-8, Interscience Publishers, John Wiley & Sons, Inc., New York, 1967.
34. A. Raave, "Organic Chemistry of Macromolecules," chaps. 14-19, Marcel Dekker, Inc., New York, 1967.
35. R. E. Wilfong, *J. Polymer Sci.,* **54**:385 (1961).
36. R. W. Stevenson and H. R. Nettleton, *ibid.,* **A-1(6)**:889 (1968).
37. D. J. Lyman, *J. Macromol. Sci.–Revs. Macromol. Chem.,* **1(1)**:191 (1966).
38. A. J. Barry and H. N. Beck, Silicone Polymers, in F. G. A. Stone and W. A. G. Graham (eds.), "Inorganic Polymers," chap. 5, Academic Press, Inc., New York, 1962.
39. P. W. Morgan and S. L. Kwolek, *J. Chem. Ed.,* **36**:Cover and p. 182 (1959); *J. Polymer Sci.,* **40**:299 (1959).
40. P. W. Morgan, "Condensation Polymers: By Interfacial and Solution Methods," Interscience Publishers, John Wiley & Sons, Inc., New York, 1965.
41. J. R. Schaefgen and P. J. Flory, *J. Am. Chem. Soc.,* **70**:2709 (1948).
42. *Mod. Plastics,* **46(1)**:25 (1969); *Chem. & Eng. News,* **47(36)**: 64A (1969).
43. S. H. Pinner, *J. Polymer Sci.,* **21**:153 (1956).
44. W. H. Stockmayer, *ibid.,* **9**:69 (1952) and **11**:424 (1953); *J. Chem. Phys.,* **11**:45 (1943).
45. R. H. Kienle and F. E. Petke, *J. Am. Chem. Soc.,* **62**:1053 (1940); **63**:481 (1941).
46. P. J. Flory, *ibid.,* **63**:3083 (1941).
47. W. H. Stockmayer, in S. B. Twiss (ed.), "Advancing Fronts in Chemistry," chap. 6, Reinhold Book Corp., New York, 1945.
48. S. Strella and A. A. Bibeau, *J. Macromol. Chem.,* **1(3)**:417 (1966).
49. M. Jonason, *J. Appl. Polymer Sci.,* **4**:129 (1960).
50. E. G. Bobalek, E. R. Moore, S. S. Levy, and C. C. Lee, *ibid.,* **8**:625 (1964).
51. D. H. Solomon, "The Chemistry of Organic Film Formers," chap. 3, John Wiley & Sons, Inc., New York, 1967.
52. P. J. Flory, *Chem. Rev.,* **39**:137 (1946).

53. S. H. Rider and E. E. Hardy, Prepolymer Technology for Crosslinked Plastics, in N. A. J. Platzer (ed.), "Polymerization and Polycondensation Processes," chap. 13, American Chemical Society, Reinhold Book Corp., New York, 1962.
54. L. M. Yeddanapalli and V. V. Gopalakrishna, *Makromol. Chem.*, **32**:90, 124, 130 (1959).
55. J. H. Freeman and C. W. Lewis, *J. Am. Chem. Soc.*, **76**:2080 (1954).
56. C. P. Vale and W. G. K. Taylor, "Aminoplastics," Iliffe Books, Ltd., London, 1964.
57. J. I. deJong and J. deJong, *Rec. Trav. Chim.*, **72**:139 (1953).
58. R. A. H. Strecker and D. M. French, *Polymer Preprints*, **7(2)**:952 (1966).
59. J. H. Saunders and K. C. Frisch, "Polyurethanes: Chemistry and Technology," part II, Interscience Publishers, John Wiley & Sons, Inc., New York, 1964.
60. G. D. Edwards, *J. Appl. Polymer Sci.*, **9**:3845 (1965).
61. I. Skeist and G. R. Somerville, "Epoxy Resins," Reinhold Book Corp., New York, 1958.
62. C. R. Martens, "Alkyd Resins," Reinhold Book Corp., New York, 1961.
63. H. V. Boenig, "Unsaturated Polyesters: Structure and Properties," American Elsevier Publishing Co., Inc., New York, 1964.
64. F. Dobinson and J. Preston, *J. Macromol. Sci. (Chem.)*, **A1(1)**:179 (1967).
65. K. Saotome and K. Sata, *Makromol. Chem.*, **102**:105 (1967).
66. D. Coleman, *J. Polymer Sci.*, **14**:15 (1954).
67. E. P. Goldberg, *ibid.*, **C4**:707 (1964).
68. S. H. Merrill and S. E. Petrie, *ibid.*, **A3**:2189 (1965).
69. E. M. Hicks, Jr., A. J. Ultee, and J. Drougas, *Science*, **147**:373 (1965).
70. E. A. Tippetts and J. Zimmerman, *J. Appl. Polymer Sci.*, **8**:2465 (1964).
71. H. Mark, *Pure and Appl. Chem.*, **12**:9 (1966).
72. H. Lee, D. Stoffey, and K. Neville, "New Linear Polymers," McGraw-Hill Book Company, New York, 1967.
73. H. Schnell, "Chemistry and Physics of Polycarbonates," Interscience Publishers, John Wiley & Sons, Inc., New York, 1964.
74. L. Starr, *J. Polymer Sci.*, **A-1(4)**:3041 (1966).
75. J. Preston and W. B. Black, *ibid.*, **C19**:17 (1967).
76. A. S. Hay, *Fortschr. Hochpolymer.-Forsch. (Advan. Polymer Sci.)*, **4**:496 (1967); *Macromolecules*, **2(1)**:107 (1969).
77. R. N. Johnson, A. G. Farnham, R. A. Clendinning, W. F. Hale, and C. N. Merriam, *J. Polymer Sci.*, **A-1(5)**:2375 (1967).
78. R. B. Fox et al., *Polymer Preprints*, **8(2)**:e (1967).
79. E. J. McNelis, *J. Org. Chem.*, **31**:1255 (1966).
80. L. A. Errede and M. Szwarc, *Quart. Rev. (London)*, **12**:301 (1958).
81. W. F. Gorham, *J. Polymer Sci.*, **A-1(4)**:3027 (1966).
82. G. M. Bower and L. W. Frost, *ibid.*, **A1**:3135 (1963).

83. C. E. Sroog, A. L. Endrey, S. V. Abramo, C. E. Berr, W. M. Edwards, and K. L. Olivier, *J. Polymer Sci.*, **A3**:1373 (1965).
84. H. Vogel and C. S. Marvel, *ibid.*, **50**:511 (1961); **A1**:1531 (1963).
85. W. Wrasidlo and H. H. Levine, *ibid.*, **A2**:4795 (1964).
86. C. S. Marvel, *J. Macromol. Sci. (Chem.)*, **A1(1)**:7 (1967).
87. W. DeWinter, *J. Macromol. Sci.–Revs. Macromol. Chem.*, **1(2)**:329 (1966).
88. V. L. Bell and R. A. Jewell, *J. Polymer Sci.*, **A-1(5)**:3043 (1967).
89. P. M. Hergenrother, W. Wrasidlo, and H. H. Levine, *ibid.*, **3A**:1665 (1965).
90. J. K. Stille and E. L. Mainen, *Macromolecules*, **1**:36 (1968).
91. A. H. Frazer and F. T. Wallenberger, *J. Polymer Sci.*, **A2**:1181 (1964).
92. J. R. Holsten and H. R. Lilyquist, *ibid.*, **A3**:3915 (1965).
93. W. J. Bailey, J. Economy, and M. E. Hermes, *J. Org. Chem.*, **27**:3295 (1962).
94. J. K. Stille et al., *J. Polymer Sci.*, **A-1(5)**:2721 (1967); *Macromolecules*, **2(1)**:85 (1969).
95. C. G. Overberger and S. Fujimoto, *J. Polymer Sci.*, **B3**:735 (1965).
96. J. K. Stille and F. W. Harris, *ibid.*, **B4**:333 (1966) and **A-1(6)**:2317 (1968).
97. J. K. Stille and L. D. Gotten, *ibid.*, **B6**:11 (1968).
98. J. K. Stille and M. A. Bedford, *ibid.*, **A-1(6)**:2331 (1968); *Polymer Preprints*, **9(1)**:636 (1968).
99. W. J. Bailey and A. A. Volpe, *Polymer Preprints*, **8(1)**:292 (1967).
100. J. Heller, J. H. Hodgkin, and F. J. Martinelli, *J. Polymer Sci.*, **B6**:153 (1968).
101. W. R. Dunnavant, *ibid.*, **B6**:49 (1968).
102. B. M. Culbertson and S. Dietz, *ibid.*, **B6**:247 (1968).
103. M. F. Lappert and G. J. Leigh (eds.), "Developments in Inorganic Polymer Chemistry," Elsevier Publishing Co., Amsterdam, 1962.
104. K. Andrianov, "Metal-Organic Polymers," Interscience Publishers, John Wiley & Sons, Inc., New York, 1965.
105. J. F. Brown, L. F. Vogt, A. Katchman, J. W. Eustace, K. M. Kiser, and K. W. Krantz, *J. Am. Chem. Soc.*, **82**:6194 (1960).
106. F. G. A. Stone and W. A. G. Graham (eds.), "Inorganic Polymers," Academic Press, Inc., New York, 1962.

PROBLEMS

2-1. Derive an expression for the rate of polymerization of stoichiometric amounts of adipic acid and hexamethylene diamine. Indicate the assumptions inherent in the derivation. Derive an expression for the rate of polymerization of non-stoichiometric amounts of the two reactants.

2-2. A 21.3 gram sample of poly(hexamethylene adipamide) is found to contain 2.50×10^{-3} moles of carboxyl groups by both titration with base and infra-red spectroscopy. From this data the polymer is calculated to have a number-average molecular weight of 8,520. What assumption is made in this calculation? How can one experimentally determine its validity? If the assumption is invalid, how can one experimentally obtain the correct value of $\overline{M}_n$?

2-3. Describe and draw the structure of the polyester obtained in each of the following polymerizations:

a. $HO_2C—R—CO_2H + HO—R'—OH$

b. $HO_2C—R—CO_2H + HO—\underset{\displaystyle\overset{|}{OH}}{R''}—OH$

c. $HO_2C—R—CO_2H + HO—\underset{\displaystyle\overset{|}{OH}}{R''}—OH + HO—R'—OH$

Will the structure of the polymer produced in each case depend on the relative amounts of the reactants? If so, describe the differences.

2-4. Describe and draw the structure of the polyester obtained in each of the following polymerizations:

a. $HO—R—CO_2H$

b. $HO—R—CO_2H + HO—R'—OH$

c. $HO—R—CO_2H + HO—\underset{\displaystyle\overset{|}{OH}}{R''}—OH$

d. $HO—R—CO_2H + HO—R'—OH + HO—\underset{\displaystyle\overset{|}{OH}}{R''}—OH$

Will the structure of the polymer produced in each of cases *b, c,* and *d* depend on the relative amounts of the reactants? If so, describe the differences.

2-5. Compare the molecular weight distributions that are expected for the polymerizations in Questions 2-3*a*, 2-4*a*, 2-4*b*, and 2-4*c*.

2-6. Discuss the possibility of cyclization in the polymerization of *a.* $H_2N{-}(CH_2)_m{-}CO_2H$

b. $HO{-}(CH_2)_2{-}OH + HO_2C{-}(CH_2)_m{-}CO_2H$

for the cases where m has values from 2 to 10? At what stage(s) in the reaction is cyclization possible? What factors determine whether cyclization or linear polymerization is the predominant reaction?

2-7. Calculate the number-average degree of polymerization of an equimolar mixture of adipic acid and hexamethylene diamine for extents of reaction 0.500, 0.800, 0.900, 0.950, 0.970, 0.980, 0.990, 0.995.

2-8. Calculate the feed ratio of adipic acid and hexamethylene diamine which should be employed to obtain a polyamide of approximately 15,000 molecular weight at 99.5% conversion. What is the identity of the end-groups of this product? Do the same calculation for a 19,000 molecular weight polymer.

2-9. What is the proportion of benzoic acid which should be used with an equimolar mixture of adipic acid and hexamethylene diamine to produce a polymer of 10,000 molecular weight at 99.5% conversion? Do the same calculation for 19,000 and 28,000 molecular weight products.

2-10. Calculate the extent of reaction at which gelation occurs for the following mixtures:

a. phthalic anhydride and glycerol in stoichiometric amounts,
b. phthalic anhydride and glycerol in the molar ratio 1.500:0.980,
c. phthalic anhydride, glycerol, and ethylene glycol in the molar ratio 1.500:0.990:0.002,
d. phthalic anhydride, glycerol, and ethylene glycol in the molar ratio 1.500:0.500:0.700.

Compare the gel-points calculated from the Carothers equation (and its modifications) with those using the statistical approach.

2-11. Show by equations the polymerization of melamine and formaldehyde to form a crosslinked structure.

2-12. Describe by means of equations how random and block copolymers having the following compositions could be synthesized

a. 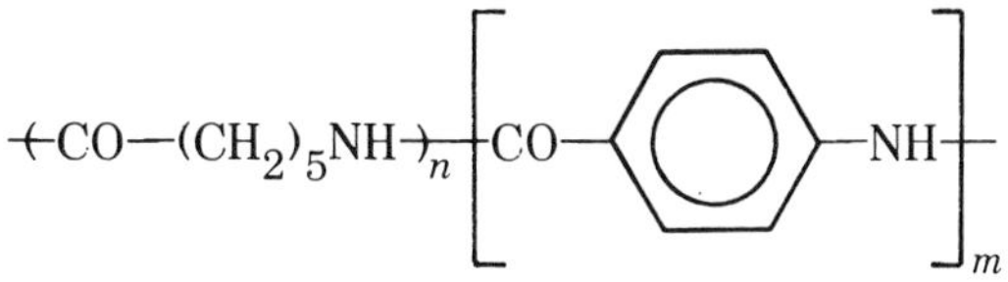 $-\!\!\left(CO{-}(CH_2)_5NH\right)\!\!-_n \left[CO{-}C_6H_4{-}NH\right]_m$

b. 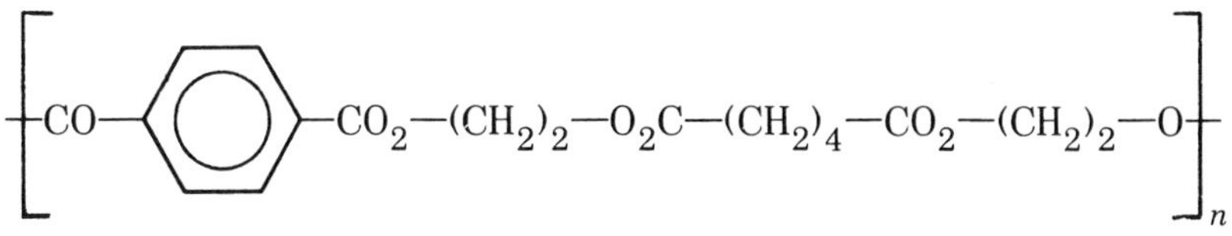 $\left[CO{-}C_6H_4{-}CO_2{-}(CH_2)_2{-}O_2C{-}(CH_2)_4{-}CO_2{-}(CH_2)_2{-}O\right]_n$

2-13. How would you synthesize a block copolymer having segments of the following structures

$$\left(CH_2CH_2CH_2—O \right)_m \quad \text{and} \quad \left[O—CH_2CH_2—OCONH—C_6H_3(CH_3)—NHCO \right]_p$$

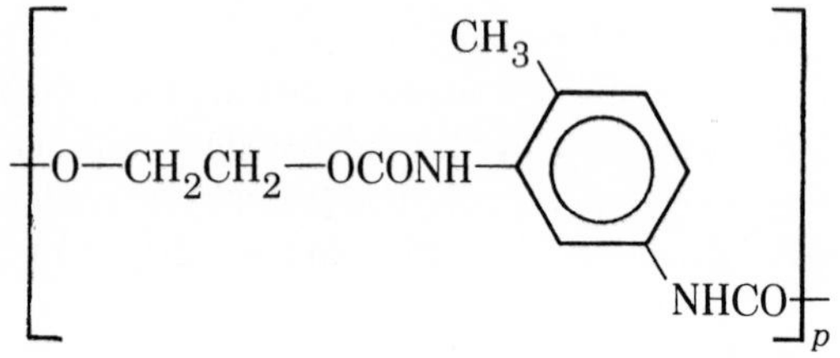

2-14. Distinguish between spiro, ladder, and semi-ladder polymers. Give examples of each.

3

RADICAL CHAIN POLYMERIZATION

In the previous chapter, the synthesis of polymers by step polymerization was considered. Polymerization of unsaturated monomers by chain polymerization will be discussed in this and several of the subsequent chapters. Chain polymerization is initiated by a reactive species R* produced from some compound I termed an *initiator* or *catalyst.*

$$I \longrightarrow R^* \tag{3-1}$$

The reactive species, which may be a free radical, cation, or anion, adds to a monomer molecule by opening the π-bond to form a new radical, cation, or anion center as the case may be. The process is repeated as many more monomer molecules are successively added to continuously propagate the reactive center

$$\text{R}^* \xrightarrow{\text{CH}_2=\text{CHY}} \text{R—CH}_2\text{—}\underset{\text{Y}}{\overset{\text{H}}{\text{C}}}{}^* \xrightarrow{\text{CH}_2=\text{CHY}} \text{R—CH}_2\text{—}\underset{\text{Y}}{\overset{\text{H}}{\text{C}}}\text{—CH}_2\text{—}\underset{\text{Y}}{\overset{\text{H}}{\text{C}}}{}^*$$

$$\xrightarrow{\text{CH}_2=\text{CHY}} \text{R}\left[\text{CH}_2\text{—}\underset{\text{Y}}{\overset{\text{H}}{\text{C}}}\right]_m\text{CH}_2\text{—}\underset{\text{Y}}{\overset{\text{H}}{\text{C}}}{}^* \qquad (3\text{-}2)$$

Polymer growth is terminated at some point by destruction of the reactive center by an appropriate reaction depending on the type of reactive center and the particular reaction conditions.

3-1 NATURE OF RADICAL CHAIN POLYMERIZATION

3-1a Comparison of Chain and Step Polymerization

Chain polymerization proceeds by a distinctly different mechanism from step polymerization. The most significant difference is that high molecular weight polymer is formed immediately in a chain polymerization. A radical, anionic, or cationic reactive center, once produced, adds many monomer units in a chain reaction and grows rapidly to a large size. The monomer concentration decreases throughout the course of the reaction as the number of high polymer molecules increases. At any instant, the reaction mixture contains only monomer, high polymer, and the growing chains. The molecular weight of the polymer is relatively unchanged during the polymerization although the overall percent conversion of monomer to polymer increases with reaction time.

The situation is quite different for a step polymerization. Whereas only monomer and the propagating species can react with each other in chain polymerization, any two molecular species present can react in step polymerization. Monomer disappears much faster in step polymerization as one proceeds slowly to produce dimer, trimer, tetramer, etc. The molecular weight increases throughout the course of the reaction and high molecular weight polymer is not obtained until the end of the polymerization. Long reaction times are necessary for both high percent conversion and high molecular weights.

3-1b Radical versus Ionic Chain Polymerizations

3-1b-1 General Considerations of Polymerizability. Whether a particular monomer can be converted to polymer depends on both thermodynamic and kinetic considerations. The polymerization will be impossible under any and all reaction conditions if it does not pass the test of thermodynamic feasibility. Polymerization is possible only if the free energy difference ΔG between monomer and polymer is negative (Sec. 3-9b). A negative ΔG does not, however, mean that polymerization will be observed under a particular set of reaction conditions (i.e., type of initiation, temperature, etc.). The ability to carry out a thermodynamically feasible polymerization depends on its kinetic feasibility—on whether the process proceeds at a reasonable rate under a proposed set of reaction conditions. Thus, whereas the polymerization of a wide variety of unsaturated monomers is thermodynamically feasible, very specific reaction conditions are often required to achieve kinetic feasibility in order to accomplish a particular polymerization.

Although radical, cationic, and anionic initiators are used in chain polymerizations, they cannot be used indiscriminately since all three types of initiation do not work for all monomers. Monomers show varying degrees of selectivity with regard to the type of reactive center which will cause their polymerization. Most monomers will undergo polymerization with a radical initiator although at varying rates. However, monomers show high selectivity toward ionic initiators. Some monomers may not polymerize with cationic initiators while others may not polymerize with anionic initiators. The variety of behaviors can be seen in Table 3-1. The types of initiation which bring about the polymerization of various monomers to high molecular weight polymer are indicated. Thus, although the polymerization of all the monomers in Table 3-1 is thermodynamically feasible, kinetic feasibility is achieved in many cases only with a specific type of initiation.

The carbon-carbon double bond in alkenes and the carbon-oxygen double bond in aldehydes and ketones are the two main types of linkages which undergo chain polymerization. The polymerization of the carbon-carbon double bond is by far the most important of the two types of monomers. The carbonyl group is not prone to polymerization by radical initiators because of its polarized nature

Table 3-1 Types of Chain Polymerization Undergone by Various Unsaturated Monomers

Monomers	Type of initiation		
	Radical	Cationic	Anionic
Ethylene	+	+	+
1-Alkyl olefins (α-olefins)	−	−	−
1,1-Dialkyl olefins	−	+	−
1,3-Dienes	+	+	+
Styrene, α-methyl styrene	+	+	+
Halogenated olefins	+	−	−
Vinyl esters ($CH_2{=}CHOCOR$)	+	−	−
Acrylates, methacrylates	+	−	+
Acrylonitrile, methacrylonitrile	+	−	+
Acrylamide, methacrylamide	+	−	+
Vinyl ethers	−	+	−
N-Vinyl carbazole	+	+	−
N-Vinyl pyrrolidone	+	+	−
Aldehydes, ketones	−	+	+

$$\begin{array}{c} O \\ \| \\ -C- \end{array} \longleftrightarrow \begin{array}{c} O{:}^{-} \\ | \\ -\underset{+}{C}- \end{array} \tag{3-3}$$

Aldehydes and ketones are polymerized by both anionic and cationic initiators (Chap. 5).

3-1b-2 Effects of Substituents. Unlike the carbonyl linkage, the alkene double bond undergoes polymerization by both radical and ionic initiators. The difference arises because the π-bond of an alkene can respond appropriately to the initiator species by either homolytic or heterolytic bond breakage

$$^{+}\overset{|}{\underset{|}{C}}-\overset{|}{\underset{|}{C}}{:}^{-} \longleftrightarrow \overset{|}{\underset{|}{C}}=\overset{|}{\underset{|}{C}} \longleftrightarrow \cdot\overset{|}{\underset{|}{C}}-\overset{|}{\underset{|}{C}}\cdot \tag{3-4}$$

A wide range of carbon-carbon double bonds undergo chain polymerization. Table 3-1 shows monomers with alkyl, alkenyl, aryl, halogen, alkoxy, ester, amide, nitrile, and heterocyclic substituents on the alkene double bond.

Whether an alkene polymerizes by radical, anionic, or cationic initiators depends on the inductive and resonance characteristics of the substituent(s) present. The effect of the substituent manifests itself by its alteration of the electron-cloud density on the double bond and its ability to stabilize the possible radical, anion, or cation formed. Electron-pushing substituents such as alkoxy, alkyl, alkenyl, and phenyl increase the electron-density on the carbon-carbon double bond

$$\overset{\delta-}{CH_2}{=}CH{\leftarrow}\overset{\delta+}{Y}$$

and facilitate its bonding to a cationic species. Further, these substituents stabilize the cationic propagating species by resonance, e.g., in the polymerization of vinyl ethers

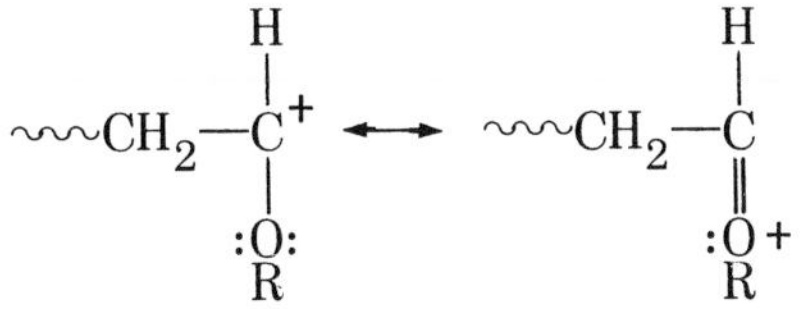

$$\sim\!CH_2{-}\overset{H}{\underset{:\ddot{O}R}{C^+}} \longleftrightarrow \sim\!CH_2{-}\overset{H}{\underset{:O^+R}{C}}\ \text{(C=O)} \qquad (3\text{-}5a)$$

The alkoxy substituent allows a delocalization of the positive charge. If the substituent were not present (e.g., in ethylene), the positive charge would be localized on the single α-carbon atom. The presence of the alkoxy group leads to stabilization of the carbonium ion by delocalization of the positive charge over two atoms—the carbon and the oxygen. Similar delocalization effects occur with phenyl, vinyl, and alkyl substituents, e.g., for styrene polymerization

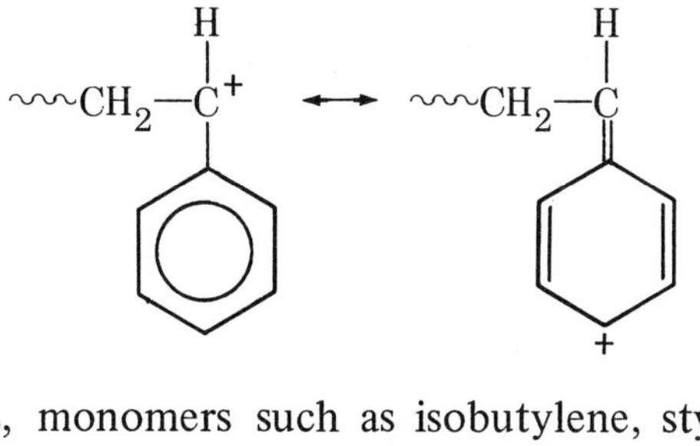

$$\sim\!CH_2{-}\overset{H}{C^+}{-}C_6H_5 \longleftrightarrow \sim\!CH_2{-}\overset{H}{C}{=}C_6H_5^{+}\ \text{(quinoid, + at para position)} \qquad (3\text{-}5b)$$

Thus, monomers such as isobutylene, styrene, methyl vinyl ether, and isoprene undergo polymerization by cationic initiators. The effect of alkyl groups in facilitating cationic polymerization is weak and it is only the 1,1-disubstituted alkenes which undergo cationic polymerization.

Electron-withdrawing substituents such as cyano and carbonyl (aldehyde, ketone, acid, or ester) facilitate the attack of an anionic species by decreasing the electron-density on the double bond

$$\overset{\delta+}{CH_2{=}}CH\overset{\delta-}{\longrightarrow Y}$$

They stabilize the propagating anionic species by resonance, e.g., for acrylonitrile polymerization

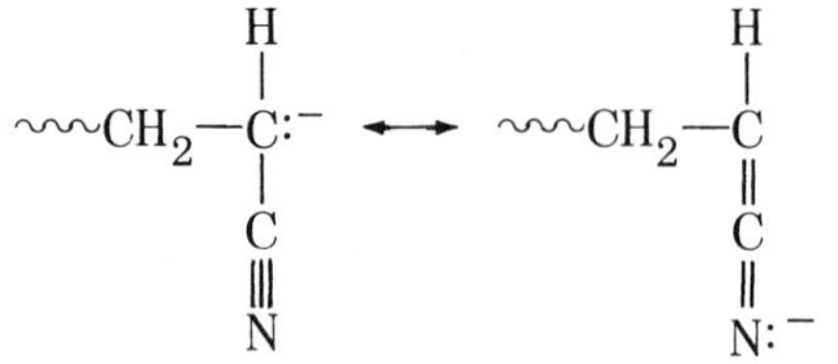

$$\sim\!\sim CH_2-\underset{\underset{\underset{N}{|||}}{C}}{\overset{H}{\overset{|}{\underset{|}{C}}}}:^- \longleftrightarrow \sim\!\sim CH_2-\underset{\underset{\underset{N:^-}{\|}}{C}}{\overset{H}{\overset{|}{\underset{\|}{C}}}} \tag{3-6}$$

Stabilization of the propagating carbanion occurs by delocalization of the negative charge over the α-carbon and the nitrogen of the nitrile group. Alkenyl and phenyl substituents, although electron-pushing inductively, can resonance stabilize the anionic propagating species in the same manner as a cyano group. Monomers such as styrene and 1,3-butadiene can, therefore, undergo anionic as well as cationic polymerization. Halogens withdraw electrons inductively and push electrons by resonance, but both effects are relatively weak and neither anionic nor cationic polymerization is appreciably facilitated for halogenated monomers such as vinyl chloride.

Contrary to the high selectivity shown in cationic and anionic polymerization, radical initiators bring about the polymerization of almost any carbon-carbon double bond. Radical species are neutral and do not have stringent requirements for attacking the π-bond or for the stabilization of the propagating radical species. Resonance stabilization of the propagating radical occurs with almost all substituents, for example

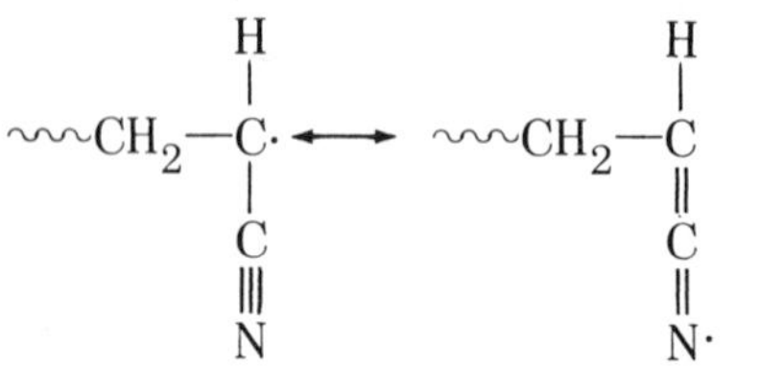

$$\sim\!\sim CH_2-\underset{\underset{\underset{N}{|||}}{C}}{\overset{H}{\overset{|}{\underset{|}{C}}}}\cdot \longleftrightarrow \sim\!\sim CH_2-\underset{\underset{\underset{N\cdot}{\|}}{C}}{\overset{H}{\overset{|}{\underset{\|}{C}}}} \tag{3-7a}$$

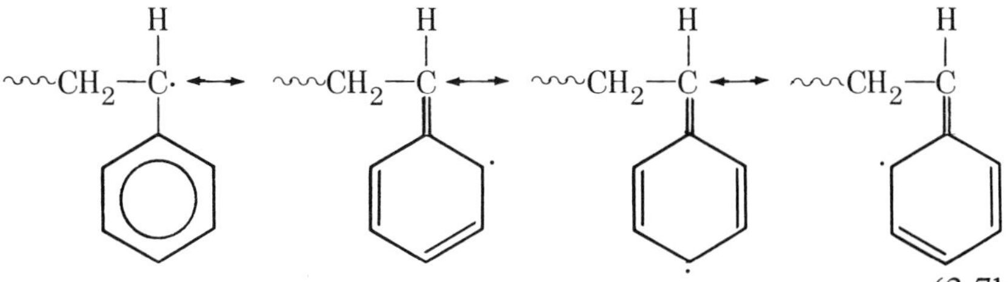

$$\sim\!\sim CH_2-\overset{H}{\underset{|}{\overset{|}{C}}}\cdot \longleftrightarrow \sim\!\sim CH_2-\overset{H}{\underset{\|}{\overset{|}{C}}} \longleftrightarrow \sim\!\sim CH_2-\overset{H}{\underset{\|}{\overset{|}{C}}} \longleftrightarrow \sim\!\sim CH_2-\overset{H}{\underset{\|}{\overset{|}{C}}} \qquad (3\text{-}7b)$$

$$\sim\!\sim CH_2-\overset{H}{\underset{:\ddot{Cl}:}{\overset{|}{\underset{|}{C}}}}\cdot \longleftrightarrow \sim\!\sim CH_2-\overset{H}{\underset{:\ddot{Cl}\cdot}{\overset{|}{\underset{\|}{C}}}} \qquad (3\text{-}7c)$$

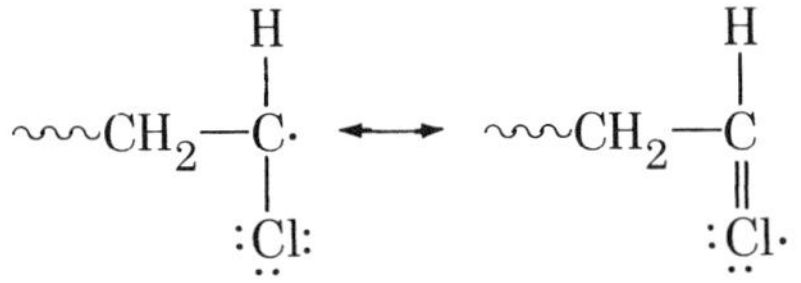

Thus, almost all substituents are able to stabilize the propagating radical by delocalization of the radical over two or more atoms. The remainder of this chapter will be concerned with the detailed characteristics of radical chain polymerization. Ionic chain polymerizations will be considered in Chap. 5.

3-2 STRUCTURAL ARRANGEMENT OF MONOMER UNITS

3-2a Possible Modes of Propagation

There are two possible points of attachment on monosubstituted ($X = H$) or 1,1-disubstituted monomers for a propagating radical—either on carbon 1

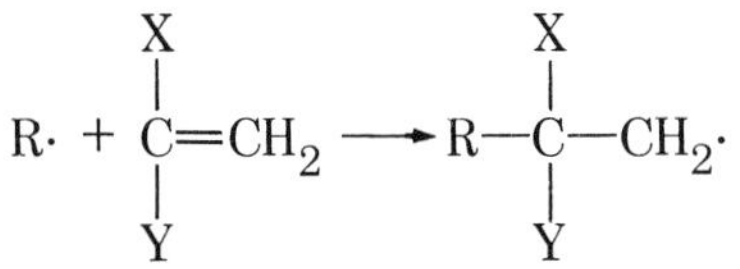

$$R\cdot + \overset{X}{\underset{Y}{\overset{|}{\underset{|}{C}}}}=CH_2 \longrightarrow \underset{\text{I}}{R-\overset{X}{\underset{Y}{\overset{|}{\underset{|}{C}}}}-CH_2\cdot} \qquad (3\text{-}8)$$

or carbon 2

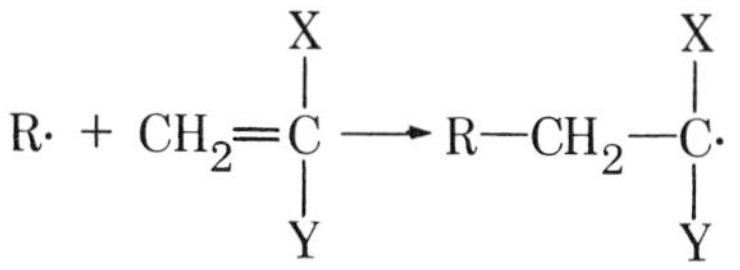

$$R\cdot + CH_2=\overset{X}{\underset{Y}{\overset{|}{\underset{|}{C}}}} \longrightarrow \underset{\text{II}}{R-CH_2-\overset{X}{\underset{Y}{\overset{|}{\underset{|}{C}}}}\cdot} \qquad (3\text{-}9)$$

If each successive addition of monomer molecules to the propagating radical occurs in the same manner as Eq. 3-9, the final polymer product will have an arrangement of monomer units in which the substituents are on alternate carbon atoms

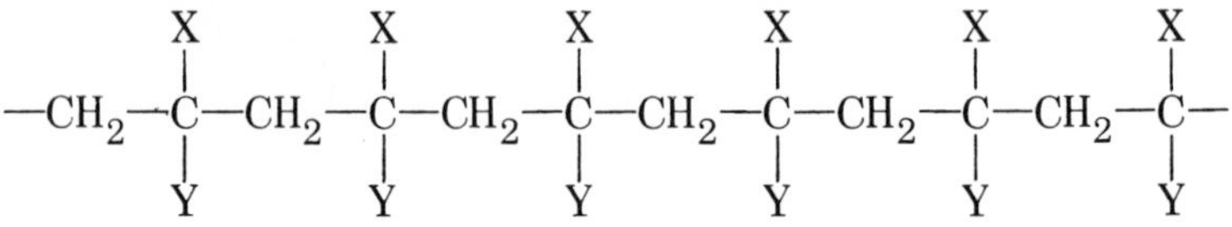

$$-CH_2-\underset{Y}{\overset{X}{\underset{|}{\overset{|}{C}}}}-CH_2-\underset{Y}{\overset{X}{\underset{|}{\overset{|}{C}}}}-CH_2-\underset{Y}{\overset{X}{\underset{|}{\overset{|}{C}}}}-CH_2-\underset{Y}{\overset{X}{\underset{|}{\overset{|}{C}}}}-CH_2-\underset{Y}{\overset{X}{\underset{|}{\overset{|}{C}}}}-CH_2-\underset{Y}{\overset{X}{\underset{|}{\overset{|}{C}}}}-$$

III

This type of arrangement is usually referred to as a *head-to-tail* or *1,3-placement* of monomer units. An inversion of this mode of addition by the polymer chain propagating alternately via Eqs. 3-9 and 3-8 would lead to a polymer structure with a *1,2-placement* of substituents at one or more places in the final polymer chain

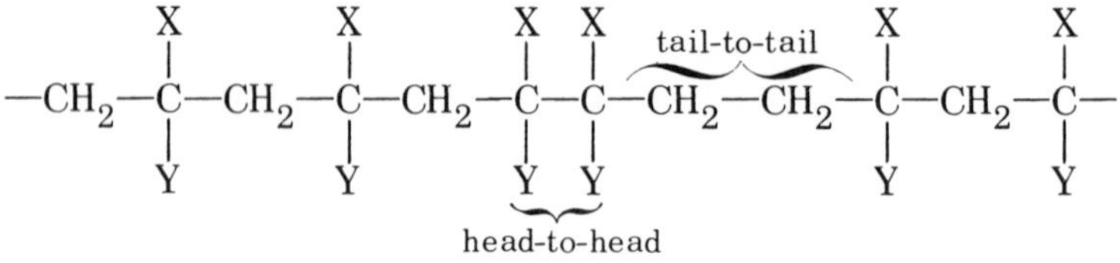

$$-CH_2-\underset{Y}{\overset{X}{\underset{|}{\overset{|}{C}}}}-CH_2-\underset{Y}{\overset{X}{\underset{|}{\overset{|}{C}}}}-CH_2-\underbrace{\underset{Y}{\overset{X}{\underset{|}{\overset{|}{C}}}}-\underset{Y}{\overset{X}{\underset{|}{\overset{|}{C}}}}}_{\text{head-to-head}}-\overbrace{CH_2-CH_2}^{\text{tail-to-tail}}-\underset{Y}{\overset{X}{\underset{|}{\overset{|}{C}}}}-CH_2-\underset{Y}{\overset{X}{\underset{|}{\overset{|}{C}}}}-$$

IV

The 1,2-placement is variously termed *head-to-head placement* or *tail-to-tail placement* or *head-to-head, tail-to-tail placement*.

The head-to-tail placement would be expected to be overwhelmingly predominant since successive propagations by Eq. 3-9 are favored on both steric and resonance grounds. The propagating radical (radical II) formed by attachment of a radical at carbon 2 is the more stable one. Radical II can be stabilized by the resonance effects of the X and Y substituents. The substituents cannot stabilize radical I since they are not attached to the carbon bearing the unpaired electron. Further, the approach (and subsequent attachment) of a propagating radical at the unsubstituted carbon (carbon 2) of a monomer molecule is much less sterically hindered compared to the approach at the substituted carbon (carbon 1).

3-2b Experimental Evidence

These theoretical predictions have been experimentally verified for a number of polymers. Marvel and coworkers [1] studied intramolecular cyclization reactions in certain polymers. These included the formation of cyclopropane rings in poly(vinyl chloride) by dechlorination with zinc

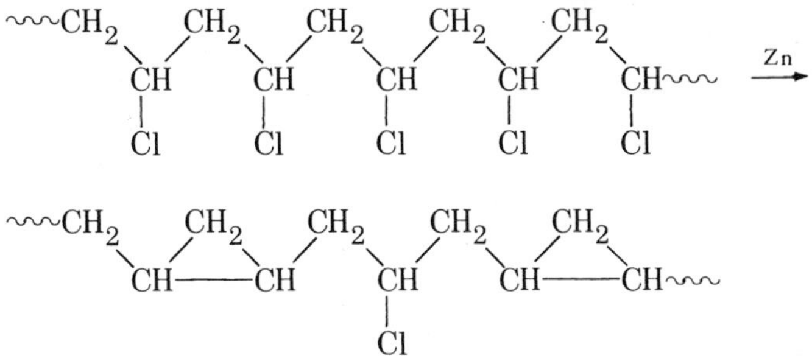

$$\sim\!CH_2-\underset{\underset{Cl}{|}}{CH}-CH_2-\underset{\underset{Cl}{|}}{CH}-CH_2-\underset{\underset{Cl}{|}}{CH}-CH_2-\underset{\underset{Cl}{|}}{CH}-CH_2-\underset{\underset{Cl}{|}}{CH}\sim \xrightarrow{Zn}$$

$$\sim\!CH_2-\overbrace{CH-CH_2-CH}^{\text{ring}}-CH_2-\underset{\underset{Cl}{|}}{CH}-CH_2-\overbrace{CH-CH_2-CH}^{\text{ring}}\sim \qquad (3\text{-}10)$$

(in each ring the two CH groups are also bonded directly to each other, forming a cyclopropane ring with the CH_2)

and the cyclization of poly(methyl vinyl ketone) by intramolecular aldol condensation.

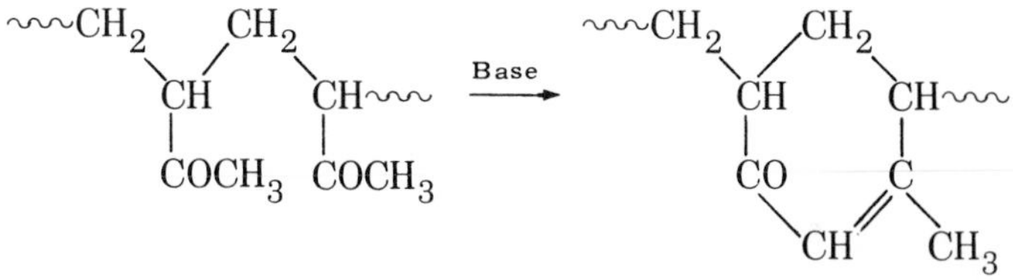

$$\sim\!CH_2-\underset{\underset{COCH_3}{|}}{CH}-CH_2-\underset{\underset{COCH_3}{|}}{CH}\sim \xrightarrow{\text{Base}} \sim\!CH_2-\underset{\underset{CO-CH=}{|}}{CH}-CH_2-\underset{\underset{C-CH_3}{|}}{CH}\sim \qquad (3\text{-}11)$$

(product: six-membered ring CH–CO–CH=C(CH$_3$)–CH–CH$_2$)

The extent of these cyclization reactions depends on the extent of 1,3-placement. The presence of 1,2-placement decreases the extent of cyclization which can occur. However, one would not achieve 100 percent cyclization even for polymers which contain all monomer units in the 1,3-placement. Some functional groups will become isolated (for example, as shown in Eq. 3-10) on a statistical basis due to the reactions of neighboring groups on its two sides. The isolated functional groups are unreactive and decrease the extent of cyclization. The experimentally observed extents of cyclization in the two reactions above were found to be within a few percent of the statistically calculated conversion.

The presence of 1–2 percent head-to-head placement in poly(vinyl acetate) has been determined [2] by hydrolysis of the polymer to poly(vinyl alcohol) and then periodate oxidation of the 1,2-glycol units

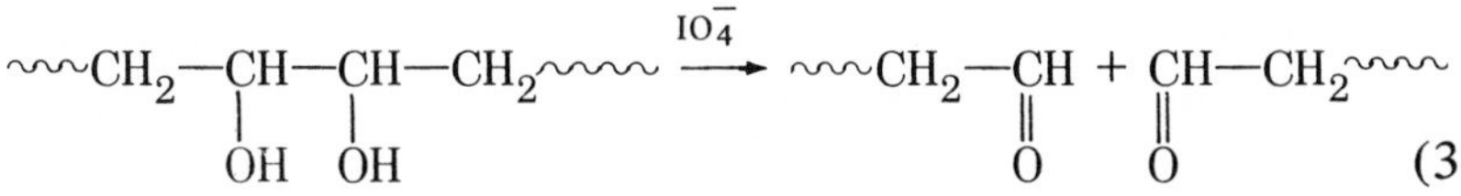

$$\sim\!CH_2-\underset{\underset{OH}{|}}{CH}-\underset{\underset{OH}{|}}{CH}-CH_2\sim \xrightarrow{IO_4^-} \sim\!CH_2-\underset{\underset{O}{\|}}{CH} + \underset{\underset{O}{\|}}{CH}-CH_2\sim \qquad (3\text{-}12)$$

High-resolution NMR studies have shown the presence of substantial amounts of head-to-head placement in some polymers [3]. Thus, poly(vinylidene fluoride) and poly(vinyl fluoride) contain approximately 10 percent and 30 percent head-to-head placement.

In general, head-to-tail addition is considered to be the predominant mode of propagation in all polymerizations. However, when the substituents on the monomer are small (and do not offer appreciable steric hindrance to the approaching radical) or do not have a large resonance stabilizing effect, as in the case of fluorine atoms, sizable amounts of head-to-head propagation may occur. The effect of increasing polymerization temperature is to increase the amount of head-to-head placement [2, 3]. Increased temperature leads to a less selective (more random) propagation but the effect is not large. Thus, the head-to-head content in poly(vinyl acetate) only increases from 1.30 to 1.98 percent when the polymerization temperature is increased from 30 to 90°C.

3-3 OVERALL KINETICS OF CHAIN POLYMERIZATION

3-3a Sequence of Events

Radical chain polymerization is a chain reaction consisting of a sequence of three steps—*initiation, propagation,* and *termination.* The initiation step is considered to involve two reactions. The first is the production of free radicals by any one of a number of reactions. The usual case is the homolytic dissociation of an initiator or catalyst species I to yield a pair of radicals R·

$$\mathrm{I} \xrightarrow{k_d} 2\mathrm{R}\cdot \tag{3-13}$$

where k_d is the rate constant for the catalyst dissociation. The second part of the initiation involves the addition of this radical to the first monomer molecule to produce the chain initiating species $M_1\cdot$

$$\mathrm{R}\cdot + \mathrm{M} \xrightarrow{k_i} \mathrm{M}_1\cdot \tag{3-14a}$$

where M represents a monomer molecule and k_i is the rate constant for the initiation step (Eq. 3-14a). For the polymerization of $CH_2{=}CHY$, Eq. 3-14a takes the form

$$\text{R}\cdot + \text{CH}_2{=}\text{CHY} \longrightarrow \text{R}{-}\text{CH}_2{-}\underset{\text{Y}}{\overset{\text{H}}{\text{C}}}\cdot \tag{3-14b}$$

(The radical R· is often referred to as an *initiator radical* or a *primary radical*.)

Propagation consists of the growth of $M_1\cdot$ by the successive additions of large numbers (hundreds, and perhaps, thousands) of monomer molecules according to Eq. 3-2. Each addition creates a new radical which has the same identity as the one previously, except that it is larger by one monomer unit. The successive additions may be represented by

$$M_1\cdot + M \xrightarrow{k_p} M_2\cdot$$

$$M_2\cdot + M \xrightarrow{k_p} M_3\cdot$$

$$M_3\cdot + M \xrightarrow{k_p} M_4\cdot$$

or in general terms

$$M_n\cdot + M \xrightarrow{k_p} M_{n+1}\cdot \tag{3-15}$$

where k_p is the rate constant for propagation. Propagation with growth of the chain to high polymer proportions takes place very rapidly. The value of k_p for most monomers is in the range 10^2–10^4 liter/mole-sec. This is a large rate constant—much larger than those usually encountered in chemical reactions.

At some point, the propagating polymer chain stops growing and terminates. Termination with the annihilation of the radical centers occurs by bimolecular reaction between radicals. Two radicals react with each other by *combination* (*coupling*)

$$\sim\text{CH}_2{-}\underset{\text{Y}}{\overset{\text{H}}{\text{C}}}\cdot + \cdot\underset{\text{Y}}{\overset{\text{H}}{\text{C}}}{-}\text{CH}_2\sim \xrightarrow{k_{tc}} \sim\text{CH}_2{-}\underset{\text{Y}}{\overset{\text{H}}{\text{C}}}{-}\underset{\text{Y}}{\overset{\text{H}}{\text{C}}}{-}\text{CH}_2\sim \tag{3-16a}$$

or, more rarely, by *disproportionation* in which a hydrogen radical that is *beta* to one radical center is transferred to another radical center. This results in the formation of two polymer molecules—one saturated and one unsaturated.

$$\sim\sim CH_2-\underset{Y}{\overset{H}{C}}\cdot + \cdot\underset{Y}{\overset{H}{C}}-\underset{H}{\overset{H}{C}}\sim\sim \xrightarrow{k_{td}} \sim\sim CH_2-\underset{Y}{\overset{H}{C}}H + \underset{Y}{\overset{H}{C}}=\overset{H}{C}\sim\sim \quad (3\text{-}16b)$$

Termination can also occur by a combination of coupling and disproportionation. The two different modes of termination can be represented in general terms by

$$M_n\cdot + M_m\cdot \xrightarrow{k_{tc}} M_{n+m} \quad (3\text{-}17a)$$

$$M_n\cdot + M_m\cdot \xrightarrow{k_{td}} M_n + M_m \quad (3\text{-}17b)$$

where k_{tc} and k_{td} are the rate constants for termination by coupling and disproportionation, respectively. One can also express the termination step by

$$M_n\cdot + M_m\cdot \xrightarrow{k_t} \text{dead polymer} \quad (3\text{-}17c)$$

where the particular mode of termination is not specified and

$$k_t = k_{tc} + k_{td} \quad (3\text{-}18)$$

The term *dead polymer* signifies the cessation of growth for the propagating radical. The propagation reaction would proceed indefinitely until all the monomer in a reaction system were exhausted if it were not for the strong tendency toward termination. Typical termination rate constants are in the range of 10^6–10^8 liter/mole-sec or orders of magnitude greater than the propagation rate constants. The much greater value of k_t (whether k_{tc} or k_{td}) compared to k_p does not prevent propagation because the radical species are present in very low concentrations and because the polymerization rate is dependent on only the one-half power of k_t.

3-3b Rate Expression

Equations 3-13 through 3-16 constitute the detailed mechanism of a free radical initiated chain polymerization. The chain nature of the process resides in the propagation step (Eq. 3-15) in which large numbers of monomer molecules are converted to polymer for each initial radical species produced in the first step (Eq. 3-13). In order to obtain a kinetic expression for the overall rate of polymerization, it is necessary to assume that k_p and k_t are independent of the size of the radical. This is exactly the same type of assumption which was employed in deriving the kinetics of step polymerization. There is ample experimental evidence which indicates that although radical reactivity depends on molecular size, the effect of size vanishes after the pentamer or hexamer.

Monomer disappears by the initiation reaction (Eq. 3-14) as well as by the propagation reactions (Eq. 3-15). The *rate of monomer disappearance,* which is synonymous with the *rate of polymerization,* is given by

$$\frac{-d[\mathrm{M}]}{dt} = R_i + R_p \tag{3-19}$$

where R_i and R_p are the rates of initiation and propagation, respectively. However, the number of monomer molecules reacting in the initiation step is far less than the number in the propagation step for a process producing high polymer. To a very close approximation, the former can be neglected and the polymerization rate is given simply by the rate of propagation

$$\frac{-d[\mathrm{M}]}{dt} = R_p \tag{3-20}$$

The rate of propagation, and therefore, the rate of polymerization, is the sum of many individual propagation steps. Since the rate constants for all the propagation steps are the same, one can express the polymerization rate by

$$R_p = k_p[\mathrm{M}\cdot][\mathrm{M}] \tag{3-21}$$

where [M] is the monomer concentration and [M·] is the total concentration of all chain radicals, i.e., all radicals of size $\mathrm{M}_1\cdot$ and larger.

Equation 3-21 for the polymerization rate is not directly usable because it contains a term for the concentration of radicals. Radical concentrations are difficult to measure since they are very low (approximately 10^{-8} molar) and it is therefore desirable to eliminate them from Eq. 3-21. In order to do this, the *steady-state* assumption is made that the concentration of radicals increases initially, but almost instantaneously reaches a constant, steady-state value. The rate of change of the concentration of radicals quickly becomes and remains zero during the course of the polymerization. This is equivalent to stating that the rates of initiation R_i and termination R_t of radicals are equal or

$$R_i = 2k_t[\text{M}\cdot]^2 \tag{3-22}$$

The theoretical validity of the steady-state assumption has been discussed [4]. Its experimental validity has been shown in many polymerizations. Typical polymerizations achieve a steady-state after an induction period which may be at most a few seconds.

The right side of Eq. 3-22 represents the rate of termination. There is no specification as to whether termination is by coupling or disproportionation since both follow the same kinetic expression. The use of the factor of 2 in the termination rate equation follows the generally accepted convention for reactions destroying radicals in pairs. It is also generally employed for reactions creating radicals in pairs as in Eq. 3-13. (In using the polymer literature one should be aware that the factor of 2 is not universally employed.) Rearrangement of Eq. 3-22 to

$$[\text{M}\cdot] = \left(\frac{R_i}{2k_t}\right)^{1/2} \tag{3-23}$$

and substitution into Eq. 3-21 yields

$$R_p = k_p[\text{M}]\left(\frac{R_i}{2k_t}\right)^{1/2} \tag{3-24}$$

for the rate of polymerization. It is seen that Eq. 3-24 has the significant conclusion of the dependence of the polymerization rate on the square root of the initiation rate. Doubling the rate of initiation does not double the polymerization rate; the polymerization rate is increased only by the factor $\sqrt{2}$. This behavior is a consequence of the bimolecular termination reaction between radicals.

The polymerization rate may be experimentally followed by measuring the changes in any of several properties of the system such as density, refractive index, viscosity, or light absorption. Density measurements are among the most accurate and sensitive of the techniques. The density increases by 20–25 percent on polymerization for many monomers. In actual practice the volume of the polymerizing system is measured by carrying out the reaction in a *dilatometer.* This is a specially constructed vessel with a capillary tube which allows a highly accurate measurement of small volume changes. It is not uncommon to be able to detect a few hundredths of a percent polymerization by the dilatometer technique.

3-4 INITIATION

The derivation of Eq. 3-24 is general in that the reaction for the production of radicals (Eq. 3-13) is not specified. The initiation rate is simply shown as R_i. A variety of initiator (catalyst) systems can be used to bring about the polymerization. (The term catalyst is not used in the classical sense of the word but is used to indicate that very large numbers of monomer molecules are converted to polymer for each catalyst molecule which is consumed.) Radicals can be produced by a variety of thermal, photochemical, and redox methods [5]. In order to function as a useful source of radicals, an initiator system should be readily available, stable under ambient or refrigerated conditions, and possess a practical rate of radical generation at temperatures which are not excessive (approximately $<$ 150°C).

3-4a Thermal Decomposition of Initiators

3-4a-1 Types of Initiators. The *thermal, homolytic dissociation* of initiators is the most widely used mode of generating radicals to initiate polymerization—for both commercial polymerizations and theoretical studies. Polymerizations initiated in this manner are often referred to as *thermal catalyzed* polymerizations. The number of different types of compounds which can be used as initiators is rather limited. One is usually limited to compounds with bond dissociation energies in the range 25–40 kcal/mole. Compounds with higher or lower dissociation energies will dissociate too slowly or too rapidly. Only a few classes of compounds–including those with O—O, S—S, N—O bonds–possess the desired range of dissociation energies. However, it is only the peroxides which find extensive use as radical sources. The other classes of compounds are usually either not readily available or not stable enough. Several different types of peroxides are widely used. These are acyl peroxides such as acetyl and benzoyl peroxides

$$CH_3-\overset{\overset{\displaystyle O}{\|}}{C}-O-O-\overset{\overset{\displaystyle O}{\|}}{C}-CH_3 \longrightarrow 2\ CH_3-\overset{\overset{\displaystyle O}{\|}}{C}-O\cdot \tag{3-25a}$$

$$\phi-\overset{\overset{\displaystyle O}{\|}}{C}-O-O-\overset{\overset{\displaystyle O}{\|}}{C}-\phi \longrightarrow 2\ \phi-\overset{\overset{\displaystyle O}{\|}}{C}-O\cdot \tag{3-25b}$$

alkyl peroxides such as cumyl and *t*-butyl peroxides

$$\phi-\underset{\underset{\displaystyle CH_3}{|}}{\overset{\overset{\displaystyle CH_3}{|}}{C}}-O-O-\underset{\underset{\displaystyle CH_3}{|}}{\overset{\overset{\displaystyle CH_3}{|}}{C}}-\phi \longrightarrow 2\ \phi-\underset{\underset{\displaystyle CH_3}{|}}{\overset{\overset{\displaystyle CH_3}{|}}{C}}-O\cdot \tag{3-25c}$$

$$CH_3-\underset{\underset{\displaystyle CH_3}{|}}{\overset{\overset{\displaystyle CH_3}{|}}{C}}-O-O-\underset{\underset{\displaystyle CH_3}{|}}{\overset{\overset{\displaystyle CH_3}{|}}{C}}-CH_3 \longrightarrow 2\ CH_3-\underset{\underset{\displaystyle CH_3}{|}}{\overset{\overset{\displaystyle CH_3}{|}}{C}}-O\cdot \tag{3-25d}$$

hydroperoxides such as *t*-butyl and cumyl hydroperoxide

$$CH_3-\underset{\underset{\displaystyle CH_3}{|}}{\overset{\overset{\displaystyle CH_3}{|}}{C}}-O-OH \longrightarrow CH_3-\underset{\underset{\displaystyle CH_3}{|}}{\overset{\overset{\displaystyle CH_3}{|}}{C}}-O\cdot + \cdot OH \tag{3-25e}$$

$$\phi-\underset{\underset{\displaystyle CH_3}{|}}{\overset{\overset{\displaystyle CH_3}{|}}{C}}-O-OH \longrightarrow \phi-\underset{\underset{\displaystyle CH_3}{|}}{\overset{\overset{\displaystyle CH_3}{|}}{C}}-O\cdot + \cdot OH \tag{3-25f}$$

and peresters such as *t*-butyl perbenzoate

$$\phi-\overset{\overset{\displaystyle O}{\|}}{C}-O-O-\underset{\underset{\displaystyle CH_3}{|}}{\overset{\overset{\displaystyle CH_3}{|}}{C}}-CH_3 \longrightarrow \phi-\overset{\overset{\displaystyle O}{\|}}{C}-O\cdot + \cdot O-\underset{\underset{\displaystyle CH_3}{|}}{\overset{\overset{\displaystyle CH_3}{|}}{C}}-CH_3 \tag{3-25g}$$

Aside from the peroxides, the only other class of compounds used extensively as catalysts are the azo compounds. 2,2′-Azobisisobutyronitrile (AIBN)

$$CH_3-\underset{\underset{\displaystyle CN}{|}}{\overset{\overset{\displaystyle CH_3}{|}}{C}}-N{=}N-\underset{\underset{\displaystyle CN}{|}}{\overset{\overset{\displaystyle CH_3}{|}}{C}}-CH_3 \longrightarrow 2\ CH_3-\underset{\underset{\displaystyle CN}{|}}{\overset{\overset{\displaystyle CH_3}{|}}{C}}\cdot + N_2 \tag{3-25h}$$

is by far the most important member of this class of initiators. The facile dissociation of azo compounds is not caused by the presence of a weak bond as is the case with the peroxides. The C—N bond dissociation energy is high (approximately 70 kcal/mole) but the driving force for homolysis is the formation of the highly stable nitrogen molecule.

The various catalysts are used at different temperatures depending on their rates of decomposition. Thus, azobisisobutyronitrile (AIBN) is commonly used at 50–70°C, acetyl peroxide at 70–90°C, benzoyl peroxide at 80–95°C, and dicumyl or di-*t*-butyl peroxide at 120–140°C. (The value of the decomposition rate constant k_d is usually in the range 10^{-4}–10^{-6} sec^{-1} for the temperature range in which the catalyst is employed—see Table 3-10.) The great utility of the peroxides as a class of initiators arises from the availability in stable form of many different compounds with a wide variety of use temperatures. The differences in the rates of decomposition of the various initiators are related to differences in the structures of the initiators and of the radicals produced. The effects of structure on initiator reactivity have been discussed elsewhere [5].

3-4a-2 Kinetics of Initiation and Polymerization. The rate of thermal homolysis of an initiator R_d (Eqs. 3-13 and 3-25) is given by

$$R_d = 2fk_d[\mathrm{I}] \tag{3-26}$$

where [I] is the concentration of the initiator and f is the *initiator efficiency*. The initiator efficiency is defined as the fraction of the radicals produced in the homolysis reaction which initiate polymer chains. The value of f is usually less than unity due to wastage reactions. The factor of 2 in Eq. 3-26 follows the convention previously discussed.

The initiation reaction in polymerization is composed of two steps (Eqs. 3-13 and 3-14) as discussed previously. In most polymerizations, the second step (the addition of the primary radical to monomer) is much faster than the first step. The homolysis of the initiator is the rate determining step in the initiation sequence and the rate of initiation is then given by

$$R_i = 2fk_d[\mathrm{I}] \tag{3-27}$$

Substitution of Eq. 3-27 into Eq. 3-24 yields

$$R_p = k_p[\mathrm{M}]\left(\frac{fk_d[\mathrm{I}]}{k_t}\right)^{1/2} \tag{3-28}$$

3-4a-3 Dependence of Polymerization Rate on Initiator. Equation 3-28 describes the most common case of radical chain polymerization. It shows the polymerization rate to be dependent on the square root of the initiator concentration. This dependence has been abundantly confirmed for many different monomer-initiator combinations over wide ranges of [M] and [I]. Figure 3-1 shows typical data illustrating the square root dependence [6–8]. Deviations from this behavior are found under certain conditions. The order of dependence of R_p on [I] may be observed to be less than one-half at very high initiator concentrations. However, such an effect is not truly a deviation from Eq. 3-28. It may be caused by a decrease in f with increasing initiator concentration. Alternately, the termination mode may change [9] to one between growing polymer radicals and primary radicals

$$\mathrm{M}_n\cdot + \mathrm{R}\cdot \longrightarrow \mathrm{M}_n\text{—R} \tag{3-29}$$

This mode of termination and the accompanying change in the order of dependence of R_p on [I] may also be found in the Trommsdorff polymerization region (Sec. 3-10). Situations also arise where the

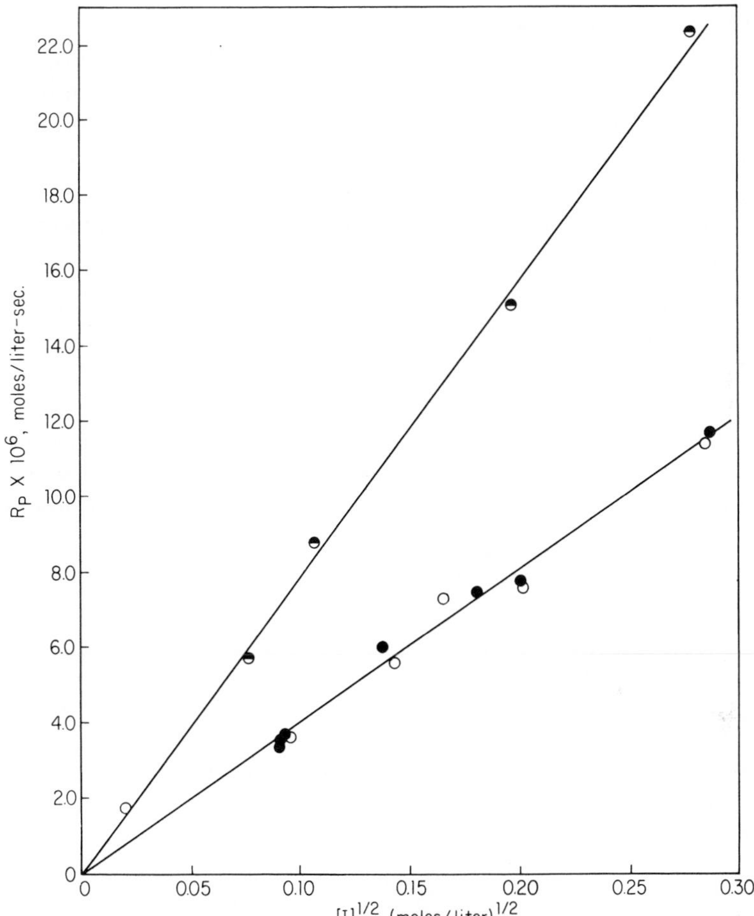

FIG. 3-1 *Square root dependence of the polymerization rate R_p on the initiator concentration [I]. ◓ = Methyl methacrylate, benzoyl peroxide, 50°C. After [6] (by permission of Akademische Verlagsgesellschaft, Geest and Portig K.-G., Leipzig). ○,● = Vinyl benzoate, azobisisobutyronitrile, 60°C. After [7] and [8] (by permission of Hüthig and Wepf Verlag, Basel).*

order of dependence of R_p on [I] will be greater than one-half. This behavior may be observed in the Trommsdorff region if the polymer radicals do not undergo termination or under certain conditions of chain transfer or inhibition (Sec. 3-7).

3-4a-4 Dependence of Polymerization Rate on Monomer. The rate expression Eq. 3-28 requires a first order dependence of the polymerization rate on the monomer concentration. This is indeed found to be the general behavior for many polymerizations. Figure 3-2 shows the first order relationship for the polymerization of methyl methacrylate [10]. However, there are many polymerizations where R_p shows a higher than first order dependence on [M]. Thus, the rate of polymerization depends on the 3/2-power of the monomer concentration in the polymerization of styrene in chlorobenzene solution at 120°C initiated by *t*-butyl peresters [11]. The benzoyl peroxide initiated polymerization of styrene in toluene at 80°C shows an increasing order of dependence of R_p on [M] as [M] decreases [12]. The dependence is 1.18 order at [M] = 1.8 and increases to 1.36 order at [M] = 0.4. These effects may be caused by a dependence of the initiation rate on the monomer concentration. Equation 3-28 was derived on the assumption that R_i is independent of [M]. The initiation rate can be monomer dependent in several ways. The initiator efficiency f may vary directly with the monomer concentration

$$f = f'[\mathrm{M}] \tag{3-30}$$

which would lead (by substitution of Eq. 3-30 into Eqs. 3-27 and 3-28) to first order dependence of R_i on [M] and 3/2 order dependence of R_p on [M]. (This effect has been observed and is discussed in Sec. 3-4f.) The equivalent result arises if the second step of the initiation reaction (Eq. 3-14) were to become the rate determining step instead of the first step (Eq. 3-13).

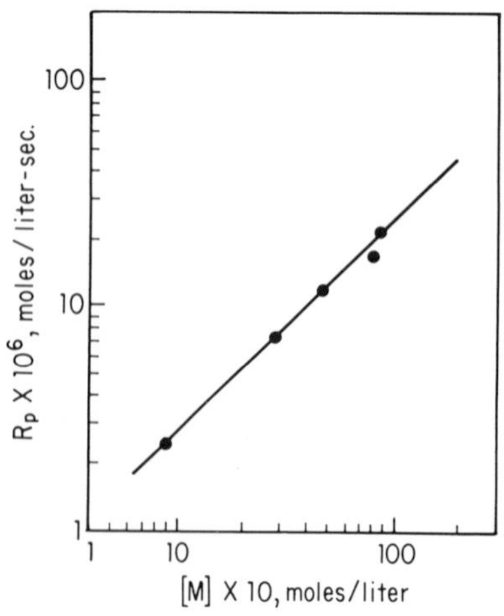

FIG. 3-2 *First order dependence of the polymerization rate R_p of methyl methacrylate on the monomer concentration [M]. The initiator is the t-butyl perbenzoate-diphenylthiourea redox system. After [10] (by permission of Interscience Publishers, John Wiley & Sons, Inc., New York).*

In some systems, it appears that the initiation step differs from the usual two-step sequence of Eqs. 3-13 and 3-14. Thus, in the *t*-butyl hydroperoxide-styrene system, only a minor part of the initiation occurs by the first order homolysis reaction (Eq. 3-25f) which accounts for the complete decomposition of *t*-butyl hydroperoxide in the absence of styrene. Homolysis of the hydroperoxide occurs at a much faster rate in the presence of styrene than in its absence. The increased decomposition rate in the *t*-butyl hydroperoxide-styrene system occurs by a *molecule-induced homolysis* reaction which is first order in both styrene and hydroperoxide [13]. The initiation reaction may be written as

$$\mathrm{M} + \mathrm{I} \longrightarrow \mathrm{M}\cdot + \mathrm{R}\cdot \tag{3-31}$$

and will result in a 3/2 order dependence of R_p on [M]. Exception to the first order dependence of the polymerization rate on the monomer concentration may also be observed due to a change in the termination mode to that (Eq. 3-29) involving primary radicals (Sec. 3-10d).

3-4b Photochemical Initiation

Polymerization can also be initiated by *photochemical* means [14, 15]. Radicals can be produced by the ultraviolet irradiation of a pure monomer or of a monomer containing either a catalyst or a photosensitizer.

3-4b-1 Pure Monomer. The photolysis of some monomers results in the formation of an excited state (M)* by the absorption of light quanta

$$\mathrm{M} + h\nu \longrightarrow (\mathrm{M})^* \tag{3-32}$$

The excited species undergoes homolysis to produce radicals

$$(\mathrm{M})^* \longrightarrow \mathrm{R}\cdot + \mathrm{R}'\cdot \tag{3-33}$$

capable of initiating the polymerization of the monomer. The identity of the radicals R· and R′· are not usually well established. Thus, in the photochemical polymerization of styrene (whose main absorption band is at 250 mμ), bond breakage has been [16] variously considered as occurring by

$$\phi{-}CH{=}CH_2 \longrightarrow \phi\cdot + \cdot CH{=}CH_2 \tag{3-34}$$

or

$$\phi{-}CH{=}CH_2 \longrightarrow \phi{-}CH{=}\dot{C}H + H\cdot \tag{3-35}$$

Initiation by diradicals

$$\phi{-}CH{=}CH_2 \longrightarrow \phi{-}\dot{C}H{-}\dot{C}H_2 \tag{3-36}$$

has also been postulated but is unlikely for reasons to be discussed in Sec. 3-4d.

The rate of photochemical initiation is given by

$$R_i = 2fI_a = 2\Phi I_a \tag{3-37}$$

where I_a is the intensity of absorbed light in moles (called einsteins in photochemistry) of light quanta per liter-second and f is redefined as the number of pairs of radicals produced per light quantum absorbed. The symbol Φ is usually used instead of f in photochemical polymerizations and is called the *quantum yield for radical production*. The absorbed light intensity is given by

$$I_a = \epsilon I_o [\mathrm{M}] \tag{3-38}$$

where I_o is the light intensity incident on the monomer in moles of light quanta per liter-second and ϵ is the molar absorptivity (extinction coefficient) of the monomer for the particular wavelength of radiation absorbed. Substitution of Eq. 3-38 into Eq. 3-37 yields

$$R_i = 2\Phi\epsilon I_o [\mathrm{M}] \tag{3-39}$$

which can be substituted into Eq. 3-24 to give

$$R_p = k_p [\mathrm{M}]^{3/2} \left(\frac{\Phi\epsilon I_o}{k_t}\right)^{1/2} \tag{3-40}$$

for the rate of photo-initiated polymerization.

The light intensities delivered by various light sources are usually known in units such as kcal/sec or erg/sec and it is necessary to convert them into the appropriate units of einsteins (moles) of light quanta per liter-second before use in Eq. 3-40. This is accomplished by a knowledge of the wavelength λ or frequency ν of the light energy employed. The energy in an einstein of light is $Nh\nu$ or Nhc/λ where h is Planck's constant, c is the speed of light, and N is Avogadro's number.

The use of Eq. 3-40 assumes that the incident light intensity does not vary appreciably throughout the thickness of the reaction vessel. This will be true only when the absorption of light is quite low or very thin reaction vessels are employed. For most polymerizations, the light absorption will not be negligible and I_o and I_a will vary with thickness. Under these conditions an expression for I_a can be obtained from Beer's law

$$I = I_o e^{-\epsilon[\mathrm{M}]b} \tag{3-41}$$

where I is the incident light intensity at a distance b into the reaction vessel. The light intensity absorbed by the reaction system is then given by

$$I_a = I_o\left[1 - e^{-\epsilon[\mathrm{M}]b}\right] \tag{3-42}$$

where b is now the thickness of the reaction vessel. The polymerization rate can then be analyzed by combining Eqs. 3-24, 3-37, and 3-42 to yield

$$R_p = k_p[\mathrm{M}]\left(\frac{\Phi I_a}{k_t}\right)^{1/2} \tag{3-43}$$

and

$$R_p = k_p[\mathrm{M}]\left(\frac{\Phi I_o\left[1 - e^{-\epsilon[\mathrm{M}]b}\right]}{k_t}\right)^{1/2} \tag{3-44}$$

The use of Eq. 3-44 is often preferentially avoided by directly measuring I_a in a particular polymerization system. The measurement of light intensity is referred to as *actinometry* [5]. An instrument or actinometer which can be used for this purpose is the thermopile. This consists of a number of thermocouples connected in series with their hot junctions imbedded at a blackened surface which absorbs all incident light and converts it into heat. I_a is measured by placing the thermopile directly behind the reaction vessel and measuring the difference in light intensities when the vessel is empty and when it holds the reaction mixture. One can also use a chemical actinometer—a chemical reaction whose quantum yield is known via primary calibration with the thermopile. Such a reaction is the decomposition of oxalic acid (in the presence of uranyl salts)

$$(CO_2H)_2 \xrightarrow{h\nu} CO_2 + CO + H_2O \tag{3-45}$$

with a quantum yield of 0.5. The reaction is followed by titrating unreacted oxalic acid with permanganate. The absorbed light intensity can be easily calculated from the amount of decomposition products and the time of irradiation. Another useful chemical actinometer is the photochemical hydrolysis of chloroacetic acid

$$ClCH_2CO_2H + H_2O \xrightarrow{h\nu} HOCH_2CO_2H + HCl \tag{3-46}$$

which has a quantum yield of 1.0.

3-4b-2 Photolytic Dissociation of Initiators. The initiators which produce radicals by thermal homolysis can also be employed in photo-initiation. In the usual case, photolytic and thermal homolysis of an initiator produce the same radicals. The photochemical method allows the use of a wider range of compounds as initiators compared to the thermal catalyzed polymerization. This is due to the higher selectivity of photolytic homolysis. For compounds other than the initiators discussed previously, thermal homolysis occurs at too high a temperature and usually results in the production of a wide spectrum of different radicals as various bonds randomly break. Thus, photochemical initiation can be used with carbonyl compounds such as ketones

$$R{-}\overset{\overset{\displaystyle O}{\|}}{C}{-}R' \xrightarrow{h\nu} R{-}\overset{\overset{\displaystyle O}{\|}}{C}\cdot + \cdot R' \tag{3-47}$$

and benzoin

$$\phi-\overset{\overset{\displaystyle O}{\|}}{C}-\overset{\overset{\displaystyle OH}{|}}{C}H\phi \xrightarrow{h\nu} \phi-\overset{\overset{\displaystyle O}{\|}}{C}\cdot + \cdot\overset{\overset{\displaystyle OH}{|}}{C}H\phi \tag{3-48}$$

as well as alkyl halides, organometallics, and other types of compounds.

The rate of initiation in this case will be given by

$$R_i = 2\Phi\epsilon I_o[\mathrm{I}] \tag{3-49}$$

and the rate of polymerization can be expressed as

$$R_p = k_p[\mathrm{M}]\left(\frac{\Phi\epsilon I_o[\mathrm{I}]}{k_t}\right)^{1/2} \tag{3-50}$$

or

$$R_p = k_p[\mathrm{M}]\left(\frac{\left[\Phi I_o\left(1 - e^{-\epsilon[\mathrm{I}]b}\right)\right]}{k_t}\right)^{1/2} \tag{3-51}$$

or the general equation Eq. 3-43, depending on the particular case.

3-4b-3 Photosensitizers. Another means of photochemical initiation involves the use of *photosensitizers* to bring about the homolysis of a monomer or initiator which does not undergo sufficient excitation at the available frequencies of light. The photosensitizer Z undergoes excitation

$$\mathrm{Z} + h\nu \longrightarrow (\mathrm{Z})^* \tag{3-52}$$

and then transfers energy to a compound C

$$(\mathrm{Z})^* + \mathrm{C} \longrightarrow \mathrm{Z} + (\mathrm{C})^* \tag{3-53}$$

Radicals are subsequently produced by decomposition of the excited state of compound C

$$(\mathrm{C})^* \longrightarrow \mathrm{R}\cdot + \mathrm{R}'\cdot \tag{3-54}$$

Thus, whereas (C)* cannot be produced by direct irradiation of C with light of frequency ν, the absorption of energy is accomplished because (Z)* is able to transfer the energy to C at an appropriate frequency which can be absorbed by C. Benzophenone is a commonly employed photosensitizer for radical reactions. Various dyes such as fluorescein and eosin are other useful photosensitizers.

The rates of initiation and polymerization for photosensitized polymerization will be expressed by Eqs. 3-49 through 3-51 with [I] redefined as the concentration of photosensitizer. Additionally, there may be a dependence of R_i on [M] in these polymerizations at low monomer concentrations or low quantum yields. This would lead to appropriately different dependencies of R_p on [M] than those shown by Eqs. 3-50 and 3-51.

3-4b-4 General Observations. Inspection of the rate equations developed above for photochemical polymerizations indicates a square root dependence of the polymerization rate on the light intensity in all instances. This has been confirmed with many different monomers using various photo-initiation systems. The dependence of R_p on [M], on the other hand, varies depending on the particular mode of photo-initiation. The dependence of R_p on the initiator or photosensitizer concentration depends on the type of experimental setup employed, i.e., whether Eq. 3-50 or 3-51 is applicable.

Photochemical polymerizations have been extensively studied although their commercial utility has been negligible. The lack of practical application of photo-initiation arises from the general availability of initiators which undergo facile thermal homolysis over the whole spectrum of reaction temperatures. Photochemical polymerizations are, however, very important from the theoretical viewpoint. Photochemical polymerizations offer the best means of obtaining values of the individual rate constants k_p and k_t for polymerization (Sec. 3-8).

3-4c Initiation by Ionizing Radiations

The increasing availability of radioactive sources has stimulated studies on their use for initiating chain polymerizations. Electrons (β-rays), neutrons, and α-particles (He^{2+}) are particulate radiations while γ- and x-rays are electromagnetic radiations. The interactions of these radiations with matter are more complex than those of light [17]. The chemical effects of the different types of radiation are qualitatively the same although there are quantitative differences. Molecular excitation may occur with the subsequent formation of radicals in the same manner as in photolysis, but ionization of a compound C by ejection of an electron

$$\text{C} + \text{radiation} \longrightarrow \text{C}^+ + e^- \tag{3-55}$$

is more probable because of the higher energies of these radiations. For this reason, such radiations are termed *ionizing radiations*. The cation may then form a radical by dissociation

$$\text{C}^+ \longrightarrow \text{A}\cdot + \text{B}^+ \tag{3-56}$$

The ejected electron may be attracted to the cation B^+ with the formation of another radical

$$\text{B}^+ + e^- \longrightarrow \text{B}\cdot \tag{3-57}$$

Radicals may also be produced by a sequence of reactions initiated by the capture of an ejected electron by C

$$\text{C} + e^- \longrightarrow \text{C}^- \tag{3-58}$$

$$\text{C}^- \longrightarrow \text{B}\cdot + \text{A}^- \tag{3-59}$$

$$\text{A}^- \longrightarrow \text{A}\cdot + e^- \tag{3-60}$$

The radiolysis of olefinic monomers results in the formation of cations, radicals, and free radicals as described above. It is then possible for these species to initiate chain polymerizations. Whether a polymerization is initiated by the radicals, cations, or anions depends on the reaction conditions. Most radiation-induced polymerizations are radical polymerizations. It is usually only at low temperatures that the ionic species are stable enough to initiate polymerization. At ambient temperatures or higher, the ionic species usually are not stable and dissociate to yield radicals. The radiolytic radical polymerizations show the same kinetic characteristics as photolytic polymerizations. Radiolytic initiation can also be carried out using initiators or other compounds which are prone to undergo decomposition upon irradiation.

3-4d Pure Thermal Initiation

Many monomers appear to undergo a spontaneous polymerization when heated in the apparent absence of catalysts. On careful investigation few of these involve the thermal production of radicals from the monomer. In most cases the observed polymerizations are initiated by the thermal homolysis of impurities that are present in the monomer. Most monomers when carefully and exhaustively purified do not undergo a *purely thermal, self-initiated polymerization.* Only styrene and methyl methacrylate have been unequivocally shown to undergo self-initiated polymerization when heated. Presumably, substituted styrenes and methacrylates will act similarly. The rates of the thermal, self-initiated polymerizations are much slower than the corresponding polymerizations initiated by the thermal homolysis of an initiator such as AIBN, but can be appreciable under certain conditions. The thermal polymerization rate for styrene is 0.1 percent per hour at 60°C and 14 percent per hour at 127°C while that for methyl methacrylate is only about 1 percent of the rate for styrene [4]. The rate of self-initiated polymerization must be accounted for in any polymerization study conducted at temperatures such that the self-initiation constitutes an appreciable portion of the total initiation process.

The mode of initiation in the thermal, self-initiated polymerization of styrene has been studied but is not clearly understood. The rate of polymerization has been found to be second order in styrene [18]. This result means that the rate of initiation is also second order in styrene since R_p varies with $[M] R_i^{1/2}$ in accordance with Eq. 3-24. Bimolecular initiation by the formation of biradicals

$$2\,\phi{-}CH{=}CH_2 \longrightarrow \phi{-}\dot{C}HCH_2CH_2\dot{C}H{-}\phi \qquad (3\text{-}61)$$

has been proposed but does not appear feasible. Biradical species would be expected to produce only low molecular products due to cyclization by coupling of the radical ends. Evidence for this comes from the many unsuccessful attempts which have been made to initiate polymerizations by biradicals formed from the thermal or photolytic homolysis of cyclic peroxides, disulfides, or azo compounds [16]. A more feasible bimolecular initiation step is the one

$$2\,\phi{-}CH{=}CH_2 \longrightarrow \phi{-}\dot{C}H{-}CH_3 + CH_2{=}\dot{C}\phi \qquad (3\text{-}62)$$

suggested by Walling [4].

The picture of self-initiation is made ambiguous by conflicting studies which show the initiation rate to be third order in monomer for polymerizations carried out in bromobenzene solution [19]. Termolecular initiation

$$3\,\phi\text{—CH=CH}_2 \longrightarrow \phi\text{—}\dot{\text{C}}\text{H—CH}_3 + \phi\text{—}\overset{\overset{\text{CH}_3}{|}}{\text{C}}\text{=CH—}\dot{\text{C}}\text{H}\phi \qquad (3\text{-}63)$$

was proposed but is considered unlikely in view of the rarity of termolecular reactions in solution. Another and more feasible suggestion [20] is that involving the sequence

$$2\,\phi\text{—CH=CH}_2 \longrightarrow \phi\text{—}\dot{\text{C}}\text{HCH}_2\text{CH}_2\dot{\text{C}}\text{H—}\phi \qquad (3\text{-}64)$$

$$\phi\text{—}\dot{\text{C}}\text{HCH}_2\text{CH}_2\dot{\text{C}}\text{H—}\phi + \phi\text{—CH=CH}_2 \longrightarrow$$

$$\phi\text{—}\dot{\text{C}}\text{H—CH}_3 + \phi\text{—}\dot{\text{C}}\text{HCH}_2\text{CH=CH—}\phi \qquad (3\text{-}65)$$

3-4e Redox Initiation

Many oxidation-reduction reactions produce radicals which can be used to initiate polymerization. This type of initiation is referred to as *redox initiation, redox catalysis,* or *redox activation*. A prime advantage of redox initiation is that radical production occurs at reasonable rates at very moderate temperatures (approximately 0–50°C). This allows a greater freedom of choice of the polymerization temperature than is possible with the thermal homolysis of initiators. A wide variety of redox reactions, including both inorganic and organic components either wholly or in part, may be employed for this purpose.

One of the oldest and best known redox sources of radicals is Fenton's reagent—the reaction of hydrogen peroxide with ferrous ion

$$H_2O_2 + Fe^{2+} \longrightarrow HO^- + HO\cdot + Fe^{3+} \qquad (3\text{-}66a)$$

Ferrous ion also promotes the decomposition of a variety of other compounds including various types of organic peroxides.

$$\text{ROOR} \xrightarrow{Fe^{2+}} \text{RO}^- + \text{RO}\cdot \qquad (3\text{-}66b)$$

$$\mathrm{ROOH} \xrightarrow{\mathrm{Fe}^{2+}} \mathrm{HO}^- + \mathrm{RO}\cdot \tag{3-66c}$$

$$\mathrm{ROO\overset{O}{\overset{\|}{C}}R'} \xrightarrow{\mathrm{Fe}^{2+}} \mathrm{R'\overset{O}{\overset{\|}{C}}O^-} + \mathrm{RO}\cdot \tag{3-66d}$$

Other reductants such as Cr^{2+}, V^{2+}, Ti^{3+}, Co^{2+} and Cu^+ can be employed in place of ferrous ion in many instances. Most of these redox systems are aqueous or emulsion systems.

Redox initiation with acyl peroxides can be carried out in organic media by using amines as the reductant. An interesting system is the combination of a benzoyl peroxide and an *N,N*-dialkylaniline. The difference in the rates of decomposition between such a redox system and the simple thermal homolysis of the peroxide alone is very striking. The decomposition rate constant k_d for pure benzoyl peroxide in styrene polymerization is 1.33×10^{-4} sec^{-1} at 90°C while that for the benzoyl peroxide-*N,N*-diethylaniline redox system is 1.25×10^{-2} liter/mole-sec at 60°C and 2.29×10^{-3} liter/mole-sec at 30°C [21]. The redox system has a much larger decomposition rate. Radical production in this redox system appears [5] to proceed via an initial ionic displacement by the nitrogen of the aniline on the peroxide linkage

$$\phi\!-\!\ddot{\mathrm{N}}(\mathrm{R})\!-\!\mathrm{R} + \phi\!-\!\overset{O}{\overset{\|}{C}}\!-\!O\!-\!O\!-\!\overset{O}{\overset{\|}{C}}\!-\!\phi \longrightarrow \left[\phi\!-\!\mathrm{N}(\mathrm{R})(\mathrm{R})\!-\!O\!-\!\overset{O}{\overset{\|}{C}}\!-\!\phi\right]^+ \phi\!-\!\overset{O}{\overset{\|}{C}}\!-\!O^- \longrightarrow$$

$$\phi\!-\!\overset{+}{\dot{\mathrm{N}}}(\mathrm{R})\!-\!\mathrm{R} + \phi\!-\!\overset{O}{\overset{\|}{C}}\!-\!O\cdot + \phi\!-\!\overset{O}{\overset{\|}{C}}\!-\!O^- \tag{3-66e}$$

Other redox reactions that have been employed include

1) The reduction of persulfate ion by ferrous, argentous, sulfite, or thiosulfate ions, for example

$$^-O_3S\!-\!O\!-\!O\!-\!SO_3^- + Fe^{2+} \longrightarrow Fe^{3+} + SO_4^{2-} + SO_4^{-}\cdot \tag{3-67a}$$

$$^-O_3S\!-\!O\!-\!O\!-\!SO_3^- + S_2O_3^{2-} \longrightarrow SO_4^{2-} + SO_4^{2\overline{\cdot}} + \cdot S_2O_3^- \tag{3-67b}$$

2) The use of reductants such as HSO_3^-, SO_3^{2-}, $S_2O_3^{2-}$, and $S_2O_5^{2-}$ in combination with oxidants such as Cu^{2+}, Fe^{3+}, ClO_3^-, and H_2O_2

3) The oxidation of thiourea by BrO_4^-, MnO_4^-, $S_2O_8^{2-}$, H_2O_2, and Fe^{3+} [22]

4) The oxidation of various organic compounds with Ce^{4+} or V^{5+} [23–25], for example

$$R{-}CH_2{-}OH + Ce^{4+} \longrightarrow Ce^{3+} + H^+ + R{-}\dot{C}H{-}OH \tag{3-68}$$

The kinetics of redox initiated polymerizations generally fall into two categories. Many of these polymerizations proceed in the same manner as other polymerizations in terms of the propagation and termination steps, the only difference being the source of radicals for the initiation step. For these polymerizations, the initiation and polymerization rates will be given by appropriate expressions which are very similar to those developed previously. Thus, for the benzoyl peroxide-dialkylaniline redox system, the kinetics are given by

$$R_i = k_d[\text{peroxide}][\text{amine}] \tag{3-69}$$

$$R_p = k_p[M]\left(\frac{k_d[\text{peroxide}][\text{amine}]}{2k_t}\right)^{1/2} \tag{3-70}$$

Equations 3-69 and 3-70 differ from those (Eqs. 3-27 and 3-28) previously discussed for other initiation systems in the absence of the factor of 2 in the initiation rate equation. The reason for this is that one benzoyl peroxide molecule yields only one radical ($\phi CO_2\cdot$) capable of initiating polymerization. The amino radical cation produced (Eq. 3-66e) in the peroxide-amine system is not effective in initiating polymerization as shown by the absence of nitrogen in the final polymer product. The amino radical cation disappears by some unknown side reaction. For many other systems, the rate expressions will be similar to Eqs. 3-69 and 3-70 in showing a first order dependence of R_i on both the oxidant and the reductant as well as the absence of the factor of 2. Initiation by reactions such as Eqs. 3-66a–d involve only one radical produced per each molecule of catalyst.

Some redox polymerizations involve a change in the termination step from the usual bimolecular reaction to one involving the reaction between the propagating radicals and a component of the redox system. This leads to kinetics which are appreciably different than those previously encountered. Thus, in the alcohol-Ce^{4+}system (Eq. 3-68), termination occurs according to

$$M_n\cdot + Ce^{4+} \longrightarrow Ce^{3+} + H^+ + \text{dead polymer} \tag{3-71}$$

The propagating radical loses a hydrogen to form a dead polymer molecule with an olefinic endgroup. The rates of initiation and termination are given by

$$R_i = k_d[Ce^{4+}][\text{alcohol}] \tag{3-72a}$$

$$R_t = k_t[Ce^{4+}][M\cdot] \tag{3-72b}$$

By making the usual steady-state assumption (i.e., $R_i = R_t$), one obtains the radical concentration as

$$[M\cdot] = \frac{k_d[\text{alcohol}]}{k_t} \tag{3-73}$$

Substitution of this result into Eq. 3-21 yields the polymerization rate as

$$R_p = \frac{k_d k_p[M][\text{alcohol}]}{k_t} \tag{3-74}$$

3-4f Initiator Efficiency

3-4f-1 Definition of *f*. When a material balance is performed on the amount of initiator which is decomposed during a polymerization and compared with that which initiates polymerization, it is apparent that the initiator is inefficiently used. There is wastage of initiator due to two reactions. One is the *induced decomposition of initiator* by the attack of propagating radicals on the initiator, for example

$$M_n\cdot + \phi\overset{\overset{\displaystyle O}{\|}}{C}O{-}O\overset{\overset{\displaystyle O}{\|}}{C}\phi \longrightarrow M_n{-}O\overset{\overset{\displaystyle O}{\|}}{C}\phi + \phi\overset{\overset{\displaystyle O}{\|}}{C}O\cdot \tag{3-75}$$

This reaction is termed "chain transfer to initiator" and is considered further in Sec. 3-6b. The induced decomposition of initiator does not change the radical concentration during the polymerization since the newly formed radical (ϕCOO·) will initiate a new polymer chain. However, the reaction does result in a wastage of initiator. A molecule of initiator is decomposed without an increase in the amount of monomer being converted to polymer.

The second wastage reaction is that involving the side reaction(s) of the radicals formed in the primary step of initiator decomposition. Some of the radicals formed in the primary decomposition step, for example, in the reactions

$$\phi\overset{\overset{\displaystyle O}{\|}}{C}O{-}O\overset{\overset{\displaystyle O}{\|}}{C}\phi \longrightarrow 2\,\phi COO\cdot \tag{3-76a}$$

$$Fe^{2+} + \phi C(CH_3)_2OOH \longrightarrow Fe^{3+} + HO^- + \phi C(CH_3)_2O\cdot \tag{3-76b}$$

undergo reactions to form neutral molecules instead of initiating polymerization. It is this wastage reaction that is referred to when discussing the initiator efficiency f. The initiator efficiency f is defined as the fraction of radicals formed in the primary step of initiator decomposition which are successful in initiating polymerization. The initiator efficiency is considered exclusive of any initiator wastage by induced decomposition. The reader is cautioned, however, that reported literature values of f do not always make this distinction. Very frequently, the calculations of f neglect and do not correct for the occurrence of induced decomposition. Such f values may be considered as the "effective" or "practical" initiator efficiency in that they give the net or overall initiation efficiency of the initial catalyst concentration. The preferred method of quantitatively handling induced decomposition of initiator, however, is that which is discussed in Sec. 3-6b-3.

3-4f-2 Mechanism of $f < 1$. The values of f for most initiators lie in the range of 0.3–0.8. To understand why the initiator efficiency will be less than unity, consider the following reactions which occur in polymerizations initiated by benzoyl peroxide

$$\phi COO{-}OOC\phi \rightleftharpoons [2\,\phi COO\cdot] \tag{3-77}$$

$$[2\,\phi COO\cdot] \longrightarrow [\phi COO\phi + CO_2] \tag{3-78}$$

$$[2\,\phi COO\cdot] + M \longrightarrow \phi CO_2\cdot + \phi COOM\cdot \tag{3-79}$$

$$[2\,\phi COO\cdot] \longrightarrow 2\,\phi COO\cdot \tag{3-80}$$

$$\phi COO\cdot + M \longrightarrow \phi COOM\cdot \tag{3-81}$$

$$\phi COO\cdot \longrightarrow \phi\cdot + CO_2 \tag{3-82}$$

$$\phi\cdot + M \longrightarrow \phi M\cdot \tag{3-83}$$

$$\phi\cdot + \phi COO\cdot \longrightarrow \phi COO\phi \tag{3-84}$$

$$2\,\phi\cdot \longrightarrow \phi{-}\phi \tag{3-85}$$

The brackets indicate the presence of a solvent cage which traps the radicals for some period before they diffuse apart. Equation 3-77 represents the primary step of initiator decomposition into two radicals which are held within the solvent cage. The radicals in the solvent cage may undergo recombination (the reverse of Eq. 3-77), reaction with each other (Eq. 3-78), reaction with monomer (Eq. 3-79), or diffusion out of the solvent cage (Eq. 3-80). Once outside the solvent cage, the radicals may react with monomer (Eq. 3-81) or decompose according to Eq. 3-82 to yield a radical which may undergo various reactions (Eqs. 3-83 to 3-85).

Recombination of the primary radicals (Eq. 3-77) has no effect on the initiator efficiency. Initiation of the polymerization occurs by Eqs. 3-79, 3-81, and 3-83. The initiator efficiency is decreased by the reactions indicated by Eqs. 3-78, 3-84, and 3-85 since their products are stable and cannot give rise to radicals. Of these reactions, the decomposition within the solvent cage (Eq. 3-78) is usually much more significant than the others in decreasing the value of f. That this reaction is competitive with those leading to initiation of polymerization can be seen by considering the time scale [4] of the various events. The average life of neighboring radicals is perhaps 10^{-10}–10^{-9} sec. Since rate constants for radical-radical reactions are in the range 10^7 liter/mole-sec and higher, and the concentration of radicals in the solvent cage is approximately 10 molar, there is a reasonable probability that Reaction 3-78 will occur. Reaction 3-79 cannot compete effectively with Reaction 3-78 since radical addition reactions have much lower rate constants ($10-10^5$ liter/mole-sec).

Lowering of the initiator efficiency by reactions analogous to Eq. 3-78 is a general phenomenon with almost all initiators. Thus, acetoxy radicals from acetyl peroxide undergo decarboxylation faster than benzoxy radicals and radical combination within the solvent cage leads to stable products incapable of producing radicals

$$CH_3COO{-}OOCCH_3 \longrightarrow [2\ CH_3COO\cdot] \begin{cases} \nearrow [CH_3COOCH_3 + CO_2] & (3\text{-}86a) \\ \searrow [CH_3CH_3 + 2\ CO_2] & (3\text{-}86b) \end{cases}$$

t-Butoxy radicals from di-*t*-butyl peroxide undergo an intramolecular elimination of methyl radicals followed by dimerization of the latter

$$CH_3{-}\underset{CH_3}{\overset{CH_3}{\underset{|}{\overset{|}{C}}}}{-}O\cdot \longrightarrow CH_3{-}\overset{O}{\overset{\|}{C}}{-}CH_3 + CH_3\cdot \xrightarrow{\quad} \tfrac{1}{2}\,CH_3CH_3 \qquad (3\text{-}87)$$

and cumyloxy radicals from dicumyl peroxide or cumyl hydroperoxide undergo a similar dissociation [5]. The homolysis of AIBN occurs in a concerted process with simultaneous breakage of the two C—N bonds to yield nitrogen and 2-cyano-2-propyl radicals. Reaction of the radicals with each other can occur in two ways to yield tetramethylsuccinodinitrile and dimethyl-*N*-(2-cyano-2-isopropyl)ketenimine.

$$(CH_3)_2\overset{CN}{\overset{|}{C}}{-}N{=}N{-}\overset{CN}{\overset{|}{C}}(CH_3)_2 \longrightarrow \left[2\ (CH_3)_2\overset{CN}{\overset{|}{C}}\cdot + N_2\right]$$

$$\swarrow \left[(CH_3)_2\overset{CN}{\overset{|}{C}}{-}\overset{CN}{\overset{|}{C}}(CH_3)_2 + N_2\right] \qquad (3\text{-}88a)$$

$$\downarrow \left[(CH_3)_2C{=}C{=}N{-}\overset{CN}{\overset{|}{C}}(CH_3)_2 + N_2\right] \qquad (3\text{-}88b)$$

The initiator efficiency is generally independent of the monomer concentration and of the sequence of reactions indicated by Eqs. 3-82 through 3-85. The prime reason for $f < 1$ is the reactions occurring within the solvent cage. An interesting observation is the decrease of f for AIBN in styrene polymerization as the viscosity of the medium is increased [26]. The increased viscosity apparently results in a longer lifetime for the caged radicals—leading to an increase in the extent of Reactions 3-88a and 3-88b.

Once a radical has diffused out of the solvent cage, the reaction with monomer (Eq. 3-81) occurs predominantly in preference to other reactions. Even if Reaction 3-82 occurs, this will be followed by Reaction 3-83 in preference to the two radical combination reactions (Eqs. 3-84 and 3-85). The preferences for polymerization initiation arise from the much greater monomer concentrations (10^{-1}–10 molar) compared to the radical concentrations (10^{-7}–10^{-9} molar) which are normally present in polymerization systems. However, one can observe a variation of f with the monomer concentration at low monomer concentrations. Figure 3-3 shows this effect in the AIBN initiation of styrene polymerization [27]. The initiator efficiency increases very rapidly with [M] and a limiting value is quickly reached.

The value of f varies in the presence of solvents. The initiator efficiencies of AIBN [28] and benzoyl peroxide [29] are lower in carbon tetrachloride than in aromatic solvents. These effects are due to competition between reaction of the radicals with the monomer compared to reaction with solvent. Reactions of radicals with solvents will be discussed in greater detail in Sec. 3-6c. The initiator efficiency for any particular initiator may also vary for the polymerization of different monomers. Thus, the value of f for AIBN in the polymerizations of methyl methacrylate, vinyl acetate, styrene, vinyl chloride, and acrylonitrile ranged from 0.6 to 1.0, increasing in that order [30]. This order is a consequence of the relative rates with which radicals add to the different monomers.

3-4f-3 Experimental Determination of f. Various methods are employed for the experimental evaluation of the initiator efficiency. One method involves the determination and comparison of both the initiator decomposition and the production of polymer molecules. The initiator decomposition is best determined during an actual polymerization. Independent measurement of initiator decomposition in the absence of monomer can give erroneous results. The

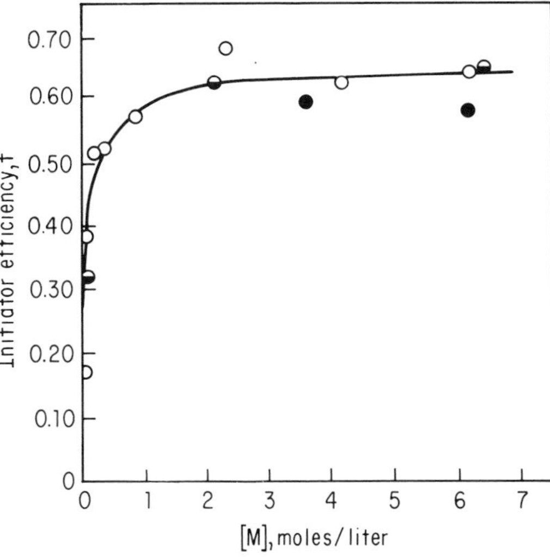

FIG. 3-3 *Effect of styrene concentration on the initiator efficiency of azobisisobutyronitrile.* ●, ○, *and* ◒ *refer to experiments with initiator concentrations of 0.20, 0.50 and 1.00 grams/liter, respectively. After [27] by permission of Interscience Publishers, John Wiley & Sons, Inc., New York.*

rates of decomposition of initiator can be quite different for pure initiator as compared to initiator in the presence of monomer. (Recall the molecule-induced homolysis of *t*-butyl hydroperoxide—Sec. 3-4a-4.) AIBN decomposition can be followed relatively easily by following the evolution of nitrogen. Measurement of the polymer number-average molecular weight allows a determination of f by comparison of the number of radicals produced with the number of polymer molecules obtained. This method requires a knowledge of whether termination occurs by coupling or by disproportionation since the former results in two initiator fragments per polymer molecule and the latter in only one. The occurrence of induced decomposition must be taken into account in calculating the number of radicals produced. Induced decomposition is negligible for azonitriles but occurs to an appreciable extent with many peroxides.

The second and a most useful method is a variation of the first in which the number of initiator fragments in the polymer is determined by direct analysis of the polymer end-groups. The analysis is relatively difficult to perform accurately because of the low concentration of the end-groups. For a 50,000 molecular weight polymer, the end-groups comprise only about 0.1 percent of the total weight of the sample. The use of isotopically labelled initiators such as C^{14} labelled AIBN [26] and S^{35} labelled potassium persulfate is an exceptionally sensitive method for determining the number of initiator fragments.

A third method involves the use of *radical scavengers* which count the number of radicals in a system by stopping their growth. The free radical diphenylpicrylhydrazyl (DPPH) obtained by oxidation of diphenylpicrylhydrazine

$$\phi_2N\text{—}NH\text{—}C_6H_2(NO_2)_3 \xrightarrow{PbO_2} \phi_2N\text{—}\dot{N}\text{—}C_6H_2(NO_2)_3 \qquad (3\text{-}89)$$

is frequently used for this purpose. The DPPH radical terminates other radicals, probably by the reaction

$$R\cdot + \phi_2N\text{—}\dot{N}\text{—}C_6H_2(NO_2)_3 \longrightarrow R\text{—}C_6H_4\text{—}N(\phi)\text{—}NH\text{—}C_6H_2(NO_2)_3 \qquad (3\text{-}90)$$

The reaction can be easily followed spectrophotometrically since the DPPH radical is deep violet and the product is usually light yellow or colorless. Ferric chloride has also been used to count radicals via the reaction

$$R\cdot + FeCl_3 \longrightarrow RCl + FeCl_2 \qquad (3\text{-}91)$$

Other radical scavengers are duroquinone and benzoquinone. This method of determining the initiator efficiency leaves much to be desired in that the reaction between the scavenger and radicals is very often not quantitative. Thus, the DPPH radical is an extremely efficient scavenger in many systems. It completely stops vinyl acetate [31] and styrene polymerizations even at concentrations below 10^{-4} molar. However, the scavenging effect of DPPH is not universally quantitative.

A fourth and most useful method is the *dead-end polymerization* technique recently developed by Tobolsky and coworkers [32–34] for the simultaneous determination of k_d and f. Dead-end polymerization refers to a polymerization in which the initiator concentration decreases to such a low value that the half-life of the propagating polymer chains approximates that of the initiator. Under such circumstances, the polymerization stops short of completion and one observes a limiting conversion of monomer to polymer at infinite reaction time. Consider a dead-end polymerization initiated by the thermal homolysis of an initiator. The rate of initiator disappearance is given by

$$\frac{-d[\mathrm{I}]}{dt} = k_d[\mathrm{I}] \tag{3-92}$$

Integration of Eq. 3-92 yields

$$[\mathrm{I}] = [\mathrm{I}]_0 e^{-k_d t} \tag{3-93}$$

where $[\mathrm{I}]_0$ is the initiator concentration at the start of the polymerization. Substitution of Eq. 3-93 into Eq. 3-28 and rearrangement yields

$$\frac{-d[\mathrm{M}]}{[\mathrm{M}]} = k_p\left(\frac{f[\mathrm{I}]_0}{k_t k_d}\right)^{1/2} e^{-k_d t/2}\, dt \tag{3-94}$$

which on integration leads to

$$-\ln\frac{[\mathrm{M}]}{[\mathrm{M}]_0} = -\ln(1-p) = 2k_p\left(\frac{f[\mathrm{I}]_0}{k_t k_d}\right)^{1/2}(1-e^{-k_d t/2}) \tag{3-95}$$

where p is the extent of conversion of monomer to polymer and is defined by $([\mathrm{M}]_0-[\mathrm{M}])/[\mathrm{M}]_0$. At long reaction times ($t \to \infty$), [M] and p

reach the limiting values of $[M]_\infty$ and p_∞, respectively, and Eq. 3-95 becomes

$$-\ln\frac{[M]_\infty}{[M]_0} = -\ln(1-p_\infty) = 2k_p\left(\frac{f[I]_0}{k_t k_d}\right)^{1/2} \tag{3-96}$$

Dividing Eq. 3-95 by Eq. 3-96, rearranging, and then taking logarithms of both sides leads to the useful expression

$$\ln\left[1 - \frac{\ln(1-p)}{\ln(1-p_\infty)}\right] = \frac{-k_d t}{2} \tag{3-97}$$

The value of k_d is then easily found from the slope of a plot of the left side of Eq. 3-97 versus time. Figure 3-4 shows this plot for the AIBN initiated polymerization of isoprene at three different temperatures [34]. The value of f can then be obtained from either of Eqs. 3-28 or 3-96 if the ratio $k_p/k_t^{1/2}$ for the monomer is known from other studies.

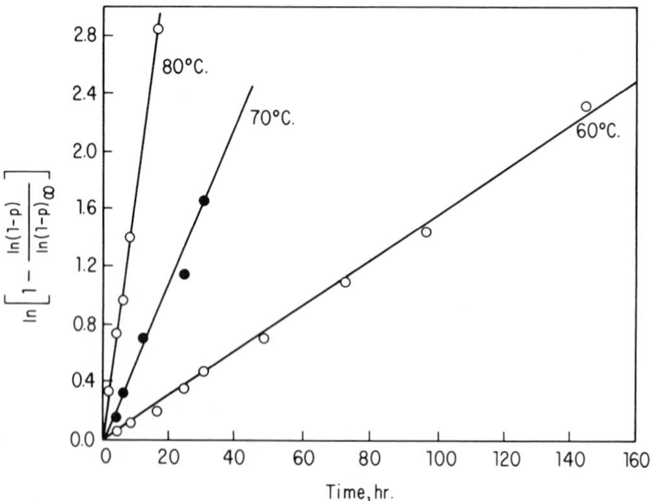

FIG. 3-4 *Dead-end polymerization of isoprene initiated by azobisisobutyronitrile. After [34] (by permission of Interscience Publishers, John Wiley & Sons, Inc., New York).*

Mathematical treatments have been developed to extend the dead-end polymerization technique to many different situations [35, 36]. These include polymerizations which are not dead-end polymerizations, i.e., polymerizations which go to completion. Also included are treatments for polymerizations involving appreciable induced decomposition of initiator and polymerizations involving bimolecular initiator decompositions (e.g., the benzoyl peroxide-dialkylaniline system).

3-5 MOLECULAR WEIGHT

3-5a Kinetic Chain Length

The *kinetic chain length* ν of a radical chain polymerization is defined as the average number of monomer molecules consumed (polymerized) per each radical which initiates a polymer chain. This quantity will obviously be given by the ratio of the polymerization rate to the initiation rate or to the termination rate since the latter two rates are equal.

$$\nu = \frac{R_p}{R_i} = \frac{R_p}{R_t} \tag{3-98}$$

Combination of Eqs. 3-21, 3-22, and 3-98 yields

$$\nu = \frac{k_p[\mathrm{M}]}{2k_t[\mathrm{M}\cdot]} \tag{3-99}$$

which can be combined with Eq. 3-24 to give

$$\nu = \frac{k_p^2[\mathrm{M}]^2}{2k_t R_p} \tag{3-100}$$

For a polymerization initiated by the thermal homolysis of an initiator, Eq. 3-28 can be substituted into Eq. 3-100 to yield

$$\nu = \frac{k_p[\mathrm{M}]}{2(fk_d k_t[\mathrm{I}])^{1/2}} \tag{3-101}$$

Equations 3-100 and 3-101 show a very significant characteristic of radical chain polymerizations. The kinetic chain length is inversely dependent on the radical concentration or the polymerization rate. Increasing the polymerization rates and radical concentrations in radical polymerizations leads to smaller sized polymer molecules. The kinetic chain length at constant polymerization rate is a characteristic of the particular monomer and independent of the method of initiation. Thus, for any monomer the kinetic chain length will be independent of whether the polymerization is initiated by thermal, redox, or photochemical means, whether initiators are used, or of the particular initiator used, if the $[M\cdot]$ or R_p is the same.

3-5b Mode of Termination

The *number-average degree of polymerization* $\overline{X}_n$, defined as the average number of monomer molecules contained in a polymer molecule, is related to the kinetic chain length. If the propagating radicals terminate by coupling, a dead polymer molecule is composed of two kinetic chain lengths or

$$\overline{X}_n = 2\nu \qquad (3\text{-}102a)$$

For termination by disproportionation, the kinetic chain length is synonymous with the number-average degree of polymerization

$$\overline{X}_n = \nu \qquad (3\text{-}102b)$$

The number-average molecular weight of a polymer is given by

$$\overline{M}_n = M_o \overline{X}_n \qquad (3\text{-}103)$$

where M_o is the molecular weight of the monomer.

The mode of termination is experimentally determined from the observation of the number of initiator fragments per polymer molecule. This requires the analysis of the molecular weight of a polymer sample as well as the total number of initiator fragments contained in that sample. Although the experimental data are not available for all monomers, most polymer radicals appear to terminate predominantly or entirely by coupling. Studies with small, aliphatic radicals such as ethyl, isopropyl, and *t*-butyl indicate that disproportionation will become progressively more important for branched radicals at high polymerization temperatures. The coupling of branched radicals will be sterically hindered. Further, the increase in the number of β-hydrogens available for transfer in most branched radicals leads to a statistical favoring of disproportionation. Thus, whereas styrene undergoes termination by coupling, methyl methacrylate undergoes termination by both coupling and disproportionation. The extent of disproportionation in methyl methacrylate increases with temperature since the activation energy for disproportionation is about 5 kcal/mole greater than that for coupling. Disproportionation accounts for about 60 percent of the termination reaction at 60°C [37]. Disproportionation also appears to be significant for vinyl acetate [38].

3-6 CHAIN TRANSFER

3-6a Effect of Chain Transfer

In many polymerization systems the polymer molecular weight is observed to be lower than predicted on the basis of termination by coupling or disproportionation. This effect is due to the premature termination of a growing polymer by the transfer of a hydrogen or other atom or species to it from some compound present in the system—the monomer, initiator, or solvent, as the case may be. These radical displacement reactions are termed *chain transfer* reactions and may be depicted as

$$M_n\cdot + XA \xrightarrow{k_{tr}} M_n\text{—}X + A\cdot \tag{3-104}$$

where XA may be monomer, initiator, solvent, or other substance and X is the atom or species transferred. Chain transfer to initiator was referred to earlier as induced initiator decomposition (Sec. 3-4f-1).

The rate of a chain transfer reaction is given by

$$R_{tr} = k_{tr}[M\cdot][XA] \tag{3-105}$$

where k_{tr} is the chain transfer rate constant. Chain transfer results in the production of a new radical A· which then reinitiates polymerization

$$A\cdot + M \xrightarrow{k_a} M\cdot \tag{3-106}$$

Chain transfer results in a decrease in polymer size. The effect of chain transfer on the polymerization rate is not evident but is dependent on whether the rate of reinitiation is comparable to that of the original propagating radical. Table 3-2 shows the four main possible situations that may be encountered. Reinitiation is rapid in Cases 1 and 2 and one observes no change in the polymerization rate. The same number of monomer molecules are consumed per unit time with the formation of larger numbers of smaller sized polymer molecules. The relative decrease in $\overline{X}_n$ depends on the magnitude of the transfer constant. When the transfer rate constant k_{tr} is much larger than that for propagation (Case 2), the result is a very small sized polymer ($\overline{X}_n \simeq 1$–5)—referred to as a *telomer.* When reinitiation is slow compared to propagation (Cases 3 and 4), one observes a decrease in R_p as well as in $\overline{X}_n$. The magnitude of the decrease in R_p is determined by the relative values of k_p and k_{tr}. The remainder of this section will be concerned with Case 1. Cases 3 and 4 will be considered further in Sec. 3-7. Case 2 (telomerization) is not within the scope of this text.

Table 3-2 Effect of Chain Transfer on R_p and $\overline{X}_n$

Case	Relative rate constants for transfer, propagation, and reinitiation	Type of effect	Effect on R_p	Effect on $\overline{X}_n$
1	$k_p \gg k_{tr}$ $k_a \simeq k_p$	Normal chain transfer	None	Decrease
2	$k_p \ll k_{tr}$ $k_a \simeq k_p$	Telomerization	None	Large decrease
3	$k_p \gg k_{tr}$ $k_a < k_p$	Retardation	Decrease	Decrease
4	$k_p \ll k_{tr}$ $k_a < k_p$	Degradative chain transfer	Large decrease	Large decrease

For chain transfer by Case 1, the kinetic chain length remains unchanged but the number of polymer molecules produced per kinetic chain length is altered. The number-average degree of polymerization is no longer given by ν or 2ν for disproportionation and coupling, respectively. Chain transfer is important in that it may alter the molecular weight of the polymer product in an undesirable manner. On the other hand, controlled chain transfer may be employed to advantage in the control of molecular weight at a specified level.

The degree of polymerization must now be redefined as the polymerization rate divided by the sum of all termination rates (i.e., the normal termination mode plus all chain transfer reactions). For the general case of a polymerization initiated by the thermal homolysis of a catalyst and involving termination by coupling and chain transfer to monomer, initiator, and the compound S (referred to as a *chain transfer agent*), the number-average degree of polymerization follows from Eq. 3-105 as

$$\overline{X}_n = \frac{R_p}{(R_t/2) + k_{tr,\mathrm{M}}[\mathrm{M}\cdot][\mathrm{M}] + k_{tr,\mathrm{S}}[\mathrm{M}\cdot][\mathrm{S}] + k_{tr,\mathrm{I}}[\mathrm{M}\cdot][\mathrm{I}]} \tag{3-107}$$

The first term in the denominator denotes coupling and the other three denote chain transfer by monomer, chain transfer agent, and initiator, respectively. A *chain transfer constant* C for a substance is defined as the ratio of the rate constant k_{tr} for the chain transfer of a propagating radical with that substance to the rate constant k_p for propagation of the radical. The chain transfer constants for monomer, chain transfer agent, and initiator are then given by

$$C_\mathrm{M} = \frac{k_{tr,\mathrm{M}}}{k_p} \qquad C_\mathrm{S} = \frac{k_{tr,\mathrm{S}}}{k_p} \qquad C_\mathrm{I} = \frac{k_{tr,\mathrm{I}}}{k_p} \tag{3-108}$$

Combining Eqs. 3-21, 3-27, 3-28, 3-107, and 3-108 yields

$$\frac{1}{\overline{X}_n} = \frac{k_t R_p}{k_p^2[\mathrm{M}]^2} + C_\mathrm{M} + C_\mathrm{S}\frac{[\mathrm{S}]}{[\mathrm{M}]} + C_\mathrm{I}\frac{k_t R_p^2}{k_p^2 f k_d [\mathrm{M}]^3} \tag{3-109}$$

which shows the quantitative effect of the various transfer reactions on the number-average degree of polymerization. Various methods can be employed to determine the values of the chain transfer constants.

3-6b Transfer to Monomer and Initiator

3-6b-1 Determination of C_M and C_I. Two special cases of Eq. 3-109 are of interest. When a chain transfer agent is absent, the term in [S] disappears and

$$\frac{1}{\overline{X}_n} = \frac{k_t R_p}{k_p^2 [\mathrm{M}]^2} + C_\mathrm{M} + C_\mathrm{I} \frac{k_t R_p^2}{k_p^2 f k_d [\mathrm{M}]^3} \tag{3-110a}$$

Equation 3-110a can be given in another form by combining it with Eq. 3-28

$$\frac{1}{\overline{X}_n} = \frac{k_t R_p}{k_p^2 [\mathrm{M}]^2} + C_\mathrm{M} + C_\mathrm{I} \frac{[\mathrm{I}]}{[\mathrm{M}]} \tag{3-110b}$$

Equation 3-110a is quadratic in R_p and the appropriate plot of $1/\overline{X}_n$ versus R_p in Figure 3-5 for styrene polymerization shows the effect to varying degrees depending on the initiator [39]. The initial portion of the plot is linear but at higher concentrations of initiator and therefore, high values of R_p, the plot deviates from linearity as the contribution of transfer to initiator increases. The intercept of the linear portion yields the value of C_M. The slope of the linear portion is given by $k_t/k_p^2[\mathrm{M}]^2$ from which the important quantity k_p^2/k_t can be determined since the monomer concentration is known. For systems in which chain transfer to initiator is negligible (e.g., the AIBN initiated polymerization), a plot of $1/\overline{X}_n$ versus R_p will be linear over the whole range.

Several methods are available for the determination of C_I. Equation 3-110a can be rearranged and divided through by R_p to yield

$$\left[\frac{1}{\overline{X}_n} - C_\mathrm{M}\right]\frac{1}{R_p} = \frac{k_t}{k_p^2 [\mathrm{M}]^2} + \frac{C_\mathrm{I} k_t R_p}{k_p^2 f k_d [\mathrm{M}]^3} \tag{3-111}$$

A plot of experimental data as the left side of Eq. 3-111 versus R_p yields a straight line whose slope is $(C_\mathrm{I} k_t/k_p^2 f k_d [\mathrm{M}]^3)$. The initiator transfer constant can be determined from the slope because the various other quantities are known or can be related to known quantities through Eq. 3-28. When chain transfer to monomer is negligible, one can rearrange Eq. 3-110b to yield

$$\left[\frac{1}{\overline{X}_n} - \frac{k_t R_p}{k_p^2 [\mathrm{M}]^2}\right] = C_\mathrm{I} \frac{[\mathrm{I}]}{[\mathrm{M}]} \tag{3-112}$$

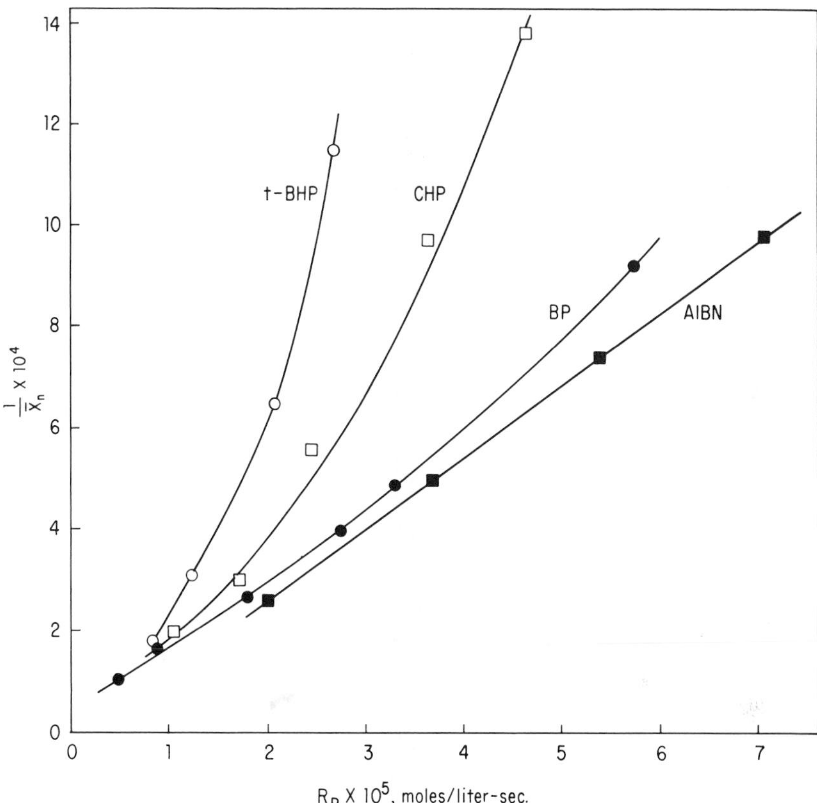

FIG. 3-5 *Dependence of the degree of polymerization of styrene on the polymerization rate. The effect of chain transfer to initiator is shown for t-butyl hydroperoxide (○), cumyl hydroperoxide (□), benzoyl peroxide (●), and azobisisobutyronitrile (■) at 60°C. After [39] (by permission of Interscience Publishers, John Wiley & Sons, Inc., New York).*

A plot of the left side of Eq. 3-112 versus [I]/[M] yields a straight line whose slope is C_I. Figure 3-6 shows the appropriate plot for the *t*-butyl hydroperoxide polymerization of styrene [13].

3-6b-2 Monomer Transfer Constants. Using the methods described, the values of C_M and C_I in the benzoyl peroxide polymerization of styrene have been found to be 0.00006 and 0.055, respectively [40]. The amount of chain transfer to monomer which occurs is negligible in this polymerization. The chain transfer constant for benzoyl peroxide is appreciable and chain transfer with initiator becomes increasingly important as the initiator concentration increases. These effects are shown in Figure 3-7 where the

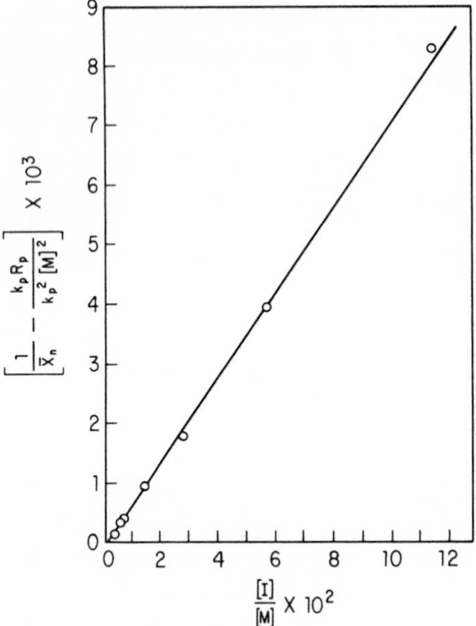

FIG. 3-6 *Determination of initiator chain transfer constants in the t-butyl hydroperoxide catalyzed polymerization of styrene in benzene solution at 70°C. After [13] (by permission of American Chemical Society, Washington).*

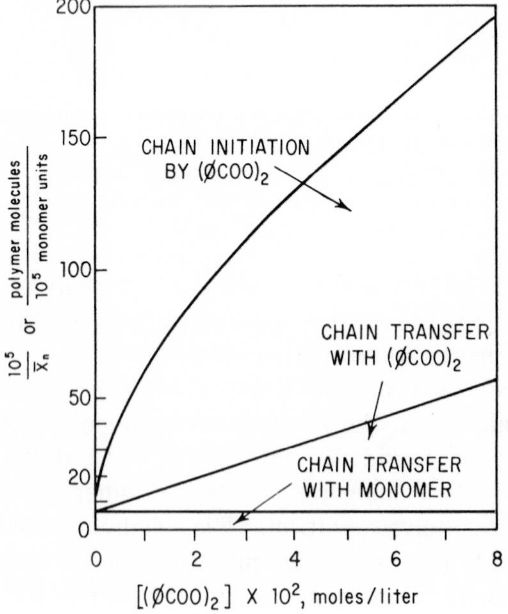

FIG. 3-7 *Contribution of various sources of chain termination in the benzoyl peroxide catalyzed polymerization of styrene at 60°C. After [40] (by permission of American Chemical Society, Washington).*

contributions of the various sources of chain ends are indicated. The topmost curve shows the total number of polymer molecules per 10^5 styrene monomer units. The difference between successive curves gives the number of polymer molecules terminated by normal coupling termination, transfer to benzoyl peroxide, and transfer to styrene.

The monomer chain transfer constants are generally small for most monomers (Table 3-3) [41]. Many monomers have C_M values in the range 10^{-5}–10^{-4} and self-chain transfer is not a problem in limiting the polymer molecular weight that can be obtained in the polymerization. Monomer chain transfer is low because the reaction

$$M_n\cdot + CH_2{=}\underset{Y}{\overset{H}{C}} \longrightarrow M_n{-}H + CH_2{=}\underset{Y}{C}\cdot \tag{3-113}$$

involves breaking the strong vinyl C—H bond. Vinyl acetate and vinyl chloride have the largest self-transfer constants. The large value of C_M for vinyl acetate has been attributed to transfer from the acetoxy methyl group. There is no corresponding explanation for vinyl chloride. The high values of C_M for vinyl acetate and vinyl chloride are probably a consequence of the high reactivities of the propagating radical in these two cases.

Although the high C_M values for vinyl acetate and vinyl chloride place an upper limit on the polymer size that can be obtained, that limit is not abnormally small as is often indicated in various texts. C_M values of 2–5 $\times$ 10^{-4} limit the number-average degree of

Table 3-3 Monomer Chain Transfer Constants[a,b]

Monomer	$C_M \times 10^4$
Acrylamide	0.6
Acrylonitrile	0.26–0.3
Methyl acrylate	0.036–0.325
Methyl methacrylate	0.07–0.18
Styrene	0.6–1.1
Vinyl acetate	1.75–2.8
Vinyl chloride (30°C)	6.25

[a]Data from [41], p. II-77.
[b]All C_M values are for 60°C except where otherwise noted.

polymerization to about 2000–5000 according to Eq. 3-110. This corresponds to $\overline{M}_n$ values of approximately 140,000 and 450,000 for vinyl chloride and vinyl acetate, respectively. The situation for vinyl acetate is especially contrary to that which is generally believed. The value of $C_M = 0.002$ for vinyl acetate which has frequently appeared in many texts (for example, [4]) appears to be too high, by an order of magnitude, as shown by many different references in the literature.

3-6b-3 Initiator Transfer Constants. Different initiators have varying transfer constants (Table 3-4). Azonitriles are generally considered to have no tendency toward chain transfer and to produce polymerizations which are clean in the sense of being devoid of complications from transfer even at high initiator concentrations. (Recent work [9], however, indicates that AIBN may have an appreciable transfer constant.) Many peroxides have very significant transfer constants. Dialkyl peroxides and diacyl peroxides undergo transfer (induced initiator decomposition) by the displacement reaction

Table 3-4 Initiator Chain Transfer Constants[a,b]

Initiator	C_I for polymerization of	
	Styrene	Methyl methacrylate
2,2′-Azobisisobutyronitrile	0	0
t-Butyl peroxide	0.0003–0.0013	–
Cumyl peroxide (50°C)	0.01	–
Lauroyl peroxide (70°C)	0.024	–
Benzoyl peroxide	0.048–0.055	0.02
t-Butyl hydroperoxide	0.035	1.27
Cumyl hydroperoxide	0.063	0.33

[a]Data from [41], p. II-77.
[b]All C_I values are for 60°C except where otherwise noted.

$$M_n\cdot + RO{-}OR \longrightarrow M_n{-}OR + RO\cdot \tag{3-114}$$

where R = alkyl or acyl. The acyl peroxides have higher transfer constants than the alkyl peroxides due to the weaker O—O bond of the former. The hydroperoxides are usually the strongest transfer agents among the initiators. Transfer probably involves hydrogen atom abstraction

$$M_n\cdot + ROO\text{—}H \longrightarrow M_n\text{—}H + ROO\cdot \qquad (3\text{-}115)$$

The typical effect of initiator chain transfer [39] can be seen graphically in Fig. 3-5. The decrease of polymer size due to chain transfer to initiator is much less than indicated from the C_I values because it is the quantity $C_I[I]/[M]$ which affects $\overline{X}_n$ (Eq. 3-110b). The initiator concentrations are quite low (10^{-4}–10^{-2} molar) in polymerization and the ratio [I]/[M] is typically in the range 10^{-3}–10^{-5}.

3-6c Transfer to Chain Transfer Agent

3-6c-1 Determination of C_S. The second special case of Eq. 3-109 consists of the situation where transfer with the chain transfer agent is most important. In some instances the chain transfer agent is the solvent, while in others it is an added compound. In such a case the third term on the right side of Eq. 3-109 makes the biggest contribution to the determination of the degree of polymerization. By the appropriate choice of polymerization conditions, one can determine the value of C_S for various chain transfer agents [42]. By using low concentrations of initiators or initiators with negligible C_I values (e.g., AIBN), the last term in Eq. 3-109 becomes negligible. The first term on the right side of the equation may be kept constant by keeping $R_p/[M]^2$ constant by appropriately adjusting the initiator concentration throughout the course of the reaction. Under these conditions, Eq. 3-109 takes the form

$$\frac{1}{\overline{X}_n} = \left(\frac{1}{\overline{X}_n}\right)_0 + C_S\frac{[S]}{[M]} \qquad (3\text{-}116)$$

where $\left(1/\overline{X}_n\right)_0$ is the value of $1/\overline{X}_n$ in the absence of the chain transfer agent. $\left(1/\overline{X}_n\right)_0$ is the sum of the first, second, and fourth terms on the right side of Eq. 3-109. C_S is then determined as the slope of the linear plot of $1/\overline{X}_n$ versus [S]/[M]. Such plots are shown in Figure 3-8 for several chain transfer agents in styrene polymerization [18]. This method has been found to be of general utility in determining values of C_S.

An alternate method includes a modification of the first method by plotting $\left[1/\overline{X}_n - \left(1/\overline{X}_n\right)_0\right]$ instead of $1/\overline{X}_n$ versus [S]/[M]. Under

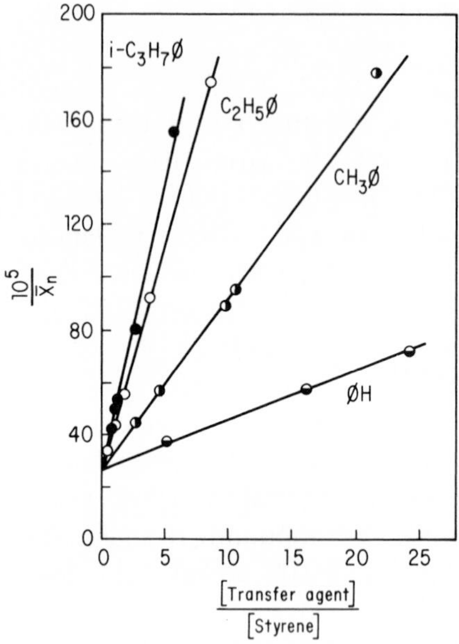

FIG. 3-8 *The effect of various chain transfer agents on the degree of polymerization of styrene at 100°C. After [42] (by permission of American Chemical Society, Washington).*

conditions where $R_p/[\mathrm{M}]^2$ is not constant, one may plot the quantity $\left(1/\bar{X}_n - k_t R_p/k_p^2[\mathrm{M}]^2\right)$ against $[\mathrm{S}]/[\mathrm{M}]$. This yields a straight line with slope C_S. Another method involves dividing the rate expression for transfer (Eq. 3-105) by that for propagation (Eq. 3-21) to yield

$$\frac{d[\mathrm{S}]/dt}{d[\mathrm{M}]/dt} = \frac{k_{tr,\mathrm{S}}[\mathrm{S}]}{k_p[\mathrm{M}]} = C_\mathrm{S}\frac{[\mathrm{S}]}{[\mathrm{M}]} \tag{3-117}$$

The value of C_S is obtained as the slope of the line obtained by plotting the ratio of the rates of disappearance of transfer agent and monomer $d[\mathrm{S}]/d[\mathrm{M}]$ versus $[\mathrm{S}]/[\mathrm{M}]$.

3-6c-2 Structure and Reactivity. The transfer constants for various compounds are shown in Table 3-5. These data are useful for the information they yield regarding the relationship between structure and reactivity in radical displacement reactions. Aliphatic hydrocarbons such as cyclohexane with strong C—H bonds show low transfer constants. Benzene also has a low C_S because of its strong bonds. Transfer to benzene appears to occur by addition of the radical

$$\mathrm{M}_n\cdot + \mathrm{C_6H_6} \longrightarrow \mathrm{M}_n\text{—}\mathrm{C_6H_6}\cdot \tag{3-118}$$

Table 3-5 Transfer Constants for Chain Transfer Agents[a,b]

Transfer agent	$C_S \times 10^4$ for polymerization of	
	Styrene	Vinyl acetate
Benzene	0.023	1.2
Cyclohexane	0.031	7.0
Heptane	0.42	17.0 (50°C)
Toluene	0.125	21.6
Ethylbenzene	0.67	55.2
Isopropylbenzene	0.82	89.9
t-Butylbenzene	0.06	3.6
n-Butyl chloride	0.04	10
n-Butyl bromide	0.06	50
Acetone	0.40 (80°C)	11.7
Acetic acid	0.20 (80°C)	1.1, 10
n-Butyl alcohol	0.40 (80°C)	20
Chloroform	0.5	150
n-Butyl iodide	1.85	800
Butylamine	0.5	–
Triethylamine	7.1	370
n-Butyl disulfide	24	10,000
Carbon tetrachloride	90	9,600
Carbon tetrabromide	22,000	28,700 (70°C)
t-Butyl mercaptan	37,000	–
n-Butyl mercaptan	210,000	480,000

[a]Data are typical values taken from [41], p. II-77.
[b]All values are for 60°C unless otherwise noted.

The presence of the weak benzylic hydrogens in toluene, ethylbenzene, and isopropylbenzene leads to higher C_S values relative to benzene. The benzylic C—H breaks easily because the resultant radical is resonance stabilized.

$$\text{C}_6\text{H}_5\text{—}\dot{\text{C}}\text{H}_2 \longleftrightarrow \cdot\text{C}_6\text{H}_5\text{=CH}_2 \longleftrightarrow \cdot\text{C}_6\text{H}_5\text{=CH}_2 \longleftrightarrow \cdot\text{C}_6\text{H}_5\text{=CH}_2 \qquad (3\text{-}119)$$

The transfer constant for *t*-butylbenzene drops since there are no benzylic C—H bonds present. *n*-Butyl chloride and bromide behave like aliphatics with low transfer constants—corresponding to aliphatic C—H bond breakage. The iodide on the other hand transfers an iodide atom and shows a high C_S value due to the weakness of the C—I bond.

Acids, carbonyl compounds, ethers, amines, and alcohols have transfer constants comparable to those of aliphatic hydrocarbons—corresponding to C—H breakage. Some secondary and tertiary compounds, however, have higher C_S values than the hydrocarbons.

The weak S—S bond leads to high transfer constants for disulfides

$$M_n\cdot + RS{-}SR \longrightarrow M_n{-}SR + RS\cdot \tag{3-120}$$

The high C_S values for carbon tetrachloride and carbon tetrabromide are due to the weak carbon-halogen bonds. These bonds are especially weak because of the excellent stabilization of the trihalocarbon radicals formed by resonance involving the halogen free pairs of electrons

$$\text{Cl}_2\dot{\text{C}}{-}\text{Cl} \longleftrightarrow \text{Cl}{=}\text{C}(\text{Cl}){-}\text{Cl}\cdot \longleftrightarrow \text{Cl}{-}\text{C}(\text{Cl}){=}\dot{\text{Cl}} \longleftrightarrow \text{Cl}{-}\text{C}(\text{Cl}){=}\text{Cl}\cdot \tag{3-121}$$

The greater transfer constant for carbon tetrabromide compared to the tetrachloride is due to the weaker C—Br bond. The low C_S value for chloroform compared to carbon tetrachloride is explained by C—H bond breakage in the former. The thiols have the largest transfer constants of any known compounds due to the weak S—H bond.

Two interesting observations are made when the C_S values for various compounds are compared in the polymerization of various different monomers. The absolute value of the transfer constant for any one compound may change very significantly depending on the monomer being polymerized. This is clearly seen in Table 3-5 where many of the transfer agents are 1–2 orders of magnitude more active in vinyl acetate polymerization compared to styrene polymerization. This effect is a consequence of the greater reactivity of the vinyl acetate propagating radical. The chain transfer constant for any one compound generally increases in the order of increasing radical reactivity. The order of radical reactivity is vinyl chloride > vinyl acetate > acrylonitrile > methyl acrylate > methyl methacrylate >

styrene > 1,3-butadiene. Radical reactivity is discussed in greater detail in Chap. 6.

The order of reactivity of a series of transfer agents usually remains the same irrespective of the monomer when the transfer agents are relatively neutral in polarity. However, there are many very significant deviations from this generalization for polar transfer agents. Table 3-6 shows data for carbon tetrachloride and triethylamine with several monomers. The monomers are listed in decreasing order of reactivity for transfer reactions with neutral transfer agents such as hydrocarbons. It is apparent that the electron-rich (electron-donor) transfer agent triethylamine has enhanced reactivity with the electron-poor (electron-acceptor) monomers acrylonitrile, methyl acrylate, and methyl methacrylate. The electron-poor (electron-acceptor) transfer agent carbon tetrachloride has enhanced reactivity with the electron-rich (electron-donor) monomers vinyl acetate and styrene.

Table 3-6 Polar Effects in Chain Transfer[a,b,c]

Monomer	Chain transfer agent			
	CCl_4		$(C_2H_5)_3N$	
	$C_S \times 10^4$	k_{tr}	$C_S \times 10^4$	k_{tr}
Vinyl acetate	9,600	2,500	370	85
Acrylonitrile	0.85	0.17	3,800	760
Methyl acrylate	1.25[c]	0.26[c]	400	84
Methyl methacrylate	2.4	0.12	1,900	98
Styrene	90	1.6	7.1	0.13

[a] C_S values are taken from [41], p. II-77 and are for 60°C unless otherwise noted.

[b] k_{tr} values were calculated from Eq. 3-64 using the k_p values from Table 3-9.

[c] C_S value is at 80°C. The k_{tr} was calculated using the k_p value for 60°C.

The enhancement of chain transfer reactivity has been postulated [4] as occurring by stabilization of the respective transition states for the transfer reactions by contributions from polar structures such as

$$\sim\!\sim CH_2-\dot{C}H + Cl-CCl_3 \longleftrightarrow \sim\!\sim CH_2-\overset{+}{C}H\cdots\dot{C}l\cdots\bar{\ddot{C}}Cl_3 \qquad (3\text{-}122)$$

$$\sim\!\sim\!\sim CH_2-\underset{\displaystyle CN}{\overset{\bullet}{C}H} + H-\underset{\displaystyle CH_3}{CH}-N(CH_3)_2 \longleftrightarrow$$

$$\sim\!\sim\!\sim CH_2-\underset{\displaystyle CN}{\overset{-}{C}H}\cdots\cdots\overset{\bullet}{H}\cdots\cdots\underset{\displaystyle CH_3}{\overset{+}{C}H}-N(CH_3)_2 \qquad (3\text{-}123)$$

in which there is partial charge transfer between an electron-donor and an electron-acceptor. This type of *polar effect* is a general one encountered in free radical reactions. One usually observes the reactivity of an electron-donor radical to be greater with an electron-acceptor substrate than with an electron-donor substrate. The reverse is true of an electron-acceptor radical. The effect of polar effects on radical addition reactions will be considered in Sec. 6-3b-3.

3-6c-3 Applications of Chain Transfer Agents. The use of Eqs. 3-109, 3-110, and 3-116 allows one to quantitatively determine the effects of transfer to monomer, initiator, and solvent on the molecular weight of the product which can be obtained from a reaction system. Of even greater importance is the use of deliberately added chain transfer agents to control the molecular weight of a polymerization. Equation 3-116 can be used to determine the concentration of transfer agent needed to obtain a specifically desired molecular weight. When used in this manner, transfer agents are called "regulators" or "modifiers." Transfer agents with transfer constants of one or greater are especially useful since they can be used in small concentrations. Thus, mercaptans such as *n*-dodecyl mercaptan are used in the industrial emulsion copolymerization of styrene and butadiene for SBR rubbers. The production of very low molecular weight polymers by chain transfer (telomerization) is an industrially useful reaction. Ethylene polymerized in chloroform yields, after fluorination of its end groups, a starting material for fluorinated lubricants. Low molecular weight acrylic ester polymers have been used as plasticizers. On the other hand, benzene is used as the solvent for the production of high molecular weight polyethylene because of its very low transfer constant.

It is also useful to point out that chain transfer studies yield further corroboration of the concept of functional group reactivity independent of molecular size. Thus, one can vary the degree of polymerization for a monomer by using different chain transfer agents or different concentrations of the same transfer agent. Under these conditions, the propagation rate constant k_p is found to be independent of $\overline{X}_n$. Further, the transfer constant k_{tr} for a particular transfer agent is also independent of the size of the propagating radical.

3-6d Chain Transfer to Polymer

The previous discussion has ignored the possibility of chain transfer to polymer molecules. Transfer to polymer results in the formation of a radical site on a polymer chain. The polymerization of monomer at this site leads to the production of a branched polymer, for example

$$M_n\cdot + \sim\sim CH_2-\underset{H}{\overset{Y}{C}}\sim\sim \longrightarrow M_n-H + \sim\sim CH_2-\overset{Y}{\underset{\cdot}{C}}\sim\sim \xrightarrow{M} \sim\sim CH_2-\overset{Y}{\underset{\underset{\wr}{M_m}}{C}}\sim\sim \tag{3-124}$$

Ignoring chain transfer to polymer does not present a difficulty in obtaining precise values of C_I, C_M, and C_S since these are determined from data at low conversions. Under these conditions the polymer concentration is low and the extent of transfer to polymer is negligible.

Transfer to polymer cannot, however, be neglected for the practical situation where polymerization is carried to complete or high conversion. The effect of chain transfer to polymer plays a very significant role in determining the physical properties and the ultimate applications of a polymer. As indicated in Chap. 1, branching drastically decreases the crystallizability of a polymer.

The transfer constant C_P for chain transfer to polymer is determined with much difficulty. C_P cannot be simply determined by introducing the term $C_P[P]/[M]$ into Eq. 3-109 as is indicated in many introductory polymer texts. Transfer to polymer does not necessarily lead to a decrease in the overall degree of polymerization. Each act of transfer produces a branched polymer molecule of larger size than initially present in addition to prematurely terminating a propagating polymer chain.

The evaluation of C_P involves the difficult determination of the number of branches produced in a polymerization relative to the number of monomer molecules polymerized. This can be done by polymerizing a monomer in the presence of a known concentration of polymer of known molecular weight. The product of such an experiment consists of three different types of molecules:

Type 1. Unbranched molecules of the initial polymer.

Type 2. Unbranched molecules produced by polymerization of the monomer.

Type 3. Branched molecules arising from transfer of Type 2 radicals to Type 1 molecules.

The number of new polymer molecules produced in the system yields the number of Type 2 molecules. The total number of branches is obtained by performing a mass balance on the system and assuming the size of a branch is the same as a Type 2 molecule. This experimental analysis is inherently difficult and is additionally complicated if chain transfer to initiator, monomer, or some other species is occurring simultaneously. Other methods of determining the polymer transfer constant have also been employed but are usually not without ambiguity. Thus, for example, C_P for poly(vinyl acetate) has been determined by degradative hydrolysis [43]. This method assumes that transfer occurs at the acetoxy methyl group leading to polymer branches

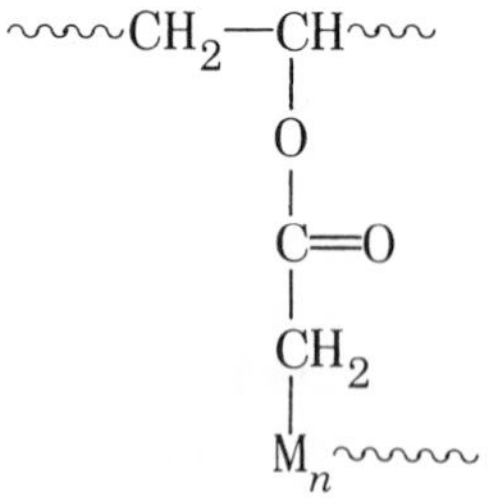

$$
\begin{array}{l}
\sim\sim CH_2-\underset{|}{C}H\sim\sim \\
\qquad\quad\; O \\
\qquad\quad\; | \\
\qquad\quad\; C{=}O \\
\qquad\quad\; | \\
\qquad\quad\; CH_2 \\
\qquad\quad\; | \\
\qquad\quad\; M_n\sim\sim\sim
\end{array}
$$

V

which can be cleaved from the original polymer molecule by ester hydrolysis of the linkage. However, there are much conflicting data which indicate that all of the transfer to polymer does not take place at the acetoxy methyl site.

Because of the experimental difficulties involved, there are relatively few reliable C_P values available in the literature. The values that are available [40] for any one polymer often vary considerably from each other. It is often most useful to consider the small model compound analog of a polymer (e.g., ethylbenzene or isopropylbenzene for polystyrene) to gain a correct perspective of the importance of polymer chain transfer. A consideration of the best available C_P values and those of the appropriate small model compounds indicates that the amount of transfer to polymer will not be high in most cases even at high conversion. C_P values are about 10^{-4} or slightly higher for many polymers such as polystyrene and poly(methyl methacrylate).

Flory [44] has derived the equation

$$\rho = -C_P\left[1 + \left(\frac{1}{p}\right)\ln(1-p)\right] \tag{3-125}$$

to express the *branching density* ρ as a function of the polymer transfer constant C_P and the extent of reaction p. The branching density ρ is the number of branches per monomer molecule polymerized. Using a C_P value of 1×10^{-4} and an 80% conversion, one calculates from Eq. 3-125 that there will be one branch for every 10^4 monomer units polymerized. Experimental data verify this result quite well [16]. In a typical styrene polymerization at 80% conversion, there is about one branch for every 4–10 $\times$ 10^3 monomer units for polymer molecular weights of 10^5–10^6. This corresponds to about one polymer chain in ten containing a branch [45].

The extent of branching is greater in polymers, such as poly(vinyl acetate), poly(vinyl chloride), and polyethylene, which have very reactive propagating radicals. Poly(vinyl acetate) has a C_P value which is probably in the range 2–5 $\times$ 10^{-4}. Further, vinyl acetate monomer was earlier noted (Table 3-3) as having a large C_M value. Transfer to monomer yields the species

$$CH_2{=}\overset{H}{C}{-}O{-}CO{-}\dot{C}H_2$$

VI

which can initiate polymerization at its radical end and can also enter into the propagation reaction of some other propagating radical. The result of this behavior is the formation of a branched polymer. Thus, extensive branching occurs in poly(vinyl acetate) since a branch is formed for each act of transfer to either monomer or polymer. Figure 3-9 shows the large extent of branching which occurs in vinyl acetate polymerization [46]. The extent of branching increases very rapidly during the last stages of the polymerization.

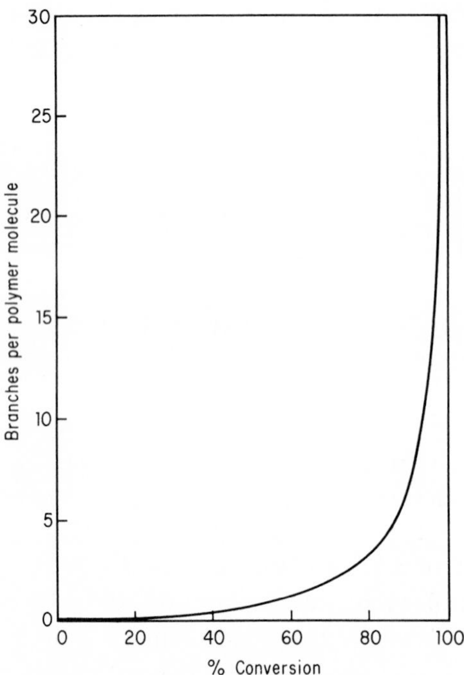

FIG. 3-9 *Extent of branching in vinyl acetate polymerization at 60°C. After [46] (by permission of Hüthig and Wepf Verlag, Basel).*

The extent of branching in polyethylene varies considerably depending on the polymerization temperature and other reaction conditions, but may reach as high as 30 branches per 500 monomer units. The branches in polyethylene are mainly short branches. These are evenly divided between ethyl and butyl branches and outnumber long branches by a factor of approximately 50. Butyl and ethyl branching probably arise from the following sequence of reactions

$$\sim\!\sim CH(H)-CH_2-CH_2-CH_2-\dot{C}H_2 \xrightarrow{\text{transfer}} \sim\!\sim \dot{C}H-CH_2-CH_2-CH_2-CH_3 \qquad (3\text{-}126a)$$

$$\downarrow CH_2{=}CH_2$$

$$\sim\!\sim CH(CH_2-\dot{C}H_2)-CH_2-CH(H)-CH_2-CH_3 \qquad (3\text{-}126b)$$

$$\xleftarrow{\text{transfer}}$$

$$\sim\!\sim CH(CH_2-CH_3)-CH_2-\dot{C}H-CH_2-CH_3 \qquad (3\text{-}126c)$$

Butyl branches are obtained by the unique "back-biting" self-transfer reaction in which the radical end abstracts a hydrogen from the fifth methylene linkage from its end (Eq. 3-126a). Ethyl branching arises from a second self-transfer (Eq. 3-126c) after one monomer molecule has been added (Eq. 3-126b).

3-7 INHIBITION AND RETARDATION

3-7a Types of Inhibitors and Retarders

The addition of certain substances suppresses the polymerization of monomers. These substances act by reacting with the initiating and propagating radicals and converting them either to non-radical species or radicals of reactivity too low to undergo propagation. Such polymerization suppressors are classified according to their effectiveness. *Inhibitors* stop every radical and polymerization is completely halted until they are consumed. *Retarders* are less efficient and stop only a portion of the radicals. In this case, polymerization occurs, but at a slower rate. The difference between inhibitors and retarders is simply one of degree and not kind. Figure 3-10 shows these effects in the thermal polymerization of styrene [47]. Polymerization is completely stopped by benzoquinone, a typical inhibitor, during an *induction* or *inhibition period* (curve 2). At the end of this period, when the benzoquinone has been consumed, polymerization proceeds at the same rate as in the absence of inhibitor (curve 1). Nitrobenzene, a retarder, lowers the polymerization rate without an inhibition period (curve 3). The behavior of nitrosobenzene, ϕNO, is

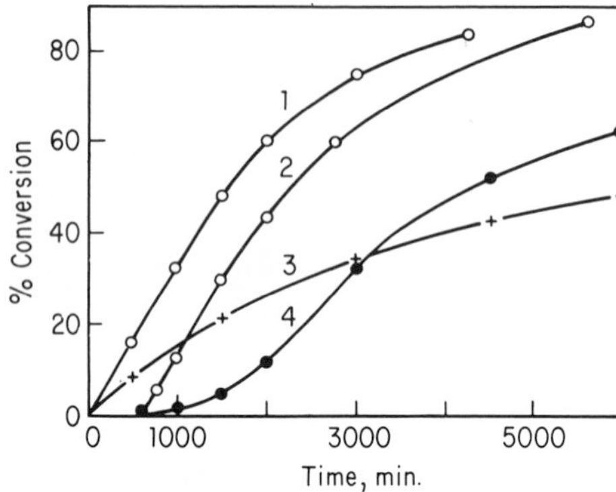

FIG. 3-10 *Inhibition and retardation in the thermal, self-catalyzed polymerization of styrene at 100°C. Curve 1: no inhibitor; Curve 2: 0.1% benzoquinone; Curve 3: 0.5% nitrobenzene; Curve 4: 0.2% nitrosobenzene; After [47] (by permission of Verlag Chemie GmbH, Weinheim).*

more complex (curve 4). It is initially an inhibitor but is apparently converted to a product which acts as a retarder after the inhibition period. This latter behavior is not at all uncommon. Inhibition and retardation are usually the cause of the irreproducible polymerization rates observed with insufficiently purified monomers. Impurities present in the monomer may act as inhibitors or retarders. On the other hand, inhibitors are invariably added to commercial monomers to prevent premature thermal polymerization during storage and shipment. These inhibitors are usually removed prior to polymerization or, alternately, an appropriate excess of initiator may be used to compensate for their presence.

Various types of compounds act as inhibitors and retarders. Stable free radicals which are too stable to initiate polymerization but which can still react with radicals are one type of radical terminator. Diphenylpicrylhydrazyl (DPPH) is such a radical and its use as a radical scavenger has been discussed (Sec. 3-4f-3). The stoichiometry between the number of kinetic chains terminated and the number of DPPH radicals consumed is 1:1. There are essentially no other stable radicals which are of practical utility as polymerization inhibitors.

The most useful class of inhibitors are molecules which react with chain radicals to yield radicals of low reactivity. Quinones are probably the most important class of inhibitors. Benzoquinone completely stops the polymerization of a variety of monomers including vinyl acetate [31] and styrene [16]. The behavior of quinones is quite complex. The stoichiometry between the number of kinetic chains terminated and the number of quinone molecules consumed varies appreciably. For benzoquinone with many monomers the stoichiometry is 1:1. Chloranil (2,3,5,6-tetrachlorobenzoquinone) is an efficient inhibitor for vinyl acetate but undergoes copolymerization (Chap. 6) with styrene

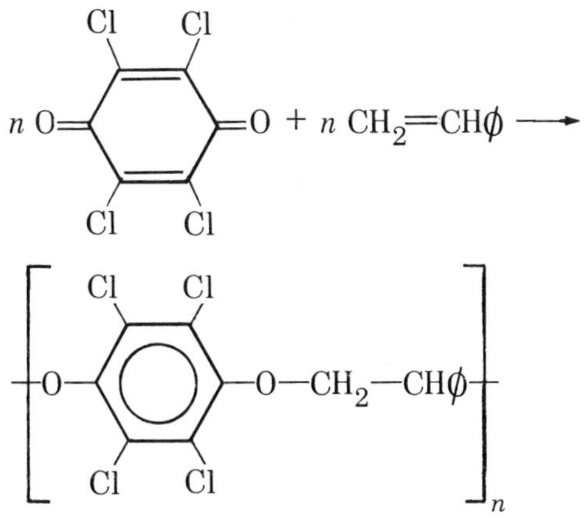

$$n\ \mathrm{O{=}C_6Cl_4{=}O} + n\ \mathrm{CH_2{=}CH\phi} \longrightarrow \left[\mathrm{-O{-}C_6Cl_4{-}O{-}CH_2{-}CH\phi-}\right]_n \tag{3-127}$$

with retardation of the overall polymerization rate [48]. The mechanism of inhibition by quinones is not completely understood [5, 16]. Termination of chain radicals by quinones probably involves addition to the oxygen atom or the ring of the quinone

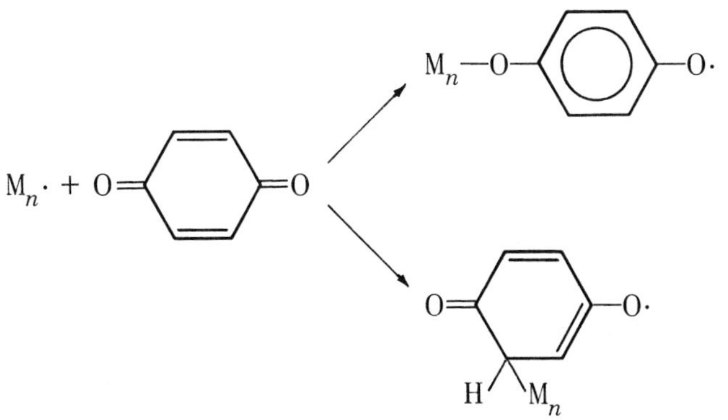

$$\mathrm{M}_n\cdot + \mathrm{O{=}C_6H_4{=}O} \longrightarrow \mathrm{M}_n\mathrm{{-}O{-}C_6H_4{-}O}\cdot \tag{3-128a}$$

$$\mathrm{M}_n\cdot + \mathrm{O{=}C_6H_4{=}O} \longrightarrow \mathrm{O{=}C_6H_4(H)(M_n){-}O}\cdot \tag{3-128b}$$

although the disproportionation reactions

$$\sim\!\sim CH_2-\underset{Y}{\overset{H}{C}}\cdot + O=\langle C_6H_4\rangle=O \;\nearrow\; \sim\!\sim CH=\underset{Y}{\overset{H}{C}} + HO-\langle C_6H_4\rangle-O\cdot \tag{3-128c}$$

$$\searrow\; \sim\!\sim CH_2-\underset{Y}{\overset{H}{C}}H + O=\langle C_6H_4\rangle=O\;\cdot \tag{3-128d}$$

may also be important. The radical to inhibitor stoichiometry is determined by the fate of the inhibitor radicals produced in Eqs. 3-128a–d. The possible reactions involve dimerization, disproportionation between themselves, or reaction with other chain radicals. Disproportionation results in the regeneration of one inhibitor molecule per each pair of inhibitor radicals. Dimerization would lead to a 1:1 radical to quinone ratio while the other two reactions yield a 2:1 ratio. Stoichiometric ratios of both 2:1 and 1:1 have been observed. The complexity of quinone action is shown by the observation that they act only as retarders for methyl methacrylate and methyl acrylate.

Hydroquinone (p-HOϕOH) and other dihydroxybenzenes such as t-butylcatechol also act as inhibitors but only in the presence of oxygen. The inhibiting effect is due to their oxidation to quinones [48]. Polyalkyl ring-substituted phenols and anilines act as inhibitors in some instances. The mechanism may involve hydrogen abstraction

$$M_n\cdot + \text{2,4,6-}R_3C_6H_2\text{-OH} \longrightarrow M_n\!-\!H + \text{2,4,6-}R_3C_6H_2\text{-}\dot{O} \tag{3-129}$$

followed by coupling of the phenoxy radical (either at the oxygen atom or on the ring) with other polymer radicals. The unsubstituted phenol and aniline are relatively unreactive as inhibitors.

Aromatic di- and trinitro compounds terminate chain radicals although the inhibition is not as complete generally as in the case of the quinones. The nitro compounds act as inhibitors only in a few instances such as in vinyl acetate polymerization [4]. They retard styrene polymerization [47] and have no effect on methacrylate or acrylate polymerizations [49]. The stoichiometry varies appreciably depending on the monomer. The mechanism of radical termination may involve radical attack on both the aromatic ring and the nitro group

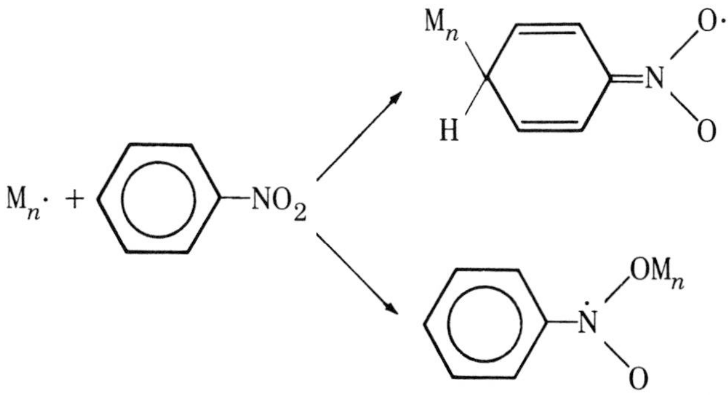

$$M_n\cdot + C_6H_5\text{—}NO_2 \longrightarrow \text{(}M_n\text{, H)}C_6H_5\text{=}N(O\cdot)O \qquad (3\text{-}130a)$$

$$M_n\cdot + C_6H_5\text{—}NO_2 \longrightarrow C_6H_5\text{—}\dot{N}(OM_n)O \qquad (3\text{-}130b)$$

High radical:nitrobenzene ratios up to 5 or 6 have been observed for 1,3,5-trinitrobenzene.

A large number of other substances such as oxygen, sulfur, carbon, and ferric chloride (Sec. 3-4f-3) also show the ability to inhibit polymerization [16]. An interesting inhibitor is molecular oxygen (a diradical) which reacts with chain radicals to form the relatively unreactive peroxy radical

$$M_n\cdot + O_2 \longrightarrow M_n\text{—}OO\cdot \qquad (3\text{-}131)$$

However, oxygen has been known to initiate the polymerization of many monomers. Some commercial processes for ethylene polymerization involve initiation by oxygen. Initiation in this case may occur by the thermal decomposition of the peroxy radical in Eq. 3-131 or of other oxygenated species formed in the system.

3-7b Kinetics of Inhibition or Retardation

The kinetics of retarded polymerizations can be analyzed [50] using a scheme consisting of the usual initiation (Eq. 3-14), propagation (Eq. 3-15), and termination (Eq. 3-16) reactions in addition to the inhibition reaction

$$\mathrm{M}_n\cdot + \mathrm{Z} \xrightarrow{k_z} \mathrm{M}_n + \mathrm{Z}\cdot \tag{3-132}$$

where Z is the inhibitor. The kinetics are relatively simplified if one assumes that the inhibitor radicals Z· do not reinitiate polymerization and that they terminate without regeneration of the original inhibitor molecule.

The steady-state assumption for the radical concentration leads to

$$\frac{d[\mathrm{M}\cdot]}{dt} = R_i - k_t[\mathrm{M}\cdot]^2 - k_z[\mathrm{Z}][\mathrm{M}\cdot] = 0 \tag{3-133}$$

which can be combined with Eq. 3-8 to yield

$$\frac{R_p^2 k_t}{k_p^2[\mathrm{M}]^2} + \frac{R_p[\mathrm{Z}]k_z}{k_p[\mathrm{M}]} - R_i = 0 \tag{3-134}$$

Equation 3-134 has been used to correlate rate data in inhibited polymerizations [51]. A consideration of Eq. 3-134 shows that R_p is inversely proportional to the ratio k_z/k_p of the rate constants for inhibition and propagation. This ratio is often referred to as the *inhibition constant* z, that is

$$z = \frac{k_z}{k_p} \tag{3-135}$$

It is further seen that R_p depends on R_i to a power between one-half and unity depending on the relative magnitudes of the first two terms in Eq. 3-134. Two limiting cases of Eq. 3-134 exist. When the second term is negligible compared to the first, the polymerization is not retarded and Eq. 3-134 simplifies to Eq. 3-24.

For the case where the retardation is strong ($k_z/k_p \gg 1$), normal bimolecular termination will be negligible. Under these conditions the first term in Eq. 3-134 is negligible and one has

$$\frac{R_p[\mathrm{Z}]k_z}{k_p[\mathrm{M}]} - R_i = 0 \tag{3-136a}$$

or

$$R_p = \frac{k_p[\mathrm{M}]R_i}{k_z[\mathrm{Z}]} = \frac{-d[\mathrm{M}]}{dt} \tag{3-136b}$$

Equation 3-136 shows the rate of retarded polymerization to be dependent on the first power of the initiation rate. Further, R_p is inversely dependent on the inhibitor concentration. The induction period observed for inhibited polymerization is directly proportional to the inhibitor concentration.

The inhibitor concentration will decrease with time and [Z] at any time is given by

$$[\mathrm{Z}] = [\mathrm{Z}]_0 - \frac{R_i t}{y} \tag{3-137}$$

where $[\mathrm{Z}]_0$ is the initial concentration of Z, t is time, and y is the number of radicals terminated per inhibitor molecule. Combination of Eqs. 3-135, 3-136b, and 3-137 yields

$$\frac{-d[\mathrm{M}]}{dt} = \frac{R_i[\mathrm{M}]}{z([\mathrm{Z}]_0 - R_i t/y)} \tag{3-138a}$$

or, by rearrangement

$$\frac{-1}{d\ln[\mathrm{M}]/dt} = \frac{z[\mathrm{Z}]_0}{R_i} - \frac{zt}{y} \tag{3-138b}$$

A plot of the left side of Eq. 3-138b versus time is linear and the values of z and y can be obtained from the intercept and slope, respectively, if $[\mathrm{Z}]_0$ and R_i are known. The method involves difficult experimentation since the polymerization rates being measured are quite small, especially if z is large. Figure 3-11 shows Eq. 3-138b plotted for inhibited vinyl acetate polymerization [31]. Table 3-7 shows selected z values for various systems. One can again observe that, as with chain transfer constants, the inhibition constant for a

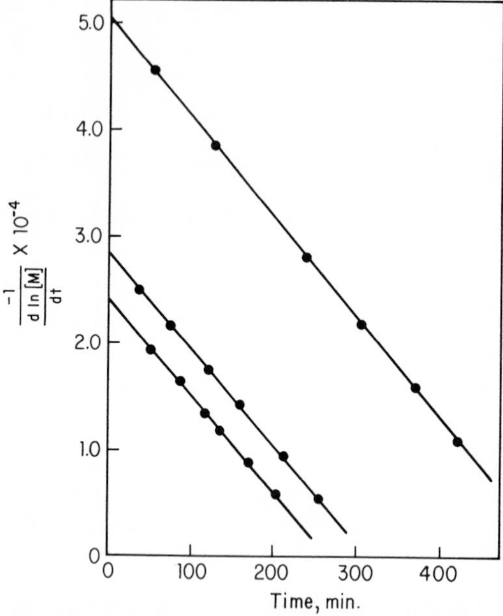

FIG. 3-11 *The inhibition of the benzoyl peroxide catalyzed polymerization of vinyl acetate by duroquinone at 45°C. The three lines are for different concentrations of duroquinone. After [31] (by permission of American Chemical Society, Washington).*

compound varies considerably depending on the reactivity of the propagating radical. Thus, 1,3,5-trinitrobenzene acts as an inhibitor with the highly reactive vinyl acetate radical but only a retarder with the less reactive methyl acrylate radical.

A careful consideration of Eq. 3-138b shows that for a strong retarder ($z \gg 1$), the polymerization rate will be negligible until the inhibitor concentration is markedly reduced. When the inhibitor concentration becomes sufficiently low, propagation can become competitive with the inhibition reaction. This is more readily seen by considering the equation

$$\frac{d[Z]}{d[M]} = \frac{z[Z]}{[M]} \tag{3-139}$$

obtained by dividing the rate expression for the disappearance of inhibitor (Eq. 3-132) by that for monomer disappearance (Eq. 3-15).

Table 3-7 Inhibitor Constants[a]

Inhibitor	Monomer[b]	$z = k_z/k_p$
Nitrobenzene	Methyl acrylate	0.00464
	Styrene	0.326
	Vinyl acetate	11.2
1,3,5-Trinitrobenzene	Methyl acrylate	0.204
	Styrene	64.2
	Vinyl acetate	404
p-Benzoquinone	Acrylonitrile	0.91
	Methyl methacrylate (60°C)	4.5
	Styrene	518
DPPH	Methyl methacrylate (44°C)	2,000
$FeCl_3$ in DMF	Acrylonitrile (60°C)	3.3
	Styrene (60°C)	536
	Vinyl acetate (60°C)	~800[c]
Oxygen	Methyl methacrylate	33,000
	Styrene	14,600
Sulfur	Methyl methacrylate (44°C)	0.075
	Vinyl acetate (44°C)	470
Aniline	Methyl acrylate	0.0001
	Vinyl acetate	0.015
Phenol	Methyl acrylate	0.0002
	Vinyl acetate	0.012

[a]Data are taken from [41], p. II-71.
[b]All data are for 50°C unless otherwise noted.
[c]Estimated from separate values of k_p and k_z.

Integration of Eq. 3-139 yields

$$\log\left(\frac{[Z]}{[Z]_0}\right) = z \log\left(\frac{[M]}{[M]_0}\right) \tag{3-140}$$

where $[Z]_0$ and $[M]_0$ are initial concentrations. It is apparent from this expression that the inhibitor must be almost completely consumed before the monomer can be polymerized. Equation 3-140 can also be used to determine the inhibition constant from the slope of a plot of log [Z] versus log [M].

3-7c Autoinhibition of Allylic Monomers

An especially interesting case of inhibition is the internal or *autoinhibition* of allylic monomers ($CH_2{=}CH{-}CH_2Y$). Allylic monomers such as allyl acetate polymerize at abnormally low rates with the unexpected dependence of the rate on the first power of the initiator concentration. Further, the degree of polymerization, which is independent of the polymerization rate, is very low—being only 14 for allyl acetate. These effects are the consequence of *degradative chain transfer* (Case 4 in Table 3-2). The propagating radical in such a polymerization is very reactive while the allylic C—H (the C—H bond alpha to the double bond) in the monomer is quite weak—resulting in facile chain transfer to monomer

$$\sim\!\!\sim CH_2{-}\underset{\substack{|\\ CH_2Y}}{\overset{H}{C}}\cdot \quad + \; CH_2{=}CH{-}\underset{H}{\overset{H}{C}}Y \longrightarrow$$

$$\sim\!\!\sim CH_2{-}\underset{\substack{|\\ CH_2Y}}{CH_2} \quad + \; CH_2{=}CH{-}\underset{H}{\dot{C}}Y \;\updownarrow\; \dot{C}H_2{-}CH{=}\underset{H}{C}Y \tag{3-141}$$

The weakness of the allylic C—H bond arises from the high resonance stability of the allylic radical which is formed. Degradative chain transfer competes exceptionally well with normal propagation and the polymer chains are terminated by transfer after the addition of only a very few monomer units. That the allylic C—H bond is the one broken in the transfer reaction has been shown [52] by experiments with $CH_2{=}CH{-}CD_2OCOCH_3$. The deuterated allyl acetate polymerizes 1.9–2.9 times as fast as normal allyl acetate and has a degree of polymerization 2.4 times as large under the same conditions. This is what would be expected since the C—D bond is stronger than the C—H bond due to its lower zero point energy [4] and degradative chain transfer would therefore be decreased in the deuterated monomer.

The allylic radicals which are formed are too stable to initiate polymerization and the kinetic chain also terminates when the transfer occurs. The fate of the allylic radicals is unclear. Reaction 3-141 is equivalent to termination by an inhibitor which is the monomer itself in this case. In this polymerization the propagation and termination reactions will have the same general kinetic expression with first order dependencies on initiator and monomer concentrations since the same reactants and stoichiometry are involved. The degree of polymerization is simply the ratio of the rate constants for propagation and termination and is independent of the initiator concentration. In addition to the termination by degradative chain transfer of the allylic hydrogen atom, additional termination occurs in some allyl monomers by radical displacement according to

$$M_n\cdot + CH_2{=}CH{-}CH_2OCOR \longrightarrow M_n{-}CH_2{-}CH{=}CH_2 + RCOO\cdot \quad (3\text{-}142)$$

Hydrogen abstraction is, however, the predominant termination reaction for allyl monomers.

The low reactivity of α-olefins such as propylene or of 1,1-dialkyl olefins such as isobutylene toward radical polymerization is probably a consequence of degradative chain transfer with the allylic hydrogens. It should be pointed out, however, that other monomers such as methyl methacrylate and methacrylonitrile which also contain allylic C—H bonds do not undergo extensive degradative chain transfer. This is due to the lowered reactivity of the propagating radicals in these monomers. The ester and nitrile substituents stabilize the radicals and decrease their reactivity toward transfer. Simultaneously the reactivity of the monomer toward propagation is enhanced. These monomers, unlike the α-olefins and 1,1-dialkyl olefins, yield high polymers in radical polymerizations.

3-8 DETERMINATION OF ABSOLUTE RATE CONSTANTS

3-8a Non-Steady-State Kinetics

There are five different types of rate constants which are of concern in radical chain polymerization—those for initiation, propagation, termination, chain transfer, and inhibition. The use of polymerization data under steady-state conditions allows the evaluation of only the initiation rate constant k_d (or k_i for thermal initiation). The ratio $k_p/k_t^{1/2}$ or k_p^2/k_t can be obtained from Eq. 3-24 since R_p, R_i, and [M] are measurable. Similarly, the chain transfer constant k_{tr}/k_p and the inhibition constant k_z/k_p can be obtained by any of several methods discussed. However, steady-state data do not allow the evaluation of the individual k_p, k_t, k_{tr}, and k_z values. It is necessary to employ non-steady-state conditions to determine these individual rate constants. The treatment discussed here is essentially that of Flory [53] and Walling [4].

Consider a photochemical polymerization. The rate of change of the radical concentration will be given by the difference between their rates of production and termination

$$\frac{d[\mathrm{M}\cdot]}{dt} = R_i - 2k_t[\mathrm{M}\cdot]^2 \tag{3-143}$$

The various terms in this and subsequent equations in this section apply to non-steady-state quantities; appropriate steady-state quantities are denoted by the subscript s. For steady-state conditions Eq. 3-143 becomes

$$(R_i)_s = 2k_t[\mathrm{M}\cdot]_s^2 \tag{3-144}$$

Combining Eqs. 3-143 and 3-144 yields

$$\frac{d[\mathrm{M}\cdot]}{dt} = 2k_t([\mathrm{M}\cdot]_s^2 - [\mathrm{M}\cdot]^2) \tag{3-145}$$

It is convenient and indeed necessary at this point to define the parameter τ_s as the *average lifetime of a growing radical* under steady-state conditions. The radical lifetime is given by the steady-state radical concentration divided by its steady-state rate of disappearance

$$\tau_s = \frac{[\mathrm{M}\cdot]_s}{2k_t[\mathrm{M}\cdot]_s^2} = \frac{1}{2k_t[\mathrm{M}\cdot]_s} \tag{3-146}$$

Combination of Eq. 3-146 with Eq. 3-21 at steady-state yields

$$\tau_s = \frac{k_p[\mathrm{M}]}{2k_t(R_p)_s} \tag{3-147}$$

The individual constants k_p and k_t could be determined from Eqs. 3-147 and 3-24 if τ_s were known. It is the objective of non-steady-state experiments to determine τ_s for just this purpose.

Integration of Eq. 3-145 yields

$$\ln\left[\frac{(1 + [\mathrm{M}\cdot]/[\mathrm{M}\cdot]_s)}{(1 - [\mathrm{M}\cdot]/[\mathrm{M}\cdot]_s)}\right] = 4k_t[\mathrm{M}\cdot]_s(t-t_0) \tag{3-148}$$

where t_0 is the integration constant such that $[\mathrm{M}\cdot] = 0$ at time t_0. Combining Eqs. 3-146 and 3-148 gives

$$\tanh^{-1}\left(\frac{[\mathrm{M}\cdot]}{[\mathrm{M}\cdot]_s}\right) = \frac{(t-t_0)}{\tau_s} \tag{3-149}$$

or

$$\frac{[\mathrm{M}\cdot]}{[\mathrm{M}\cdot]_s} = \frac{R_p}{(R_p)_s} = \tanh\left(\frac{(t-t_0)}{\tau_s}\right) \tag{3-150}$$

(The reader should be familiar with the hyperbolic tangent and inverse hyperbolic tangent so as to derive Eqs. 3-149 and 3-150.) The t in these equations is the time of illumination. Now consider this polymerization as proceeding with intermittent illumination, i.e., with alternate light and dark periods. At the very beginning, the radical concentration is zero but at any time following, the radical concentration never falls to zero again. It has, instead, some value $[\mathrm{M}\cdot]_2 > 0$ at the start of a period of illumination or light period (which corresponds to the end of a dark period). Therefore, Eq. 3-149 becomes

$$\frac{t_0}{\tau_s} = -\tanh^{-1}\left(\frac{[\mathrm{M}\cdot]_2}{[\mathrm{M}\cdot]_s}\right) \tag{3-151}$$

and

$$-\tanh^{-1}\left(\frac{[\mathrm{M}\cdot]_1}{[\mathrm{M}\cdot]_s}\right) - \tanh^{-1}\left(\frac{[\mathrm{M}\cdot]_2}{[\mathrm{M}\cdot]_s}\right) = \frac{t}{\tau_s} \tag{3-152}$$

where $[M\cdot]_1$ is the radical concentration after a light period of time t. $[M\cdot]_1$ also corresponds to the radical concentration at the start of a dark period. The curve OAE in Figure 3-12 shows the buildup in radical concentration during a light period according to Eq. 3-152 when the initial radical concentration is zero at $t_0 = 0$.

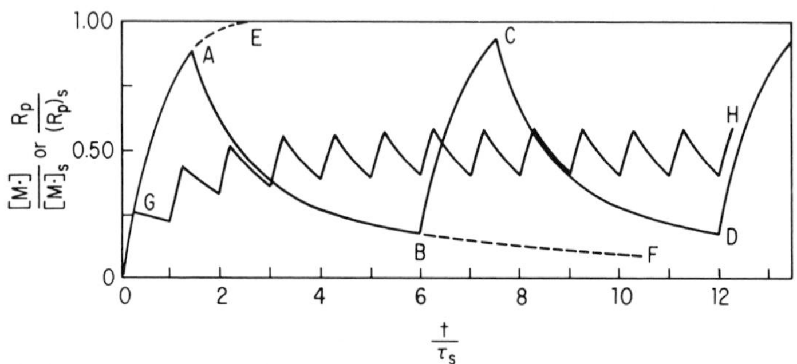

FIG. 3-12 *Plot of $[M\cdot]/[M\cdot]_s$ versus time during alternating light and dark periods. Adapted from [53], P. J. Flory, "Principles of Polymer Chemistry." Copyright 1953 by Cornell University. Used by permission of Cornell University Press, Ithaca.*

The light is now turned off at time t and radical decay occurs during the dark period according to

$$\frac{d[M\cdot]}{dt} = -2k_t[M\cdot]^2 \tag{3-153}$$

which on integration yields

$$\frac{1}{[M\cdot]} - \frac{1}{[M\cdot]_1} = 2k_t t' \tag{3-154}$$

where $[M\cdot]$ is the radical concentration after a further time interval t' corresponding to the time of darkness. Multiplying Eq. 3-154 through by $[M\cdot]_s$ and combining with Eq. 3-146 yields

$$\frac{[M\cdot]_s}{[M\cdot]} - \frac{[M\cdot]_s}{[M\cdot]_1} = \frac{t'}{\tau_s} \tag{3-155a}$$

$$\text{or} \quad \frac{(R_p)_s}{R_p} - \frac{(R_p)_s}{(R_p)_1} = \frac{t'}{\tau_s} \tag{3-155b}$$

The radical decay according to Eq. 3-155 is shown as curve ABF in Fig. 3-13.

One method of determining τ_s is the *after-effect* technique which employs Eq. 3-155b. The polymerization rate $(R_p)_s$ under steady-state conditions is observed using constant illumination. The illumination is stopped and the subsequent rate R_p is determined as a function of the time t' after the start of darkness. The ratio $(R_p)_s/R_p$ is plotted against t' according to Eq. 3-155b and the slope is $1/\tau_s$. The experimental procedures for obtaining τ_s by this technique, although quite difficult because very slow reaction rates must be measured, have been successful and are used [54]. Alternately, one can use fast detection methods to follow the polymerization during illumination before steady-state has been reached. The use of flash photolysis in which high radical concentrations are produced by an intense pulse of light from a discharge tube has also been used [55].

3-8b Rotating Sector Method

The more common technique employed to determine τ_s is the *rotating sector method* involving the alternating of light and dark periods. This method requires a study of the polymerization rate as a function of cycle time (the time for one light and one dark period).

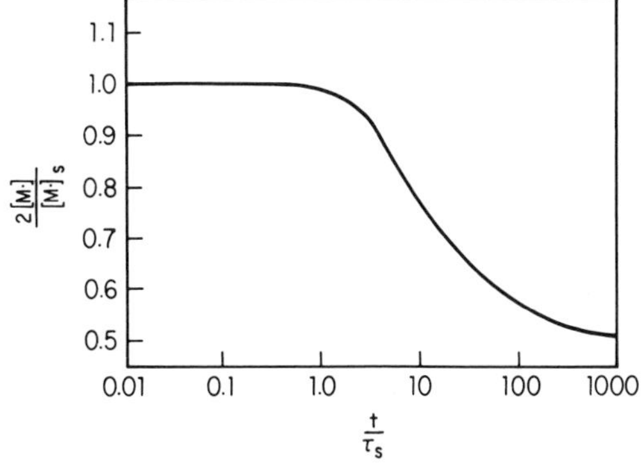

FIG. 3-13 *Semi-log plot of* $2[M\cdot]/[M\cdot]_s$ *versus* t/τ_s. *After [57] (by permission of American Chemical Society, Washington).*

Consider the specific case where the ratio r of the length t' of the dark period to the length t of a light period is 3. If the cycle time is very long compared to τ_s (slow flickering), the R_p will be equal to $(R_p)_s$ during the entire light period and zero during the entire dark period. The reason for this is that the times for the radical concentration to reach steady-state or to decay to zero are small compared to times t and t', respectively. The average polymerization rate $\bar{R}_p$ over one complete cycle will be one-fourth that of the steady-state value since the system is illuminated only one-fourth of the time, that is

$$\bar{R}_p = \frac{(R_p)_s}{4} \tag{3-156}$$

If the cycle time is reduced (fast flickering), radical decay during the dark period is incomplete and the steady-state radical concentration is not reached during the light period (Fig. 3-12). The radical concentration averaged over a cycle will be greater than $(R_p)_s/4$ because the decay during a dark period is less than the buildup during a light period. A very fast cycle time maintains the radical concentration at approximately a constant level (curve OGH in Fig. 3-12) and is equivalent to polymerization under constant illumination at an intensity $1/(1+r)$ times that actually used. The ratio of the average polymerization rate $(\bar{R}_p)_\infty$ at very high or infinite speed of sector rotation to the steady-state rate is then given by

$$\frac{(\bar{R}_p)_\infty}{(R_p)_s} = \frac{1}{(1+r)^{1/2}} \tag{3-157}$$

which equals 1/2 for the case of $r = 3$. Thus, the average rate increases from one-fourth to one-half of $(R_p)_s$ as the cycle or flickering frequency $1/(t+rt)$ increases from a very low to a very high value compared with $1/\tau_s$.

The mathematical treatment of flickering illumination was originally treated by Briers, Chapman, and Walters [56] and is applicable here. After a number of cycles, the radical concentration oscillates uniformly with a constant radical concentration $[M\cdot]_1$ at the end of each light period of duration t and a constant radical concentration

$[M\cdot]_2$ at the end of each dark period of duration $t' = rt$. Applying Eqs. 3-152 and 3-155a, one obtains

$$\tanh^{-1}\left(\frac{[M\cdot]_1}{[M\cdot]_s}\right) - \tanh^{-1}\left(\frac{[M\cdot]_2}{[M\cdot]_s}\right) = \frac{t}{\tau_s} \tag{3-158}$$

and

$$\frac{[M\cdot]_s}{[M\cdot]_2} - \frac{[M\cdot]_s}{[M\cdot]_1} = \frac{rt}{\tau_s} \tag{3-159}$$

The maximum and minimum values of the ratios $[M\cdot]_1/[M\cdot]_s$ and $[M\cdot]_2/[M\cdot]_s$ can be calculated from Eqs. 3-158 and 3-159 for given values of r and t/τ_s. The average radical concentration $\overline{[M\cdot]}$ over a cycle or several cycles is given by

$$\overline{[M\cdot]}(t+rt) = \int_0^t [M\cdot]\,dt + \int_0^{t'} [M\cdot]\,dt' \tag{3-160}$$

where the first integral (for the light period) is given by Eq. 3-157 and the second integral (for the dark period) is given by Eq. 3-159. Evaluation [57] of the integrals in Eq. 3-160 yields

$$\frac{\overline{[M\cdot]}}{[M\cdot]_s} = (r+1)^{-1}\left[1 + \frac{\tau_s}{t}\ln\left(\frac{[M\cdot]_1/[M\cdot]_2 + [M\cdot]_1/[M\cdot]_s}{1 + [M\cdot]_1/[M\cdot]_s}\right)\right] \tag{3-161}$$

Using Eq. 3-161 with Eqs. 3-158 and 3-159, one can calculate the ratio $\overline{[M\cdot]}/[M\cdot]_s$ as a function of t/τ_s for a fixed value of r. A semi-log plot of such data for $r = 3$ is shown in Fig. 3-13. In accordance with an earlier conclusion, the radical concentration falls from one-half of the steady-state value for fast flickering to one-fourth for slow flickering.

In order to experimentally determine the τ_s value for a particular system, one interposes a rotating sector or disc in between the system and the light source. The sector has a portion cut out which determines the value of r. The steady-state polymerization rate is first measured without the sector present. Then the average rate $\overline{R}_p$ is measured with the sector present at increasing rates of sector rotation. The cycle time as well as t and t' are determined by the rate of sector rotation. The data are plotted as the rate ratio $\overline{R}_p/(R_p)_s$ versus $\log t$. Alternately, one can plot the data as the rate ratio $\overline{R}_p/(\overline{R}_p)_\infty$ since this ratio is related to $\overline{R}_p/(R_p)_s$ through Eq. 3-157. The theoretical curve (e.g., Fig. 3-13) for the same r value is placed on top of the experimental curve and shifted on the abscissa until a best fit is obtained. The displacement on the abscissa of one curve from the other yields $\log \tau_s$ since the abscissa for the theoretical curve is $\log t - \log \tau_s$. Figure 3-14 shows such a determination for the polymerization of methacrylamide in water solution initiated by the photochemical decomposition of hydrogen peroxide [58].

The experimental determination of τ_s then allows the calculation of k_p, k_t, k_{tr}, and k_z. The ratios $k_p/k_t^{1/2}$ and k_p/k_t are obtained from Eqs. 3-24 and 3-147, respectively. Combination of these ratios yields the individual values of k_p and k_t. Quantities such as $[\mathrm{M}\cdot]_s$ and R_t can be calculated from Eqs. 3-21 and 3-22, respectively. k_{tr} and k_z can be obtained from the values of the chain transfer and inhibition constants.

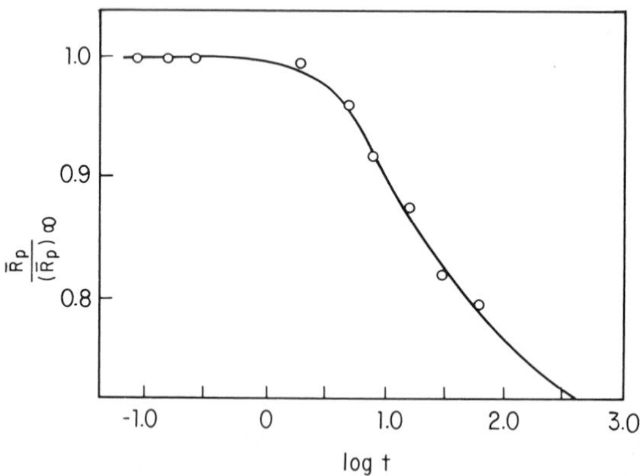

FIG. 3-14 *The ratio of the polymerization rate of methacrylamide for intermittent illumination with light periods of t seconds to the value at very high (infinite) sector speed plotted against t. The circles are the experimental points; the line is the theoretical curve. After [58] (by permission of The Faraday Society, London).*

3-8c Typical Values of Reaction Parameters

Table 3-8 shows the values of the various concentrations, rates, and rate constants involved in the photopolymerization of methacrylamide as well as the range of values that are generally encountered in radical chain polymerizations. For the methacrylamide case, the experimentally determined quantities were R_i, $(R_p)_s$, [M], [I], $k_p/k_t^{1/2}$, τ_s, and k_p/k_t. All of the other parameters were then calculated in the appropriate manner. These values are typical of radical polymerizations. The k_p value ($\sim 10^3$) is larger by many orders of magnitude than the usual reaction rate constant (for example, Tables 2-1, 2-2, and 2-5 show rate constants of approximately 10^{-3}, 10^{-2}, and 10^{-6} for esterification, urethane formation, and phenol-formaldehyde polymerization, respectively). Propagation is therefore rapid and high polymer is formed essentially instantaneously. However, the even larger k_t value ($\sim 10^7$) leads to quick termination, low radical concentrations ($\sim 10^{-8}$ molar), and short radical lifetimes. The radical lifetime for methacrylamide in these experiments was 2.62 seconds but it can be much shorter under

Table 3-8 Reaction Parameters in Radical Chain Polymerization

Quantity	Units	General range of values	Methacrylamide photopolymerization[a]
R_i	moles/liter-sec	10^{-8}-10^{-10}	8.75×10^{-9}
k_d	sec^{-1}	10^{-4}-10^{-6}	–
[I]	moles/liter	10^{-2}-10^{-4}	3.97×10^{-2}
$[M\cdot]_s$	moles/liter	10^{-7}-10^{-9}	2.30×10^{-8}
$(R_p)_s$	moles/liter-sec	10^{-4}-10^{-6}	3.65×10^{-6}
[M]	moles/liter	10-10^{-1}	0.20
k_p	liters/mole-sec	10^2-10^4	7.96×10^2
R_t	moles/liter-sec	10^{-8}-10^{-10}	8.73×10^{-9}
k_t	liters/mole-sec	10^6-10^8	8.25×10^6
τ_s	sec	10^{-1}-10	2.62
k_p/k_t	none	10^{-4}-10^{-6}	9.64×10^{-5}
$k_p/k_t^{1/2}$	$(liters/mole\text{-}sec)^{1/2}$	1-10^{-2}	2.77×10^{-1}

[a]Values are taken directly or recalculated from data in [58].

other conditions or for other monomers. It is interesting to compare the experimental value (8.75×10^{-9}) of R_i with the calculated value (8.73×10^{-9}) of R_t. The excellent agreement of the two indicates the validity of the steady-state assumption.

The rate constants for propagation and termination have been determined for many monomers. The values for some of the common monomers are shown in Table 3-9. The monomers have been listed in the order of decreasing reactivity of their radicals (see Sec. 3-6c-2). The order of k_p values follows this behavior quite well but there are some k_t values which obviously do not. As has been pointed out previously, the reactivity of a radical depends not only on its reactivity but also on the substrate it is reacting with.

3-9 ENERGETIC CHARACTERISTICS

3-9a Activation Energy and Frequency Factor

The effect of temperature on the rate and degree of polymerization is of prime importance in determining the manner of performing a polymerization. Increasing the reaction temperature usually increases the polymerization rate and decreases the polymer molecular weight. Figure 3-15 shows this effect for the thermal, self-initiated polymerization of styrene [59]. However, the quantitative effect of temperature is complex since R_p and $\overline{X}_n$ depend on a combination of three rate constants—k_d, k_p, and k_t. Each of the rate constants for initiation, propagation, and termination can be expressed by an Arrhenius type relationship

$$k = Ae^{-E/RT} \tag{3-162a}$$

or

$$\ln k = \ln A - \frac{E}{RT} \tag{3-162b}$$

where A is the *collision frequency factor*, E the *Arrhenius activation energy*, and T the Kelvin temperature. A plot of $\ln k$ versus $1/T$ allows the determination of both E and A from the slope and intercept, respectively. Values of E_p, the activation energy for propagation, and E_t, the activation energy for termination, for several monomers are shown in Table 3-9. It is interesting to note

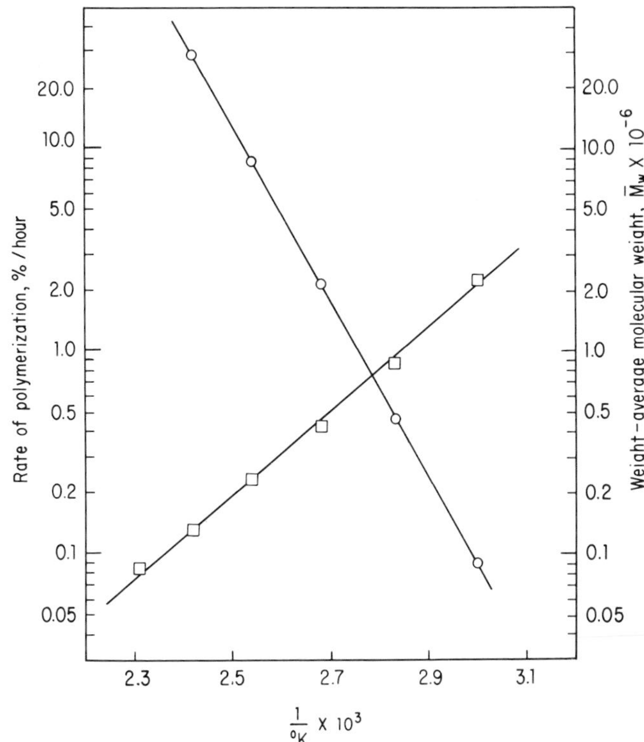

FIG. 3-15 *Dependence of the polymerization rate (○) and polymer molecular weight (□) on temperature for the thermal, self-initiated polymerization of styrene. After [59] (by permission of Dow Chemical Co., Midland).*

that the variations in the values of A_p, the frequency factor for propagation, are much greater than those in E_p—indicating that steric effects are probably the more important factor in determining the absolute value of k_p. Thus, the more hindered monomers (e.g., methyl methacrylate) have lower k_p and A_p values than the less hindered ones. The A_p values in general are much lower than the usual value (10^{11}–10^{13}) of the frequency factor for a bimolecular reaction—probably due to a large decrease in entropy on polymerization. The variations in the values of A_t, the frequency factor for termination, generally follow along the same line as the A_p values. The A_t values in general are larger than the A_p values.

3-9a-1 Rate of Polymerization. Consider the activation energy for various radical chain polymerizations. For a polymerization

Table 3-9 Kinetic Parameters in Radical Chain Polymerization[a,b,c]

Monomer	$k_p \times 10^{-3}$	E_p	$A_p \times 10^{-7}$	$k_t \times 10^{-7}$	E_t	$A_t \times 10^{-9}$
Vinyl chloride	12.3	3.7	0.33	2,300	4.2	600
Vinyl acetate	2.30	6.3	3.2	2.9	3.2	3.7
Acrylonitrile	1.96	3.9	–	78.2	3.7	–
Methyl acrylate	2.09	7.1	10	0.95	5.3	15
Methyl methacrylate	0.705	4.7	0.087	2.55	1.2	0.11
Styrene	0.145	7.3	0.45	2.9	1.9	0.058
1,3-Butadiene	0.100	9.3	12	–	–	–

[a] k_p and k_t values are for 60°C and are taken from [4] (p. 95) and [41] (p. II-67).
[b] E_p and E_t values are taken from [4] (p. 95) and [41] (p. II-67). The units of E_p are kcal per mole of polymerizing monomer; the units of E_t are kcal per mole of propagating radicals.
[c] A_p and A_t values are in liter/mole-sec and are taken from [4] (p. 95).

initiated by the thermal decomposition of a catalyst, the polymerization rate depends on the ratio of three rate constants $k_p(k_d/k_t)^{1/2}$ in accordance with Eq. 3-28. The temperature dependence of this ratio, obtained by combining three separate Arrhenius type equations, is given by

$$\ln\left[k_p\left(\frac{k_d}{k_t}\right)^{1/2}\right] = \ln\left[A_p\left(\frac{A_d}{A_t}\right)^{1/2}\right] - \frac{[E_p + (E_d/2) - (E_t/2)]}{RT} \tag{3-163}$$

The *overall activation energy for the rate of polymerization* E_R is $[E_p + (E_d/2) - (E_t/2)]$. Since R_p is given by Eq. 3-28, one can write Eq. 3-163 as

$$\ln R_p = \ln\left[A_p\left(\frac{A_d}{A_t}\right)^{1/2}\right] + \ln\left[(f[\mathrm{I}])^{1/2}[\mathrm{M}]\right] - \frac{E_R}{RT} \tag{3-164}$$

E_R and $A_p(A_d/A_t)^{1/2}$ can then be obtained from the slope and intercept, respectively, of a plot of $\ln R_p$ versus $1/T$ (similar to Fig. 3-15).

E_d, the activation energy for initiator decomposition, is about 30–35 kcal/mole for most of the initiators commonly used (Table 3-10) [41]. The E_p and E_t values for most monomers are in the ranges 5–10 kcal/mole and 2–5 kcal/mole, respectively (Tables 3-9 and [41]). The overall activation energy E_R for most polymerizations initiated by thermal initiator decomposition is therefore about 20

Table 3-10 Thermal Decomposition of Initiators[a,b]

Initiator	E_d	$k_d \times 10^5$	T (°C)
2,2′-Azobisisobutyronitrile	29.5	0.85	60
Acetyl peroxide	32.5	8.7	80
Benzoyl peroxide	29.7	4.7	85
Cumyl peroxide	40.7	1.6	115
t-Butyl peroxide	35.1	3.0	130
t-Butyl hydroperoxide	40.8	0.43	155

[a] All data are for decompositions in benzene solution.
[b] Data from [41] (p. II-1).

kcal/mole. This corresponds to a two- or three-fold rate increase for a 10°C temperature increase. The situation is different for other modes of initiation. Thus, redox initiation (for example, Fe^{2+} with thiosulfate or cumene hydroperoxide) has been discussed as taking place at lower temperatures compared to the thermal polymerizations. One indication of the difference between the two different initiation modes is the difference in activation energies. Redox initiation will have an E_d value of only about 10–15 kcal/mole—or about 20 kcal/mole less than that for thermal initiation [60]. This leads to an E_R for redox polymerization of about 10 kcal/mole—or about one-half the value for non-redox initiators.

For a purely photochemical polymerization, the initiation step is temperature-independent ($E_d = 0$) since the energy for initiator decomposition is supplied by light quanta. The overall activation energy for photochemical polymerization is then only about 5 kcal/mole. This low value of E_R indicates that R_p for photochemical polymerizations will be relatively insensitive to temperature compared to other polymerizations. The effect of temperature on photochemical polymerizations is complicated, however, since most photochemical initiators can also decompose thermally. At higher temperatures the initiators may undergo appreciable thermal decomposition in addition to the photochemical decomposition. In such cases, one must take into account both the thermal and photochemical initiations. The initiation and overall activation energies for a purely thermal self-initiated polymerization are approximately the same as for initiation by the thermal decomposition of an initiator. However, purely thermal polymerizations proceed at very slow rates because of the low probability of the initiation process due to the very low values (10^4–10^6) of the frequency factor.

3-9a-2 Degree of Polymerization. To determine the effect of temperature on the molecular weight of the polymer produced in a thermally catalyzed polymerization where transfer reactions are negligible, one must consider the ratio $k_p/(k_d k_t)^{1/2}$ since it determines the degree of polymerization (Eq. 3-101). The variation of this ratio with temperature is given by

$$\ln\left[\frac{k_p}{(k_d k_t)^{1/2}}\right] = \ln\left[\frac{A_p}{(A_d A_t)^{1/2}}\right] - \frac{[E_p - (E_d/2) - (E_t/2)]}{RT} \tag{3-165}$$

where the energy term $[E_p - (E_d/2) - (E_t/2)]$ is the *activation energy for the degree of polymerization* $E_{\overline{X}_n}$. For bimolecular termination, $\overline{X}_n$ is governed by Eqs. 3-101 and 3-102a and one can write

$$\ln \overline{X}_n = \ln\left[\frac{A_p}{(A_d A_t)^{1/2}}\right] + \ln\left[\frac{[\mathrm{M}]}{(f[\mathrm{I}])^{1/2}}\right] - \frac{E_{\overline{X}_n}}{RT} \tag{3-166}$$

$E_{\overline{X}_n}$ has a value of about -15 kcal/mole in typical cases and $\overline{X}_n$ decreases rapidly with increasing temperature. Equation 3-166 also holds for a purely thermal, self-initiated polymerization (Fig. 3-15). For a pure photochemical polymerization $E_{\overline{X}_n}$ is positive by approximately 5 kcal/mole, since E_d is zero, and $\overline{X}_n$ increases moderately with temperature. This is the only situation where $\overline{X}_n$ increases with temperature. For all other cases, $\overline{X}_n$ decreases with temperature.

When chain transfer occurs in the polymerization, $\overline{X}_n$ is given by an appropriate form of Eq. 3-109. The temperature dependence of $\overline{X}_n$ can be quite complex depending on the relative importance of the various terms in Eq. 3-109. For the case where chain transfer to compound S is controlling (Eq. 3-116), one obtains

$$-\ln\left[\frac{[\mathrm{M}]}{[\mathrm{S}]}\left(\frac{1}{\overline{X}_n} - \frac{1}{(\overline{X}_n)_0}\right)\right] = \ln\frac{k_p}{k_{tr,\mathrm{S}}} = \ln\frac{A_p}{A_{tr,\mathrm{S}}} - \frac{(E_p - E_{tr,\mathrm{S}})}{RT} \tag{3-167}$$

The quantity $(E_p - E_{tr,\mathrm{S}})$ is now $E_{\overline{X}_n}$ and can be obtained from a plot of either of the two forms of the left side of Eq. 3-167 versus $1/T$. $E_{tr,\mathrm{S}}$ usually exceeds E_p by 5–10 kcal/mole with the more active transfer agents having lower values [18, 42, 61]. The term $(E_p - E_{tr,\mathrm{S}})$ is usually -5 to -20 kcal/mole (Table 3-11) and the molecular weight therefore decreases with increasing temperature. The frequency factors for transfer reactions are usually greater than those for propagations and the low transfer constant of a particular transfer agent is a consequence of the high activation energy only.

3-9b Thermodynamics of Polymerization

3-9b-1 Significance of ΔG, ΔH and ΔS. The thermodynamic characteristics (ΔG, ΔH, ΔS) of polymerization are important to an understanding of the effect of monomer structure on polymerization. Further, knowledge of ΔH allows one to maintain the desired

Table 3-11 Activation Parameters for Chain Transfer in Styrene Polymerization (60°C)[a]

Transfer agent	$-(E_p - E_{tr,S})$	$\log (A_{tr,S}/A_p)$
Cyclohexane	13.4	3.1
Benzene	14.8	3.9
Toluene	10.1	1.7
Ethylbenzene	5.5	-0.55
Isopropylbenzene	5.5	-0.47
t-Butylbenzene	13.7	3.8
n-Butyl chloride	14	4
n-Butyl bromide	11	2
n-Butyl iodide	7	1
Carbon tetrachloride	5	1

[a]Data from [18], [42], [61].

R_p and $\overline{X}_n$ by appropriate thermal control of the process. The ΔG, ΔH, and ΔS for a polymerization are the differences in *free energy, enthalpy,* and *entropy,* respectively, between one mole of monomer and one mole of repeating units in the polymer product. The thermodynamic properties of a polymerization relate only to the propagation step since polymerization consists of single acts of initiation and termination and a large number of propagation steps.

Chain polymerizations of alkenes are exothermic (negative ΔH) and exoentropic (negative ΔS). The exothermic nature of polymerization arises because the process involves the exothermic conversion of π-bonds in monomer molecules into σ-bonds in the polymer. The negative ΔS for polymerization arises from the decreased degrees of freedom (randomness) for the polymer relative to the monomer. Thus, polymerization is favorable from the enthalpy viewpoint but unfavorable from the entropy viewpoint. Table 3-12 shows the wide range of ΔH values for various monomers [62]. The ΔS values fall in the narrow range of minus 25–30 cal/°K-mole. The methods of evaluating ΔH and ΔS have been reviewed [63]. These include direct calorimetric measurements of ΔH for the polymerization, determination by the difference between the heats of combustion of monomer and polymer, and measurements of the equilibrium constant for the polymerization. The overall thermodynamics of the polymerization of alkenes is quite favorable. The value of ΔG given by

Table 3-12 Heats and Entropies of Polymerization at 25°C[a]

Monomer	$-\Delta H$	$-\Delta S$
Ethylene	22.7	24
Propylene	20.5	27.8
1-Butene	20.0[b]	26.8
Isobutylene	12.3	28.8
1, 3-Butadiene	17.4	20.5
Isoprene	17.8	24.2
Styrene	16.7	25.0
α-Methylstyrene	8.4	24.8
Vinyl chloride	22.9	—
Vinylidene chloride	18.0	—
Vinylidene fluoride	30	—
Tetrafluoroethylene	37.2	26.8
Acrylic acid	16.0	—
Acrylonitrile	18.4	—
Maleic anhydride	14	—
Vinyl acetate	21.0	26.2
Methyl acrylate	18.8	—
Methyl methacrylate	13.5	28.0

[a] ΔH refers to the conversion of liquid monomer to amorphous or slightly crystalline polymer. ΔS refers to the conversion of monomer (at a concentration of one molar) to amorphous or slightly crystalline polymer. The subscripts lc are often used with ΔH and ΔS to show the initial and final states (that is, ΔH_{lc} and ΔS_{lc}). The units of ΔH are kcal per mole of polymerized monomer; the units of ΔS are cal/°K-mole.

[b] This value is from [41] (p. II-365). All other data are from [62] (pp. 450 and 492).

$$\Delta G = \Delta H - T\Delta S \tag{3-168}$$

is negative because the negative $T\Delta S$ term is outweighed by the negative ΔH term.

One should recall the earlier discussion (Sec. 3-1b) on the thermodynamic and kinetic feasibilities of polymerization. The data in Table 3-12 clearly show the general thermodynamic feasibility for any carbon-carbon double bond. Although the relative thermodynamic feasibility of any one monomer varies depending on the substituents present in the monomer, ΔG is negative in all cases and polymerization is favored. However, thermodynamic feasibility does not indicate the experimental conditions which may be required to bring about the polymerization. Thus, Table 3-1 showed that the kinetic feasibility of polymerization varies considerably from one monomer to another in terms of whether radical, cationic, or anionic initiation can be used for the reaction. In some instances, thermodynamically feasible polymerizations may require very specific catalyst systems. This is the case with the α-olefins which cannot be polymerized to high molecular polymers by any of the conventional radical or ionic initiators. The polymerization of these monomers was not achieved until the discovery of the Ziegler-Natta or coordination type catalysts (Chap. 8).

3-9b-2 Effect of Monomer Structure. Consider the effect of monomer structure on the enthalpy of polymerization. The ΔH for ethylene (−22.7 kcal/mole) is very close to the exact difference (approximately 20–22 kcal/mole) between the bond energies of the π-bond in an alkene and the σ-bond in an alkane. The ΔH values for the other monomers vary considerably. The variations in ΔH for differently substituted ethylene arise from any of the following effects:

1) Differences in the resonance stabilization of monomer and polymer due to differences in conjugation or hyperconjugation.

2) Steric strain differences in the monomer and polymer arising from bond angle deformation, bond stretching, or interactions between non-bonded atoms.

3) Differences in hydrogen bonding or dipole interactions in the monomer and polymer.

Many substituents stabilize the monomer but have no appreciable effect on polymer stability since resonance is only possible with the former. The net effect is to decrease the exothermicity of the polymerization. Thus, hyperconjugation of alkyl groups with the C=C lowers ΔH for propylene and 1-butene polymerizations. Conjugation of the C=C with substituents such as the benzene ring (styrene and α-methylstyrene), the alkene double bond (butadiene and isoprene), the carbonyl linkage (acrylic acid, methyl acrylate, methyl methacrylate), and the nitrile group (acrylonitrile) similarly leads to stabilization of the monomer and decreased enthalpies of polymerization. When the substituent is poorly conjugating as in vinyl acetate, the ΔH is close to the value for ethylene.

The effect of 1,1-disubstitution manifests itself by decreased ΔH values. This is a consequence of steric strain in the polymer due to interactions between substituents on alternating carbon atoms of the polymer chain

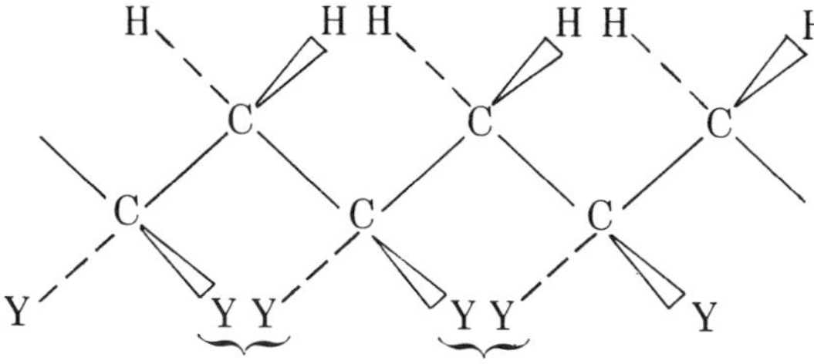

1,3-interactions

VII

In the picture above the main polymer chain is drawn in the plane of this text with the H and Y substituents placed above and below the plane of the text. The dotted and triangular lines indicate substituents below and above this plane, respectively. Such interactions are referred to as *1,3-interactions* and are responsible for the decreased ΔH values in monomers such as isobutylene, α-methylstyrene, methyl methacrylate, and vinylidene chloride. The effect in α-methylstyrene is especially significant. The ΔH value of -8.4 kcal/mole is essentially the smallest heat of polymerization of any monomer.

A contributing factor to the lowering of ΔH in some cases is a decrease in hydrogen bonding or dipole interactions on polymerization. Monomers such as acrylic acid and acylamide are significantly stabilized by strong intermolecular associations. The intermolecular associations are not as important in the polymer because its steric constraints prevent the required lining up of substituents.

The ΔH values for vinyl chloride, vinylidene fluoride, and tetrafluoroethylene are rather difficult to explain. These monomers would be expected to have lower ΔH values than ethylene due to increased steric strain in the polymer and increased resonance stabilization of the monomer. However, vinyl chloride has a ΔH value which is essentially the same as that of ethylene while vinylidene fluoride and tetrafluoroethylene have very high $-\Delta H$ values of 30 and 37.2 kcal/mole, respectively. Further, the ΔH for vinylidene chloride is much higher than expected for a 1,1-disubstituted ethylene. A possible explanation may involve increased stabilization of the polymer due to the presence of intermolecular association (dipole interaction).

While the ΔH values vary over a wide range for different monomers, the ΔS values are insensitive to monomer structure—being relatively constant within the range of 25–30 cal/°K-mole [41], 62]. The $T\Delta S$ contribution to the ΔG for polymerization will be small as indicated earlier and will vary only within a narrow range. Thus, the variation in the $T\Delta S$ term at 50°C for all monomers is in the range 8.1–9.7 kcal/mole. The entropy changes which occur upon polymerization have been analyzed for several monomers [63, 64]. The ΔS of polymerization arises primarily from the loss of the translational entropy of the monomer. Losses in the rotational and vibrational entropies of the monomer are essentially balanced by gains in the rotational and vibrational entropies of the polymer. Thus, ΔS for polymerization is essentially the translational entropy of the monomer which is relatively insensitive to the structure of the monomer.

3-9b-3 Polymerization of 1,2-Disubstituted Ethylenes. 1-2-Disubstituted ethylenes such as maleic anhydride, stilbene, and 1,2-dichloroethylene

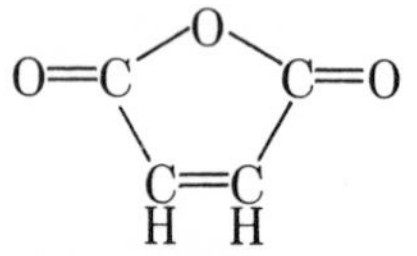

O=C–O–C=O (ring closed by HC=CH) ϕCH=CHϕ ClCH=CHCl

exhibit very little or no tendency to undergo polymerization. Steric inhibition is the cause of this behavior but the effect is different than that responsible for the difficulty with which 1,1-disubstituted monomers polymerize.

Polymers from 1,2-disubstituted monomers

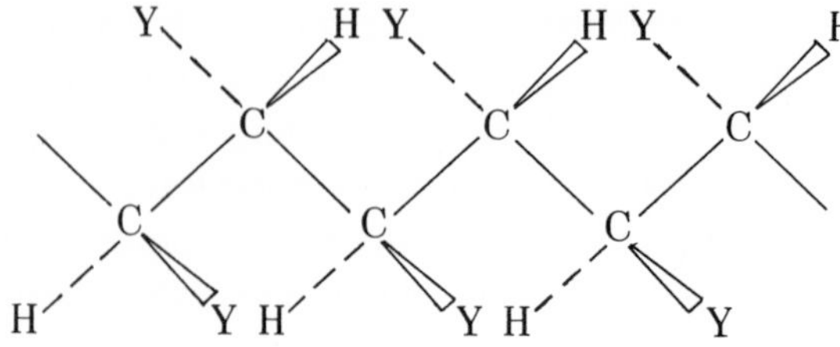

VIII

contain one substituent on every carbon atom. Models show that such structures are not excessively strained. The steric strain due to interactions between Y substituents in such structures is certainly less than in polymers from 1,1-disubstituted ethylenes (compare structures VII and VIII). Thus, the ΔH value for maleic anhydride is -14 kcal/mole which is favorable for polymerization compared to the values for some 1,1-disubstituted ethylenes.

The very low tendency of 1,2-disubstituted ethylenes to polymerize is not due primarily to thermodynamic factors but to kinetic considerations. The approach of the propagating radical to a monomer molecule is sterically hindered. The propagation step is extremely slow due to steric interactions between the β-substituent of the propagating species and the two substituents of the incoming monomer molecule

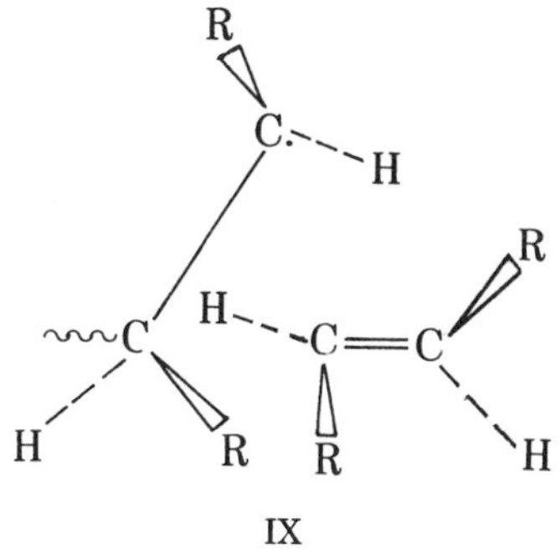

IX

Propagation is hindered in favor of termination or chain transfer reactions.

3-9c Polymerization-Depolymerization Equilibria; Ceiling Temperature

For most chain polymerizations there is some temperature at which the reaction becomes a reversible one, i.e., the propagation step (Eq. 3-15) should be written as

$$\mathrm{M}_n\cdot + \mathrm{M} \underset{k_{dp}}{\overset{k_p}{\rightleftharpoons}} \mathrm{M}_{n+1}\cdot \tag{3-169}$$

where k_{dp} is the rate constant for the reverse reaction—termed *depolymerization* or *depropagation*. The overall effect of temperature on polymerization is complex due to the presence of this propagation-depropagation equilibrium. When the temperature is initially increased for the polymerization of a monomer, the polymerization rate increases as k_p increases (Sec. 3-9a-1). However, at higher temperatures, the depropagation rate constant k_{dp} which was initially zero increases and becomes significant with increasing temperature. Finally, a temperature—the *ceiling temperature* T_c—is reached at which the propagation and depropagation rates are equal. These effects are shown in Fig. 3-16 for styrene. At the ceiling temperature, the net rate of polymer production is zero.

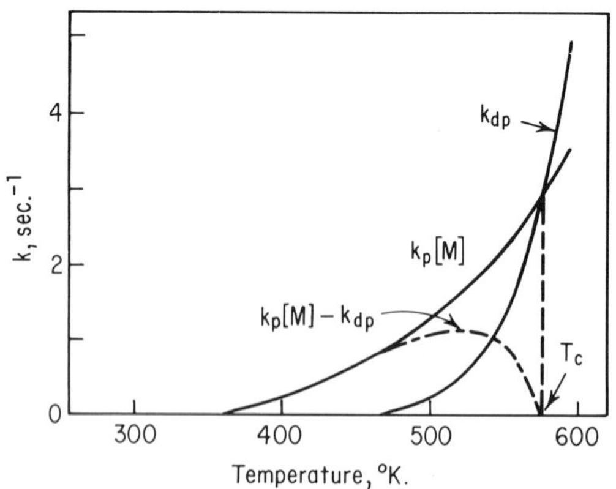

FIG. 3-16 *The variation of $k_p[M]$ and k_{dp} with temperature for styrene. After [63] (by permission of The Chemical Society, Burlington House, London).*

The equilibrium position for the monomer-polymer equilibrium in Eq. 3-169 will be dependent on the temperature with increased temperature resulting in a shift to the left since the forward reaction is exothermic. The reaction isotherm

$$\Delta G = \Delta G^o + RT \ln K \tag{3-170}$$

is applicable to an analysis of polymerization-depolymerization equilibria. ΔG^o is the ΔG of polymerization for the monomer and polymer in appropriate standard states [63, 64]. The standard state for monomer is often taken as the pure liquid or a one molar solution. The standard state for polymer is usually the solid amorphous or slightly crystalline polymer or a solution which is one molar in the repeating unit of the polymer. For an equilibrium situation, $\Delta G = 0$ by definition and Eq. 3-170 may be combined with Eq. 3-168 to yield

$$\Delta G^o = \Delta H^o - T\Delta S^o = -RT \ln K \tag{3-171}$$

The equilibrium constant is defined by k_p/k_{dp} or more conveniently by

$$K = \frac{[M_{n+1}\cdot]}{[M_n\cdot][M]} = \frac{1}{[M]} \tag{3-172}$$

Combination of Eqs. 3-171 and 3-172 yields

$$T_c = \frac{\Delta H^o}{\Delta S^o + R \ln [M]_c} \tag{3-173a}$$

or

$$\ln [M]_c = \frac{\Delta H^o}{RT_c} - \frac{\Delta S^o}{R} \tag{3-173b}$$

Equation 3-173 shows the *equilibrium monomer concentration* $[M]_c$ as a function of the reaction or ceiling temperature T_c. Since ΔH^o is a negative quantity, the monomer concentration in equilibrium with polymer increases with increasing temperature, i.e., a plot of $\ln [M]_c$ versus $1/T$ is linear with a negative slope of $\Delta H^o/R$ and an intercept of $-\Delta S^o/R$. This means that there is a series of ceiling temperatures corresponding to different equilibrium monomer concentrations. For any monomer solution of concentration $[M]_c$, there is a temperature T_c at which polymerization does not occur. (For each $[M]_c$ there is a corresponding plot analogous to Fig. 3-16 in which $k_{dp} = k_p[M]$ at its T_c.) Stated another way, the polymerization of a particular monomer solution at a particular temperature proceeds until equilibrium is established, i.e., until the monomer concentration decreases to the $[M]_c$ value corresponding to that T_c temperature. Thus, higher initial monomer concentrations are required with increasing temperature in order to observe a net production of polymer before equilibrium is established. There is an upper temperature limit above which polymer cannot be obtained even from pure monomer. The reader is cautioned to note that the literature often appears to refer only to a singular T_c value—"the ceiling temperature." It is clear from the discussion above that each monomer concentration has its own T_c value. The apparent designation of a singular T_c value usually refers to the T_c for the pure monomer or in some cases to that for the monomer at unit molarity.

For many of the alkene monomers, the equilibrium position for the propagation-depropagation equilibrium is far to the right under the usual reaction temperatures employed, i.e., there is essentially complete conversion of monomer to polymer for all practical purposes. Table 3-13 shows the monomer concentrations at 25°C for a few monomers [65–68]. Data are also shown for the ceiling temperatures of the pure monomers. The data do indicate that the polymer obtained in any polymerization will contain some concentration of residual monomer as determined by Eq. 3-173. Further, there are some monomers for which the equilibrium is not particularly favorable for polymerization, for example, α-methylstyrene. Thus, at 25°C a 2.2 molar solution of α-methylstyrene will not undergo polymerization. Pure α-methylstyrene will not polymerize at 61°C. Methyl methacrylate is a borderline case in that the pure monomer can be polymerized below 220°C but the conversion will be appreciably less than complete. Thus, for example, the value of $[M]_c$ at 110°C is 0.139 molar [41]. Equations 3-173a and 3-173b apply equally well to ionic chain and ring-opening polymerizations as will be seen in subsequent chapters. The lower temperatures of ionic polymerizations offer a useful route to the polymerization of many monomers which cannot be polymerized by radical initiation because of their low ceiling temperatures. The successful polymerization of a previously unpolymerizable monomer is often simply a matter of

Table 3-13 Polymerization-Depolymerization Equilibria[a]

Monomer	$[M]_c$ at 25°C	T_c for pure monomer (°C)
Vinyl acetate	1×10^{-9}	–
Methyl acrylate	1×10^{-9}	–
Styrene	1×10^{-6}	310
Methyl methacrylate	1×10^{-3}	220
α-Methylstyrene	2.2	61

[a]Data are from [65–68].

carrying out the reaction at a temperature below its ceiling temperature.

Interestingly, it should not be assumed that a polymer will be useless above its ceiling temperature. A dead polymer that has been removed from the reaction media will be stable and will not depolymerize unless an active end is produced by bond cleavage of an end-group or at some point along the polymer chain. When such an active site is produced by thermal, chemical, photolytic, or other means, depolymerization will follow until the monomer concentration becomes equal to $[M]_c$ for the particular temperature. The thermal behavior of many polymers, however, is much more complex. Degradative reactions other than depolymerization will often occur at temperatures below the ceiling temperature.

3-10 AUTOACCELERATION

3-10a Course of Polymerization

Radical chain polymerizations are characterized by the presence of an *autoacceleration* in the polymerization rate as the reaction proceeds. One would normally expect the reaction rate to fall with time (i.e., the extent of conversion) since the monomer concentration (and also the initiator concentration) decreases with conversion. However, the exact opposite behavior is observed in many polymerizations where the rate of polymerization increases with time. A typical example of this phenomenon is shown in Fig. 3-17 for the polymerization of methyl methacrylate in benzene solution [69]. The curve for the 10% methyl methacrylate solution shows the type of behavior that would generally be expected. The curve for the pure monomer shows a dramatic autoacceleration in the polymerization rate. Such behavior is referred to as the *gel effect*. The terms *Trommsdorff effect* and *Norrish-Smith effect* are also used in recognition of the early workers in the field.

The gel effect is caused by a decrease in the termination rate constant with increasing conversion. As the polymerization proceeds the viscosity of the system increases and termination becomes increasingly slower. Although propagation is also hindered the effect is much smaller since k_p values are smaller than k_t values by a factor of 10^4–10^5. Termination involves the reaction of two large polymer radicals while propagation involves the reaction of small monomer molecules and only one large radical. High viscosity affects the

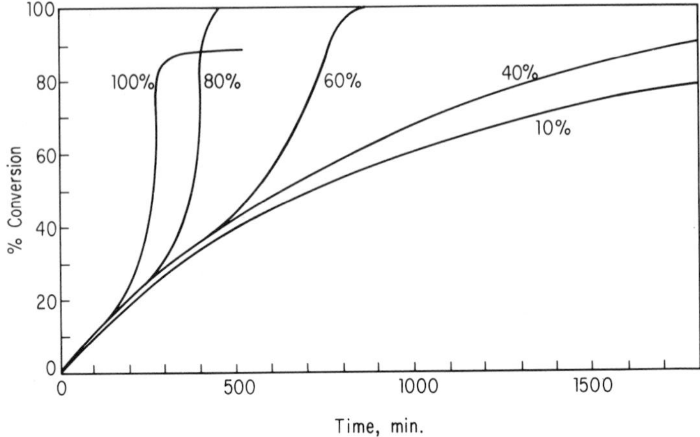

FIG. 3-17 *Autoacceleration in the benzoyl peroxide catalyzed polymerization of methyl methacrylate in benzene at 50°C. The different curves are for various concentrations of monomer in solvent. After [69] (by permission of Hüthig and Wepf Verlag, Basel).*

former much more than the latter. Therefore, the quantity $k_p/k_t^{1/2}$ increases and the result in accordance with Eq. 3-24 is an increase in R_p with conversion. A second consequence of this effect is an increase in molecular weight with conversion as required by Eq. 3-98. These conclusions have been verified by the quantitative evaluation of the k_p and k_t values as a function of the percent conversion. Thus, Table 3-14 shows data on the polymerization of methyl

Table 3-14 Effect of Conversion on the Polymerization of Methyl Methacrylate (22.5°C)[a]

% Conversion	Rate (%/hr)	τ (sec)	k_p	$k_t \times 10^{-5}$	$(k_p/k_t^{1/2}) \times 10^2$
0	3.5	0.89	384	442	5.78
10	2.7	1.14	234	273	4.58
20	6.0	2.21	267	72.6	8.81
30	15.4	5.0	303	14.2	25.5
40	23.4	6.3	368	8.93	38.9
50	24.5	9.4	258	4.03	40.6
60	20.0	26.7	74	0.498	33.2
70	13.1	79.3	16	0.0564	21.3
80	2.8	216	1	0.0076	3.59

[a]Data from [70].

methacrylate [70]. It is seen that k_p is relatively unaffected until 50% conversion (of monomer to polymer) has been reached whereas k_t has decreased by almost two orders of magnitude in the same span. The $k_p/k_t^{1/2}$ ratio and the polymerization rate simultaneously increase rapidly at first and then taper off as k_p is also affected in the later stages of reaction. The attention of the reader is also called to the data showing the increase in the radical lifetime with increasing conversion.

3-10b Diffusion-Controlled Termination

The onset of the Trommsdorff effect is often described as the point at which the termination step becomes diffusion-controlled. However, this terminology is poor since termination is probably diffusion-controlled to begin with in most if not all polymerization systems. North and coworkers [71] have described termination as occurring by the three step process:

1) Translational diffusion of two propagating radicals until they are in close proximity to each other

$$\mathrm{M}_n\cdot + \mathrm{M}_m\cdot \underset{k_2}{\overset{k_1}{\rightleftharpoons}} \underset{\mathrm{X}}{[\mathrm{M}_n\cdot \cdots\cdot \mathrm{M}_m\cdot]} \tag{3-174}$$

2) Rearrangement of the two chains so that the two radical ends are sufficiently close for chemical reaction, which occurs by segmental diffusion of the chains, i.e., by the movement of parts or segments of a polymer chain relative to its other parts

$$\underset{\mathrm{X}}{[\mathrm{M}_n\cdot \cdots\cdot \mathrm{M}_m\cdot]} \underset{k_4}{\overset{k_3}{\rightleftharpoons}} \underset{\mathrm{XI}}{[\mathrm{M}_n\cdot/\mathrm{M}_m\cdot]} \tag{3-175}$$

3) Chemical reaction of the two radical ends

$$\underset{\mathrm{XI}}{[\mathrm{M}_n\cdot/\mathrm{M}_m\cdot]} \xrightarrow{k_c} \text{dead polymer} \tag{3-176}$$

For the usual case where Reaction 3-176 is very fast, $k_c \gg k_4$, and one can obtain

$$R_t = \frac{k_1 k_3 [\mathrm{M}\cdot]^2}{k_2 + k_3} \tag{3-177}$$

by assuming steady-state concentrations of both X and XI. Two limiting cases of termination arise. For the case of slow translational diffusion, $k_3 \gg k_2$, and

$$R_t = k_1 [\mathrm{M}\cdot]^2 \tag{3-178}$$

For the case of slow segmental diffusion, $k_2 \gg k_3$, and

$$R_t = \frac{k_1 k_3 [\mathrm{M}\cdot]^2}{k_2} \tag{3-179}$$

Thus, the experimentally observed termination rate constant k_t corresponds to k_1 and $k_1 k_3/k_2$, respectively, for the two limiting situations.

The theoretical conclusions of North and coworkers have been verified. Thus, for example, the effect of viscosity on the low conversion polymerization of several methacrylates at 30°C has been studied by using diisooctyl phthalate and sucrose acetate isobutyrate to vary the viscosity [71]. The k_t/k_p ratio decreased continuously with increasing viscosity from the lowest solution viscosity on upward. Further, recent work [72] indicates that segmental diffusion is the slow step in the termination process, i.e., Eq. 3-179 is rate determining.

3-10c Effects of Reaction Conditions

The % conversion at which autoacceleration is observed varies depending on the reaction conditions and the accuracy of the experimental procedures. When highly accurate data are obtained, many monomers show the $k_p/k_t^{1/2}$ ratio as increasing from the very beginning or after only a few percent conversion—substantiating the conclusion that the termination reaction is a diffusion-controlled process. Styrene [35] and various methacrylates [71, 73] are examples of such polymerizations.

The molecular weight of the polymer obtained from a monomer can affect the point at which autoacceleration occurs and also the extent of autoacceleration. Thus, vinyl acetate yields a lower molecular weight product (due to chain transfer as previously discussed) and does not therefore show as dramatic a gel effect as other monomers. Temperature also plays a large role in determining the type and quality of gel effect observed. Higher temperatures decrease the viscosity of the reaction medium. This delays the gel effect and the autoacceleration may not be as pronounced. Similar effects are observed in the presence of solvents and chain transfer agents. Solvents lower the viscosity of the medium directly while chain transfer agents do so by lowering the polymer molecular weight. The effect of solvent in methyl methacrylate polymerization is seen in Fig. 3-17.

The use of solvents which are non-solvents for the polymer (e.g., methanol for polystyrene, hexane for polymethyl methacrylate), on the other hand, usually leads to marked acceleration of the polymerization rate. The same effect is observed for the polymerization of monomers whose polymers are insoluble or weakly soluble in their own monomers. Examples of this type of behavior are acrylonitrile, vinyl chloride, trifluorochloroethylene, and vinylidene chloride [74]. The accelerative effects observed in these instances of heterogeneous polymerization are similar to the gel effect and are caused by a decrease in k_t relative to k_p. The growing polymeric radicals become coiled up since they are essentially insoluble or on the verge of insolubility in the solvent or in their own monomer. Termination between radicals again becomes progressively more difficult while propagation may still proceed reasonably well.

3-10d Dependence of Polymerization Rate on Initiator

The occurrence of the gel effect in homogeneous polymerizations and of heterogeneity in polymerizations gives rise to deviations from the usual one-half order dependence of R_p on the initiator concentration. One usually observes a dependence of the rate of polymerization on a power of the initiator concentration between one-half and unity [43, 74]. This indicates that termination probably occurs by two processes—one is the usual second order termination and the other is a reaction which is first order in the polymeric radicals. The exact nature of the latter is not clear but it probably consists of transfer to monomer, polymer, or some other species present. The first order termination reaction becomes progressively more important as the polymerization increases and the overall dependence of R_p on R_i becomes progressively larger than one-half order. Simultaneously, the degree of polymerization will show a dependence on R_i to a power between $-1/2$ and -1. In some heterogeneous polymerization systems, the polymeric radicals may become so coiled up and inaccessible as to not undergo termination under the usual reaction conditions. The presence of buried or trapped non-terminated radicals has been shown by the ability of photochemically produced reaction mixtures to continue polymerizing for days after the discontinuation of illumination.

Another mode of termination which appears to occur, when the normal termination reaction becomes unimportant, is that between a polymeric radical and a primary radical (formed in Eq. 3-13)

$$M_n\cdot + R\cdot \longrightarrow M_n{-}R \tag{3-180}$$

One can show that for termination by Eq. 3-180, R_p will be dependent on the second power of the monomer concentration and independent of the initiator concentration (zero order). This has been partially confirmed in the polymerization of styrene in the presence of added polystyrene which is used to increase the viscosity of the medium [26]. The polymerization rate at high viscosities showed a dependence on the square of [M] and the 0.3-power of the initiator concentration. A preferred means of describing such systems may involve kinetics similar to those involved in emulsion polymerization (Chap. 4).

It is also possible that termination in the Trommsdorff region and in heterogeneous systems occurs by both of the modes discussed. The observed orders of dependence of R_p on initiator are often in the range 0.4–0.8. This observed order may be the result of a combination of the first order and zero order termination processes.

3-11 MOLECULAR WEIGHT DISTRIBUTION

3-11a Low Conversion Polymerization

The molecular weight distribution in radical chain polymerizations is more complex than those in step polymerization. Radical chain polymerization involves several possible modes by which propagation is terminated—disproportionation, coupling, and various transfer reactions. The situation is further complicated since the molecular weight of the polymer produced at any instant varies with the overall percent conversion due to changes in the monomer and catalyst concentrations and the propagation and termination rate constants. Molecular weight distributions can be relatively easily calculated for polymerizations restricted to low conversions where all of the kinetic parameters ([M], [I], k_p,k_t) are approximately constant [75–77]. Under these conditions, the polymer molecular weight does not change with conversion.

Consider the situation where one polymer molecule is produced from each kinetic chain. This is the case for termination by disproportionation or chain transfer or a combination of the two. The situation in this instance is analogous to that for linear step polymerization (Sec. 2-5) and Eqs. 2-45, 2-47, 2-48, 2-27, 2-54, and 2-55

$$\underline{N}_x = (1-p)p^{x-1} \tag{2-45}$$

$$N_x = N_0(1-p)^2 p^{x-1} \tag{2-47}$$

$$w_x = x(1-p)^2 p^{x-1} \tag{2-48}$$

$$\overline{X}_n = \frac{1}{(1-p)} \tag{2-27}$$

$$\overline{X}_w = \frac{(1+p)}{(1-p)} \tag{2-54}$$

$$\frac{\overline{X}_w}{\overline{X}_n} = (1+p) \tag{2-55}$$

describe the number-fraction, number, and weight distributions, the number- and weight-average degrees of polymerization, and the breadth of the distribution.

One difference in the use of these equations for radical chain polymerizations compared to step polymerizations is the redefinition of p as the probability that a propagating radical will continue to propagate instead of terminating. The value of p is given as the rate of propagation divided by the sum of the rates of all reactions that a propagating radical may undergo

$$p = \frac{R_p}{R_p + R_t + R_{tr}} \tag{3-181}$$

where R_p, R_t, and R_{tr} are the rates of propagation, termination by disproportionation, and chain transfer, respectively. There is a very important second difference in the use of the above equations for radical chain polymerization compared to step polymerizations. The equations apply to the whole reaction mixture for a step polymerization but only to the polymer fraction of the reaction mixture for a radical chain polymerization.

A consideration of the above equations indicates that high polymer (i.e., large values of $\overline{X}_n$ and $\overline{X}_w$) will only be produced if p is close to unity. This is certainly what one expects based on the previous discussions in Sec. 3-5. The distributions described by Eqs. 2-45, 2-47, and 2-48 have been graphically shown in Figures 2-7, 2-8, and 2-9. The breadth of the size distribution $\overline{X}_w/\overline{X}_n$ has a limiting value of two as p approaches unity.

For termination by coupling, where a polymer molecule arises from the combination of two kinetic chains, the size distribution is sharper. The following equations

$$\underline{N}_x = (1-p)^2 (x-1) p^{x-2} \tag{3-182}$$

$$w_x = \tfrac{1}{2} x (1-p)^3 (x-1) p^{x-2} \tag{3-183}$$

$$\overline{X}_n = \frac{2}{1-p} \tag{3-184}$$

$$\overline{X}_w = \frac{2+p}{1-p} \tag{3-185}$$

$$\frac{\overline{X}_w}{\overline{X}_n} = \frac{2+p}{2} \tag{3-186}$$

can be shown to be applicable. For this case, R_t in Eq. 3-181 is the rate of termination by coupling and R_{tr} is zero. The distribution here is similar to the case of multi-chain step polymerization (Sec. 2-7) with $f = 2$. The breadth of the distribution has a limiting value of 1.5 for p close to unity.

For polymerizations where termination occurs by a combination of coupling, disproportionation, and chain transfer, one can obtain the size distribution by a weighted combination of the above two sets of distribution functions. Thus, the weight distribution can be obtained as

$$w_x = Ax(1-p)^2 p^{x-1} + \frac{1}{2}(1-A)x(1-p)^3(x-1)p^{x-2} \tag{3-187}$$

where A is the fraction of polymer molecules formed by disproportionation and chain transfer reactions [78].

3-11b High Conversion Polymerization

For many practical radical chain polymerizations, the reaction is carried out to high or complete conversion. The size distributions for high conversion polymerizations become much broader than those described above or those in step polymerizations. Both the monomer and initiator concentrations decrease as a polymerization proceeds. The polymer molecular weight depends on the ratio $[M]/[I]^{1/2}$ according to Eq. 3-101. In the usual situation, [I] decreases faster than [M] and the molecular weight of the polymer produced at any instant increases with the conversion. The overall molecular weight distributions for high or complete conversion polymerizations are quite broad with the $\bar{X}_w/\bar{X}_n$ ratio being in the range 2–5. Broad molecular weight distributions are usually not desirable from the practical viewpoint since most polymer properties show optimum values at specific molecular weights. Commercial polymerization processes often involve the addition of multiple charges of initiator and/or monomer during the course of the reaction to minimize the molecular weight broadening.

When autoacceleration occurs in polymerization, there is even larger broadening of the size distribution. The large increases in the $k_p/k_t^{1/2}$ ratio (Table 3-12) which accompany the gel effect lead to large increases in the sizes of the polymers being produced as the polymerization proceeds. $\bar{X}_w/\bar{X}_n$ values as high as 5–10 may be observed when the gel effect is present. Excessive molecular weight broadening occurs when branched polymers are produced by chain transfer to polymer. Chain transfer to polymer can lead to $\bar{X}_w/\bar{X}_n$ ratios as high as 20–50. This very extensive size broadening occurs because chain transfer to polymer increases as the polymer size increases. Thus, branching leads to even more branching as a polymerization proceeds. One usually attempts to minimize molecular weight broadening due to the gel effect and chain transfer to polymer but it is quite difficult to do so successfully. Thus, for example, low temperatures minimize chain transfer to polymer but maximize the gel effect.

Various distribution functions for the broad distributions have been employed but not with large success. The use of computer techniques [79, 80] should prove most useful in allowing one to take into account the changes in [M], [I], k_p, and k_t with conversion.

3-12 EFFECT OF PRESSURE

The effect of pressure on polymerization, although not extensively studied [4, 81–83], is important from the practical viewpoint. The largest volume polymer (> 3½ billion pounds/year)—low density polyethylene—is produced by polymerization at moderately high pressures of 1,000–3,000 atmospheres. High pressures can have appreciable effects on polymerization rates and polymer molecular weights. Increased pressure usually results in increased polymerization rates and molecular weights. Figure 3-18 shows these effects for the benzoyl peroxide initiated polymerization of styrene [84].

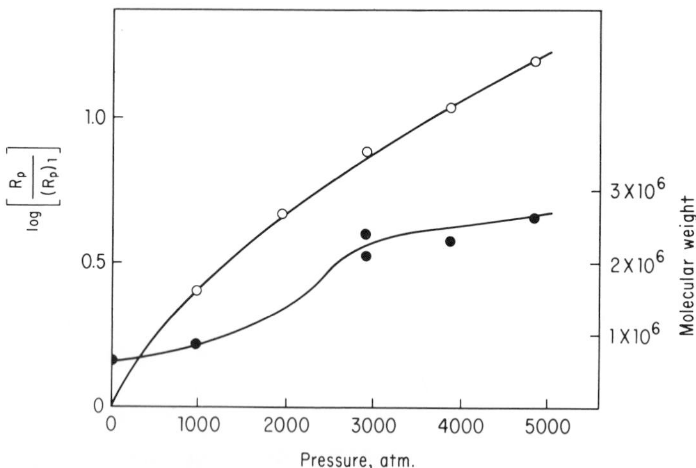

FIG. 3-18 *The effect of pressure on the polymerization rate (○) and polymer molecular weight (●) for the benzoyl peroxide catalyzed polymerization of styrene at 60°C. $R_p/(R_p)_1$ is the polymerization rate relative to the rate at 1 atmosphere. After [83] (by permission of E and F. N. Spon Ltd., London) from data in [84] (by permission of The Royal Society, London).*

3-12a Volume of Activation

The effect of pressure on R_p and $\overline{X}_n$ like that of temperature, manifests itself by changes in the three rate constants– k_d, k_p, and k_t. The quantitative effect of pressure P on the rate constant k of a reaction is given by

$$\frac{d \ln k}{dP} = \frac{-\Delta V^{\ddagger}}{RT} \tag{3-188}$$

where $\Delta V^{\ddagger}$ is the *volume of activation*, i.e., the change in volume (cm^3/mole) in going from the reactant(s) to the transition state. A negative value of $\Delta V^{\ddagger}$ corresponds to the volume of the transition state being smaller than that of the reactants; the result is that increased pressure leads to an increase in the reaction rate constant. A $\Delta V^{\ddagger}$ of -10 cm^3/mole corresponds to a 60-fold increase in reaction rate at 10,000 atmospheres pressure at room temperature. Positive values of $\Delta V^{\ddagger}$ correspond to a decrease in the reaction rate constant with increasing pressure as the volume of the transition state is larger than that of the reactants.

The $\Delta V^{\ddagger}$ term for initiation by the thermal decomposition of a catalyst $\Delta V_d^{\ddagger}$ is positive since the reaction is a unimolecular decomposition involving a volume expansion for the initiator going to the transition state. The initiation rate decreases with increasing pressure although the effect is not too large. Thus, the rate constant for AIBN decomposition decreases approximately 30 percent in going from one to 1,500 atmospheres. Similar effects have been observed [82, 83] for other initiators since $\Delta V_d^{\ddagger}$ is generally in the range of 5–10 cm^3/mole. The corresponding $\Delta V^{\ddagger}$ term for propagation $\Delta V_p^{\ddagger}$ is negative since the reaction involves two species coming together (i.e., a volume decrease occurs in going to the transition state), for example, $\Delta V_p^{\ddagger}$ for styrene is approximately -13.4 cm^3/mole [85]. The volume of activation for bimolecular termination $\Delta V_t^{\ddagger}$ is positive with values which are generally slightly larger than the $\Delta V_d^{\ddagger}$ values. At first glance, one would expect $\Delta V_t^{\ddagger}$ to be negative since termination involves a decrease in volume when two radicals come together in the transition state. However, since the termination step is diffusion-controlled, increased pressure decreases k_t by increasing the viscosity of the reaction medium [85].

3-12b Rate of Polymerization

The variation of the polymerization rate with pressure will depend on the variation of the ratio $k_p(k_d/k_t)^{1/2}$ with pressure in accordance with Eqs. 3-28 and 3-188. This latter variation will be given by

$$\frac{d \ln\left[k_p(k_d/k_t)^{1/2}\right]}{dP} = \frac{-\Delta V_R^\ddagger}{RT} \tag{3-189}$$

where $\Delta V_R^\ddagger$ is the *overall volume of activation for the rate of polymerization* and is given by

$$\Delta V_R^\ddagger = \frac{\Delta V_d^\ddagger}{2} + \Delta V_p^\ddagger - \frac{\Delta V_t^\ddagger}{2} \tag{3-190}$$

The various terms are such that the value of $\Delta V_R^\ddagger$ is negative by about 15–20 cm^3/mole for most monomers and the rate of polymerization is increased by high pressures (Fig. 3-18). Thus, $\Delta V_R^\ddagger$ is -17.4 cm^3/mole for the polymerization of vinyl acetate at 50°C and the polymerization rate increases approximately four- to five-fold at 1,000 atmospheres [86]. The polymerization rates of ethylene, propylene, styrene, and other monomers have been found to increase similarly with increasing pressure [82, 83, 87, 88].

3-12c Degree of Polymerization

The variation of the degree of polymerization with pressure depends on the variation of the ratio $k_p/(k_d k_t)^{1/2}$ with pressure as given by

$$\frac{d \ln\left[k_p/(k_d k_t)^{1/2}\right]}{dP} = \frac{-\Delta V_{\bar{X}_n}^\ddagger}{RT} \tag{3-191}$$

where $\Delta V_{\bar{X}_n}^\ddagger$ is the *overall volume of activation for the degree of polymerization* and is given by

$$\Delta V_{\bar{X}_n}^\ddagger = \Delta V_p^\ddagger - \frac{\Delta V_d^\ddagger}{2} - \frac{\Delta V_t^\ddagger}{2} \tag{3-192}$$

$\Delta V^{\ddagger}_{\bar{X}_n}$ is negative by about 20–25 cm^3/mole in most cases and the polymer molecular weight increases with increasing pressure (Fig. 3-18). However, the increase in molecular weight with pressure is not continuous. The polymer size increases initially but soon reaches a limiting value at a particular pressure and further increases in pressure have little effect on molecular weight. Actually, the initial increase in molecular weight with pressure is not as steep as one would expect based on the value of $\Delta V^{\ddagger}_{\bar{X}_n}$. $\Delta V^{\ddagger}_{\bar{X}_n}$ is more negative than $\Delta V^{\ddagger}_{R}$ and $\bar{X}_n$ should increase faster than R_p with increasing pressure; the opposite is observed (Fig. 3-18). The explanation for this effect lies in a consideration of the terms which contribute to determining the polymer molecular weight. A consideration of Eq. 3-109 in view of known values for the various quantities in styrene polymerization shows that only the first term (that for bimolecular termination) on the right side of the equation is significant at one atmosphere pressure [83, 84]. As the pressure increases, C_{M} decreases due to the increase in k_p, but the term for bimolecular termination decreases more steeply. Thus, C_{M} contributes increasingly to the determination of polymer molecular weight; at the highest pressures, bimolecular termination becomes insignificant and chain transfer to monomer is the major determinant of molecular weight.

Chain transfer reactions would be expected to increase in rate with increasing pressure since transfer is a bimolecular reaction with a negative volume of activation. The variation of chain transfer constants with pressure, however, differ depending on the relative effects of pressure on the propagation and transfer rate constants. For the case where only transfer to chain transfer agent S is important, C_{S} varies with pressure according to

$$\frac{d \ln C_{\mathrm{S}}}{dP} = \frac{d \ln (k_{tr,\mathrm{S}}/k_p)}{dP} = \frac{-(\Delta V^{\ddagger}_{tr,\mathrm{S}} - \Delta V^{\ddagger}_{p})}{RT} \tag{3-193}$$

where $\Delta V^{\ddagger}_{tr,\mathrm{S}}$ is the volume of activation for chain transfer. For some transfer agents, $\Delta V^{\ddagger}_{tr,\mathrm{S}}$ is smaller than $\Delta V^{\ddagger}_{p}$ and C_{S} increases with pressure; the opposite occurs with other transfer agents. Thus, the transfer constant for triethylamine in styrene polymerization is decreased by a factor of about 5 in going from 1 atmosphere to 4,400 atmospheres [88]. On the other hand, C_{S} for carbon tetrachloride is decreased by only about 15 percent by the same increase in pressure. An interesting observation is that on the effect of pressure on the *back-biting* self-transfer reaction (Eq. 3-126) which occurs in polyethylene. The extent of this transfer to polymer reaction decreases with increasing pressure [89]. This means that the amount of branching in polyethylene decreases as the pressure increases. The extent of transfer and branching is also temperature dependent; it increases with increasing temperature.

3-13 PROCESS CONDITIONS

The conditions under which radical polymerizations are carried out are both of the homogeneous and heterogeneous types. This classification is usually based on whether the initial reaction mixture is homogeneous or heterogeneous. Some homogeneous systems may become heterogeneous as polymerization proceeds due to insolubility of the polymer in the reaction media. Mass and solution polymerizations are homogeneous processes; suspension and emulsion polymerizations are heterogeneous processes. Emulsion polymerization will be discussed separately in Chap. 4. The other processes will be considered here. All monomers can be polymerized by any of the various processes. However, it is usually found that the commercial polymerization of any one monomer is best carried out by one or two of the processes. The technology of commercial polymerization processes has been discussed in detail [90, 91].

3-13a Bulk (Mass) Polymerization

Bulk or *mass polymerization* of a pure monomer offers the simplest process with a minimum of contamination of the product. However, bulk polymerization is difficult to control due to the characteristics of radical chain polymerization. Their highly exothermic nature, the high activation energies involved, and the tendency toward the gel effect combine to make heat dissipation difficult. Bulk polymerization requires careful temperature control. Further, there is also the need for strong and elaborate stirring equipment since the viscosity of the reaction system increases rapidly at relatively low conversion. The viscosity and exotherm effects make temperature control difficult. Local hot spots may occur—resulting in degradation and discoloration of the polymer product and a broadened molecular weight distribution due to chain transfer to polymer. In the extreme case, uncontrolled acceleration of the polymerization rate can lead to disastrous "runaway" reactions.

Bulk polymerization is not used extensively for radical chain polymerizations because of the difficulties indicated. It is, however, used in the polymerizations of ethylene, styrene, and methyl methacrylate [90, 91]. The heat dissipation problems are circumvented by carrying out the polymerizations to low conversions or in stages. Ethylene polymerization proceeds at high pressures (1,000–3,000 atm) and at temperatures above the melting point of polyethylene. The system is usually considered a homogeneous one since the polymer is usually either soluble in the ethylene or highly swollen by the ethylene. One continuous process employs very long and very narrow tubular reactors (e.g., tubes with diameters less than one inch and lengths of 100 feet). The molecular weight distribution is kept from broadening because of the relative ease of temperature control, the use of multiple charges of initiator, and limiting the polymerization to 10–20% conversion. The polyethylene is separated from the reaction mixture and the unreacted monomer is recycled.

The heat dissipation problem is controlled in methyl methacrylate and styrene polymerizations by carrying out the reactions in two steps. Styrene is polymerized at about 80°C to 30–35% conversion in a stirred reactor called a *prepolymerizer*. The resulting viscous solution or syrup of polymer in monomer is then made to flow down a cylindrical tower. The tower has a temperature gradient with increasing temperatures at the bottom. Polymerization proceeds as the reaction mixture flows downward and 98–100% conversion is obtained for the exiting stream.

Sheets, rods, tubes, and other shapes of poly(methyl methacrylate) are made in an analogous manner. Partially polymerized monomer is poured into an appropriate mold and then the assembly heated in an air or water bath to progressively higher temperatures. This procedure not only allows an easier dissipation of heat but also allows greater controls of the dimensions of the product. There is a very large volume shrinkage of about 21 percent for methyl methacrylate upon polymerization. The amount of shrinkage in the product mold is decreased by the use of partially polymerized methyl methacrylate.

3-13b Solution Polymerization

Polymerization of a monomer in a solvent overcomes many of the disadvantages of the bulk process. The solvent acts as diluent and aids in the transfer of the heat of polymerization. The solvent also allows easier stirring since the viscosity of the reaction mixture is decreased. Thermal control is much easier in *solution polymerization* compared to bulk polymerization. On the other hand, the presence of solvent may present new difficulties. Unless the solvent is chosen with appropriate consideration, chain transfer to solvent can become a problem. Further, the purity of the polymer may be affected if there are difficulties in removal of the solvent. Vinyl acetate, acrylonitrile, and esters of acrylic acid are polymerized in solution. Ethylene polymerization is sometimes a solution process since water or benzene may be added to aid in the problem of heat control. Acrylonitrile is polymerized in water solution using redox initiation. This is an interesting system in that the polymerization quickly becomes heterogeneous. Polyacrylonitrile precipitates from solution as a fine powder.

3-13c Suspension Polymerization

Heterogeneous, suspension polymerization is extensively employed. Styrene, methyl methacrylate, vinyl chloride, and vinyl acetate are polymerized by the suspension process. The process is also referred to as *bead, pearl*, or *granular polymerization* because of the forms in which the final products may be obtained. The monomer is dispersed as droplets in water. The monomer droplet size is in the range 0.01–0.5 cm in diameter. Dispersion is maintained by mechanical agitation and the addition of stabilizers. Various types of stabilizers are used to prevent agglomeration of the monomer droplets. These include water-soluble organic polymers such as gelatin, methyl cellulose, and poly(vinyl alcohol), electrolytes, and water-insoluble inorganic compounds such as kaolin, magnesium silicates, and aluminum hydroxide.

The initiators used are soluble in the monomer droplets. Such catalysts are often referred to as being *oil-soluble catalysts*. Each monomer droplet is considered to be a small bulk polymerization system. The kinetics of polymerization within each droplet are the same as those for the corresponding bulk polymerization. Heat control in suspension polymerization is relatively easy. However, the product usually must be washed, dried, and freed of additives.

3-13d Solid-State Polymerization

A number of monomers have been polymerized in the *solid-state*. These reactions have usually been carried out with the monomer in its crystalline form below its melting point using atomic radiation as the means of initiation [92]. Some of them proceed by a radical mechanism while others proceed by an ionic mechanism. Interestingly enough, the polymerization of some monomers proceeds more favorably in the solid state than in the liquid state. The crystal lattice structure must play an important role in solid-state polymerization but in an unclear manner at present. Much work remains to be done before the mechanistic details of these polymerizations are established. Solid-state polymerization is not presently employed on a commercial scale.

3-14 POLYMERIZATION OF DIENES

The polymerization of *dienes* (i.e., monomers with two double bonds per molecule) can proceed in a variety of ways depending on the chemical structure of the diene. Dienes are classified as *conjugated* or *non-conjugated dienes* depending on whether or not the two double bonds are conjugated with each other. Conjugated dienes are also referred to as *1,3-dienes.* The polymerization of non-conjugated dienes often yields branched and crosslinked products. Non-conjugated dienes are often used to bring about crosslinking in other alkene monomers by the technique of copolymerization (Sec. 6-6a). Certain non-conjugated dienes undergo a special type of cyclization polymerization (cyclopolymerization) by an alternating intra-intermolecular reaction mechanism (Sec. 6-6b).

The polymerization of conjugated dienes is of special interest. Two different types of polymerization reactions occur with 1,3-dienes such as 1,3-butadiene, isoprene(2-methyl-1,3-butadiene), and chloroprene(2-chloro-1,3-butadiene)

$$CH_2{=}CH{-}CH{=}CH_2 \qquad CH_2{=}\underset{\displaystyle CH_3}{\underset{|}{C}}{-}CH{=}CH_2 \qquad CH_2{=}\underset{\displaystyle Cl}{\underset{|}{C}}{-}CH{=}CH_2$$

1,3-Butadiene Isoprene Chloroprene

One of the polymerization routes involves polymerization of one or the other of the double bonds in the usual manner. The other route involves the two double bonds acting in a unique and concerted manner. Thus, addition of an initiating radical to a 1,3-diene such as 1,3-butadiene yields an allylic radical with the two equivalent resonance forms XII and XIII.

$$\mathrm{R\cdot + CH_2{=}CH{-}CH{=}CH_2 \longrightarrow \begin{matrix} R{-}CH_2{-}\dot{C}H{-}CH{=}CH_2 & \text{XII} \\ \updownarrow & \\ R{-}CH_2{-}CH{=}CH{-}\dot{C}H_2 & \text{XIII} \end{matrix}} \tag{3-194}$$

Propagation may then occur by attachment of the successive monomer units either at carbon 2 (propagation via XII) or at carbon 4 (propagation via XIII). The two modes of polymerizations are referred to as *1,2-polymerization* and *1,4-polymerization*, respectively. The polymers obtained have the repeating structures

$$\left[\mathrm{CH_2{-}\underset{\underset{\displaystyle CH{=}CH_2}{|}}{CH}}\right]_n \qquad\qquad \mathrm{{+}CH_2{-}CH{=}CH{-}CH_2{+}_n}$$

1,2-polymerization 1,4-polymerization

and are named 1,2-poly-1,3-butadiene and 1,4-poly-1,3-butadiene, respectively. Both polymers are unsaturated—the *1,2-polymer* has pendant unsaturation while there is unsaturation along the polymer chain in the *1,4-polymer*. The polymerization of 1,3-dienes is considered in greater detail in Sec. 8-6.

REFERENCES

1. C. S. Marvel et al., *J. Am. Chem. Soc.*, **60**:280 (1938); **61**:3241 (1939).
2. H. N. Friedlander, H. E. Harris, and J. G. Pritchard, *J. Polymer Sci.*, **A-1(4)**:649 (1966).
3. C. W. Wilson and E. R. Santee, Jr., *ibid.*, **C(8)**:97 (1965).
4. C. Walling, "Free Radicals in Solution," chaps. 3–5, John Wiley & Sons, Inc., New York, 1957.
5. W. A. Pryor, "Free Radicals," chaps. 5–11, McGraw-Hill Book Co., Inc., New York, 1966.
6. C. V. Schulz and F. Blaschke, *Z. Physik Chem. (Leipzig)*, **B51**:75 (1942).
7. G. F. Santee, R. H. Marchessault, H. G. Clark, J. J. Kearny, and V. Stannett, *Makromol. Chem.*, **73**:177 (1964).
8. A. Vrancken and G. Smets, *ibid.*, **30**:197 (1959).
9. W. A. Pryor and T. R. Fiske, *Macromolecules*, **2**:62 (1969).
10. T. Sugimura and Y. Minoura, *J. Polymer Sci.*, **A-1(4)**:2735 (1966).
11. G. S. Misra and V. R. B. Mathiu, *Makromol. Chem.*, **100**:5 (1967).

12. M. W. Horikx and J. J. Hermans, *J. Polymer Sci.*, **11**:325 (1953).
13. C. Walling and L. Heaton, *J. Am. Chem. Soc.*, **87**:38 (1965).
14. G. M. Burnett and H. W. Melville, *Proc. Roy. Soc. (London)*, **A189**:456, 494 (1947).
15. F. S. Dainton and W. D. Sisley, *Trans. Faraday Soc.*, **59**:1369 (1963).
16. M. H. George, Styrene, in G. E. Ham (ed.), "Vinyl Polymerization," vol. 1, part I, chap. 3, Marcel Dekker, Inc., New York, 1967.
17. A. Chapiro, "Radiation Chemistry of Polymer Systems," chap. IV, Interscience Publishers, John Wiley & Sons, Inc., New York, 1962.
18. R. A. Gregg and F. R. Mayo, *Disc. Faraday Soc.*, **2**:328 (1947).
19. F. R. Mayo, *J. Am. Chem. Soc.*, **75**:6133 (1953).
20. G. M. Burnett and L. D. Loan, *Trans. Faraday Soc.*, **51**:214 (1955).
21. K. F. O'Driscoll et al., *J. Polymer Sci.*, **A3**:283, 1567 (1965).
22. A. Mukherjee, R. Pal(Mitra), Amarendra, M. Biswas, and S. Maiti, *ibid.*, **A-1(5)**:135 (1967).
23. S. Saccubai and M. Santappa, *ibid.*, **A-1(7)**:643 (1969).
24. K. Kaeriyama, *Polymer*, **10**:11 (1969).
25. S. V. Subramanian and M. Santappa, *Makromol. Chem.*, **112**:1 (1968); *J. Polymer Sci.*, **A-1(6)**:493 (1968).
26. F. DeSchrijver and G. Smets, *J. Polymer Sci.*, **A-1(4)**:2201 (1966).
27. J. C. Bevington, *Trans. Faraday Soc.*, **51**:1392 (1955).
28. C. Walling, *J. Polymer Sci.*, **14**:214 (1954).
29. K. Nozaki and P. D. Bartlett, *J. Am. Chem. Soc.*, **68**:1686 (1946).
30. L. M. Arnett and J. H. Peterson, *ibid.*, **74**:2031 (1952).
31. P. D. Bartlett and H. Kwart, *ibid.*, **72**:1051 (1950).
32. A. V. Tobolsky, C. E. Rodgers, and R. D. Brickman, *ibid.*, **82**:1277 (1960).
33. R. D. Bohme and A. V. Tobolsky, Dead-End Polymerization, in "Encyclopedia of Polymer Science and Technology," vol. 4., p. 599, John Wiley & Sons, Inc., New York, N. Y., 1966.
34. R. H. Gobran, M. B. Berenbaum, and A. V. Tobolsky, *J. Polymer Sci.*, **46**:431 (1960).
35. K. F. O'Driscoll and P. J. White, *ibid.*, **B1**:597 (1963); **A3**:283 (1965).
36. K. F. O'Driscoll and S. A. McArdle, *ibid.*, **40**:557 (1959).
37. J. C. Bevington, H. W. Melville, and R. P. Taylor, *ibid.*, **12**:449 (1954); **14**:463 (1954).
38. B. L. Funt and W. Pasika, *Can. J. Chem.*, **38**:1865 (1960).
39. B. Baysal and A. V. Tobolsky, *J. Polymer Sci.*, **8**:529 (1952).
40. F. R. Mayo, R. A. Gregg, and M. S. Matheson, *J. Am. Chem. Soc.*, **73**:1691 (1951).
41. J. Brandup and E. H. Immergut (eds.), "Polymer Handbook," Interscience Publishers, John Wiley & Sons, Inc., New York, 1966.
42. R. A. Gregg and F. R. Mayo, *J. Am. Chem. Soc.*, **70**:2373 (1948).

43. M. K. Lindeman, The Mechanism of Vinyl Acetate Polymerization, in G. E. Ham (ed.), "Vinyl Polymerization," vol. 1, part I, chap. 4, Marcel Dekker, Inc., New York, 1967.
44. P. J. Flory, *J. Am. Chem. Soc.*, **69**:2893 (1947).
45. J. C. Bevington, G. M. Guzman, and H. W. Melville, *Proc. Roy. Soc. (London)*, **A221**:453, 547 (1947).
46. D. J. Stein, *Makromol. Chem.*, **76**:170 (1964).
47. G. V. Schulz, *Chem. Ber.*, **80**:232 (1947).
48. K. K. Georgieff, *J. Appl. Polymer Sci.*, **9**:2009 (1965).
49. Y. Tabata, K. Ishigure, K. Oshima, and H. Sobue, *J. Polymer Sci.*, **A2**:2445 (1964).
50. P. G. Ashmore, "Catalysis and Inhibition of Chemical Reactions," pp. 304-310, Butterworth and Co. (Publishers) Ltd., London, 1963.
51. H. W. Melville and W. F. Watson, *Trans. Faraday Soc.*, **44**:886 (1948).
52. P. D. Bartlett and F. A. Tate, *J. Am. Chem. Soc.*, **75**:91 (1953).
53. P. J. Flory, "Principles of Polymer Chemistry," chap. IV, Cornell University Press, Ithaca, 1953.
54. S. W. Benson and A. M. North, *J. Am. Chem. Soc.*, **81**:1339 (1959).
55. R. G. W. Norrish and B. A. Thrush, *Quart. Rev. (London)*, **10**:149 (1956).
56. F. Briers, D. L. Chapman, and E. Walters, *J. Chem. Soc.*, **1926**:562.
57. M. S. Matheson, E. E. Auer, E. B. Bevilacqua, and E. J. Hart, *J. Am. Chem. Soc.*, **71**:497 (1949).
58. F. S. Dainton and W. D. Sisley, *Trans. Faraday Soc.*, **59**:1369 (1963).
59. Dow Chemical Co., A. Roche, and C. C. Price in R. H. Boundy, R. F. Boyer, and S. M. Stoesser (eds.), "Styrene: Its Polymers, Co-Polymers, and Derivatives," unpublished data in Table 7-1, p. 216, Reinhold Book Corp., New York, 1952.
60. W. G. Barb, J. H. Baxendale, P. George, and K. R. Hargrave, *Trans. Faraday Soc.*, **47**:462, 591 (1951).
61. R. A. Gregg and F. R. Mayo, *J. Am. Chem. Soc.*, **75**:3530 (1953).
62. R. M. Joshi and B. J. Zwolinski, Heats of Polymerization and Their Structural and Mechanistic Implications, in G. E. Ham (ed.), "Vinyl Polymerization," vol. 1, part I, chap. 8, Marcel Dekker, Inc., New York, 1967.
63. F. S. Dainton and K. J. Ivin, *Quart. Rev. (London)*, **12**:61 (1958).
64. F. S. Dainton and K. J. Ivin, *Trans. Faraday Soc.*, **46**:331 (1950).
65. L. A. Wall, *Soc. Plastic Eng. J.*, **16**:1 (1960).
66. H. McCormick, *J. Polymer Sci.*, **25**:488 (1957).
67. D. J. Worsfold and S. Bywater, *ibid.*, **26**:299 (1957).
68. R. E. Cook, F. S. Dainton, and K. J. Ivin, *ibid.*, **29**:549 (1958).
69. G. V. Schulz and G. Haborth, *Makromol. Chem.*, **1**:106 (1948).
70. P. Hayden and H. W. Melville, *J. Polymer Sci.*, **43**:201 (1960).
71. A. M. North et al., *ibid.*, **A1**:1311 (1963); *Trans. Faraday Soc.*, **57**:859 (1961) and **60**:960 (1964).

72. K. Ito, *J. Polymer Sci.*, **A-1(7)**:827 (1969).
73. D. Mangaraj and S. K. Patra, *Makromol. Chem.*, **104**:125 (1967).
74. A. D. Jenkins, Occlusion Phenomena in the Polymerization of Acrylonitrile and Other Monomers, in G. E. Ham (ed.), "Vinyl Polymerization," vol. 1, part I, chap. 6, Marcel Dekker, Inc., New York, 1967.
75. C. Tanford, "Physical Chemistry of Macromolecules," pp. 603-607, John Wiley & Sons, Inc., New York, 1961.
76. P. J. Flory, "Principles of Polymer Chemistry," chap. VIII, Cornell University Press, Ithaca, 1953.
77. L. H. Peebles, Jr., p. II-421 in reference 41.
78. W. B. Smith, J. A. May, and C. W. Kim, *J. Polymer Sci.*, **A-2(4)**:365 (1966).
79. J. H. Duerksen and A. E. Hamielec, *Polymer Preprints*, **8(1)**:344 (1967).
80. R. J. Zeman and N. R. Amundson, *Chem. Eng. Sci.*, **20**:331, 637 (1965).
81. N. L. Zutty and R. D. Burkhart, Polymer Synthesis at High Pressures, in N. A. J. Platzker (ed.), "Polymerization and Polycondensation Processes," chap. 3, American Chemical Society, Reinhold Book Corp., New York, 1962.
82. K. E. Weale, *Quart. Rev. (London)*, **16**:267 (1962).
83. K. E. Weale, "Chemical Reactions at High Pressures," chaps. 8 and 9, E. and F. N. Spon, London, 1967.
84. F. M. Merrett and R. G. W. Norrish, *Proc. Roy. Soc. (London).*, **A206**:309 (1951).
85. A. E. Nicolson and R. G. W. Norrish, *Disc. Faraday Soc.*, **22**:104 (1956).
86. H. Nakamoto, Y. Ogo, and T. Imoto, *Makromol. Chem.*, **111**:93 (1968).
87. G. A. Mortimer and L. C. Arnold, *J. Polymer Sci.*, **A2**:4247 (1964).
88. A. C. Toohey and K. E. Weale, *Trans. Faraday Soc.*, **58**:2446 (1962).
89. J. C. Woodbrey and P. Ehrlich, *J. Am. Chem. Soc.*, **85**:1580 (1963).
90. W. M. Smith, "Manufacture of Plastics," vol. 1, pp. 16-32, 81-87, 100-118, 225-246, 308-323, 364-381, 414-432, Reinhold Book Corp., New York, 1964.
91. J. A. Brydson, "Plastics Materials," pp. 100-102, 159-161, 231-234, 251-254, D. Van Nostrand Co., Princeton, 1966.
92. H. Morawetz, *J. Polymer Sci.*, **A-1(4)**:2487 (1966).

PROBLEMS

3-1. When one considers the various polymers produced from alkenes, the following generalizations are apparent:

a. The polymers are produced almost exclusively from ethylene, 1-monosubstituted ethylenes or 1,1-disubstituted ethylenes. Polymers from 1,2-disubstituted ethylenes are essentially non-existent.

b. Most of the chain polymerizations are carried out by radical initiation; relatively few are produced by ionic initiation.

Why? Are there good reasons for these generalizations or are they simply a matter of chance? Discuss.

3-2. Show by chemical equations the polymerization of acrylonitrile initiated by the thermal decomposition of cumyl hydroperoxide.

3-3. Using carbon-14 labelled AIBN as an initiator, a sample of styrene is polymerized to an average degree of polymerization of 1.52×10^4. The AIBN has an activity of 9.81×10^7 counts per minute per mole in a scintillation counter. If 3.22 grams of the polystyrene has an activity of 203 counts per minute, determine the mode of termination by appropriate calculations.

3-4. Consider the polymerization of styrene catalyzed by di-*t*-butyl peroxide at 60°C. For a solution of 0.01 molar peroxide and 1.0 molar styrene in benzene, the initial rates of initiation and polymerization are 4.0×10^{-11} moles/liter-sec and 1.5×10^{-7} moles/liter-sec, respectively. Calculate the values of (fk_d), the initial kinetic chain length, and the initial degree of polymerization. Indicate how often on the average chain transfer occurs per each initiating radical from the peroxide. What is the breadth of the molecular weight distribution that is expected, i.e., what is the value of $\overline{X}_w/\overline{X}_n$? Use the following chain transfer constants:

$$C_{\mathrm{M}} = 8.0 \times 10^{-5}$$
$$C_{\mathrm{I}} = 3.2 \times 10^{-4}$$
$$C_{\mathrm{P}} = 1.9 \times 10^{-4}$$
$$C_{\mathrm{S}} = 2.3 \times 10^{-6}$$

3-5. For a particular application, the molecular weight of the polystyrene obtained in Question 3-4 is too high. What concentration of *n*-butyl mercaptan should be used to lower the molecular weight to 85,000? What will be the polymerization rate for the reaction in the presence of the mercaptan?

3-6. Consider the polymerization reaction in Question 3-4. Aside from increasing the monomer concentration, what means are available for increasing the polymerization rate? Compare the alternate possibilities with respect to any changes which are expected in the molecular weight of the product.

3-7. Show by chemical equations the reactions involved in chain transfer by hexane, benzene, isopropylbenzene, propanol, butyl iodide, carbon tetrabromide, *n*-butyl mercaptan, and di-*n*-butyl sulfide. Compare and discuss the differences in the transfer constants of these agents for vinyl acetate polymerization (Table 3-5).

3-8. The polymerization of methyl acrylate (one molar in benzene) is carried out using a photosensitizer and 3130 Angstrom light from a filtered mercury arc lamp. Light is absorbed by the system at the rate of 1.0×10^5 ergs/liter-second. If the quantum yield for radical production in this system is 0.50, calculate the rates of initiation and polymerization.

3-9. Consider the following data for the polymerization of a 0.2 molar solution of monomer Z:

Experiment	[AIBN]	UV intensity	[Photosensitizer]	Temp. (°C)	$R_p \times 10^3$	$\bar{X}_n$
1	2A	O	O	50	0.30	200
2	2A	O	O	80	?	?
3	2A	B	C	50	0.45	?
4	O	2B	C	50	0.30	200
5	A	B	C	50	?	?
6	2A	2B	C	50	?	?
7	O	2B	C	80	?	?
8	4A	8B	C	50	?	?
9	4A	8B	C	80	?	?

Fill in the question marks in the table above if E_p and E_t for monomer Z are 7.3 and 1.9 kcal/mole, respectively. Note any assumptions made in carrying out your calculations.

3-10. Most radical chain polymerizations show a one-half order dependence of the polymerization rate on the rate of initiation R_i or the initiator concentration [I]. Describe and explain under what conditions radical chain polymerizations will show the following order dependencies:

a. First order.
b. Zero order.
c. Between half order and zero order.
d. Between half order and first order.

Explain clearly the manner in which the polymerization mechanisms give rise to these different kinetic orders. Derive the appropriate kinetic expressions.

3-11. What is the breadth of the size distribution to be expected for a low conversion polymerization where termination is entirely by coupling. Discuss the manner in which each of the following situations alters the size distribution:

a. Chain transfer to *n*-butyl mercaptan.
b. High conversion.
c. Chain transfer to polymer.
d. Autoacceleration.

For those situations where there is a tendency toward a broadening of the size distribution, discuss the possible process conditions which may be used to decrease this tendency.

3-12. Calculate the rate and degree polymerization of methyl methacrylate initiated by AIBN at 50°C at 2,500 atmospheres relative to the corresponding quantities at 1 atmosphere if $\Delta V_R^{\ddagger} = -19.0$ cm^3/mole and $\Delta V_d^{\ddagger} = 3.8$ cm^3/mole.

4

EMULSION POLYMERIZATION

Emulsion polymerization refers to a unique process employed for some radical chain polymerizations. It involves the polymerization of monomers which are in the form of emulsions. The process is not similar to the previously described suspension polymerization (Sec. 3-13c) but is quite different in its mechanism and reaction characteristics. Emulsion polymerization differs from suspension polymerization in the type and smaller size of the particles in which polymerization occurs and in the kind of initiator employed.

4-1 DESCRIPTION OF PROCESS

4-1a Utility

Emulsion polymerization was first employed for the production of synthetic styrene-butadiene rubbers during the 1940's when the supplies of natural rubber were cut off during World War II. Conjugated dienes such as butadiene and isoprene are presently polymerized and copolymerized in large part by the emulsion process. In addition, emulsion polymerization is also used extensively for vinyl acetate, vinyl chloride, acrylates, methacrylates, and various copolymers of these monomers.

The emulsion polymerization process has several distinct advantages. The physical state of the emulsion system makes it easy to control the process. Thermal and viscosity problems are much less significant than in bulk polymerization. The products of emulsion polymerizations can in some instances be employed directly without further separations but with appropriate blending operations. Such applications involve coatings, finishes, floor polishes, and paints. Aside from the physical difference between the emulsion and other polymerization processes, there is one very significant kinetic difference. For the other processes, there is an inverse relationship (Eq. 3-100) between the polymerization rate and the polymer molecular weight. This drastically limits one's practical ability to make large changes in the molecular weight of a polymer, e.g., from 200,000 to 2,000,000 or from 200,000 to 20,000. Large decreases in the molecular weight of a polymer can be made without altering the polymerization rate by using chain transfer agents. However, large increases in molecular weight can only be made by decreasing the polymerization rate by lowering the initiator concentration or lowering the reaction temperature. Emulsion polymerization is a unique process in that it affords a means of increasing the polymer molecular weight without decreasing the polymerization rate. Because of a different reaction mechanism, emulsion polymerization has the advantage of being able to simultaneously attain both high molecular weights and high reaction rates. To a large extent, the molecular weight and polymerization rate can be varied independently of each other.

4-1b Qualitative Picture

4-1b-1 Components and Their Locations. The physical picture of emulsion polymerization is based primarily on the qualitative picture of Harkins [1] and the quantitative treatment of Smith and Ewart [2, 3]. Table 4-1 shows a typical recipe for an emulsion polymerization [4]. This formulation was one of the early ones employed for the production of "GR-S" rubber but is generally typical of all emulsion polymerization systems. The main components of an emulsion polymerization system are the monomer(s), *dispersing medium, emulsifying agent,* and water-soluble initiator. The dispersing

Table 4-1 Composition of a "GR-S" Recipe for Emulsion Polymerization of Styrene-Butadiene[a]

Component	Parts by weight
Styrene	25
Butadiene	75
Water	180
Emulsifier (Dresinate 731)	5
Mercaptan	0.5
NaOH	0.061
Cumene hydroperoxide	0.17
$FeSO_4$	0.017
$Na_4P_2O_7 \cdot 10\ H_2O$	1.5
Fructose	0.5

[a]Data from [4].

medium is the liquid in which the various components are dispersed in an emulsion state by means of the emulsifying agent. The dispersing medium is usually water. The emulsifying agent is a surfactant whose action is due to its having both hydrophilic and hydrophobic segments in its molecular structure. Various other components may also be present in the emulsion system. Thus, a mercaptan is used in the above formulation as a chain transfer agent to control the polymer molecular weight. The initiator is the hydroperoxide-ferrous ion redox system and the function of fructose is probably to regenerate ferrous ion by reducing the ferric ion produced in the initiation reaction (Eq. 3-66c). The sodium pyrophosphate acts to solubilize the iron salts in the strongly alkaline reaction medium. The emulsion system is usually kept in a well-agitated state during reaction.

The locations of the various components in an emulsion system will now be considered. A small fraction of the emulsifying agent is dissolved as such in the water. The bulk of the emulsifier molecules aggregate together to form small colloidal clusters or *micelles*. There is a dynamic equilibrium between the emulsifier in solution and that in the micelles. The colloidal-sized micelles are rodlike in shape as shown by light scattering measurements [5]. Each micelle consists of 50 to 100 emulsifier molecules and is 1,000 to 3,000 Å (0.1–0.3 μ) in length with diameters that are approximately twice the length of an emulsifier molecule. The emulsifier molecules are arranged in a micelle with their hydrocarbon ends pointed toward the interior of the micelle and their ionic ends outward toward the water. The number of micelles and their size depends on the amount of emulsifier used compared to the amount of monomer. Larger amounts of emulsifier yield larger numbers of smaller sized particles, i.e., the surface area of the micelles increases with the amount of emulsifier.

When a water-insoluble or only slightly water-soluble monomer is added, a very small fraction dissolves and goes into solution. A larger but still small portion of the monomer enters the interior hydrocarbon part of the micelles. This is evidenced by x-ray and light scattering measurements which show that the micelles increase in size as the monomer is added [6]. The largest portion of the monomer is dispersed as *monomer droplets* whose size depends on the intensity of agitation. The droplets are probably stabilized by emulsifier molecules adsorbed on their surfaces. The diameter of the monomer droplets is usually not less than 1 micron (10,000 Å). Thus, in a typical emulsion polymerization system, the monomer droplets are quite a bit larger than the monomer-containing micelles. Consequently, while the concentration of micelles is typically 10^{18} per milliliter, there are at most 10^{10}–10^{11} monomer droplets per milliliter. A further difference between the micelles and the monomer droplets is that the micelles have a much greater total surface area. The determinations of particle size and particle number in emulsion systems are made by electron microscope, light scattering, ultracentrifugation, and other methods [6–8].

4-1b-2 Site and Progress of Polymerization. The initiator is present in the water phase and this is where the initiating radicals are produced. The rate of radical production R_i is typically of the order of 10^{13} radicals per milliliter per second. (The symbol ρ is often used instead of R_i in emulsion polymerization terminology.) The locus of polymerization is now of prime concern. Polymerization of the monomer in solution undoubtedly takes place but is not appreciable because of the low concentration of monomer in solution. The site of polymerization is also not the monomer droplets since the initiators employed are insoluble in the organic monomer. Such initiators are referred to as oil-insoluble initiators. This situation distinguishes emulsion polymerization from suspension polymerization. Oil-soluble initiators are used in suspension polymerization and reaction occurs in the monomer droplets. The absence of polymerization in the monomer droplets in emulsion polymerization has been experimentally verified. If one halts an emulsion polymerization at an

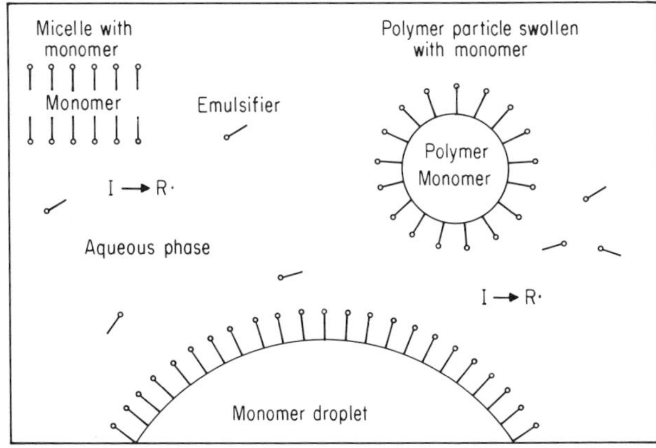

FIG. 4-1 *Simplified representation of an emulsion polymerization system.*

appropriate point before complete conversion is achieved, the monomer droplets can be separated and analyzed. An insignificant amount (approximately < 0.1 percent) of polymer is found in the monomer droplets in such experiments.

Polymerization takes place almost exclusively in the interior of the micelles. The micelles act as a meeting place for the organic (oil-soluble) monomer and the water-soluble initiator. The micelles are also favored as the site of reaction because of their high monomer concentration and their high surface to volume ratio compared to the monomer droplets. As polymerization proceeds, the micelles grow initially by the addition of monomer from the aqueous solution phase and subsequently from the monomer droplets. A simplified schematic representation of an emulsion polymerization system is shown in Fig. 4-1. The system consists of three types of particles–monomer droplets, inactive micelles in which polymerization is not occurring, and active micelles in which polymerization is occurring. An emulsifier molecule is shown as ○— to indicate that one end is polar or ionic and the other end non-polar.

The system undergoes a very significant change after only a few percent of the total monomer has been converted to polymer. Polymerization is initiated in only a fraction, of the order of 0.1 percent, of the micelles initially present. As the active micelles grow in size and contain polymer as well as monomer, they absorb more and more emulsifier molecules from that which is in solution. The point is quickly reached at which the emulsifier concentration in solution falls below its *critical micelle concentration* (CMC). This is the concentration of emulsifier in solution which must be maintained in order to form and maintain micelles. When the concentration of emulsifier falls below this value, the inactive micelles (those in which polymerization is not occurring) become unstable and micellar emulsifier dissolves. At 2–15% conversion, depending on the particular polymerization system, the active micelles have grown much larger than the original micelles. They are no longer considered as micelles but as *polymer particles* or, more precisely, as monomer-swollen polymer particles. All micelles which were not activated by the entry of an initiating radical have disappeared and essentially all of the emulsifier in the system has been adsorbed by the polymer particles. As a consequence the monomer droplets are no longer stable and will coalesce if agitation is stopped.

Polymerization proceeds homogeneously in the polymer particles as the monomer concentration in the particles is maintained at a constant concentration by diffusion of monomer from the monomer droplets. The number of polymer particles remains constant throughout the polymerization. The monomer droplets decrease in size as the size of the polymer particles increases. Finally at 50–80% conversion, the monomer droplets completely disappear and the polymer particles contain all the unreacted monomer. Polymerization continues at a steadily decreasing rate as the monomer concentration in the polymer particles decreases. Final conversions of essentially 100 percent are usually achieved. The final polymer particles have diameters of the order of 500 to 2,000 Å and are intermediate in size between the initial micelles and initial monomer droplets.

4-2 KINETICS

4-2a Rate of Polymerization

The theoretical calculations of Smith and Ewart [2, 3] allow the derivation of the kinetic expressions for emulsion polymerization. These calculations are based on the rates of radical coupling reactions compared to the diffusion rates of radicals in water. It has been shown that the initiating radicals in emulsion polymerization systems do not terminate in the aqueous phase but are long-lived enough to diffuse into the polymer particles. Thus, essentially all of the radicals produced in the aqueous phase enter the polymer particles.

It is convenient to consider the steady-state portion of the polymerization after the inactive monomer micelles have disappeared and the number of polymer particles has become constant. In emulsion polymerization systems, the *number of polymer particles* N is in the range $10^{13}-10^{15}$ particles per milliliter of aqueous phase and the rate of initiation is in the range $10^{12}-10^{14}$ radicals per milliliter of aqueous phase per second. In a typical system where there are 10^{14} polymer particles/ml and R_i is 10^{13} radicals/ml-sec, a radical diffuses into each polymer particle on an average of every ten seconds. Once inside the polymer particle, a radical propagates in the usual manner at a rate r_p dependent on the propagation rate constant k_p and the monomer concentration [M] in the particle.

$$r_p = k_p[\mathrm{M}] \tag{4-1}$$

The monomer concentration is usually quite high since in many cases the equilibrium swelling of the particle by monomer is of the order of 50 percent by weight. Values of [M] as high as 5 molar are common.

Consider now what occurs on the entry of a radical into a particle which already has a radical. It can be calculated that the radical concentration in a polymer particle is in the range of 10^{-6} molar or higher. This is a much higher radical concentration than in the homogeneous polymerization systems and the radical lifetime here is only a few thousandths of a second. The entry of a second radical into the polymer particle results in immediate bimolecular termination. Thus, the polymer particle will have either one or zero radicals. The presence of two radicals in one particle is synonymous with zero radicals since termination occurs so quickly. The particle is then dormant until another (the third) radical arrives approximately 10 seconds later. The particle is again activated and propagation proceeds until the next radical arrives in another ten seconds. The cycle of alternate growth and inactivity of the polymer particle continues until the monomer conversion is essentially complete.

Any polymer particle will be active half of the time and dormant the other half of the time. In other words, at any given moment half of the polymer particles contain one radical and are growing while the other half are dormant. The number of radicals per particle $\bar{n}$ averaged over all the particles is one-half. The overall polymerization rate per milliliter of the aqueous phase is then the sum total of $N/2$ particles polymerizing according to Eq. 4-1. This is given by

$$R_p = \frac{Nk_p[M]}{2} \tag{4-2}$$

Equation 4-2 shows that the rate of polymerization is directly

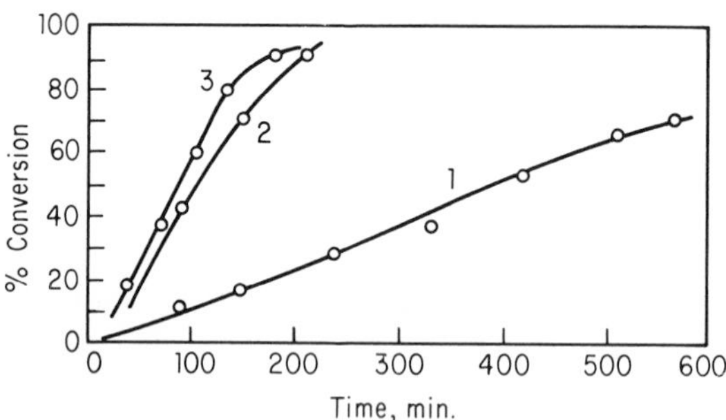

FIG. 4-2 *Plot of % conversion versus time for emulsion polymerizations of styrene with different concentrations of potassium laurate. The moles of emulsifier per polymerization charge (of 180 g H_2O, 100 g styrene, 0.5 g $K_2S_2O_8$) are 0.0035 (Curve 1), 0.007 (Curve 2), and 0.014 (Curve 3). After [9] (by permission of Interscience Publishers, John Wiley & Sons, Inc., New York).*

dependent on the number of polymer particles. A prime consequence of Eq. 4-2 is the independence of R_p on the rate of radical generation R_i. This is true as long as radicals are being produced. The polymerization will, of course, stop if the generation of radicals is stopped. An increase in R_i simply results in an increased rate of alternation of activity and inactivity in each polymer particle.

Data for the emulsion polymerization of styrene [9] are shown in Fig. 4-2. The data shown are for systems with three different emulsifier contents. The polymerization rate increases with the emulsifier concentration since N increases as the emulsifier concentration increases. Each of the curves in Fig. 4-2 is relatively typical of emulsion polymerization behavior. There is an initial stage in which autoacceleration is usually observed to varying degrees depending on the particular system. This corresponds to the time during which active micelles are being formed. When the number of active micelles becomes constant, the polymerization rate is linear with time as long as excess monomer droplets remain and [M] is constant. At high conversions the rate decreases as [M] decreases.

4-2b Degree of Polymerization

The number-average degree of polymerization in an emulsion polymerization can be obtained by considering what occurs in a single polymer particle. The rate r_i at which a primary radical enters a polymer particle is given by

$$r_i = \frac{R_i}{N} \tag{4-3}$$

This is also the same as the rate of termination of a polymer chain since termination occurs immediately upon the entry of a radical into a polymer particle in which a polymer chain is propagating. The degree of polymerization is then the rate of growth of a polymer chain divided by the rate at which primary radicals enter the polymer particle, i.e., Eq. 4-1 divided by Eq. 4-3

$$\overline{X}_n = \frac{r_p}{r_i} = \frac{Nk_p[\mathrm{M}]}{R_i} \tag{4-4}$$

Figure 4-3 shows the viscosity-average molecular weights in the emulsion polymerizations of styrene of Fig. 4-2. The results are in line with Eq. 4-4 in that the polymer size increases with the emulsifier concentration.

It should be noted that the degree of polymerization in an emulsion polymerization is synonymous with the kinetic chain length. Although termination is by bimolecular coupling, one of the radicals is a primary radical which does not significantly contribute to the size of a dead polymer molecule. The derivation of Eq. 4-4 assumes the absence of any termination by chain transfer. If chain transfer occurs, the degree of polymerization will be given by

$$\overline{X}_n = \frac{r_p}{r_i + \sum r_{tr}} \tag{4-5}$$

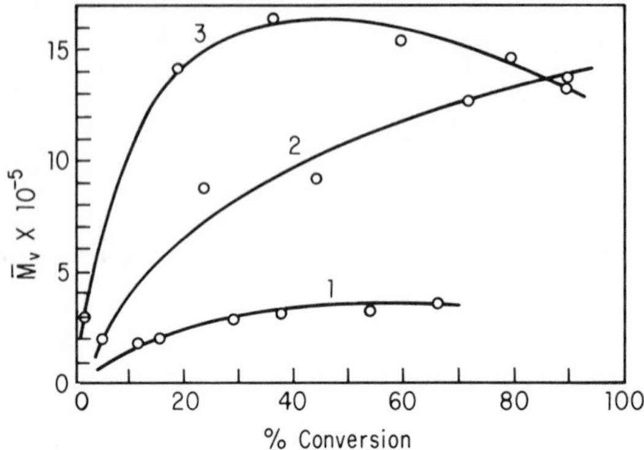

FIG. 4-3 *Plot of viscosity-average molecular weight versus % conversion for emulsion polymerizations of styrene with different concentrations of potassium laurate. The moles of emulsifier per polymerization charge (of 180 g H_2O, 100 g styrene, 0.5 g $K_2S_2O_8$) are 0.0035 (Curve 1), 0.007 (Curve 2), and 0.014 (Curve 3). After [9] (by permission of Interscience Publishers, John Wiley & Sons, Inc., New York).*

where $\sum r_{tr}$ is the sum of the rates of all transfer reactions. The rate of a chain transfer reaction in a polymer particle would be given by an equation of the type

$$r_{tr} = k_{tr}[\mathrm{XA}] \tag{4-6}$$

analogous to the case of transfer in homogeneous polymerization (Eq. 3-105).

The degree of polymerization, like the polymerization rate, varies directly with N, but the degree of polymerization also varies indirectly with R_i. A consideration of Eqs. 4-2 and 4-4 with their analogues for homogeneous, radical chain polymerization (Eqs. 3-24 and 3-100) shows the significant characteristic of the emulsion process. In homogeneous polymerization, one can increase the polymerization rate by increasing the rate of initiation, but the result is a simultaneous lowering of the polymer molecular weight. The situation is quite different in emulsion polymerization. The rate and degree of polymerization can be simultaneously increased by increasing the number of polymer particles at a constant initiation rate. These conclusions have been experimentally verified by a number of studies [3, 10–12].

4-3 NUMBER OF POLYMER PARTICLES

The number of polymer particles is a prime determinant of the rate and degree of polymerization since it appears as the first power in both Eqs. 4-2 and 4-4. The mechanism of the formation of the polymer particles from the micelles has been previously discussed. Initiator radicals enter a small fraction of the micelles and grow into polymer particles with the adsorption of the emulsifier from the other (inactive) micelles. The number of polymer particles formed depends on the number of micelles initially present (which is in turn determined by the emulsifier concentration) and the rate of radical generation. Smith and Ewart [2] derived the relationship

$$N = k\left(\frac{R_i}{\mu}\right)^{2/5}(a_s[\mathrm{E}])^{3/5} \tag{4-7}$$

where k is a constant (between 0.37 and 0.53), μ is the rate of increase in the volume of a polymer particle (and can be determined from r_p and geometrical considerations), [E] is the concentration of micellar emulsifier, and a_s is the interfacial area occupied by an emulsifier molecule in the micelles, all in cgs units.

Equation 4-7 shows the dependence of R_p and $\overline{X}_n$ (via Eqs. 4-2 and 4-4) on the 0.4 power of the rate of radical production and the 0.6 power of the emulsifier concentration. This dependence of R_p on R_i does not contradict the earlier conclusion regarding the independence of the polymerization rate on the rate of radical production. The rate of radical generation affects the number of polymer particles formed which in turn determines the polymerization rate. However, once an emulsion polymerization system has reached the steady-state situation with regard to N (that is, when N is constant and the inactive micelles have disappeared), the rate of radical generation no longer has any effect on the polymerization rate as long as some initiation is taking place. Further and very significantly, it should be noted that the number of polymer particles can be increased by increasing the emulsifier concentration while maintaining a constant rate of radical generation. Thus, from the practical viewpoint, high polymerization rates are obtained by high initial rates of radical generation and high emulsifier concentrations. The quantitative behavior defined by Eq. 4-7 has been verified in several systems [13]. The most extensively studied monomer is styrene.

The concentration of emulsifier which appears in Eq. 4-7 refers to the micellar concentration. If a particular emulsifier has a relatively high critical micelle concentration (CMC), the value of [E] which is used must be appropriately corrected for the amount of emulsifier dissolved in solution. Although there are no micelles below the CMC, an appreciable number of polymer particles are formed. This number can be as large as ten percent of the number at the CMC. The mechanism of particle formation below the CMC probably involves the precipitation of oligomers or low molecular weight polymers formed in the solution [14].

As has been mentioned previously, the number of polymer particles remains constant after the disappearance of the micelles. This is observed in many systems although the polymer particles decrease in stability since the total particle surface increases and the coverage of the surface with emulsifier decreases. Apparently the relative decrease in particle stability is not appreciable in many cases. In other systems such as vinyl chloride the stability decreases sufficiently to cause the particles to coalesce and N decreases with conversion.

4-4 OTHER CHARACTERISTICS OF EMULSION POLYMERIZATION

4-4a Initiation

The initiators used in emulsion polymerization include water-soluble initiators such as potassium or ammonium persulfate, hydrogen peroxide, and certain azo compounds, for example, 2,2′-azobis(2-methyl-4-carboxybutyronitrile). Partially water-soluble peroxides such as succinic acid peroxide and *t*-butyl hydroperoxide are also employed. However, the most commonly used initiators are the redox systems (Sec. 3-4e) such as the persulfate-ferrous system

$$S_2O_8^{2-} + Fe^{2+} \longrightarrow Fe^{3+} + SO_4^{2-} + SO_4^{-}\cdot \qquad (3\text{-}67a)$$

and the cumyl hydroperoxide-ferrous system

$$\phi-\underset{\underset{CH_3}{|}}{\overset{\overset{CH_3}{|}}{C}}-OOH + Fe^{2+} \longrightarrow Fe^{3+} + HO^- + \phi-\underset{\underset{CH_3}{|}}{\overset{\overset{CH_3}{|}}{C}}-O\cdot \tag{4-8}$$

The derivation of the kinetics of emulsion polymerization assumes the entry of radicals one by one into the polymer particles. This requirement is clearly met by the water-soluble initiator systems such as those mentioned above. The same kinetic behavior, however, has also been observed for hydrocarbon-soluble initiator systems, such as the thermal decomposition of hydroperoxides, which yield two radicals per decomposition. Although these hydrocarbon-soluble initiators decompose into pairs of radicals within the particles, polymeric radicals are apparently formed one by one although the mechanism is unclear. One possibility involves the diffusion of radicals out of the polymer particles [15]. Thus, in the thermal decomposition of cumyl hydroperoxide, one might postulate the diffusion of the inorganic radical HO· out of the polymer particle while the organic radical $\phi C(CH_3)_2O\cdot$ remains to initiate polymerization. A variation on this mechanism involves the decomposition of the initiator at the polymer particle-water interface with the HO· diffusing into the aqueous phase and the organic radical diffusing into the polymer particle. Such an effect may be especially applicable to initiator systems comprised of an oil-soluble initiator and a water-soluble activator such as the cumyl hydroperoxide-ferrous ion system.

4-4b Emulsifiers

Both anionic and non-ionic emulsifiers (or *surfactants* as they are also referred to) have been employed in emulsion polymerization. Cationic emulsifiers have an adverse effect on the efficiency of many initiators and are not employed to any appreciable extent [16]. The anionic surfactants employed include alkyl sulfates, alkylaryl sulfonates, and phosphates. Many of these are soaps such as sodium lauryl sulfate. Such emulsifiers are often referred to in the literature as *soaps.* The non-ionic emulsifiers employed are hydrophilic ones such as hydroxyethyl cellulose, poly(vinyl alcohol), and various derivatives of poly(ethylene oxide). The amount of surfactant used in an emulsion polymerization recipe is usually in the range of 1–5 percent of the weight of the monomer(s). The effect of [E] on increasing N

reaches a limit at about 8–10 percent emulsifier. Above this emulsifier concentration there is no longer an increase in the number of polymer particles with increasing emulsifier concentration.

The quality of the water used in emulsion polymerization is of importance. The reaction is usually carried out using deionized water. The presence of foreign ions can interfere with both the initiation process and the action of the emulsifier.

4-4c Propagation and Termination

Emulsion polymerization proceeds in a polymer particle where the concentration of polymer is quite high throughout the reaction. This type of system is then similar to a bulk polymerization in the later stages of reaction and one would anticipate the occurrence of the Trommsdorff effect. The propagation rate constant for an emulsion polymerization can be determined from Eq. 4-2 by measurements of R_p, [M], and N. The termination rate constant can also be obtained but with greater difficulty [12, 17]. The k_p values for a few monomers have been determined and found to be close to the values for homogeneous polymerization. Thus, styrene and methyl acrylate [18] have k_p values of 206 and 472, respectively, for emulsion polymerization at 50°C compared to the corresponding values of 145 and 2,090 for homogeneous polymerization at 60°C (Table 3-9). The absence of a large change in k_p for emulsion polymerization is not surprising since k_p is only slightly changed at high conversions in homogeneous polymerization (Table 3-12).

The situation is quite different for the termination. The values of k_t are lower in emulsion polymerization by a factor of about 10^3 compared to the values for homogeneous polymerization [18, 19]. The termination reaction in emulsion polymerization, as in homogeneous polymerization, is much more sensitive than the propagation reaction to the viscosity of the medium.

4-4d Energetics

The overall heat of an emulsion polymerization would be expected to be essentially the same as that for the corresponding bulk or solution polymerization. Thus, the heats of emulsion polymerization for acrylic acid, methyl acrylate, and methyl methacrylate were determined [20] to be 18.4, 18.6, and 13.6 kcal/mole, respectively. The values (Table 3-10) for the corresponding homogeneous polymerizations are 18.5, 18.8, and 13.5 kcal/mole. Since the heat of polymerization is essentially synonymous with the heat of the propagation step, it is not appreciably altered by the differences in the mechanisms of homogeneous and emulsion polymerizations.

The effect of temperature on emulsion polymerization, although not extensively studied, is generally similar to that on homogeneous polymerization with a few modifications. The overall rate of polymerization increases with an increase in temperature. Temperature increases the rate by increasing both k_p and N. The increase in N is a result of an increase in the value of [E] due to a decrease in the critical micelle concentration of the emulsifier. (The number of particles is also increased due to the increased rate of radical generation at higher temperatures.) Opposing this trend to a slight extent is the small decrease in the concentration of monomer in the particles at higher temperatures. Thus, the value of [M] for styrene decreases approximately 15 percent in going from 30 to 90°C [2]. The overall activation energy for emulsion polymerization is, thus, a complex combination of the activation energies for propagation, radical production, CMC, and [M]. For the few systems studied, the overall activation energies for emulsion polymerization are approximately the same or less than those for the corresponding homogeneous polymerization. Thus, the overall activation energy for methyl methacrylate is 13.2 kcal/mole in bulk polymerization and 13.0–12.2 kcal/mole in emulsion polymerization [21].

4-4e Inverse Emulsion Systems

In the conventional emulsion polymerization, a hydrophobic monomer is emulsified in water with an oil-in-water emulsifier and then the polymerization initiated usually with a water-soluble initiator. Emulsion polymerization can also be carried out with inverse emulsions. Here, an aqueous solution of a hydrophilic monomer such as acrylic acid or acrylamide is emulsified in a hydrophobic oil phase with a water-in-oil emulsifier [22]. Polymerization can be initiated with either oil- or water-soluble initiators. The mechanism of polymerization in these inverse emulsion polymerization systems appears to be similar to that in the conventional case. One major difference is that the stability of the particles in the inverse emulsions is in many cases less than that of the conventional systems due apparently to the different electrostatic forces operative in the two situations.

4-5 DEVIATIONS FROM SMITH-EWART BEHAVIOR

The Smith-Ewart theory of emulsion polymerization described in the previous sections is usually not obeyed for most of the so-called emulsion polymerizations reported in the literature. Smith-Ewart behavior (Eqs. 4-2, 4-4, and 4-7) requires the following dependencies

$$R_p \propto N, [\mathrm{I}]^{2/5}, [\mathrm{E}]^{3/5} \tag{4-9}$$

$$N \propto [\mathrm{I}]^{2/5}, [\mathrm{E}]^{3/5} \tag{4-10}$$

$$\overline{X}_n \propto N, [\mathrm{E}]^{3/5}, [\mathrm{I}]^{-3/5} \tag{4-11}$$

([I] is the initiator concentration.) Even a cursory examination of the literature [22–26] shows a rather chaotic state of affairs. Various workers have reported for different systems a wide variety of deviations from Smith-Ewart behavior. These include such apparently anomalous results as the absence of any dependence of N on [I] or of R_p on [I] or of $\overline{X}_n$ on [I]. Others report a dependence of R_p on a very small power of N, usually a 0.2 power dependence. The number of polymer particles shows a third power dependence on [E] in many instances; dependencies from the Smith-Ewart one-half power up to third power are also found as well as dependencies of less than one-half power. Even more surprising, inverse relationships have been observed [24, 25] between R_p and N, R_p and [E], and $\overline{X}_n$ and [E].

Some of the anomalous results are due to an incorrect interpretation of experimental data or incorrect application of the Smith-Ewart theory. Others are a consequence of the inapplicability of the Smith-Ewart theory in certain types of systems [27]. Some of the anomalous results appear to be best described by the newer theory of emulsion polymerization due to Medvedev and Sheinker [28].

4-5a Value of $\bar{n}$

Consider now some of the deviations from Smith-Ewart theory. One of the assumptions in that theory is that the average number of radicals per polymer particle $\bar{n}$ is one-half. However, when the particle size is larger than about 0.1–0.15 microns, more than one propagating radical can be simultaneously accommodated in a particle. This leads to an increase in the polymerization rate compared to that calculated from Eq. 4-2 since the average number of radicals per particle becomes greater than one-half. The importance of this effect is more pronounced as the particle size and the percent conversion increase. At high conversion, the particle size increases and k_t decreases—leading to an increase in $\bar{n}$. The increase in $\bar{n}$ occurs at lower conversions for the larger sized particles. For styrene polymerization, $\bar{n}$ increases from 0.5 to only 0.6 at 90% conversion for 0.7 micron particles. On the other hand, for 1.4 micron particles, $\bar{n}$ increases to about 1 at 80% conversion and more than 2 at 90% conversion [13]. (The value of $\bar{n}$ can be obtained from independent measurements of R_p, N, k_p, and [M].) This effect is probably responsible for some of the anomalous effects described above. Calculations using Eqs. 4-2 and 4-4 with $\bar{n}$ assumed to be one-half will lead to incorrect relationships between the various reaction parameters if $\bar{n}$ is not one-half.

4-5b Medvedev-Sheinker Theory

A careful evaluation of the literature data shows that for many emulsion polymerizations, especially at higher particle numbers (approximately $> 2–3 \times 10^{14}$), the number of polymer particles and the polymerization rate obey the relationships

$$N \propto [\mathrm{E}]^3, [\mathrm{I}]^0 \tag{4-12}$$

$$R_p \propto N^{1/5}, [\mathrm{E}]^{1/2}, [\mathrm{I}]^{1/2} \tag{4-13}$$

to a close approximation.

The mechanism of emulsion polymerization appears to be different in these systems. Specifically, the site of the reaction apparently becomes the particle surface instead of the interior of the particle. Medvedev and Sheinker [27, 28] suggested that the radicals cannot penetrate the interior of the particles due to the high viscosity and that polymerization therefore occurs at the particle surface. Several studies in which the polymerization rate was shown to be linearly related to the total surface area of all the particles lend support to this theory [29].

Further evidence for the particle surface as the site of polymerization in these systems has been obtained from the observation that the amount of branching in polystyrene prepared by emulsion polymerization is the same or less than that in the bulk polymerization [30]. If polymerization occurred within the polymer particle, it would take place in the presence of a high concentration of polymer throughout most of the reaction. One would expect appreciably more branching via chain transfer to polystyrene under these conditions relative to the bulk polymerization. On the other hand, polymerization at the particle surface would occur in the absence of high concentrations of polymer and branching would be expected to be negligible.

The theory proposed by Medvedev and Sheinker fits the relationships 4-12 and 4-13 quite well although some of the details of the reaction are not clear. The polymerization rate is linearly dependent on the total particle surface area. The latter, however, is relatively insensitive to the number of polymer particles. Thus, from geometrical considerations for spherical particles, a ten-fold increase in N results in only slightly more than doubling the total particle surface area. The net result is that R_p exhibits a much less than the first power dependence on N required by the Smith-Ewart theory. In addition to their differences on the dependence of R_p on N, the Smith-Ewart and Medvedev-Sheinker theories differ considerably in their dependencies of N on the emulsifier and initiator concentrations (compare Eq. 4-10 with Eq. 4-12). The dependence of N on the third power of [E] arises from a first order dependence of the total surface area on the emulsifier concentration.

The two theories of emulsion polymerization are not necessarily mutually exclusive. Both theories appear to be applicable under various conditions depending on whether the reaction site is the particle surface or the interior of the particle. Unfortunately, it is far from clear as to when the reaction site changes from one to the other. It appears that the Smith-Ewart theory describes best those polymerizations in which the polymer is soluble in its own monomer (e.g., styrene). The reaction site here appears to be the whole volume (including, no doubt, the surface) of the particles. Polymerizations in which the polymer is insoluble in its own monomer (e.g., vinyl chloride, vinylidene chloride, acrylonitrile) are usually best described by the Medvedev-Sheinker theory. Further, as indicated previously, the Medvedev-Sheinker theory appears to be more applicable at high particle numbers.

4-5c Effect of Water Solubility

Smith-Ewart behavior is usually best observed with monomers, such as styrene, butadiene, and isoprene, with low water solubilities (approximately < 0.1 weight percent). The situation is quite different for monomers with an appreciable water solubility. This includes vinyl chloride, methyl methacrylate, vinyl acetate, methyl acrylate, and acrylonitrile with solubilities of approximately 1.1, 1.5, 2.5, 5.6, and 8.5 weight percent, respectively [23]. Such water-soluble monomers often show departures from Smith-Ewart behavior. Their emulsion polymerization behavior may often but not always be more consistent with the Medvedev-Sheinker theory. A range of behaviors can be observed under different reaction conditions.

Emulsion polymerization of a water-soluble monomer involves the simultaneous polymerization of the monomer which is in solution as well as of that in the micelles. The former polymerization yields precipitating polymer molecules (or radicals) which may absorb emulsifier from the rest of the system. The consequence may be a decrease in N due to the resulting decrease in [E]. On the other hand, the precipitating particles may themselves act as polymer particles, i.e., as sites for emulsion polymerization [26]. Polymer particles may arise from precipitating species as well as from the monomer micelles. Thus, the overall polymerization process consists of the sum total of a solution polymerization, an emulsion polymerization with the initial monomer micelles, and an emulsion polymerization with the precipitated particles. (Homogeneous polymerizations taking place with precipitation of the polymer from the reaction medium bear a strong resemblance to these emulsion polymerizations. The only difference is the absence of the initial monomer micelles and of emulsifier.)

The variety of behaviors that may be observed in emulsion systems depends on the relative importance of the three polymerization processes. This in turn may be altered considerably by the specific reaction conditions employed. It is then not surprising that the emulsion polymerizations of monomers with appreciable water solubilities are described by the Smith-Ewart theory in some instances, by the Medvedev-Sheinker theory in others, and by neither in some.

4-5d Inhibition by Emulsifier

Some of the anomalous results observed in emulsion polymerization–those involving the inverse relationships between R_p and N, R_p and [E], and $\overline{X}_n$ and [E]–are unexplained by either the Smith-Ewart or Medvedev-Sheinker theories. All three inverse relationships have been observed in the polymerization of ethylene [24]. The emulsion polymerization of vinyl acetate has been found to show an inverse relationship between R_p and [E] for some emulsifiers [31]. In these systems, the emulsifier retards the polymerization by a chain transfer reaction. This occurs to an observable extent only with the highly reactive radicals from ethylene and vinyl acetate. The occurrence of extensive chain transfer is a further indication of the validity of the Medvedev-Sheinker theory. Transfer with emulsifier could only take place at the particle surface and not in the interior of the particle.

4-5e Molecular Weight Distribution

The molecular weight of the polymer produced during an emulsion polymerization following Smith-Ewart behavior changes during the course of the reaction in accordance with Eq. 4-4 due to changes in N, k_p, R_i, and [M]. Figure 4-3 shows the typical behavior as observed in the polymerization of styrene. The molecular weight increases quickly in the initial states (approximately 0–20% conversion) as the number of particles increases. Further increases with conversion are not as rapid and may be due to changes in R_i. Some decrease in the polymer molecular weight is often observed in the later stages of reaction due to decreases in [M] and k_p.

Theoretical considerations indicate that the molecular weight distribution will be narrower in emulsion polymerization compared to the corresponding homogeneous polymerization. Under the appropriate reaction conditions, the values of N, [M], k_p, and R_i remain remarkably constant during a large part of the polymerization and one finds a relatively narrow overall molecular weight distribution. The bottom curve in Fig. 4-3 shows this effect quite clearly. However, in many emulsion polymerizations, the variations in the various parameters or the non-adherence to Smith-Ewart behavior lead to wider distributions than in homogeneous polymerization.

REFERENCES

1. W. D. Harkins, *J. Am. Chem. Soc.*, **69**:1428 (1947).
2. W. V. Smith and R. W. Ewart, *J. Chem. Phys.*, **16**: 592 (1948).
3. W. V. Smith, *J. Am. Chem. Soc.*, **70**:3695 (1948).
4. E. J. Vandenberg and G. E. Hulse, *Ind. Eng. Chem.*, **40**:932 (1948).
5. E. B. Bradford and J. W. Vanderhoff, *J. Polymer Sci.*, **C1**:41 (1963).
6. P. Debye and E. W. Anacker, *J. Phys. Coll. Chem.*, **55**:644 (1951).
7. J. P. Kratohvil, *Anal. Chem.*, **36**:485R (1964).

8. J. G. Brodnyan, *J. Colloid Sci.*, **15**:76, 563 (1960).
9. D. J. Williams and E. G. Bobalek, *J. Polymer Sci.*, **A-1(4)**:3065 (1966).
10. W. V. Smith, *J. Am. Chem. Soc.*, **71**:4077 (1949).
11. F. A. Bovey, I. M. Kolthoff, A. I. Medalia, and E. J. Mechan, "Emulsion Polymerization," Interscience Publishers, John Wiley & Sons, Inc., New York, 1955.
12. B. M. E. Van Der Hoff, Kinetics of Emulsion Polymerization, in N. A. J. Platzer (ed.), "Polymerization and Polycondensation Processes," chap. 1, American Chemical Society, Reinhold Book Corp., New York, 1962.
13. H. Gerrens, *Fortschr. Hochpolymer.-Forsch. (Advan. Polymer Sci.)*, **1**: 234 (1959).
14. D. M. French, *J. Polymer Sci.*, **32**:395 (1958).
15. R. Patsiga, M. Litt, and V. Stannett, *J. Phys. Chem.*, **64**:801 (1960).
16. W. C. Mast and C. H. Fisher, *Ind. Eng. Chem.*, **41**:790 (1949).
17. J. W. Vanderhoff, E. B. Bradford, H. L. Tarkowski, and B. W. Wilkinson, *J. Polymer Sci.*, **50**:265 (1961).
18. H. Gerrens, *Polymer Preprints*, **7(2)**:699 (1966).
19. G. J. M. Ley, C. Schneider, and D. O. Hummel, *ibid.*, **7(2)**:725 (1966).
20. K. G. McCurdy and K. J. Laidler, *Can. J. Chem.*, **42**:818 (1964).
21. S. D. Stavrova, M. F. Margaritova, and S. S. Medvedev, *Vysokomolekul. Soyedin.* **7**:792 (1965).
22. J. W. Vanderhoff, E. B. Bradford, H. L. Tarkowski, J. B. Shaffer, and R. M. Wiley, Inverse Emulsion Polymerization, in N. A. J. Platzer (ed.), "Polymerization and Polycondensation Processes," chap. 2, American Chemical Society, Reinhold Book Corp., New York, 1962.
23. M. K. Lindemann, The Mechanism of Vinyl Acetate Polymerization, in G. E. Ham (ed.), "Vinyl Polymerization," vol. 1, part I, chap. 4, Marcel Dekker, Inc., New York, 1967.
24. H. K. Stryker, G. J. Mantell, and A. F. Helin, *J. Polymer Sci.*, **11**:1 (1967).
25. G. J. Mantell, H. K. Stryker, A. F. Helin, D. R. Jamieson, and C. R. Wright, *ibid.*, **10**:1845 (1966).
26. Z. Izumi, *J. Polymer Sci.*, **A-1(5)**:469 (1967).
27. J. L. Gardon, *ibid.*, **A-1(6)**:623, 643, 665, 687 (1968).
28. A. Sheinker and S. S. Medvedev, *Dokl. Akad. Nauk SSR*, **97**:111 (1954).
29. J. G. Brodnyan, J. A. Cala, T. Konen, and E. L. Kelley, *J. Colloid Sci.*, **18**:73 (1963).
30. A. F. Helin, H. K. Stryker, and G. J. Mantell, *J. Appl. Polymer Sci.*, **9**:1797 (1965).
31. S. Okamura and T. Motoyama, *J. Polymer Sci.*, **58**:221 (1962).

PROBLEMS

4-1. Describe the components of an emulsion polymerization system on a macroscopic level. Compare the pros and cons of emulsion polymerization as a process condition in comparison to bulk and solution polymerization.

4-2. Describe the microscopic picture of emulsion polymerization according to Harkins, Smith, and Ewart. Where are the monomer, initiator, and emulsifier located? Describe the changes which take place as the reaction proceeds to 100% conversion.

4-3. What are the characteristic overall features which distinguish emulsion polymerization from homogeneous polymerization? Compare the two with regard to the heat of polymerization and the effect of temperature on the polymerization rate.

4-4. Calculate the rate and degree of polymerization for the emulsion polymerization of styrene at 60°C with $N = 3.2 \times 10^{13}$ particles per ml, [M] = 5.0 molar, and $R_i = 1.1 \times 10^{12}$ radicals per ml-sec. Assume that Smith-Ewart behavior is followed and that k_p is unchanged from its value in homogeneous polymerization.

5

IONIC CHAIN POLYMERIZATION

The ionic chain polymerization of the carbon-carbon and carbon-oxygen double bonds was briefly described in Chap. 3. Ionic chain polymerizations will now be considered in detail. The bulk of the discussion will involve the polymerization of the carbon-carbon double bond by cationic and anionic catalysts (Secs. 5-2 and 5-3). The last part of the chapter will consider the polymerization of other unsaturated linkages. A few of the polymerizations in this chapter, although not classified as ionic chain polymerizations, are included for the sake of convenience. Polymerizations initiated by coordination compounds and solid metals or metal oxides are usually also ionic in nature. These are termed stereospecific or coordination polymerizations and will be considered separately in Chap. 8. The polymerizations of dienes will also not be considered in this chapter. Cyclopolymerization of non-conjugated dienes and the 1,2- and 1,4-polymerizations of conjugated dienes will be discussed in Chaps. 6 and 8.

5-1 COMPARISON OF RADICAL AND IONIC POLYMERIZATIONS

Almost all monomers undergo radical polymerization while ionic polymerizations are highly selective (Table 3-1). Cationic polymerization is essentially limited to those monomers with electron-releasing substituents such as alkoxy, phenyl, vinyl, and 1,1-dialkyl. Anionic polymerization takes place with monomers possessing electron-withdrawing groups such as nitrile, carboxyl, phenyl, and vinyl. The selectivity of ionic polymerization is due to the very strict requirements for stabilization of anionic and cationic propagating species (Sec. 3-1b-2). The commercial utilization of cationic and anionic polymerizations is rather limited due to this high selectivity of ionic polymerizations compared to radical polymerization and due also to the advent of coordination polymerization.

Ionic polymerizations are not as well understood as radical polymerizations due to experimental difficulties involved in their study. The nature of the reaction media in ionic polymerizations is often not clear since heterogeneous inorganic catalysts are often involved. Further, it is extremely difficult in most instances to obtain reproducible kinetic data because ionic polymerizations proceed at very fast rates which are extremely sensitive to the presence of small concentrations of cocatalysts, impurities, and other materials. The rates of ionic polymerizations are usually faster than those of radical polymerizations.

Cationic and anionic polymerizations have many similar characteristics. Both depend on the formation and propagation of ionic species, a positive one in one case and a negative one in the other. Although ions of low stability (high energy) would be expected to react with the olefinic double bond at fast rates, they are invariably not formed or easily destroyed. Only an ion of fairly high stability will form and have a reasonable lifetime for growth by propagation. The energies required to form a pair of ions from a neutral molecule are very high. Thus, the formation in the gas phase of the *t*-butyl and ethyl carbonium ions from the corresponding alkyl chlorides requires 155 and 195 kcal/mole, respectively [1]. Such ions are too unstable and stabilization by solvation and low temperatures must take place before polymerization will occur.

Although solvents of high polarity are highly desirable to solvate the ions, they often cannot be employed for several reasons. The highly polar hydroxylic solvents (water, alcohols) will react with and destroy most ionic catalysts. Other polar solvents such as ketones will prevent initiation of polymerization by forming highly stable complexes with the catalysts. Such solvents may also not be fluid at reaction temperatures which may be below −100°C. Ionic polymerizations are therefore usually carried out in solvents of low polarity such as methyl chloride, ethylene dichloride, pentane, and nitrobenzene. In such solvents, one does not have distinctly separate ions present as is the case in water solution. The ions in such systems are present as tightly bound *ion-pairs*. Thus, a propagating cationic chain end in cationic polymerization has a negative *counter-* or *gegen-ion* close to it throughout its lifetime. Similarly, a propagating anionic chain end in anionic polymerization has a positive gegen-ion close to it. The distance between an ion and its gegen-ion increases as the solvating power of the medium increases.

Ionic polymerizations are characterized by a wide variety of modes of initiation and termination. Unlike radical polymerization, termination in ionic polymerization never involves the bimolecular reaction between two propagating polymer chains of like charge. Termination usually involves reactions of the growing chain unimolecularly or by transfer to monomer or solvent.

5-2 CATIONIC POLYMERIZATION OF ALKENES

5-2a Initiation

The various different catalysts which can be used to initiate the cationic polymerization of monomers with electron-releasing substituents are described below. More details on these and many other useful cationic initiators can be found in Sec. 7-2b-1.

5-2a-1 Protonic Acids. Protonic acids can be used to some extent to initiate cationic polymerization by protonation of the olefin. The method depends on the use of an acid which is strong enough to produce a reasonable concentration of the protonated species

$$\mathrm{HA} + \mathrm{RR'C{=}CH_2} \longrightarrow \mathrm{RR'\overset{+}{C}{-}CH_3(A)^-} \tag{5-1}$$

but the anion of the acid should not be highly nucleophilic, otherwise it will terminate the protonated olefin by combination (i.e., by covalent bond formation)

$$RR'\overset{+}{C}-CH_3(A)^- \longrightarrow RR'\underset{}{\overset{A}{\overset{|}{C}}}-CH_3 \qquad (5\text{-}2)$$

(The method used in drawing the ionic species in the above two equations and throughout this chapter is meant to show that the ionic species usually do not exist as free ions but as ion-pairs. The parentheses around the anionic fragment is used to indicate that the negative gegen-ion remains close to the positive fragment.)

The second consideration usually limits the utility of most strong acids as cationic catalysts. Halogen acids are often excluded for this purpose due to the highly nucleophilic character of the halide ion. Other strong acids such as perchloric, sulfuric, and phosphoric acids do, however, find utility for the polymerization of some monomers. The molecular weights of the products obtained by such polymerizations rarely exceed a few thousand. Low molecular weight polymers produced from hydrocarbons find commercial applications as gasolines, diesel fuels, lubricants, and a variety of other products. The catalysts used are phosphoric or sulfuric acid, usually supported on an inert material, or Lewis acids, and the polymerizations are usually performed at 200–300°C. The polymerizations of coumarone (benzofuran) and indene

by sulfuric acid yield polymers (molecular weight approximately 1,000 or below) which are used in surface coatings, adhesives, floor tiles, waxed papers, and other applications.

5-2a-2 Lewis Acids. Friedel-Crafts catalysts such as $AlCl_3$, BF_3, $SnCl_4$, $ZnCl_2$, $TiBr_4$, and other Lewis acids are used at low temperatures to obtain high molecular weight products. By far the most important commercial high molecular weight polymer produced by cationic polymerization is butyl rubber, a copolymer of isobutylene and a 1,3-diene (usually isoprene). Polymerization is usually carried out at approximately −100°C in chlorinated solvents using $AlCl_3$ as the catalyst. All of the Friedel-Crafts catalysts used in cationic polymerization require some *cocatalyst* which acts as a proton donor. The cocatalyst can be water, an organic acid, or even an organic hydrocarbon. Thus, isobutylene is unaffected by dry boron trifluoride but polymerizes instantly when a trace amount of water is added [2]. The cocatalyst water apparently reacts with the catalyst boron trifluoride to form a *catalyst-cocatalyst complex* which then proceeds to protonate the olefin and initiate propagation

$$BF_3 + H_2O \rightleftharpoons H^+(BF_3OH)^- \tag{5-3a}$$

$$H^+(BF_3OH)^- + (CH_3)_2C{=}CH_2 \longrightarrow (CH_3)_3C^+(BF_3OH)^- \tag{5-4a}$$

The initiation process can be generalized as

$$C + RH \overset{K}{\rightleftharpoons} H^+(CR)^- \tag{5-3b}$$

$$H^+(CR)^- + M \xrightarrow{k_i} HM^+(CR)^- \tag{5-4b}$$

where C, RH, and M represent the catalyst, cocatalyst, and monomer, respectively. The need for a cocatalyst is widely accepted for all Friedel-Crafts catalysts although it has been clearly demonstrated only in a few cases. The detailed study of the need for cocatalysts is made very difficult by the experimental problems encountered in preparing catalysts and monomers completely free of materials which can act as cocatalysts.

The activity of a catalyst-cocatalyst complex is dependent on its ability to donate a proton. Thus, in the polymerization of isobutylene with $SnCl_4$ as the catalyst, the rate of polymerization was found to increase with the acid strength of the cocatalyst. The rate increases in the order acetic acid > nitroethane > phenol > water with ethanol and *t*-butyl alcohol showing no cocatalyst activity [3]. Most polymerizations exhibit a maximum rate at some ratio of cocatalyst to catalyst. The polymerization rate decreases above and below this optimum value of [cocatalyst]/[catalyst]. Figure 5-1 shows this behavior for the stannic chloride catalyzed polymerization of styrene in carbon tetrachloride with water as the cocatalyst [4]. The optimum cocatalyst to catalyst ratio varies considerably from one catalyst-cocatalyst complex to another and even for the same complex in different solvents. Thus, the maximum rate of styrene polymerization occurs at $[H_2O]/[SnCl_4]$ values of 0.002 and 1.0 in carbon tetrachloride and 30% nitrobenzene-70% carbon tetrachloride, respectively [4, 5]. These results have been interpreted as

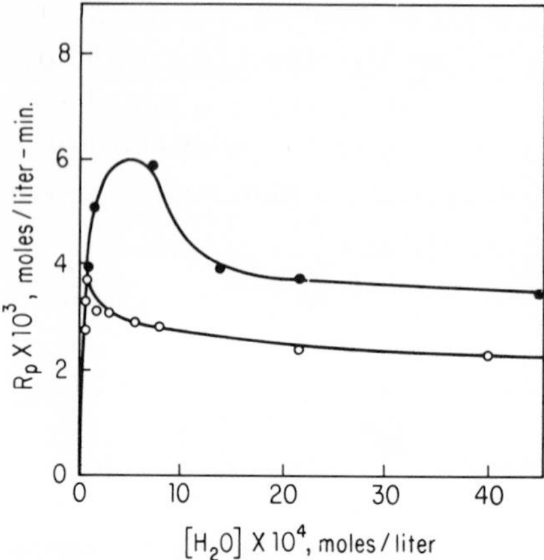

FIG. 5-1 *Effect of water concentration on the $SnCl_4$ catalyzed polymerization rate of styrene in carbon tetrachloride at 25°C.* ○ *and* ● *refer to catalyst concentrations of 0.08 and 0.12 molar, respectively. After [4] (by permission of The Faraday Society, London).*

indicating that the polymerization is catalyzed by stannic chloride dihydrate or equivalent (e.g., the trichlorostannic acid hydrate $SnCl_3OH{\cdot}H_2O$) in the polar nitrobenzene medium and by the monohydrate in the non-polar carbon tetrachloride. Another interpretation of the effect is given in Sec. 5-2c-2.

5-2a-3 Other Catalysts. The reaction of an alkyl halide with a Friedel-Crafts catalyst may yield a carbonium ion which is capable of initiating cationic polymerization, for example

$$RCl + SnCl_4 \longrightarrow R^+(SnCl_5)^- \tag{5-5}$$

This type of reaction can also be used to explain the observation of cocatalysis by certain chlorinated hydrocarbon solvents in some cationic polymerizations [4]. A variety of other cationic catalysts such as I_2, Cu^{2+}, oxonium ions, and high energy radiations are also known [4, 6–8]. Molecular iodine initiates polymerization via the reaction

$$I_2 + I_2 \longrightarrow I^+(I_3)^- \tag{5-6}$$

(The negative gegen-ion is probably a combination of I^-, I_3^-, and I_5^-.) Cupric ion probably initiates polymerization either by oxidation of the π-bond (electron transfer from monomer to Cu^{2+}) or by bonding to the π-bond. High energy radiations such as gamma rays, electrons, and neutrons can initiate both radical and ionic polymerizations depending on the particular reaction conditions, i.e., depending on the temperature and the particular monomer and solvent(s) used.

5-2b Propagation

The *initiator ion-pair* (consisting of carbonium ion and its negative gegen-ion) produced in the initiation step (Eq. 5-4) proceeds to grow by the successive addition of monomer molecules

$$H \!\left[CH_2C(CH_3)_2 \right]_n^+ (BF_3OH)^- + (CH_3)_2C{=}CH_2 \longrightarrow$$

$$H \!\left[CH_2C(CH_3)_2 \right]_n CH_2\overset{+}{C}(CH_3)_2(BF_3OH)^- \tag{5-7a}$$

or
$$HM_n^+(CR)^- + M \xrightarrow{k_p} HM_nM^+(CR)^- \tag{5-7b}$$

This addition can be thought of as occurring by an insertion of monomer between the carbonium ion and its negative gegen-ion.

The propagation reaction can be complicated in some cases by the occurrence of intramolecular rearrangement reactions. Carbonium ion rearrangements or isomerizations by hydride ($H:^-$) ion or carbanion ($R:^-$) shifts are well known in organic chemistry. The extent of rearrangement during cationic propagation will depend on the relative stabilities of the propagating and rearranged carbonium ions and on the relative rates of propagation and rearrangement. Both factors favor propagation without rearrangement for most of the common monomers polymerized by cationic means. Extensive rearrangement during polymerization has, however, been observed for certain olefins. Thus, the product from the polymerization of 3-methyl-1-butene contains both the normal (I) and rearranged (II) repeating units

$$\underset{\text{I}}{-CH_2-\underset{\displaystyle CH(CH_3)_2}{\underset{|}{CH}}-} \qquad\qquad \underset{\text{II}}{-CH_2-CH_2-C(CH_3)_2-}$$

in varying amounts depending on the reaction temperature [9]. Such polymerizations are often referred to as *isomerization polymerizations*. Isomerization occurs by hydride ion shift from the normal propagating carbonium ion (III) prior to the addition of the next monomer unit

$$\underset{\text{III}}{\sim\sim CH_2-\overset{\overset{\displaystyle H}{|}}{\underset{\underset{\displaystyle (CH_3)_2C{:}H}{|}}{C^+}}} \longrightarrow \underset{\text{IV}}{\sim\sim CH_2-CH_2-\overset{+}{C}(CH_3)_2}$$

The rearranged ion (IV) is a tertiary carbonium ion and is more stable than the normal ion (III) which is a secondary carbonium ion. The product contains mostly the rearranged repeating unit but some normal propagation occurs at higher temperatures due to kinetic reasons. The product contains approximately zero and 30 percent of the normal repeating unit at −130 and −100°C, respectively. Other monomers which undergo isomerization polymerization include 4-methyl-1-pentene, 5-methyl-1-hexene, and 6-methyl-1-heptene [10, 11]. Isomerization polymerization occurs in 4,4-dimethyl-1-pentene by methyl group shifts while ring rearrangements occur in α- and β-pinene [11].

5-2c Termination

5-2c-1 Non-Termination of Kinetic Chain. Chain transfer to monomer is one of the most common chain terminating reactions for cationic polymerization. This involves transfer of the cocatalyst-catalyst complex to a monomer molecule with the formation of terminal unsaturation in the polymer molecule

$$H\!\left(CH_2C(CH_3)_2\right)_n CH_2\overset{+}{C}(CH_3)_2(BF_3OH)^- + CH_2{=}C(CH_3)_2 \longrightarrow$$
$$(CH_3)_3C^+(BF_3OH)^- + H\!\left(CH_2C(CH_3)_2\right)_n CH_2C(CH_3){=}CH_2 \tag{5-8a}$$

$$\text{or}\quad HM_nM^+(CR)^- + M \xrightarrow{k_{tr,M}} M_{n+1} + HM^+(CR)^- \tag{5-8b}$$

It should be noted that the kinetic chain is not terminated by this reaction since the initiating ion-pair is regenerated. Many polymer molecules are produced for each catalyst-cocatalyst species present. Chain transfer to monomer is on much more favorable terms with propagation in cationic polymerization compared to radical polymerization. Since it is kinetically indistinguishable from propagation, the relative rates of transfer and propagation are given by the ratio $k_{tr,\mathrm{M}}/k_p$ which is the chain transfer constant for monomer C_M. The value of C_M determines the molecular weight of the polymer if other termination processes are not significant. The larger the value of C_M the lower will be the molecular weight.

Another type of chain transfer to monomer reaction which may be important is that involving a hydride ion abstraction from the monomer by the propagating species

$$\mathrm{H{+}CH_2C(CH_3)_2{+}_n CH_2\overset{+}{C}(CH_3)_2(BF_3OH)^- + CH_2{=}C(CH_3)_2 \longrightarrow}$$

$$\mathrm{CH_2{=}C(CH_3){-}\overset{+}{C}H_2(BF_3OH)^- + H{+}CH_2C(CH_3)_2{+}_n CH_2CH(CH_3)_2} \tag{5-8c}$$

The two types of chain transfer to monomer reactions are kinetically indistinguishable but one (Eq. 5-8a) yields an unsaturated endgroup while the other (Eq. 5-8c) yields a saturated endgroup.

Termination can also take place by rearrangement of the propagating ion-pair. This type of termination is often referred to as *spontaneous termination* or *chain transfer to counterion*. The original catalyst-cocatalyst complex is regenerated by expulsion from the ion-pair and the polymer molecule is left with terminal unsaturation

$$\mathrm{H{+}CH_2C(CH_3)_2{+}_n CH_2\overset{+}{C}(CH_3)_2(BF_3OH)^- \longrightarrow}$$

$$\mathrm{H^+(BF_3OH)^- + H{+}CH_2C(CH_3)_2{+}_n CH_2C(CH_3){=}CH_2} \tag{5-9a}$$

or $$\mathrm{HM_nM^+(CR)^-} \xrightarrow{k_t} \mathrm{M_{n+1} + H^+(CR)^-} \tag{5-9b}$$

Termination in this manner is similar to that by chain transfer to monomer in that the kinetic chain is not terminated and many polymer molecules are produced for each catalyst-cocatalyst species.

5-2c-2 Termination of Kinetic Chain. Termination by *combination* of the propagating carbonium ion with the gegen-ion occurs when the latter is sufficiently nucleophilic so that a covalent bond is formed

$$\mathrm{HM}_n\mathrm{M}^+(\mathrm{CR})^- \xrightarrow{k_t} \mathrm{HM}_n\mathrm{MCR} \tag{5-10a}$$

for example, in the trifluoroacetic acid catalyzed polymerization of styrene

$$\mathrm{H{+}CH_2CH\phi{+}_nCH_2\overset{+}{C}H\phi(OCOCF_3)^-} \longrightarrow$$

$$\mathrm{H{+}CH_2CH\phi{+}_nCH_2CH\phi{-}OCOCF_3} \tag{5-10b}$$

Alternately, the propagating ion may combine with an anionic fragment from the gegen-ion, for example

$$\mathrm{H{+}CH_2C(CH_3)_2{+}_nCH_2\overset{+}{C}(CH_3)_2(BF_3OH)^-} \longrightarrow$$

$$\mathrm{H{+}CH_2C(CH_3)_2{+}_nCH_2C(CH_3)_2OH + BF_3} \tag{5-10c}$$

Termination by combination differs from the other modes of termination in that it results in lowering the catalyst-cocatalyst concentration.

In addition to chain transfer to monomer, a variety of other transfer reactions may be important in any particular polymerization system. Various transfer agents (denoted by the symbol S or XA as in Chap. 3), present as a solvent, impurity, or deliberately added to the system, can terminate the growing polymer chain by transfer and covalent bonding of a negative fragment A^-

$$\mathrm{HM}_n\mathrm{M}^+(\mathrm{CR})^- + \mathrm{XA} \xrightarrow{k_{tr,\mathrm{S}}} \mathrm{HM}_n\mathrm{MA} + \mathrm{XCR} \tag{5-11}$$

Water, alcohols, acids, anhydrides, esters, ethers, and amines have varying chain transfer properties [12]. The presence of most of these transfer agents results in Reaction 5-11 becoming the most important mode of termination. The termination by amines probably does not involve chain transfer but, instead, the formation of stable quaternary ions which are unreactive, for example

$$\mathrm{HM}_n\mathrm{M}^+(\mathrm{CR})^- + :\mathrm{NR}_3 \longrightarrow \mathrm{HM}_n\mathrm{M}\overset{+}{\mathrm{N}}\mathrm{R}_3\mathrm{C}\overline{\mathrm{R}} \tag{5-12}$$

Aromatic compounds and alkyl halides also act as chain transfer agents in some instances. Transfer to aromatics occurs both by transfer of a negative fragment and by alkylation of the aromatic nucleus, depending on the substituents present in the aromatic compound.

Transfer to polymer has also been noted to varying extents. Chain transfer to polymer probably accounts for the synthesis of only low molecular weight polymers from α-olefins such as propylene. (This type of polymerization is sometimes referred to as *conjunct polymerization* although this terminology also includes the alkylation, isomerization, and cyclization of alkenes.) The propagating carbonium ions are reactive secondary carbonium ions which can [13] abstract tertiary hydride ions from the polymer

$$\sim\!\sim CH_2-\overset{+}{\underset{H}{C}}R + \sim\!\sim CH_2-\overset{H}{\underset{R}{C}}\sim\!\sim \longrightarrow$$

$$\sim\!\sim CH_2-\overset{H}{\underset{H}{C}}R + \sim\!\sim CH_2-\overset{+}{\underset{R}{C}}\sim\!\sim \qquad (5\text{-}13)$$

Benzoquinone acts as an inhibitor due to transfer of protons from the propagating species or the catalyst-cocatalyst to the quinone molecule

$$2\,HM_nM^+(CR)^- + O{=}C_6H_4{=}O \longrightarrow M_{n+1} + \left[HO-C_6H_4-OH\right]^{2+}(\bar{CR})_2 \qquad (5\text{-}14)$$

It should be noted that many of the substances which act as cocatalysts (e.g., water) are also good chain transfer agents. This is one of the reasons that one usually observes maxima in plots of the polymerization rate (and also the degree of polymerization) versus cocatalyst concentration. The maximum in such a plot (Fig. 5-1) corresponds to the optimum concentration of the catalyst-cocatalyst complex. Above the optimum cocatalyst concentration, chain transfer to cocatalyst becomes important.

5-2d Kinetics

5-2d-1 Different Kinetic Situations. The overall kinetics vary considerably depending largely on the mode of termination in a particular system. Consider the case of unimolecular termination by rearrangement of the propagating ion-pair (Eq. 5-9). The kinetic scheme of initiation, propagation, and termination consists of Eqs. 5-3, 5-4, 5-7, and 5-9, respectively. The derivation of the rate expression for this polymerization follows in a manner analogous to that used in radical polymerization (Chap. 2). The rates of initiation, propagation, and termination are given by

$$R_i = Kk_i[\mathrm{C}][\mathrm{RH}][\mathrm{M}] \tag{5-15}$$

$$R_p = k_p[\mathrm{HM}^+(\mathrm{CR})^-][\mathrm{M}] \tag{5-16}$$

$$R_t = k_t[\mathrm{HM}^+(\mathrm{CR})^-] \tag{5-17}$$

where $[\mathrm{HM}^+(\mathrm{CR})^-]$ is the total concentration of all propagating ion-pairs and K is the equilibrium constant for Reaction 5-3.

By assuming a steady-state for the concentration of the propagating species, the rates of initiation and termination are set equal and one obtains

$$[\mathrm{HM}^+(\mathrm{CR})^-] = \frac{Kk_i[\mathrm{C}][\mathrm{RH}][\mathrm{M}]}{k_t} \tag{5-18}$$

Combining Eqs. 5-16 and 5-18 yields the rate of polymerization as

$$R_p = \frac{Kk_ik_p[\mathrm{C}][\mathrm{RH}][\mathrm{M}]^2}{k_t} \tag{5-19}$$

The number-average degree of polymerization is obtained as

$$\overline{X}_n = \frac{R_p}{R_t} = \frac{k_p[\mathrm{M}]}{k_t} \tag{5-20}$$

Equations 5-19 and 5-20 also apply when termination occurs by combination of the propagating carbonium ion with its gegen-ion since Reaction 5-10 is kinetically indistinguishable from Reaction 5-9. One should, however, bear in mind that while the concentration of the catalyst-cocatalyst is unchanged in the former case it decreases with conversion in the latter.

If termination occurs, instead, by chain transfer to monomer (Eq. 5-8), the concentration of $[HM^+(CR)^-]$ is given by

$$[HM^+(CR)^-] = \frac{Kk_i[C][RH]}{k_{tr,M}} \tag{5-21}$$

and the rate and degree of polymerization by

$$R_p = \frac{Kk_ik_p[C][RH][M]}{k_{tr,M}} \tag{5-22}$$

$$\bar{X}_n = \frac{k_p}{k_{tr,M}} = \frac{1}{C_M} \tag{5-23}$$

where C_M is the chain transfer constant for monomer.

For the case where chain transfer to a transfer agent S (Eq. 5-11) predominates

$$[HM^+(CR)^-] = \frac{Kk_i[C][RH][M]}{k_{tr,S}[S]} \tag{5-24}$$

and the rate and degree of polymerization are given by

$$R_p = \frac{Kk_ik_p[C][RH][M]^2}{k_{tr,S}[S]} \tag{5-25}$$

$$\bar{X}_n = \frac{k_p[M]}{k_{tr,S}[S]} = \frac{[M]}{C_S[S]} \tag{5-26}$$

where C_S is the transfer constant for the chain transfer agent.

The various rate expressions were derived on the assumption that the rate-determining step in the initiation process is Reaction 5-4. If this is not the situation and Reaction 5-3 is rate-determining, the initiation rate becomes independent of the monomer concentration. Each of the expressions (Eqs. 5-19, 5-20, 5-22, 5-23, 5-25, 5-26) for the rate and degree of polymerization will show a one-order lower dependence on [M], and k_i will be the rate constant for Reaction 5-3 instead of for Reaction 5-4. In many instances, Reaction 5-4 is rate determining and the equilibrium for Reaction 5-3 is completely to the right. In such cases the initiation rate is given by

$$R_i = k_i[\mathrm{RH}][\mathrm{M}] \tag{5-27a}$$

when C is present in excess or by

$$R_i = k_i[\mathrm{C}][\mathrm{M}] \tag{5-27b}$$

when RH is in excess. The various kinetic expressions must then be modified accordingly.

The rate equations for cationic polymerization (Eqs. 5-19, 5-22, 5-25) point out one very significant difference between cationic and radical polymerization. Radical polymerizations show a one-half order dependence of R_p on R_i. However, cationic polymerizations exhibit a first order dependence of R_p on R_i. The difference between the two polymerizations is a consequence of their different modes of termination. Termination is second order in the propagating species in radical polymerization but only first order in ionic polymerization.

5-2d-2 Validity of the Steady-State Assumption. The assumption of a steady-state for $[\mathrm{HM}^+(\mathrm{CR})^-]$ is probably not valid in many cationic polymerizations. Some ionic chain polymerizations proceed so rapidly that steady-state is not achieved. Some of these reactions (e.g., isobutylene polymerization by $AlCl_3$ at $-100°$C) can be essentially complete in a matter of seconds or minutes. Even in slower polymerizations, the steady-state may not be valid until late in the polymerization. Thus, steady-state in the rhenium pentachloride polymerization of styrene at 0°C is not reached until after 10^3–10^4 seconds at which point the monomer conversion is approximately 20–30 percent [14]. Another consideration in the application of the various kinetic expressions is the uncertainty as to whether many of the catalyst-monomer-solvent systems are homogeneous or heterogeneous. In spite of the complications noted, the kinetic equations derived above have been found to be generally followed [3, 12].

5-2e Absolute Rate Constants

5-2e-1 Experimental Methods. The determination of the various individual rate constants (k_i, k_p, k_t, k_{tr}) for an ionic chain polymerization have not been carried out to as large an extent as in radical polymerization. The degree of polymerization can be used to obtain the k_t/k_p and k_{tr}/k_p ratios. Consider the general case where termination by unimolecular termination, transfer to monomer, and transfer to transfer agent are all occurring. The reciprocal of $\bar{X}_n$, obtained by combining Eqs. 5-20, 5-23, and 5-26, is given by

$$\frac{1}{\bar{X}_n} = \frac{k_t}{k_p[\mathrm{M}]} + \frac{k_{tr,\mathrm{M}}}{k_p} + \frac{k_{tr,\mathrm{S}}[\mathrm{S}]}{k_p[\mathrm{M}]} \tag{5-28a}$$

or

$$\frac{1}{\bar{X}_n} = \frac{k_t}{k_p[\mathrm{M}]} + C_\mathrm{M} + \frac{C_\mathrm{S}[\mathrm{S}]}{[\mathrm{M}]} \tag{5-28b}$$

Equation 5-28 is the cationic polymerization analogue of the previously discussed equation (Eq. 3-109) for radical polymerization.

The three ratios of rate constants (k_t/k_p, $k_{tr,\mathrm{M}}/k_p$, and $k_{tr,\mathrm{S}}/k_p$) can be obtained by appropriate methods. In the absence of a chain transfer agent, a plot of $1/\bar{X}_n$ versus $1/[\mathrm{M}]$ yields a straight line with k_t/k_p as the slope and $k_{tr,\mathrm{M}}/k_p$ or C_M as the intercept. When a chain transfer agent is present, $k_{tr,\mathrm{S}}/k_p$ or C_S is obtained as the slope of a plot of $1/\bar{X}_n$ versus $[\mathrm{S}]/[\mathrm{M}]$.

The determination of the individual rate constants requires the determination of the propagation rate constant. Experimental determination of k_p has been carried out to some extent using rate and degree of polymerization data from non-steady-state experiments [15, 16]. In most instances, however, k_p is obtained directly from Eq. 5-16 using experiments carried out under conditions where one assumes

$$[\mathrm{HM}^+(\mathrm{CR})^-] = [\mathrm{C}] \tag{5-29}$$

or where $[\mathrm{HM}^+(\mathrm{CR})^-]$ can be experimentally determined. The condition in Eq. 5-29 may be satisfied for those systems in which the initiation process is much faster than propagation. The direct determination of the concentration of the reactive intermediate $[HM^+(CR)^-]$ is possible in cationic polymerization since the concentrations are quite high. (This is quite different from the situation in radical polymerization where the reactive intermediates are present in very low concentrations.) Spectroscopic techniques are often used for analytical purposes. In some instances, the carbonium ions are colored, e.g., the polystyryl ion. The direct determination of $[HM^+(CR)^-]$ is, however, often ambiguous because the exact identity of the species is not clearly known (Sec. 5-2f).

5-2e-2 Comparison of Cationic and Radical Polymerization Rates. Table 5-1 shows the various kinetic parameters in the sulfuric acid catalyzed polymerization of styrene in ethylene dichloride at 25°C. Comparison of these data with the corresponding data for radical polymerization (Tables 3-8 and 3-9) is informative. It is evident that propagation and all of the termination reactions are much slower by orders of magnitude in cationic polymerizations. More significantly, however, cationic polymerization rates are generally faster than those of radical polymerizations. It is not the individual rate constants which determine R_p but the ratios $k_p/k_t^{1/2}$ in radical polymerization and k_p/k_t (or k_p/k_{tr} as the case may be) in cationic polymerization. For styrene, the ratio $k_p/k_t^{1/2}$ from Table 3-9 is approximately 10^{-2} while k_p/k_t from Table 5-1 is approximately 10^2 The cationic polymerization rate is, thus, favored by four orders of magnitude. This is a general phenomenon of cationic polymerizations in that the ratio of the propagation rate constant to the sum of the rate constants for all modes of termination is usually of the order of 10^2.

Table 5-1 Kinetic Parameters in H_2SO_4 Polymerization of Styrene[a]

Parameter	Value
$[H_2SO_4]$	$\sim 10^{-3}$ M
k_p	7.6 liter/mole-sec
$k_{tr,M}$	1.2×10^{-1} liter/mole-sec
k_t (spontaneous termination)	4.9×10^{-2} sec^{-1}
k_t (combination)	6.7×10^{-3} sec^{-1}

[a]Data from [16].

Cationic polymerization is further favored since the concentration of the propagating species is also usually much larger than in a radical polymerization. The $[HM^+(CR)^-]$ is not far from the catalyst concentration which is usually of the order of 10^{-3} molar. The situation is quite different in radical polymerization where $[M\cdot]$ is in the range 10^{-7}–10^{-9} molar.

5-2e-3 C_M and C_S Values. Monomer transfer constants are shown in Tables 5-2 and 5-3 for various polymerizations of styrene and isobutylene [17–21]. It is apparent that the C_M values for styrene are, in general, larger than those for isobutylene by one or two orders of magnitude. This corresponds to the greater reactivity of isobutylene toward propagation. Although extensive data are not available, one generally observes that the monomers with the larger k_p values will usually possess lower C_M or $k_{tr,M}/k_p$ values. The subject of the relative reactivities of different monomers in cationic polymerization will be considered in Chap. 6. In general, one observes the reactivity to increase in the order

vinyl ether > isobutylene > styrene, isoprene

The values of C_S for some compounds in the polymerization of styrene [17–19, 22–25] are shown in Table 5-4. The larger transfer constants are associated with transfer agents which possess a weakly

Table 5-2 Monomer Transfer Constants in Cationic Polymerization of Styrene

Catalyst	Solvent	Temperature (°C)	$C_M \times 10^2$	Ref.
$SnCl_4$	ϕH	30	1.88	[17]
$SnCl_4$	30% CCl_4-70% ϕNO_2	0	0.51	[18]
$SnCl_4$	C_2H_5Br	−63	0.02	[19]
$TiCl_4$	ϕH	30	2.0	[20]
$TiCl_4$	30% $(CH_2Cl)_2$-70% ϕH	30	1.5	[20]
$TiCl_4$	CH_2Cl_2	−60	0.04	[12]
$TiCl_4$	CH_2Cl_2	−90	< 0.005	[12]
$FeCl_3$	ϕH	30	1.2	[19]
$BF_3 \cdot (C_2H_5)_2O$	ϕH	30	0.82	[19]

Table 5-3 Monomer Transfer Constants in Cationic Polymerization of Isobutylene[a]

Catalyst-Cocatalyst	Temperature (°C)	$C_M \times 10^4$ for solvent		
		n-C_6H_{14}	$CHCl_3$	CH_2Cl_2
$TiCl_4$-H_2O	−20	10.3	12.0	21.2
	−50	2.6	3.00	6.60
	−78	0.80	1.00	1.52
$TiCl_4$-Cl_3CCO_2H	−20	6.6	25.2	26.9
	−50	2.00	4.48	5.68
	−78	0.72	1.56	2.44
$SnCl_4$-Cl_3CCO_2H	−20		60.0	60.0
	−50	17.0	22.8	36.0
	−78	6.7	8.1	5.7

[a]Data from [21].

Table 5-4 Chain Transfer Constants in Cationic Polymerization of Styrene

Catalyst	Solvent	Temperature (°C)	Transfer agent	$C_S \times 10^2$	Ref.
$SnCl_4$	ϕH	30	ϕH	0.22	[19]
H_2SO_4	$(CH_2Cl)_2$	25	i-$C_3H_7\phi$	4.5	[22]
$SnCl_4$	C_6H_{12}	0	i-$C_3H_7\phi$	0.60	[23]
$SnCl_4$	30% CCl_4-70% ϕNO_2	0	$CH_3O\phi$	162	[18]
$SnCl_4$	CCl_4	30	CCl_4	0.52	[24]
$SnCl_4$	C_6H_6	30	CH_3OH	312	[17]
$SnCl_4$	$(CH_2Cl)_2$	30	CH_3OH	90	[17]
$SnCl_4$	C_6H_6	30	CH_3CO_2H	350	[17]
$SnCl_4$	$(CH_2Cl)_2$	30	CH_3CO_2H	40	[17]
BF_3	C_6H_6	30	CH_3CO_2H	144	[17]
$SnCl_4$	C_6H_6	30	$(CH_3CO)_2O$	960	[17]
$SnCl_4$	C_6H_6	30	$CH_3CO_2C_2H_5$	120	[17]
H_2SO_4	$(CH_2Cl)_2$	25	$(C_2H_5)_2O$	19	[22]
CCl_3CO_2H	None	25	Benzoquinone	24	[25]

bonded negative fragment (for example, CH_3O^- in CH_3OH) or are readily alkylated (for example, $CH_3O\phi$). However, the value of C_S for a transfer agent is seen to vary considerably when either the catalyst or solvent is changed.

5-2f Effect of Reaction Media

It has already been noted that the reactive intermediates in cationic polymerization are usually not free carbonium ions but relatively tightly bound ion-pairs. For any propagating species ∿∿BA, one can visualize the range of behaviors from one extreme of complete covalency (V) to the other of *completely free ions* (VIII)

$$\underset{\text{V}}{\sim\!\sim\text{BA}} \qquad \underset{\text{VI}}{\sim\!\sim\text{B}^+(\text{A})^-} \qquad \underset{\text{VII}}{\sim\!\sim\text{B}^+ \,||\, \text{A}^-} \qquad \underset{\text{VIII}}{\sim\!\sim\text{B}^+ + \text{A}^-} \tag{5-30}$$

The intermediate behaviors include the *tightly bound* or *contact ion-pair* VI and the *solvent-separated ion-pair* VII. The latter involves ions that are partially separated by solvent molecules. It is often best to consider ionic polymerization systems as consisting of two types of propagating species–an ion-pair and a free ion VIII–in equilibrium with each other. The covalent species V can generally be ignored since it is unreactive. The identity of the ion-pair (i.e., whether the ion-pair is best described as species VI or species VII) will depend on the particular reaction conditions.

The nature of the reaction media plays a most significant role in cationic polymerization. More specifically, the nature of the negative gegen-ion and the solvent can greatly alter the course of a polymerization by changing the relative concentrations of the ion-pair and the free ion. Since the free ion propagates faster than the ion-pair, one observes significant changes in polymerization rates with changes in the media. Changes in the gegen-ion and solvent also affect the binding energy between the propagating ion and its gegen-ion (as well as the distance of separation between the two). These changes affect the rate of propagation of the ion-pair since monomer insertion between the propagating carbonium ion and the gegen-ion is facilitated by a decrease in the binding energy between the two. Thus, changes in the solvent and gegen-ion alter the course of polymerization by changes in the free ion concentration and in the nature of the ion-pair.

In the ideal case, one would express the observed polymerization rate in an ionic polymerization as the sum of the polymerization rates of the ion-pair and the free ion—each with its respective propagation rate constant. The effect of changes in the reaction media could then be expressed as changes in the concentration of the free ion and changes in the propagation rate constants. However, such an analysis of a polymerization reaction is not easily performed experimentally. The result is that most literature reports on the effects of reaction media do not quantitatively delineate the basic causes of the changes observed in a system. The effects of reaction media are usually reported as changes in the k_p values experimentally determined from rate expressions such as Eqs. 5-19, 5-22, and 5-25. The k_p values determined in this manner are the composite of the k_p values for the ion-pair and the free ion weighted in proportion to the relative amounts of the two propagating species. Such k_p values are best referred to as *composite* or *pseudo propagation rate constants.*

5-2f-1 Solvent Effects. Large increases in the rate and degree of polymerization are usually observed as one increases the solvating power of the reaction medium. The effect of solvent usually manifests itself in two ways. The free ion concentration increases with increased solvating power and one observes an increase in R_p since the free ion propagates faster than the ion-pair. Further, increasing the solvating power of the reaction media increases the k_p for the ion-pair by facilitating the separation of the carbonium ion and its gegen-ion to allow monomer insertion for chain growth. As noted above, the effect of solvent is generally expressed by noting the changes in the pseudo or composite propagation rate constant. Table 5-5 shows data for the perchloric acid catalyzed polymerization of styrene carried out in solvents of differing solvating power [26]. The propagation rate constant increases by five orders of magnitude in going from the low dielectric constant ($\epsilon = 2.3$) carbon tetrachloride to the high dielectric constant ($\epsilon = 9.7$) 1,2-dichloroethane. (Although the dielectric constant is generally used as an indication of the solvating power of a solvent, it is not necessarily a quantitative measure. Specific solvation effects and polarizability are also of importance.) The changes in k_p are paralleled by appropriate changes in the activation energy and frequency factor for the reaction.

The need for solvation is clearly evident when polymerization is carried out in media of low dielectric constant. In addition to

Table 5-5 Effect of Solvent on Cationic Polymerization of Styrene[a,b]

Solvent	Dielectric constant (ϵ)	k_p at 25°C (liter/mole-sec)
CCl_4	2.3	0.0012
$CCl_4/(CH_2Cl)_2$, 40/60	5.16	0.40
$CCl_4/(CH_2Cl)_2$, 20/80	7.0	3.2
$(CH_2Cl)_2$	9.72	17.0

[a]Data from [26].
[b]Initiation by $HClO_4$

lowered rates of polymerization in poorly solvating media, one frequently observes increased kinetic orders in one of the reactants. The polymerization rate may show an increased order of dependence on the monomer, catalyst, or cocatalyst corresponding to the solvation of the ion-pairs by those components. Thus, the rate for the $SnCl_4$ catalyzed polymerization of styrene is dependent on $[M]^2$ in benzene solution and $[M]^3$ in carbon tetrachloride solution [17]. The carbon tetrachloride is a poor solvating agent compared to benzene and the higher order in styrene concentration is due to the styrene taking part in the solvation of the propagating ion and its gegen-ion. At high concentrations of styrene monomer (and also in pure styrene) the order in styrene decreases to two as the reaction medium becomes equivalent to the benzene system.

The polymerization of styrene by di- and trichloroacetic acid in pure styrene or in ethylene dichloride and nitroethane solutions shows the situation where the catalyst solvates the ion-pairs [25]. The kinetic order in the concentration of chloroacetic acid increases from one in the highly polar nitromethane to two in the less polar ethylene dichloride to three in pure styrene. One should note that the propagating ion-pairs are apparently adequately solvated by benzene or pure styrene when the catalyst is stannic chloride but not when it is the chloroacetic acid. This is due to the differences in the polarity and solvating requirements of the two different catalyst systems (see Sec. 5-2f-2).

5-2f-2 Effect of Gegen-Ion. The identity of the negative gegen-ion can also exert an influence on a cationic polymerization. The larger and the less tightly bound the gegen-ion, the greater will be the ease of propagation. The effect of the gegen-ion, like that of solvent, can be quite large. Thus, the pseudo k_p for styrene polymerization at 25°C in 1,2-dichloroethane solution increases from 0.003 for iodine as the catalyst to 0.42 and 17.0 for $SnCl_4$-H_2O and $HClO_4$, respectively [26, 27].

Extensive data are not available but it appears that most of the gegen-ion effects are exerted by changes in the frequency factor for propagation. The value of A_p for the perchloric acid catalyzed polymerization is about 10^7–10^9 which is in the same range as for radical propagation (Table 3-9). However, A_p is decreased by many orders of magnitude, to about 10^2, for the iodine catalyzed polymerization [28]. This indicates that the I_3^- gegen-ion is very close to and tightly bound by the propagating carbonium ion. The ability of the monomer to insert itself into the propagating chain is greatly hindered. The tightness with which the I_3^- is bound to the propagating center is also apparent from the lack of any effect of an externally applied electric field (direct current) on the polymerization [7]. An applied electric field increases the rate and degree of cationic chain polymerizations in which there is some degree of separation of the ion-pair. The electric field brings about a further separation of the carbonium ion and its gegen-ion. The result is an increase in k_p, R_p, and $\overline{X}_n$. (Such electric field effects should not be confused with the use of electric fields to initiate polymerizations by the electrolytic formation of radicals, anions, or cations [29]. The latter type of polymerization is referred to as an *electrolytic* or *electro-initiated polymerization*.) In an analogous manner, the effect of solvent on k_p is greatest when the separation of the ion-pair is appreciable to begin with.

5-2f-3 Pseudocationic Polymerization. In recent years, Plesch and coworkers [30, 31] have concluded that many so-called cationic polymerizations do not proceed through intermediates of an ionic nature—neither through ion-pairs, solvent-separated ions, or free ions. Under certain reaction conditions, the propagating intermediates appear to be covalent species. Such polymerizations have been referred to as *pseudocationic polymerizations*.

The perchloric acid catalyzed polymerization of styrene has been discussed in terms of both cationic and pseudocationic mechanisms [30]. A fast polymerization involving ions or ion-pairs takes place when $[HClO_4]$ is high. The pseudocationic polymerization takes place at low $[HClO_4]/[Styrene]$ values. The pseudocationic reaction is orders of magnitude slower than the cationic polymerization. The reactive intermediate in the pseudocationic styrene polymerization appears to be the covalently bound perchlorate ester. Polymerization occurs by insertion of monomer at the C—O bond

$$\sim\!\sim CH_2-\underset{\phi}{\overset{H}{\underset{|}{\overset{|}{C}}}}-OClO_3 + CH_2{=}CH\phi \longrightarrow$$

$$\sim\!\sim CH_2-\underset{\phi}{\overset{H}{\underset{|}{\overset{|}{C}}}}-CH_2-\underset{\phi}{\overset{H}{\underset{|}{\overset{|}{C}}}}-OClO_3 \qquad (5\text{-}31)$$

The evidence in favor of the pseudocationic polymerization mechanism appears to be reasonably established in many systems. Thus, for example, the absence of any effect of an applied electric field on the iodine catalyzed styrene polymerization is consistent with a covalent propagating intermediate. The invoking of a pseudocationic mechanism is not as dramatic a departure from the cationic mechanism as appears. It appears to be the more appropriate description of the extreme of cationic polymerizations under conditions (of the reaction medium or the catalyst) where the ion-pair is best considered as being covalently bonded.

5-2g Energetics

Cationic polymerizations, like their radical counterparts, are quite exothermic since the reaction involves the conversion of π-bonds to σ-bonds. The heat of polymerization for any particular monomer is essentially the same irrespective of the mode of initiation (if the monomer can be polymerized by both radical and cationic catalysts).

From a consideration of Eqs. 5-19 and 5-20, the activation energies E_R and $E_{\overline{X}_n}$ for the rate and degree of polymerization, respectively, are obtained as

$$E_R = E_i + E_p - E_t \qquad (5\text{-}32)$$

$$E_{\overline{X}_n} = E_p - E_t \qquad (5\text{-}33)$$

where E_i, E_p, and E_t are the activation energies for the initiation, propagation, and chain termination steps, respectively. E_t will be replaced by E_{tr} when termination occurs by a transfer reaction. Propagation involves the addition of an ion to a monomer in a

Table 5-6 Activation Energy for Rate of Cationic Polymerization of Styrene

Catalyst system	Solvent	E_R (kcal/mole)
$TiCl_4$-H_2O[a]	$(CH_2Cl)_2$	−8.5
$TiCl_4$-CCl_3CO_2H[a]	ϕCH_3	−1.5
CCl_3CO_2H	C_2H_5Br	3.0
$SnCl_4$-H_2O	ϕH	5.5
CCl_3CO_2H	$(CH_2Cl)_2$	8.0
CCl_3CO_2H	CH_3NO_2	14.0

[a]Data from [13]; all other data are from [25].

medium of low polarity and does not require a large activation energy. The values of E_i and E_t are greater than E_p in most cases. The net interaction of the various activation energies leads to values of E_R which are in the range of −5 to +10 kcal/mole. For many polymerization systems E_R is negative and one observes the rather unusual phenomenon of increasing polymerization rates with decreasing temperatures. The negative activation energy for the polymerization rate is not, however, a complete generalization. The sign and value of E_R vary from one monomer to another. Even for the same monomer, the value of E_R may vary considerably depending on the catalyst, cocatalyst, and solvent employed. Table 5-6 shows that E_R may vary from −8.5 to +14 kcal/mole for styrene polymerization. The variations in E_R are a consequence of the differences in E_i, E_p, and E_t caused by the differences in the catalyst and the solvating power of the reaction medium. It should be noted that, irrespective of sign, the values of E_R are generally smaller than in radical polymerizations. The rates of cationic polymerizations do not quantitatively change with temperature as much as those of radical polymerizations.

The activation energy $E_{\bar{X}_n}$ for the degree of polymerization is always negative because E_t is greater than E_p for all cases irrespective of the mode of termination. This means that the degree of polymerization decreases as the polymerization temperature is increased. $E_{\overline{X}_n}$ has greater negative values when termination is by transfer reactions than when termination is by spontaneous termination or by combination since the transfer reactions have greater activation energies. As the polymerization temperature is increased, the mode of chain breaking will shift from termination to transfer. Further, there may be a shift from one transfer mode to another as the temperature is changed. Figure 5-2 shows a plot of log $\overline{X}_n$ versus $1/T$ for the $AlCl_3$ catalyzed polymerization of isobutylene in dichloromethane solution [32]. There is a change in the slope of the plot at approximately $-100°C$ from an $E_{\overline{X}_n}$ value of -5.6 to one of -0.73 kcal/mole. This has been attributed to a change in the termination step from chain transfer to monomer below $-100°C$ to chain transfer to solvent above $-100°C$.

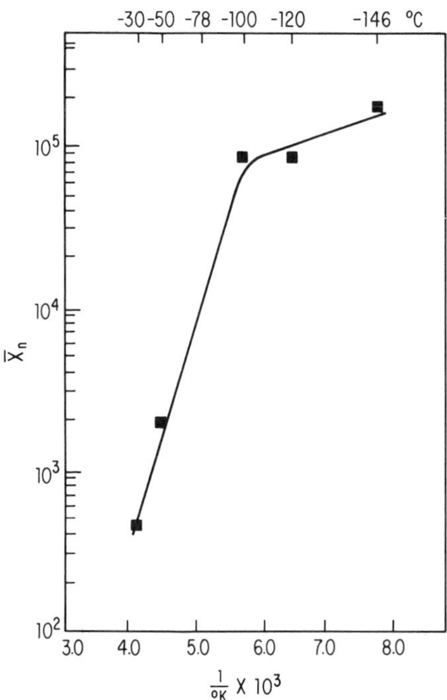

FIG. 5-2 *Temperature dependence of X_n for the $AlCl_3$ catalyzed polymerization of isobutylene. After [32] (by permission of Butterworth and Co. (Publishers) Ltd., London).*

5-3 ANIONIC POLYMERIZATION OF ALKENES

A variety of basic catalysts have been used to initiate anionic polymerization [33]. These include covalent or ionic metal amides, alkoxides, alkyls, aryls, hydroxides, and cyanides. The initiation reaction involves the addition of a negative fragment B:$^-$ such as NH_2^- or R^- to form a carbanion

$$\mathrm{B{:}^- + CH_2{=}\underset{\displaystyle Y}{\overset{\displaystyle H}{\overset{|}{\underset{|}{C}}}} \longrightarrow B{-}CH_2{-}\underset{\displaystyle Y}{\overset{\displaystyle H}{\overset{|}{\underset{|}{C}}}}{:}^-} \tag{5-34}$$

Anionic polymerization can also be initiated by the unique process of direct electron transfer from some donor species to the monomer to form an *anion-radical*

$$e^- + \mathrm{CH_2{=}\underset{\displaystyle Y}{\overset{\displaystyle H}{\overset{|}{\underset{|}{C}}}} \longrightarrow \cdot CH_2{-}\underset{\displaystyle Y}{\overset{\displaystyle H}{\overset{|}{\underset{|}{C}}}}{:}^-} \tag{5-35}$$

Chain growth proceeds by successive additions of monomer to the propagating anion.

Anionic chain polymerizations show many of the same characteristics as cationic polymerizations although there are also many very distinct differences. The propagating anion is usually not a distinct ion but exists as an ion-pair as in the case of cationic polymerizations. Anionic polymerizations generally proceed rapidly at low temperatures. However, they are not usually as temperature sensitive. Further, most anionic polymerizations possess positive E_R values and proceed well at room temperature and above.

Termination usually occurs by transfer of a positive fragment such as a proton from the solvent or some transfer agent although other modes of termination are also known. Many anionic chain polymerizations are, however, devoid of any termination reaction. Such polymerizations without termination comprise a significant departure from the corresponding behaviors in radical and cationic polymerizations.

Different catalysts have varying reactivities in the initiation step depending on their basicities. Monomers, such as acrylonitrile and methyl methacrylate, with strongly electron-pulling substituents can be polymerized with weakly basic catalysts such as hydroxide and cyanide ions. However, strong bases such as amide ion or alkyl anion are required to polymerize monomers, such as styrene or 1,3-butadiene, with relatively weak electron-pulling substituents. Consider now some of the more well-studied initiation systems for anionic polymerization.

5-3a Initiation by Metal Amides

The first detailed study of anionic polymerization was that on the polymerization of styrene by potassium amide in liquid ammonia [34]. This polymerization is one of the few ionic polymerizations which involves free ions instead of ion-pairs. The reason for this is the high dielectric constant and solvating power of liquid ammonia. The situation would be different in solvents of lower dielectric constant and solvating power such as ethers and hydrocarbons.

The polymerization was carried out typically at the boiling point of ammonia (−33°C). The polymerization rate was found to increase with the amide concentration and the square of the monomer concentration and to decrease with added potassium ion. Analysis showed that the polymer contained one nitrogen atom per molecule and was free of unsaturation. Furthermore, the molecular weight of the polymer was independent of potassium and amide ions. The mechanism of polymerization in this system follows readily from these and other experimental data. Initiation involves the dissociation of potassium amide followed by addition of amide ion to the first monomer unit.

$$\mathrm{KNH_2} \overset{K}{\rightleftharpoons} \mathrm{K^+} + \mathrm{H_2N{:}^-} \tag{5-36}$$

$$\mathrm{H_2N{:}^-} + \phi\,\mathrm{CH{=}CH_2} \xrightarrow{k_i} \mathrm{H_2N{-}CH_2{-}\overset{\displaystyle H}{\underset{\displaystyle \phi}{C}}{:}^-} \tag{5-37}$$

The rate of initiation is given by

$$R_i = k_i[\mathrm{H_2N{:}^-}][\mathrm{M}] \tag{5-38a}$$

or
$$R_i = \frac{k_i K[\mathrm{M}][\mathrm{KNH_2}]}{[\mathrm{K^+}]} \tag{5-38b}$$

Propagation proceeds according to

$$\mathrm{H_2N{-}M_n^-} + \mathrm{M} \xrightarrow{k_p} \mathrm{H_2N{-}M_nM^-} \tag{5-39}$$

with a rate given by

$$R_p = k_p[\mathrm{M}^-][\mathrm{M}] \tag{5-40}$$

where $[\mathrm{M}^-]$ represents the total concentration of the propagating anionic centers.

Termination in this system does not occur by transfer of a hydride ion (H^-) to monomer as evidenced by the absence of unsaturation in the polymer. Combination of the propagating ion with potassium ion, an unlikely possibility, also does not occur since potassium amide is not consumed in the polymerization. Termination occurs by chain transfer to solvent

$$\mathrm{H_2N{+}CH_2CH\phi{+}_nCH_2{-}\overset{\displaystyle H}{\underset{\displaystyle \phi}{C}}:^- + NH_3} \xrightarrow{k_{tr,\mathrm{S}}}$$

$$\mathrm{H_2N{+}CH_2CH\phi{+}_nCH_2CH_2\phi + H_2N:^-} \tag{5-41a}$$

or $$\mathrm{H_2N{-}M_nM^- + NH_3 \longrightarrow H_2N{-}M_nMH + H_2N:^-} \tag{5-41b}$$

with regeneration of the initiator amide ion. The rate of termination is given by

$$R_{tr} = k_{tr,\mathrm{S}}[\mathrm{M}^-][\mathrm{NH_3}] \tag{5-42}$$

The rate of polymerization, derived in the usual manner by combining Eqs. 5-38, 5-40, and 5-42 with the assumption of a steady-state for $[\mathrm{M}^-]$, is obtained as

$$R_p = \frac{Kk_ik_p[\mathrm{M}]^2[\mathrm{KNH_2}]}{k_{tr,\mathrm{S}}[\mathrm{K}^+][\mathrm{NH_3}]} \tag{5-43a}$$

or $$R_p = \frac{k_ik_p[\mathrm{M}]^2[\mathrm{H_2N:^-}]}{k_{tr,\mathrm{S}}[\mathrm{NH_3}]} \tag{5-43b}$$

This polymerization mechanism has also been confirmed for other monomers such as methacrylonitrile and ethyl acrylate [35] as well as for styrene. For the usual experimental situation where the potassium ion and amide ion concentrations are equal (i.e., there is no external added K^+), the initiation and polymerization rates are given by the somewhat different expressions

$$R_i = k_i K^{1/2} [M][KNH_2]^{1/2} \tag{5-44}$$

$$R_p = \frac{k_i K^{1/2} k_p [M]^2 [KNH_2]^{1/2}}{k_{tr,S} [NH_3]} \tag{5-45}$$

The number-average degree of polymerization in this system, obtained by dividing Eq. 5-40 by Eq. 5-42, is given by

$$\overline{X}_n = \frac{k_p [M]}{k_{tr,S} [NH_3]} = \frac{[M]}{C_S [NH_3]} \tag{5-46}$$

where $C_S = k_{tr,S}/k_p$ is the chain transfer constant of ammonia.

Consider now the effect of temperature on the rate and degree of polymerization. The activation energy for the degree of polymerization $E_{\overline{X}_n}$ follows from Eq. 5-46 as $(E_p - E_{tr})$. $E_{\overline{X}_n}$ has been found [33] to have a value of -4 kcal/mole for the potassium amide polymerization of styrene. The activation energy for termination is greater than that for propagation. This is the same situation as in cationic polymerization and one observes a decrease in the degree of polymerization as the temperature of polymerization increases. The activation energy for the overall polymerization rate E_R is given by $(E_i + E_p - E_{tr})$ and has a value of approximately 9 kcal/mole since E_i has a value of 13 kcal/mole. The rate of polymerization in this system decreases as the temperature decreases. The heat of dissociation of potassium amide ΔH_i also enters into E_R since the ionization constant for potassium amide occurs in the rate equation for polymerization (Eq. 5-43a or 5-45). However, in this system ΔH_i has a value very close to zero and can be ignored.

5-3b Polymerizations without Termination

Many anionic polymerizations take place under conditions in which there is no termination reaction. Propagation occurs with complete consumption of monomer. The anionic centers remain intact because transfer of a proton (or other positive species) from the solvent does not occur. Such non-terminated polymeric anions are referred to as *living polymers*. Living polymers are produced as long as one employs solvents (e.g., tetrahydrofuran, 1,2-dimethoxyethane, dioxane) which are inactive in terms of terminating the propagating anion by chain transfer.

The non-terminating character of these polymerizations is apparent in several different ways. Many of the propagating carbanions are colored. If a system is highly purified so that impurities are absent, the color of the carbanions is observed to persist throughout polymerization and does not disappear or change at 100% conversion. Further, after 100% conversion is reached, additional polymerization can be effected by adding more monomer to the living polymer system. The added monomer is also polymerized quantitatively. The molecular weight of the living polymer is increased accordingly as the number of polymer molecules does not change. Figure 5-3 shows this effect for the polymerization of methyl methacrylate initiated by a complex of butyllithium and diethylzinc [36]. The initiating species in this case is $C_4H_9^-[LiZn(C_2H_5)_2]^+$.

5-3b-1 Initiation by Electron Transfer. Szwarc and coworkers have studied the interesting polymerizations initiated by aromatic radical-anions such as sodium naphthalene and sodium biphenyl [37]. These radical-anion initiators are both radicals and anions. The polymerization of styrene by sodium naphthalene in tetrahydrofuran at temperatures from −78 to 0°C was the first living polymer system to be studied in detail [38, 39]. Initiation in this polymerization proceeds by the prior formation of the active catalyst—the naphthalene radical-ion

Na + [naphthalene] → [naphthalene radical-anion]$^-$ Na$^+$ (5-47)

The reaction involves the transfer of an electron from sodium to naphthalene. The naphthalene anion-radical (which is colored green) then transfers an electron to the styrene monomer to form the styryl radical-anion

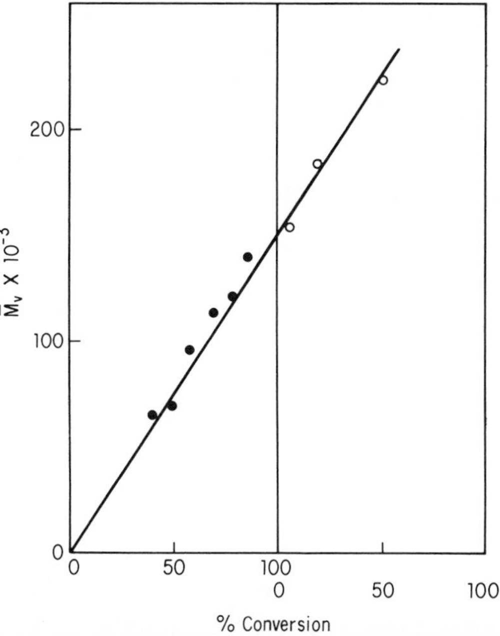

FIG. 5-3 *Dependence of polymer molecular weight on percent conversion of the anionic polymerization of methyl methacrylate.* ● *represents polymerization initiated by* $C_4H_9Li\text{-}Zn(C_2H_5)_2$ *and* ○ *represents polymerization of living anions by addition of a second batch of monomer. After [36] (by permission of Interscience Publishers, John Wiley & Sons, Inc., New York).*

$$\left[\mathrm{C_{10}H_8}\right]^{\cdot -}\mathrm{Na}^+ + \phi\mathrm{CH{=}CH_2} \longrightarrow$$

$$\mathrm{C_{10}H_8} + \left[\phi\dot{\mathrm{C}}\mathrm{H{-}}\ddot{\mathrm{C}}\mathrm{H_2} \longleftrightarrow \phi\ddot{\mathrm{C}}\mathrm{H{-}}\dot{\mathrm{C}}\mathrm{H_2}\right]^{-}\mathrm{Na}^+ \qquad (5\text{-}48)$$

The styryl radical-anion is shown as a resonance hybrid of the forms wherein the anion and radical centers are alternately on the α- or β-carbon atoms.

In a few polymerization systems, the monomer radical-anions may propagate by both anionic and radical mechanisms from the two active ends. However, in the usual case, such radical-anions undergo dimerization via their free radical ends to form dianions

$$2\left[\underset{\text{IX}}{\phi\dot{C}H-\ddot{C}H_2} \longleftrightarrow \underset{\text{X}}{\phi\ddot{C}H-\dot{C}H_2}\right]^- Na^+ \longrightarrow$$

$$Na^+\left[{}^-:\underset{H}{\overset{\phi}{C}}-CH_2-CH_2-\underset{H}{\overset{\phi}{C}}:^-\right]Na^+ \tag{5-49}$$

That this reaction occurs is shown by electron spin resonance studies which indicate the complete absence of radicals in the system. The dimerization occurs through the resonance form X instead of IX to yield the more stable styryl carbanions. The styryl dianions so-formed are colored red and undergo anionic propagation at both ends

$$Na^+\left[{}^-:\underset{H}{\overset{\phi}{C}}-CH_2-CH_2-\underset{H}{\overset{\phi}{C}}:^-\right]Na^+ + (n+m)\,\phi CH{=}CH_2 \longrightarrow$$

$$Na^+\left[{}^-:\underset{H}{\overset{\phi}{C}}-CH_2\left(CH\phi-CH_2\right)_n\left(CH_2-CH\phi\right)_m CH_2-\underset{H}{\overset{\phi}{C}}:^-\right]Na^+ \tag{5-50}$$

In addition to radical-anions, initiation by electron transfer has also been observed when one uses certain alkali metals in liquid ammonia. Polymerizations initiated by alkali metals in liquid ammonia proceed by two different mechanisms. In some systems, such as the polymerizations of styrene and methacrylonitrile by potassium, the initiation is due to amide ion formed in the system [34, 35]. Such polymerizations are analogous to those initiated by alkali amides. Polymerization in other systems cannot be due to amide ion. Thus, polymerization of methacrylonitrile by lithium in liquid ammonia proceeds at a much faster rate than that initiated by lithium amide in liquid ammonia [40]. The mechanism of polymerization is considered to involve the formation of a *solvated electron*

$$\mathrm{Li} + \mathrm{NH_3} \longrightarrow \mathrm{Li^+(NH_3)} + e^-(\mathrm{NH_3}) \qquad (5\text{-}51)$$

Such ammonia solutions are noted by their characteristic deep blue color. The solvated electron is then transferred to the monomer to form a radical-anion

$$e^-(\mathrm{NH_3}) + \mathrm{CH_2{=}CHY} \longrightarrow \left(\dot{\mathrm{C}}\mathrm{H{-}}\ddot{\mathrm{C}}\mathrm{HY} \longleftrightarrow \ddot{\mathrm{C}}\mathrm{H{-}}\dot{\mathrm{C}}\mathrm{HY}\right)^-(\mathrm{NH_3}) \qquad (5\text{-}52)$$

The radical-anion proceeds to propagate in the same manner as discussed above for initiation by sodium naphthalene. Electron transfer is probably also the mode of initiation in polymerizations involving alkali metals as dispersions in hydrocarbons.

5-3b-2 Initiation by Metal Alkyls. A variety of organometallic compounds can initiate anionic polymerizations. The most useful of these are metal alkyls such as butyllithium [41] or triphenylmethylsodium. Butyllithium is commercially useful to some extent in the polymerization of butadiene and isoprene (Chap. 8). Polymerizations initiated by a metal alkyl such as butyllithium proceed by addition of the catalyst to the monomer

$$\mathrm{C_4H_9Li} + \mathrm{CH_2{=}CHY} \longrightarrow \mathrm{C_4H_9{-}CH_2{-}}\underset{\mathrm{H}}{\overset{\mathrm{Y}}{\mathrm{C}}}\mathrm{:^-(Li^+)} \qquad (5\text{-}53)$$

followed by propagation

$$\mathrm{C_4H_9{-}CH_2{-}}\underset{\mathrm{H}}{\overset{\mathrm{Y}}{\mathrm{C}}}\mathrm{:^-(Li^+)} + n\,\mathrm{CH_2{=}CHY} \longrightarrow$$

$$\mathrm{C_4H_9{+}CH_2CHY{+}_{\!n}CH_2{-}}\underset{\mathrm{H}}{\overset{\mathrm{Y}}{\mathrm{C}}}\mathrm{:^-(Li^+)} \qquad (5\text{-}54)$$

5-3b-3 Polymerization Rate. The rate of polymerization in non-terminating systems is usually expressed simply as the rate of propagation given by

$$R_p = k_p[\mathrm{M}^-][\mathrm{M}] \tag{5-55}$$

where $[\mathrm{M}^-]$ is the total concentration of living anionic propagating ends. The concentration of living ends can be determined spectrophotometrically or by reaction with an appropriate transfer agent. If chain transfer agents are completely absent in a system, $[\mathrm{M}^-]$ will be given by the concentration of catalyst (i.e., the concentration of sodium naphthalene or butyllithium or lithium as the case may be). The living ends are mono-anions in butyllithium polymerizations and di-anions in polymerizations initiated by electron-transfer. The two types of anions are referred to as *one-ended* or *two-ended living anions*.

Many anionic polymerizations are too fast to be followed by the usual experimental techniques such as dilatometry. The polymerization of styrene by sodium naphthalene in tetrahydrofuran, for example, is essentially complete in seconds. A *fast flow technique* has been developed for studying such fast polymerizations [42]. Solutions of monomer and living ends are kept in two separate reservoirs. The two solutions are forced into a mixing chamber and then through an appropriate capillary tube in which reaction takes place. The polymerization is stopped at the outlet of the capillary by running the mixture into a solvent containing a terminating agent with a high chain transfer constant (e.g., water). The reaction time is given by the ratio of the capillary volume to the flow rate. Short reaction times from approximately 0.05 to 2 seconds can be accurately studied in this manner. The conversion and, hence, R_p and k_p are obtained by analyzing the quenched reaction mixture for either polymer or residual monomer.

It is of interest to understand the reasons for the faster reaction rates encountered in many anionic polymerizations compared to their radical counterparts. This can be done by comparing the kinetic parameters in the appropriate rate equations–Eqs. 3-21 and 5-55. The value of k_p in the anionic polymerization of styrene is close to the k_p value in radical polymerization although it may be larger by an order of magnitude for polymerization in a highly polar solvent [37]. The large difference in the rates of anionic and radical polymerizations is due mostly to the difference in the concentrations of the propagating anions and radicals. The concentration of propagating radicals in a typical radical polymerization is 10^{-9}–10^{-7} molar while that of propagating anions is 10^{-3}–10^{-2}. Thus, the rate of anionic polymerization is larger by a factor of 10^4–10^7 than that of radical polymerization.

5-3b-4 Effects of Reaction Media. The propagation rate constant and the polymerization rate for anionic polymerization are dramatically affected both by the nature of the solvent and the gegen-ion. Thus, the data in Table 5-7 show the pronounced effect of solvents in the polymerization of styrene by sodium naphthalene (3×10^{-3} molar) at 25°C. The propagation rate constant is increased by two and three orders of magnitude in tetrahydrofuran and 1,2-dimethoxyethane, respectively, compared to the rate constants in benzene or dioxane. The polymerization is much faster in the more polar solvents. That the dielectric constant is not a quantitative measure of the solvating power of a solvent is shown by the higher reaction rate in 1,2-dimethoxyethane compared to tetrahydrofuran (THF). The faster rate in the former must be due to a specific solvation effect of the ether groups.

The need for solvation in anionic polymerization also manifests itself in a few instances in deviations from the normal rate expression. Thus, the butyllithium polymerization of methyl methacrylate in toluene at −60°C shows a second order dependence of R_p on the monomer concentration [36]. In the non-polar toluene, the monomer is involved in solvating the propagating ions and ion-pairs. When polymerization is carried out in the mixed solvent system

Table 5-7 Effect of Solvent on Anionic Polymerization of Styrene[a]

Solvent	Dielectric constant (ϵ)	k_p (liter/mole-sec)
Benzene	2.2	2
Dioxane	2.2	5
Tetrahydrofuran	7.6	550
1,2-Dimethoxyethane	5.5	3,800

[a]Data from [37].

dioxane-toluene (which is more polar than toluene), the normal first order dependence of R_p on [M] is observed.

The k_p values in Table 5-7 were calculated from Eq. 5-55. As indicated previously (Sec. 5-2f), the k_p obtained in this manner for ionic chain polymerizations is usually best thought of as a composite or pseudo propagation rate constant. Szwarc and coworkers [43, 44] have expressed the polymerization rate in the living polymer systems as the sum of the polymerization rates for the ion-pair $P^-(C^+)$ and the free propagating ion P^-. Thus, one may write

$$R_p = k_{P^-(C^+)}[P^-(C^+)][M] + k_{P^-}[P^-][M] \tag{5-56}$$

where $k_{P^-(C^+)}$ and k_{P^-} are the rate constants for the propagation of the ion-pair and the free ion, respectively. $[P^-(C^+)]$ and $[P^-]$ are the concentrations of the two propagating species and [M] is the monomer concentration. C^+ in the above notation is the positive gegen-ion.

The two propagating species are in equilibrium according to

$$P^-(C^+) \overset{K}{\rightleftharpoons} P^- + C^+ \tag{5-57}$$

governed by the dissociation constant K given by

$$K = \frac{[P^-][C^+]}{[P^-(C^+)]} \tag{5-58}$$

or

$$K = \frac{[P^-]^2}{[P^-(C^+)]} \tag{5-59}$$

for the case where $[P^-] = [C^+]$.

Combination of Eqs. 5-56 and 5-59 yields

$$\frac{R_p}{[M][P^-(C^+)]} = k_{P^-(C^+)} + \frac{K^{1/2}k_{P^-}}{[P^-(C^+)]^{1/2}} \tag{5-60}$$

The right side of Eq. 5-60 is the equivalent of k_p in Eq. 5-55 if one assumes that the concentration of free anions is small. This is usually the case and $[P^-(C^+)]$ can be closely approximated by the total concentration of living ends (i.e., by the catalyst concentration).

A comparision of Eqs. 5-55 and 5-60 shows that a plot of the experimentally determined k_p values versus $[P^-(C^+)]^{-1/2}$ should be linear. Figure 5-4 shows this behavior for styrene polymerizations at 25°C in tetrahydrofuran with different gegen-ions. The plots are most useful in that $K^{1/2}k_{P^-}$ and $k_{P^-(C^+)}$ are obtained as the slope and intercept, respectively. The dissociation constant K for the various ion-pairs can be obtained from conductivity and polymerization rate data and combined with the $K^{1/2}k_{P^-}$ values to yield the propagation rate constant for the free anion [43, 44]. Table 5-8 shows the results

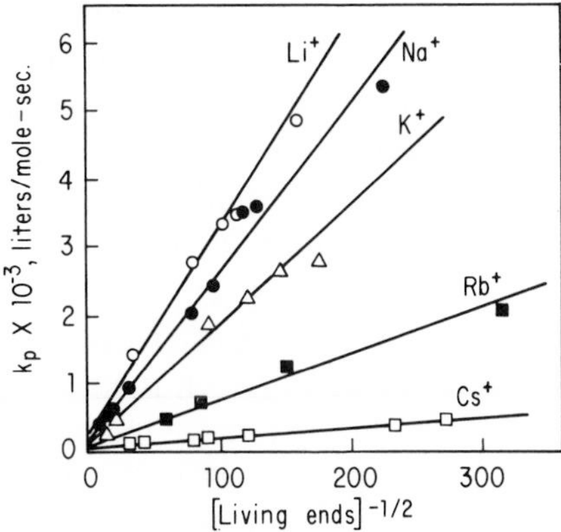

FIG. 5-4 *Dependence of the experimentally observed propagation rate constant of styrene on the concentration of living ends for different gegen-ions. After [43] (by permission of American Chemical Society, Washington).*

Table 5-8 Effect of Gegen-Ion on Anionic Polymerization of Styrene[a]

Gegen-ion	Polymerization in tetrahydrofuran				$k_{P^-(C^+)}$ for dioxane
	$k_{P^-(C^+)}$	$K^{1/2}k_{P^-}$	$K \times 10^7$	k_{P^-}	
Li^+	160	30.3	2.2	6.5×10^4	0.94
Na^+	80	25.2	1.5		3.4
K^+	60–80	18.0	0.8		19.8
Rb^+	50–80	6.7	0.1		21.5
Ca^+	22	3.0	0.02		24.5

[a]Data from [43] and [44].

of such an analysis of the data for styrene polymerization in tetrahydrofuran. The values of $k_{P^-(C^+)}$ for styrene polymerization in dioxane are also shown.

The data for polymerization in tetrahydrofuran show the much greater reactivity of the free anion compared to any of the ion-pairs. The value of k_{P^-} is 6.5×10^4 liter/mole-sec which is larger by a factor of 10^2–10^3 than the $k_{P^-(C^+)}$ values. The dissociation constants for the ion-pairs increase in going from cesium to lithium as the gegen-ion. This order is the order of increasing solvation of the gegen-ion. The smaller Li^+ is solvated to the greatest extent. The reactivities of the various ion-pairs also increase in the same order as shown by the $k_{P^-(C^+)}$ values. Table 5-8 also shows that the reactivities of the ion-pairs are generally lower in dioxane than in tetrahydrofuran—due to the lower solvating power of dioxane. However, it is interesting to note that the order of reactivity for the different ion-pairs in dioxane is the reverse of that in tetrahydrofuran. In the poor solvent dioxane, solvation of the gegen-ion is not an important consideration. The ion-pair with the highest reactivity is that with the weakest coulombic binding energy between the anion and gegen-ion. The binding energy decreases, and reactivity increases with the size of the gegen-ion. Monomer insertion between the anion and its gegen-ion is facilitated by a decrease in the binding energy between the two ions.

The effect of solvent on $k_{P^-(C^+)}$ has been expressed in a quantitative manner by Bywater and Worsfold [45]. The $k_{P^-(C^+)}$ values for polystyryllithium in various tetrahydrofuran-benzene solutions were correlated with the dielectric constant of the medium by a plot of log $k_{P^-(C^+)}$ against the term $(\epsilon - 1)/(2\epsilon + 1)$. Figure 5-5 shows the results of this correlation. This type of plot, i.e., a plot of the logarithm of a rate constant versus $(\epsilon - 1)/(2\epsilon + 1)$, is the standard method of showing the effect of solvent on a reaction involving polar species [46]. One should note that the $(\epsilon - 1)/(2\epsilon + 1)$ term increases as ϵ increases. The positive slope of the plot is in accordance with what is expected for reactions involving transition states of higher polarity than the reactants [46]. The transition state for propagation involves a separation of the propagating anion and gegen-ion as the monomer molecule becomes inserted between the two. This separation is increasingly facilitated as the dielectric constant of the reaction medium increases.

5-3b-5 Degree of Polymerization. The number-average degree of polymerization for a living polymer is given simply by the ratio of

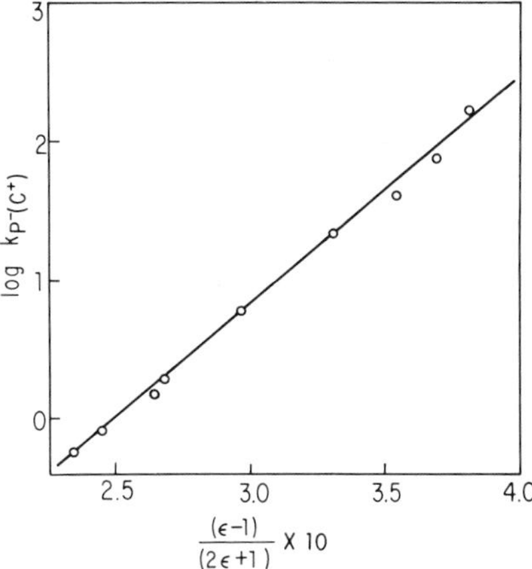

FIG. 5-5 *Dependence of the propagation rate constant for the polystyryllithium ion-pair on the dielectric constant of the reaction medium. After [45] (by permission of American Chemical Society, Washington).*

the concentrations of monomer and living ends

$$\bar{X}_n = \frac{[M]}{[M^-]} \tag{5-61}$$

For the usual situation where all of the catalyst is converted into propagating living anionic ends, Eq. 5-61 becomes

$$\bar{X}_n = \frac{2[M]}{[C]} \tag{5-62a}$$

or
$$\bar{X}_n = \frac{[M]}{[C]} \tag{5-62b}$$

depending on the mode of initiation. Equation 5-62a applies to polymerizations initiated by electron-transfer since each final polymer molecule originates from two catalyst molecules (via the di-anionic propagating species). Initiation processes other than electron-transfer (e.g., butyllithium) involve one polymer molecule per catalyst molecule and Eq. 5-62b is applicable.

A consequence of the absence of a termination reaction in the polymerization is that the polymer produced should be essentially monodisperse (that is, $\overline{M}_n \simeq \overline{M}_w$) under certain conditions. If initiation is reasonably fast so that all of the active centers begin to propagate almost simultaneously, all polymer molecules will grow for close to the same length of time. The size distribution will specifically be given by the Poisson distribution [47]

$$\frac{\overline{X}_w}{\overline{X}_n} = 1 + \frac{\overline{X}_n}{(\overline{X}_n + 1)^2} \tag{5-63a}$$

which can be approximated by

$$\frac{\overline{X}_w}{\overline{X}_n} \simeq 1 + \frac{1}{\overline{X}_n} \tag{5-63b}$$

Equation 5-63 shows that for any but a very low molecular weight polymer, the size distribution will be very narrow with $\overline{X}_w/\overline{X}_n$ being close to unity. This has been found in many systems. Thus, the ratio $\overline{M}_w/\overline{M}_n$ has been found to be in the narrow range 1.06–1.12 for styrene polymerization by sodium naphthalene. Theoretical studies indicate that the molecular weight distribution should be narrower than in radical polymerization even if the initiation rate is orders of magnitude less than the propagation rate [48]. The living polymer technique offers a unique means of synthesizing standard polymer samples of known and well-defined molecular weight. It is of interest to note in this respect that recent papers [49, 50] report the initiation of some cationic polymerizations by radical-cations in a manner analogous to the radical-anion polymerizations. This has promise in expanding the range of polymers which can be produced as standard samples of narrow molecular weight distribution.

Although these living polymerizations do not involve termination, the presence of reactive impurities can change the situation. One normally takes precautions to purge the system of oxygen, carbon dioxide, and water. Oxygen and carbon dioxide would add to the propagating anions to form peroxy and carboxy anions. These normally are not reactive enough to propagate and the kinetic chain is terminated. Water and other substances with acidic hydrogens (e.g., carboxylic acid) terminate chains by transfer of a proton. The transfer constant for water is approximately 10 in the polymerization of styrene at 25°C with sodium naphthalene [51] and its presence in sizable concentrations can limit the molecular weight of the polymer. Ethanol, on the other hand, has a transfer constant of only 10^{-3}. Its presence would allow the formation of high polymer because of the slow termination reaction although the polymer would not be living. Living polymers are, in fact, terminated when desired (usually at 100% conversion) by the addition of chain transfer agents such as water.

5-3b-6 Association Phenomena. A complication for polymerizations initiated by organolithium compounds in non-polar solvents, such as benzene, hexane, and toluene, is association of the various organolithium species present in the system. The phenomenon is important since only the unassociated species are active in polymerization. The effects of association have been extensively studied in the butyllithium polymerization of styrene [41, 52, 53]. Both the initiation and propagation rates are affected by association phenomena. At low total concentrations of butyllithium (below approximately 10^{-4} molar), there is little or no association and the initiation and propagation rates are both first order in butyllithium. However, extensive association takes place at high butyllithium concentrations. Under these conditions, the initiation and propagation rates are found to be proportional to only the 1/6 and 1/2 powers of butyllithium concentration, respectively. Above butyllithium concentrations of about 0.02 molar, R_i and R_p are independent of the total butyllithium concentration.

These results indicate that the following association equilibria are present

$$(C_4H_9Li)_6 \overset{K_1}{\rightleftharpoons} 6\,C_4H_9Li \tag{5-64}$$

$$(C_4H_9{-}M_n^-Li^+)_2 \overset{K_2}{\rightleftharpoons} 2\,C_4H_9{-}M_n^-Li^+ \tag{5-65}$$

with the butyllithium and the propagating ion-pairs in equilibria with the corresponding hexamer and dimer, respectively.

The concentrations of undissociated butyllithium and undissociated ion-pairs are given by

$$[C_4H_9Li] = K_1^{1/6}[(C_4H_9Li)_6]^{1/6} \tag{5-66}$$

$$[C_4H_9{-}M_n^- Li^+] = K_2^{1/2}[(C_4H_9{-}M_n^- Li^+]^{1/2} \tag{5-67}$$

which explain the dependence of R_i and R_p on the 1/6 and 1/2 power, respectively, of the total butyllithium concentration.

The association of the catalyst and of the propagating centers in non-polar media results in very slow polymerization rates. A typical styrene polymerization by butyllithium in benzene takes orders of magnitude longer for complete conversion compared to the corresponding sodium naphthalene polymerization. When butyllithium polymerizations are carried out in polar solvents such as tetrahydrofuran, the association vanishes completely and the polymerizations are much more rapid. The association phenomena can also be disrupted by adding a Lewis base which can coordinate with the catalyst [52–54]. The diethylzinc in the butyllithium-diethylzinc catalyst system described earlier (Sec. 5-3b) is probably used for this purpose. Increased temperature also decreases the extent of association.

5-3b-7 Energetics. The data available on the temperature dependence of the rates of non-termination polymerizations show the activation energy E_R to be relatively low and positive. One should note that the E_R for living polymers is simply the activation energy for propagation. The polymerization rates are relatively insensitive to temperature but increase with increasing temperature. Furthermore, the activation energy varies considerably depending on the solvent employed in the polymerization as was the case for cationic polymerization. Thus, the activation energy for propagation in the system styrene-sodium naphthalene is 9 ± 3 kcal/mole in dioxane and only about 1 kcal/mole in tetrahydrofuran [42, 55]. The molecular weight of the polymer produced in a non-termination polymerization is unaffected by temperature if transfer agents are absent. The situation can be different if transfer agents are present.

Most of the activation energy data reported in the literature are the values for the pseudo or composite propagation rate constant. Szwarc and coworkers have been able to determine the separate activation energies for propagation by the free anion and by the ion-pair by the kinetic analysis previously described (Sec. 5-3b-4). A recent study of the polystyryl living polymer system in tetrahydrofuran and 1,2-dimethoxyethane, with sodium and cesium gegen-ions, is especially interesting [56]. The activation energy for propagation by the free ion is 5–6 kcal/mole with the value being independent of the gegen-ion and the solvent. The frequency factor for propagation of the free ion is also the same in the two solvents. The actual value of A_p is 10^8–10^9 liter/mole-sec or slightly greater than the usual value for radical chain polymerization. Further, the activation energy for propagation E_p by the polystyrylcesium ion-pair is about the same as that for the free ion and also independent of solvent. The frequency factor A_p for the polystyrylcesium ion-pair is about 10^5 liters/mole-sec or several orders of magnitude less than that for the free ion—accounting for the much greater values of the propagation rate constant of the free ion.

The surprising result of this study is the observed activation energy for propagation E_p by the polystyrylsodium ion-pair. The activation energy is low and negative (−1.5 kcal/mole) for polymerization in tetrahydrofuran over the temperature range from −80 to 25°C. However, for polymerizations in 1,2-dimethoxyethane, the activation energy for ion-pair propagation passes through a maximum at about 0°C with the value being positive below and negative above this temperature. This behavior in 1,2-dimethoxyethane has been attributed to the presence of appreciable amounts of both tightly bound (or contact) ion-pairs and solvent-separated ion-pairs. (The two types of ion-pairs correspond to structures of types VI and VII in Eq. 5-30.) The absence of this behavior in tetrahydrofuran indicates the absence of a significant concentration of the solvent-separated ion-pair in that less polar solvent.

The observed ion-pair propagation rate constant $k_{P^-(C^+)}$ in 1,2-dimethoxyethane is a composite of that for the contact ion-pair (k_c) and that for the solvent-separated ion-pair (k_s) according to

$$k_{P^-(C^+)} = xk_s + (1 - x)\,k_c \tag{5-68}$$

or

$$k_{P^-(C^+)} = \frac{(k_c + k_s K_i)}{(1 + K_i)} \tag{5-69}$$

where x and $(1 - x)$ are the fractions of solvent-separated and contact ion-pairs, respectively, and K_i is the equilibrium constant for the equilibrium between the two types of ion-pairs

$$\sim\!\sim P^-(C^+) \overset{K_i}{\rightleftharpoons} \sim\!\sim P^- \| C^+ \tag{5-70}$$

The observed activation energy E_i is then given by

$$E_p = E_s + \frac{\Delta H_i}{(1 + K_i)} \tag{5-71}$$

where E_s is the activation energy for propagation of the solvent-separated ion-pair and ΔH_i is the heat of Reaction 5-70. Applying this type of analysis to the experimental data, Szwarc and coworkers were able to estimate k_s as about one-half the value of the rate constant for propagation of the free anion. The fraction of the ion-pairs present as solvent-separated ion-pairs was estimated to be about $2\text{–}3 \times 10^{-3}$. Thus, in summary, it has been seen (from Sec. 5-3f-4 and the above) that the pseudo propagation rate constant can in principle, although with experimental difficulty, be separated into the separate propagation rate constants for the free ion, the solvent-separated ion-pair, and the contact ion-pair.

5-4 DISTINGUISHING BETWEEN RADICAL, CATIONIC, AND ANIONIC POLYMERIZATIONS

There is sometimes a question as to whether a particular catalyst system initiates polymerization by radical, cationic, or anionic means. Such a question can easily arise, for example, in polymerizations initiated by atomic radiations. The mode of initiation of a particular catalyst can be distinguished by a consideration of its characteristics compared to those of known radical, cationic, and anionic initiators:

1) Ionic polymerizations usually proceed at lower temperatures than radical polymerizations. Although the ionic reaction temperatures are usually below 0°C, there are numerous ionic polymerizations which proceed at temperatures somewhat above 0°C. Radical polymerizations, on the other hand, almost always proceed at temperatures appreciably above approximately 50°C. Furthermore, ionic polymerizations invariably have lower activation energies than their radical counterparts and, in many cases, they may actually possess negative activation energies.

2) Ionic polymerizations are distinguished by their marked sensitivity to changes in the polarity and solvating ability of the reaction media. Radical polymerizations do not show such effects.

3) The addition of known radical scavengers such as the DPPH radical to a polymerizing system will halt polymerization if it is a radical reaction. Ionic polymerizations will be unaffected by such additions. One must be careful, however, not to use a radical scavenger which also affects ionic polymerization. Thus, benzoquinone would be a poor choice as a radical scavenger since it can also act as an inhibitor in cationic polymerization.

4) The chain transfer constant for an additive or solvent in the polymerization can be determined. This value can then be compared with the transfer constants for the same substance in the polymerization of the same monomer by known radical, cationic, and anionic initiators.

5) Copolymerization behavior can also be used to distinguish between radical and ionic polymerizations (see Chap. 6).

5-5 CARBONYL POLYMERIZATION

The polymerization of the carbonyl group yields polymers containing the acetal repeating structure

$$\underset{R'}{\overset{R}{\overset{|}{\underset{|}{C}}}}{=}O \longrightarrow \sim\!\!\sim \underset{R'}{\overset{R}{\overset{|}{\underset{|}{C}}}}{-}O{-}\underset{R'}{\overset{R}{\overset{|}{\underset{|}{C}}}}{-}O{-}\underset{R}{\overset{R}{\overset{|}{\underset{|}{C}}}}{-}O \sim\!\!\sim \tag{5-72}$$

Besides the carbon-carbon double bond, this is the only other unsaturated linkage whose polymerization has been successfully carried out to an appreciable extent [57]. The polymerization of formaldehyde has been studied much more intensely than that of other compounds. Although formaldehyde was successfully polymerized over a hundred years ago, it is only relatively recently that high molecular weight polymers of other carbonyl compounds have been generally obtained.

The recent progress in the polymerization of the carbonyl linkage is a result of the realization and understanding of the effect of ceiling temperature (T_c) on polymerization (Sec. 3-9c). With the prime exception of formaldehyde, carbonyl monomers have low ceiling temperatures. Table 5-9 shows the ceiling temperatures and equilibrium monomer concentrations for the polymerizations of several aldehydes in the gaseous and liquid states as well as in solution [58].

Table 5-9 Ceiling Temperatures and Monomer Concentrations[a]

Monomer (reaction conditions)	T_c (°C)	Monomer concentration
Formaldehyde (gaseous)	126	1 atm
Formaldehyde (in CH_2Cl_2 solution)	30	0.06 molar
Acetaldehyde (liquid)	−31	pure monomer
Propionaldehyde (liquid)	−31	pure monomer
Trichloroacetaldehyde (in pyridine solution)	12.5	0.1 mole fraction

[a]Data from [58].

The ceiling temperatures of almost all carbonyl monomers are at or appreciably below ambient temperatures. T_c is usually in the range of −20 to −30°C for the polymerization of all aldehydes except formaldehyde in the liquid state. The low T_c values for carbonyl polymerization are primarily due to the ΔH factor. The entropy of polymerization of the carbonyl-oxygen double bond is approximately the same as that for the alkene double bond. The enthalpy of polymerization for the carbonyl linkage, however, is appreciably lower. Thus, ΔH for acetaldehyde polymerization [59] is only about 7 kcal/mole compared to the usual 15–20 kcal/mole for the polymerization of the carbon-carbon double bond (Table 3-12).

Most of the early attempts to polymerize carbonyl compounds were carried out at temperatures that were, in retrospect, too high. The use of temperatures above T_c resulted in the absence of polymer formation due to the unfavorable equilibrium between monomer and polymer. Carbonyl monomers were successfully polymerized to high polymer when the polymerization reactions were carried out at temperatures below the ceiling temperatures of the monomers. Both anionic and cationic catalysts, of the types used in alkene polymerizations, can be used to initiate the polymerization of the carbonyl double bond. These polymerizations are similar in their general characteristics to the ionic polymerizations of alkene monomers. The number of detailed mechanistic studies of carbonyl polymerization is, however, small.

5-5a Anionic Polymerization

The carbonyl group is polymerized by a variety of basic catalysts. The strength of the base required to initiate polymerization depends on the substituent(s) attached to the carbonyl group.

5-5a-1 Formaldehyde. The carbonyl group of formaldehyde is highly susceptible to nucleophilic attack and this monomer can be polymerized with almost any basic catalyst. Metal alkyls, alkoxides, phenolates and carboxylates, hydrated alumina, tertiary aliphatic amines, phosphines, arsines, and nitrogen heterocyclics are among the bases which have been found to be effective catalysts [60].

The polymerization of formaldehyde to polyoxymethylene by tertiary amines is one of the more thoroughly studied reactions. The actual initiating species is considered to be the quaternary ammonium salt derived by reaction of the amine with water, alcohol, or some other cocatalyst [61]. The polymerization with water as the cocatalyst can be pictured as occurring in the following manner:

Initiation:

$$R_3N + H_2O \overset{K}{\rightleftharpoons} (R_3NH^+)OH^- \tag{5-73}$$

$$(R_3NH^+)OH^- + CH_2{=}O \xrightarrow{k_i} HO{-}CH_2{-}O^-(R_3NH^+) \tag{5-74}$$

Propagation:

$$HO{\leftarrow}CH_2{-}O{\rightarrow}_n CH_2{-}O^-(R_3NH^+) + CH_2{=}O \xrightarrow{k_p}$$

$$HO{\leftarrow}CH_2{-}O{\rightarrow}_{(n+1)} CH_2{-}O^-(R_3NH^+) \tag{5-75}$$

Termination by transfer with R′OH:

$$HO{\leftarrow}CH_2{-}O{\rightarrow}_n CH_2{-}O^-(R_3NH^+) + R'OH \xrightarrow{k_{tr}}$$

$$HO{\leftarrow}CH_2{-}O{\rightarrow}_n CH_2{-}OH + (R_3NH^+)OR^- \tag{5-76}$$

The above polymerization mechanism is quite similar to the general schemes discussed for the ionic chain polymerization of alkenes. Kinetic expressions such as Eqs. 5-25 and 5-26 should be applicable to this polymerization. However, there is a general lack of detailed experimental data to verify the kinetics of the polymerization.

The chain transfer agent R′OH may be any of a variety of compounds that can transfer a proton to the propagating anion. The cocatalyst water can itself act as the chain transfer agent. The chain transfer agent can also have an effect on the polymerization rate. Thus, both formic and acetic acids decrease the molecular weight of polyoxymethylene to the same extent but acetic acid also decreases the polymerization rate [60]. Formic acid has no effect on the polymerization rate. The effect of acetic acid on R_p must be due to the lowered activity of the initiator which is regenerated in the transfer reaction. The acetate corresponding to $(R_3NH^+)OR^-$ should undergo reverse hydrolysis (analogous to Eq. 5-73) to a greater extent than the formate since acetate ion is the stronger base.

5-5a-2 Other Carbonyl Monomers. The polymerization of carbonyl monomers other than formaldehyde follows in a similar manner although the basicity of the catalyst required may be quite different. Strong bases are required to initiate the polymerization of aliphatic aldehydes such as *n*-butyraldehyde [62]. The inductive effect of the alkyl substituent destabilizes the propagating anion IX by increasing the negative charge density on the oxygen

$$\sim\!\!\sim\!\!\sim \underset{\text{H}}{\overset{\text{R}\,\downarrow}{\text{C}}}\text{—O}^-$$

IX

Thus, weak bases such as amines cannot be used to polymerize aldehydes. Alkali metal alkyls and alkoxides are good catalysts for these monomers. Ketones are extremely difficult to polymerize due to the inductive effects of two alkyl groups. Steric considerations are, no doubt, also of significance in the general unreactivity of ketones toward polymerization. The one exception to this is the polymerization of acetone by coordination catalysts (Chap. 8).

The substitution of halogens on the alkyl group of an aliphatic aldehyde enhances its polymerizability. Trichloroacetaldehyde (chloral) is easily polymerized by such weak bases as pyridine and alkali thiocyanates [63]. Further, the polymerization of trifluoroacetaldehyde (fluoral) by butyllithium at $-78°C$ is complete in less than one second [64]. The electron-pulling inductive effect of the halogens acts to stabilize the propagating anion X by decreasing the charge density on the negative oxygen

$$\sim\!\!\sim\!\!\sim \underset{\text{H}}{\overset{\text{Cl}_3\text{C}\,\uparrow}{\text{C}}}\text{—O}^-$$

X

This effect is seen even more clearly in the ease of polymerization of fluorothiocarbonyl compounds such as thiocarbonyl fluoride

$$\mathrm{F_2C{=}S} \longrightarrow \left(\!\mathrm{CF_2{-}S}\!\right)_n \tag{5-77}$$

and hexafluorothioacetone

$$\mathrm{(CF_3)_2C{=}S} \longrightarrow \left[\!\mathrm{C(CF_3)_2{-}S}\!\right]_n \tag{5-78}$$

Thiocarbonyl fluoride is polymerized by a trace of a mild base such as dimethylformamide [65]. The polymerization of hexafluorothioacetone is an extreme example of the effect of ceiling temperature on polymerization. T_c is very low but polymerization proceeds smoothly at $-110°C$.

5-5b Cationic Polymerization

The carbonyl double bond is also polymerized by acidic catalysts. The strength of the acid required for cationic polymerization is usually greater than that of the base needed for anionic polymerization. Protonic acids such as hydrochloric and acetic acids and Lewis acids of the metal halide type are effective in catalyzing the cationic polymerization of carbonyl monomers. The initiation and propagation steps in polymerizations initiated with protonic acids can be pictured as

$$\mathrm{O{=}CHR} + \mathrm{HA} \longrightarrow \mathrm{HO{-}C^{+}HR\,(A^{-})} \tag{5-79}$$

$$\mathrm{H\!\left(O{-}CHR\right)_{\!n}O{-}C^{+}HR\,(A^{-})} + \mathrm{O{=}CHR} \longrightarrow \mathrm{H\!\left(O{-}CHR\right)_{\!(n+1)}O{-}C^{+}HR\,(A^{-})} \tag{5-80}$$

The termination reaction probably involves chain transfer with water or some other species present

$$\text{H}\!\left(\!\text{O—CHR}\!\right)_{(n+1)}\text{O—}\underset{\text{H}}{\overset{\text{R}}{\text{C}^{+}}}(\text{A}^{-}) + \text{H}_2\text{O} \longrightarrow$$

$$\text{H}\!\left(\!\text{O—CHR}\!\right)_{(n+1)}\text{O—}\underset{\text{H}}{\overset{\text{R}}{\text{C}}}\text{—OH} + \text{HA} \qquad (5\text{-}81)$$

The mechanism of Lewis acid catalyzed polymerization has not been well elucidated. In particular, whether cocatalysts are required or not is not clear. Some of the polymerizations appear to proceed in the same manner as the cationic polymerization of alkenes with the need for the usual type of cocatalyst (e.g., water). However, the following initiation step has been postulated [66] for the $AlBr_3$ catalyzed polymerization of chloral

$$\text{Cl}_3\text{C—CHO} + \text{AlBr}_3 \longrightarrow \text{Br}_3\bar{\text{A}}\text{lO—}\underset{\text{H}}{\overset{\text{CCl}_3}{\text{C}^{+}}} \qquad (5\text{-}82)$$

Similar initiation processes devoid of the need for cocatalysts have been put forth for polymerization by other Lewis acids. However, initiation by a species such as that in Eq. 5-82 has one glaring deficiency in that it requires propagation to occur with increasing separation and localization of the negative and positive charges as the propagating species XI

$$\text{Br}_3\bar{\text{A}}\text{lO—}\underset{\text{H}}{\overset{\text{CCl}_3}{\text{C}}}\!\left(\!\text{O—CHCCl}_3\!\right)_{n}\text{O—}\underset{\text{H}}{\overset{\text{CCl}_3}{\text{C}^{+}}}$$

XI

increases in size. This difficulty can be avoided by postulating

$$\mathrm{CCl_3{-}CHO + 2\,AlBr_3 \longrightarrow Br_2AlO{-}\overset{\overset{\displaystyle CCl_3}{|}}{\underset{\underset{\displaystyle H}{|}}{C^+}}(AlBr_4)^-} \qquad (5\text{-}83)$$

as the initiation reaction [66]. (Reaction 5-83 would probably involve a two step sequence–possibly the initial formation of a 1:1 complex of the aldehyde and catalyst followed by reaction with a second molecule of catalyst.) This is equivalent to the usual type of cationic polymerization mechanism (Sec. 5-2) with the catalyst also acting as the cocatalyst.

5-5c Radical Polymerization

The carbonyl double bond has not generally been susceptible to polymerization by radical initiators. There are two reasons for this behavior. First, the carbonyl group is highly polarized and not prone to attack by a radical. Second, most radicals are produced at temperatures above the ceiling temperatures of carbonyl monomers. There are, however, a few recent and isolated cases of carbonyl polymerizations by radical initiators. Trifluoroacetaldehyde has been polymerized using benzoyl peroxide at 22°C. The polymerization is slow with 18 hours required to obtain 90% conversion [64]. However, fluorothiocarbonyl monomers such as thiocarbonyl fluoride have been polymerized [65] at high rates by using a trialkylboron-oxygen redox system at −78°C. Radicals are produced [67] by the reaction sequence

$$\mathrm{R_3B + O_2 \longrightarrow R_2BOOR} \qquad (5\text{-}84)$$

$$\mathrm{R_2BOOR + 2\,R_3B \longrightarrow R_2BOBR_2 + R_2BOR + 2\,R\cdot} \qquad (5\text{-}85)$$

Radical polymerizations are observed with these monomers because the electron-pulling substituents on the carbonyl and thiocarbonyl group decrease its polarity (and polarizability). The greater susceptibility of the thiocarbonyl double bond to radical polymerization is due to the lower electronegativity of sulfur compared to oxygen. The thiocarbonyl group is less polar than the carbonyl group and more prone to attack by a radical. The successful radical polymerization of thiocarbonyl monomers is also due in large part to the low temperature initiation process employed.

5-5d Step Polymerization

Some carbonyl monomers have been polymerized by a step mechanism (Chap. 2) using an aqueous or alcohol solution of the monomer. The polymerization of formaldehyde has been most extensively studied [60]. The reaction involves step polymerization of the gem-diol or the hemiformal depending on whether the reaction is carried out in water or alcohol. The process can be depicted as

Initiation:

$$\mathrm{ROH} + \mathrm{H_2CO} \longrightarrow \mathrm{ROCH_2OH} \tag{5-86}$$

Propagation:

$$\mathrm{ROCH_2OH} \overset{\mathrm{H_2CO}}{\rightleftharpoons} \mathrm{RO(CH_2O)_2H} \overset{\mathrm{H_2CO}}{\rightleftharpoons} \mathrm{RO(CH_2O)_3H} \text{ etc.} \tag{5-87a}$$

or, in general terms

$$\mathrm{RO{\left(CH_2O\right)}_{n}H} \overset{\mathrm{H_2CO}}{\rightleftharpoons} \mathrm{RO{\left(CH_2O\right)}_{(n+1)}H} \tag{5-87b}$$

where R is H for polymerization in water and alkyl for polymerization in alcohol solution. This type of polymerization mechanism is similar in its kinetic characteristics to ring-opening polymerizations (Chap. 7).

5-5e End-Capping

The polyacetals obtained by the chain polymerization of carbonyl monomers are generally unstable at ambient or moderate temperature due to the effect of ceiling temperature. Because of their low ceiling temperatures, they undergo facile depolymerization to monomer. Thus, it would appear that this class of polymers would not be of any practical utility. However, the low ceiling temperatures of polyacetals have been circumvented by converting their reactive hydroxyl end groups into unreactive ester linkages by reaction with acid chlorides or anhydrides, for example

$$\mathrm{HO{\left(CH_2O\right)}_{n}CH_2OH} \xrightarrow[\mathrm{(RCO)_2O}]{\mathrm{RCOCl\ or}} \mathrm{RCOO{\left(CH_2O\right)}_{n}CH_2OCOR} \tag{5-88}$$

This reaction is referred to as *end-capping* or *end-blocking*. The result is that a reactive site (i.e., an anion or cation) does not form at the chain ends and depolymerization does not occur at the ceiling temperature of the polymer. In other words, the polymer chains are end-blocked from depolymerizing. A variety of end-capping reagents such as acetyl and benzoyl chlorides or acetic anhydride can be used for this purpose. The decomposition temperatures of the polyacetals are in many cases increased by a couple of hundred degrees Centigrade by the end-capping technique. (Copolymerization can also be used to prevent depolymerization—see Sec. 7-6.)

5-6 MISCELLANEOUS MONOMERS

5-6a Monomers with Two Different Polymerizable Groups

Most monomers contain only one polymerizable linkage. There are, however, some monomers with two polymerizable linkages per molecule. The polymerization of these monomers can lead to more than one polymer structure. The polymerization of dienes is an example of this behavior. There are several monomers which, unlike the dienes, contain two different types of polymerizable linkages. Examples of this type of monomer include

$$(CH_3)_2C{=}C{=}O \qquad\qquad CH_2{=}CH{-}CH{=}O$$

Dimethylketene   Acrolein

The polymerizations of dimethylketene and acrolein are of interest because the differences in the reactivities of the two polymerizable groups can lead to the formation of different polymer structures depending on the reaction conditions.

5-6a-1 Dimethylketene. Dimethylketene has been polymerized by anionic initiators. The reaction can proceed through the alkene double bond to yield a polyketone

$$n(CH_3)_2C{=}C{=}O \longrightarrow \left[C(CH_3)_2{-}\overset{\displaystyle O}{\overset{\|}{C}} \right]_n \tag{5-89}$$

or through the carbonyl linkage to yield an unsaturated polyacetal

$$n(CH_3)_2C{=}C{=}O \longrightarrow \left[\begin{array}{c} CH_3\diagdown \; \diagup CH_3 \\ C \\ \| \\ -C-O- \end{array} \right]_n \qquad (5\text{-}90)$$

or through the two groups in an alternating manner to yield an unsaturated polyester

$$2n(CH_3)_2C{=}C{=}O \longrightarrow \left[-C(CH_3)_2-\overset{\overset{\displaystyle O}{\|}}{C}-O-\underset{\underset{\displaystyle CH_3\diagup C \diagdown CH_3}{\|}}{C}- \right]_n \qquad (5\text{-}91)$$

Although two or all three structures may be formed in a particular polymerization, it is possible to obtain one or the other of these structures as the predominant repeating unit [68, 69]. Polymerization through the more polar carbonyl double bond is favored by solvents of high polarity. Polymerization of the less polar alkene linkage, either completely to form the polyketone or partially to form the polyester, is favored by non-polar solvents. Polyketone formation is favored by Li, Mg, and Al gegen-ions, and polyester by Na and K.

5-6a-2 Acrolein. The polymerization of acrolein has been studied with radical, cationic, and anionic initiators over a wide range of temperatures [70]. Radical polymerization proceeds exclusively through the vinyl linkage to produce the polyaldehyde

$$n\,CH_2{=}\underset{\underset{\displaystyle CHO}{|}}{CH} \longrightarrow \left[CH_2-\underset{\underset{\displaystyle CHO}{|}}{CH} \right]_n \qquad (5\text{-}92)$$

Cationic polymerization with the usual types of catalysts (for example, BF_3, H_2SO_4) yields polymers containing two types of repeating units

$$(n+m)\,CH_2{=}CH-CH{=}O \longrightarrow \left[CH_2-\underset{\underset{\underset{\displaystyle O}{\|}}{\displaystyle CH}}{\underset{|}{CH}} \right]_n \left[O-\underset{\underset{\underset{\displaystyle CH_2}{\|}}{\displaystyle CH}}{\underset{|}{CH}} \right]_m \qquad (5\text{-}93)$$

corresponding to reaction through both the alkene and carbonyl double bonds. The ratio n/m can be varied somewhat but polymerizations with n or m equal to zero have not been observed. Similar behavior is found for anionic polymerizations with catalysts such as butyllithium or sodium naphthalene. The only exception is the polymerization with sodium or sodium cyanide in tetrahydrofuran or toluene at −50 to −40°C which proceeds completely through the carbonyl group

$$n\,\underset{\displaystyle CH{=}CH_2}{\overset{|}{HC}}{=}O \longrightarrow \left[\underset{\displaystyle CH{=}CH_2}{\overset{|}{CH}}{-}O{-}\right]_n \tag{5-94}$$

The similarity of acrolein to 1,3-butadiene (i.e., the conjugation of the alkene and carbonyl double bonds) has led some workers to expect the possibility of a 1,4-type of polymerization

$$n\,CH_2{=}CH{-}CH{=}O \longrightarrow {+}CH_2{-}CH{=}CH{-}O{+}_n \tag{5-95}$$

but this has never been observed.

5-6b Acrylamide

The polymerization of acrylamide (or methacrylamide) by strong bases such as sodium, organolithium compounds, and alkoxides yields a polymer structure

$$n\,CH_2{=}CH{-}CO{-}NH_2 \longrightarrow {+}CH_2{-}CH_2{-}CO{-}NH{+}_n \tag{5-96}$$

which is quite unexpected. The polyamide structure of the polymer has been confirmed by the quantitative hydrolysis of the polymer to 3-aminopropionic acid.

The polymerization mechanism involves [71] addition of the anionic catalyst to the alkene linkage of the monomer

$$B^- + CH_2{=}CHCONH_2 \longrightarrow BCH_2{-}\bar{C}HCONH_2 \tag{5-97a}$$

followed by proton abstraction from another monomer molecule to form the amide anion XII

$$\mathrm{BCH_2{-}\overset{-}{C}HCONH_2 + CH_2{=}CHCONH_2 \longrightarrow}$$
$$\mathrm{BCH_2CH_2CONH_2 + \underset{XII}{CH_2{=}CHCO\overset{-}{N}H}} \qquad (5\text{-}97b)$$

The amide anion initiates polymerization, via a similar reaction sequence, by addition to monomer

$$\mathrm{CH_2{=}CHCO\overset{-}{N}H + CH_2{=}CHCONH_2 \longrightarrow}$$
$$\mathrm{CH_2{=}CHCONHCH_2\overset{-}{C}HCONH_2} \qquad (5\text{-}98a)$$

$$\mathrm{CH_2{=}CHCONHCH_2\overset{-}{C}HCONH_2 + CH_2{=}CHCONH_2 \longrightarrow}$$
$$\mathrm{CH_2{=}CHCONHCH_2CH_2CONH_2 + CH_2{=}CHCO\overset{-}{N}H} \qquad (5\text{-}98b)$$

Propagation follows in a like manner

$$\mathrm{\underset{XIII}{CH_2{=}CHCONH{+}CH_2CH_2CONH{+}_nH} + CH_2{=}CHCO\overset{-}{N}H \longrightarrow}$$
$$\mathrm{CH_2{=}CHCONH{-}CH_2{-}\overset{-}{C}HCONH{+}CH_2CH_2CONH{+}_nH \xrightarrow{Monomer}}$$
$$\mathrm{CH_2{=}CHCONH{+}CH_2CH_2CONH{+}_{(n+1)}H + CH_2{=}CHCO\overset{-}{N}H} \qquad (5\text{-}99)$$

This polymerization follows a path which is quite different than any of the previously discussed polymerizations. The propagating center is not an ion or a radical but is the alkene double bond at one end of the propagating species XIII. In addition, it is not the monomer but the monomer anion XII which adds to the propagating center. The evidence for this polymerization mechanism comes from analysis for the alkene end-group and the observation that the reaction is a step polymerization as regards the build-up of polymer molecular weight. This mechanism is very similar to that for the anionic ring-opening polymerization of cyclic amides (Sec. 7-3a). By analogy to the latter, the monomer anion can be referred to as *activated monomer*. The overall polymerization reaction is often referred to as a *hydrogen transfer polymerization.*

5-6c Isocyanates

Isocyanates can be polymerized through the carbon-nitrogen double bond

$$nR\text{—}N\text{=}C\text{=}O \longrightarrow \left[\begin{matrix} R \\ | \\ N\text{—}CO \end{matrix}\right]_n \qquad (5\text{-}100)$$

by anionic initiators such as organometallics, sodium, and sodium cyanide [72]. The polymerization has a low ceiling temperature and cyclic trimer formation

$$3\,RNCO \longrightarrow \text{(cyclic trimer: 1,3,5-tri-R-substituted ring of alternating N and C=O)} \qquad (5\text{-}101)$$

is the major product at temperatures above about $-20°C$.

5-6d Diazoalkanes

The polymerization of diazoalkanes such as diazomethane

$$nCH_2N_2 \longrightarrow (CH_2)_n + nN_2 \qquad (5\text{-}102)$$

can be carried out with BF_3 and other Lewis acids [73]. The mechanism proposed for this reaction involves the sequence

$$CH_2N_2 \xrightarrow{BF_3} F_3\overset{-}{B}CH_2\overset{+}{N}\equiv N \xrightarrow{-N_2} F_3B\overset{+}{C}H_2$$

$$F_3B\overset{+}{C}H_2 \longrightarrow F_2BCH_2F \xrightarrow{CH_2N} F_2\underset{}{B}(CH_2N_2)\text{—}CH_2F \xrightarrow{-N_2} F_2B(\overset{+}{C}H_2)\text{—}CH_2F$$

$$F_2B(\overset{+}{C}H_2)\text{—}CH_2F \longrightarrow F_2B\text{—}CH_2CH_2F \xrightarrow{CH_2N_2} F_2B(CH_2)_nF \qquad (5\text{-}103)$$

This polymerization is of interest in that it produces the equivalent of a perfectly linear polyethylene, i.e., a polyethylene without any branching. Such a linear polymer can be employed as a standard sample for basic studies on the effect of branching on polymer properties.

5-6e Triple Bonded Monomers

The polymerization of nitriles

$$n\,\mathrm{RC{\equiv}N} \longrightarrow \left[\begin{array}{c}\mathrm{R}\\ |\\ \mathrm{C{=}N}\end{array}\right]_n \qquad (5\text{-}104)$$

and acetylenes

$$n\,\mathrm{RC{\equiv}CH} \longrightarrow \left[\begin{array}{c}\mathrm{R}\\ |\\ \mathrm{C{=}CH}\end{array}\right]_n \qquad (5\text{-}105)$$

with ionic catalysts have been reported in a few rare instances [74, 75]. However, the products have not been well characterized as to structure and molecular weight. Polymer structures such as those in Eqs. 5-104 and 5-105 might be of interest in terms of their potential semi-conductor properties.

REFERENCES

1. M. L. Burstall and F. E. Treloar, Carbonium Ions, in P. H. Plesch (ed.), "The Chemistry of Cationic Polymerization," chap. 1, The Macmillan Company, New York, 1963.
2. A. G. Evans and G. W. Meadows, *Trans. Faraday Soc.,* **46**:327 (1950).
3. P. H. Plesch, Isobutene, in P. H. Plesch (ed.), "The Chemistry of Cationic Polymerization," chap. 4, The Macmillan Company, New York, 1963.
4. R. O. Colclough and F. S. Dainton, *Trans. Faraday Soc.,* **54**:886, 894 (1958).
5. C. G. Overberger, R. J. Ehrig, and R. A. Marcus, *J. Am. Chem. Soc.,* **80**:2456 (1958).
6. S. Tazuke, K. Nakagawa, and S. Okamura, *J. Polymer Sci.,* **B3**:923 (1965).
7. I. Sakurada, N. Ise, Y. Tanaka, and Y. Hayashi, *ibid.,* **A-1(4)**:2801 (1966).
8. R. C. Potter, C. L. Johnson, D. J. Metz, and R. H. Bretton, *ibid.,* **A-1(4)**:419 (1966).
9. J. P. Kennedy, L. S. Minckler, G. Wanless, and R. M. Thomas, *ibid.,* **A2**:2093 (1964).
10. A. D. Ketley, *ibid.,* **B2**:827 (1964).
11. J. P. Kennedy and A. W. Langer, Jr., *Fortschr. Hochpolymer.-Forsch., (Advan. Polymer Sci.),* **3**:508 (1964).

12. A. R. Mathieson, Styrene, in P. H. Plesch (ed.), "The Chemistry of Cationic Polymerization," chap. 6, The Macmillan Company, New York, 1963.
13. P. H. Plesch, *J. Chem. Soc.*, **1953**:1653.
14. M. Kamachi and H. Miyama, *J. Polymer Sci.*, **A3**:1337 (1965).
15. R. E. Burton and D. C. Pepper, *Proc. Roy. Soc. (London)*, **A263**:58 (1961).
16. M. J. Hayes and D. C. Pepper, *ibid.*, **A263**:63 (1961); *Proc. Chem. Soc.*, **1958**:228.
17. S. Okamura and T. Higashimura, *J. Polymer Sci.*, **21**:289 (1956); *Chem. High Polymers (Tokyo)*, **13**:342, 397 (1956) and **17**:57 (1960).
18. G. F. Endres and C. G. Overberger, *J. Am. Chem. Soc.*, **77**:2201 (1955).
19. R. H. Biddulph and P. H. Plesch, *J. Chem. Soc.*, **1960**:3913.
20. Y. Sakurda, T. Higashimura, and S. Okamura, *J. Polymer Sci.*, **33**:496 (1958).
21. Y. Imanishi, T. Higashimura, and S. Okamura, *Chem. High Polymers (Tokyo)*, **18**:333 (1961).
22. D. H. Jenkinson and D. C. Pepper, *Proc. Roy. Soc. (London)*, **A263**:82 (1961).
23. C. G. Overberger, G. F. Endres, and A. Monaci, *J. Am. Chem. Soc.*, **78**:1969 (1956).
24. S. Okamura and T. Higashimura, *J. Polymer Sci.*, **21**:289 (1956).
25. C. P. Brown and A. R. Mathieson, *J. Chem. Soc.*, **1957**:3608, 3612, 3620, 3631 and **1958**:3445.
26. D. C. Pepper and P. J. Reilly, *J. Polymer Sci.*, **58**:639 (1962).
27. N. Kanoh, A. Gotoh, T. Higashimura, and S. Okamura, *Makromol. Chem.*, **63**:115 (1963).
28. N. Kanoh, T. Higashimura, and S. Okamura, *ibid.*, **56**:65 (1962).
29. B. L. Funt, Electrolytically Controlled Polymerizations, in A. Peterlin, M. Goodman, S. Okamura, B. H. Zimm, and H. F. Mark (eds.), "Macromolecular Reviews," vol. 1, Interscience Publishers, John Wiley & Sons, Inc., New York, 1967.
30. A. Gandini and P. H. Plesch, *J. Polymer Sci.*, **B(3)**:127 (1965); "The Chemistry of Polymerization Processes," pp. 107–114, 122–129, Society of Chemical Industry, London, 1966.
31. P. H. Plesch, *Polymer Preprints*, **7(2)**:492 (1966).
32. J. P. Kennedy and R. G. Squires, *Polymer*, **6**:579 (1965).
33. M. Szwarc, *Ann. N.Y. Acad. Sci.*, **155(2)**:400 (1969).
34. W. C. Higginson and N. S. Wooding, *J. Chem. Soc.*, **1952**:760, 1178.
35. C. G. Overberger, H. Yuki, and N. Urakawa, *J. Polymer Sci.*, **45**:127 (1960)
36. G. L'Abbe and G. Smets, *ibid.*, **A-1(5)**:1359 (1967).
37. M. Szwarc and J. Smid, The Kinetics of Propagation of Anionic

Polymerization and Copolymerization, in G. Porter (ed.), "Progress in Reaction Kinetics," vol. 2, chap. 5, Pergamon Press Ltd., Oxford, 1964.
38. M. Szwarc, R. Waak, A. Rembaum, and J. D. Coombes, *J. Am. Chem. Soc.*, **79**:2026 (1957).
39. M. Szwarc, M. Levy, and R. Milkovich, *ibid.*, **78**:2656 (1956).
40. C. G. Overberger, E. M. Pearce, and N. Mayes, *ibid.*, **34**:109 (1959).
41. S. Bywater, *Fortschr. Hochpolymer.-Forsch. (Advan. Polymer Sci.)*, **4**:66 (1965).
42. C. Geacintov, J. Smid, and M. Szwarc, *J. Am. Chem. Soc.*, **84**:2508 (1962).
43. D. N. Bhattacharyya, C. L. Lee, J. Smid, and M. Szwarc, *J. Phys. Chem.*, **69**:612 (1965).
44. D. N. Bhattacharyya, J. Smid, and M. Szwarc, *ibid.*, **69**:624 (1965).
45. S. Bywater and D. J. Worsfold, *J. Phys. Chem.*, **70**:162 (1966).
46. A. A. Frost and R. G. Pearson, "Kinetics and Mechanism," 2d ed., chap. 7, John Wiley & Sons, Inc., New York, 1961.
47. P. J. Flory, *J. Am. Chem. Soc.*, **62**:1561 (1940).
48. L. Gold, *J. Chem. Phys.*, **28**:91 (1958).
49. A. Ledwith, *Ann. N.Y. Acad. Sci.*, **155(2)**:385 (1969).
50. N. Tokwia, T. Nagai, and Y. Sonoyama, *Tetrahedron Letters*, **17**:1145 (1965).
51. M. Szwarc, *Fortschr. Hochpolymer.-Forsch. (Advan. Polymer Sci.)*, **2**:275 (1960).
52. D. J. Worsfold and S. Bywater, *Can. J. Chem.*, **38**:1891 (1960).
53. K. F. O'Driscoll and A. V. Tobolsky, *J. Polymer Sci.*, **35**:259 (1959).
54. B. L. Erusalimskii and I. S. Krasinosel'skaya, *Makromol. Chem.*, **123**:80 (1969).
55. G. Allen et al., *Polymer*, **2**:151 (1961); *J. Polymer Sci.*, **48**:189 (1960).
56. T. Shimomura, J. Smid, and M. Szwarc, *Polymer Preprints*, **8(2)**:897 (1967).
57. J. Furukawa and T. Saegusa, "Polymerization of Aldehydes and Oxides," Interscience Publishers, John Wiley & Sons, Inc., New York, 1963.
58. J. Brandrup and E. H. Immergut (eds.), "Polymer Handbook," p. II-389, Interscience Publishers, John Wiley & Sons, Inc., New York, 1966.
59. O. Vogl and W. M. D. Bryant, *J. Polymer Sci.*, **A2**:4633 (1964).
60. N. Brown, *J. Macromol. Sci. (Chem.)*, **A1(2)**:209 (1967).
61. C. E. Schweitzer, R. N. MacDonald, and J. O. Punderson, *J. Appl. Polymer Sci.*, **1**:160 (1959).
62. O. Vogl, *J. Macromol. Sci. (Chem.)*, **A1(2)**:243 (1967).
63. I. Rosen, *ibid.*, **A1(2)**:267 (1967).
64. W. K. Busfield and E. Whalley, *Can. J. Chem.*, **43**:2289 (1965).
65. W. H. Sharkey, *J. Macromol. Sci. (Chem.)*, **A1(2)**:291 (1967).
66. I. Rosen, D. E. Hudgin, C. L. Sturm, G. H. McCain, and R. M. Wilmjelm, *J. Polymer Sci.*, **A3**:1535, 1545 (1965).

67. A. L. Barney, J. M. Bruce, Jr., J. N. Coker, N. W. Jacobson, and W. H. Sharkey, *ibid.*, **A-1(4)**:2617 (1966).
68. Y. Yamashita and S. Nunomoto, *Makromol. Chem.*, **58**:244 (1962).
69. G. F. Pregaglia, M. Minaghi, and M. Cambini, *ibid.*, **67**:10 (1963).
70. R. C. Schulz, Polymerization of Acrolein, in G. E. Ham (ed.), "Vinyl Polymerization," vol. 1, part I, chap. 7, Marcel Dekker, Inc., New York, 1967.
71. L. W. Bush and D. S. Breslow, *Macromolecules*, **1**:189 (1968).
72. V. E. Shashoua, W. Sweeny, and R. F. Tietz, *J. Am. Chem. Soc.*, **82**:866 (1960).
73. C. E. H. Bawn, A. Ledwith, and P. Matthies, *J. Polymer Sci.*, **34**:93 (1959).
74. L. B. Luttinger and E. C. Colthup, *J. Org. Chem.*, **27**:3752 (1962).
75. V. A. Kabanov, V. P. Zubov, V. P. Kovaleva, and V. A. Kargin, *J. Polymer Sci.*, **C4**:1009 (1963).

PROBLEMS

5-1. Consider the following monomers and catalysts:

Catalysts	*Monomers*
$(\phi CO_2)_2$	$\phi CH{=}CH_2$
$(CH_3)_3COOH + Fe^{2+}$	$CH_2{=}C(CN)_2$
Na + Naphthalene	$CH_2{=}C(CH_3)_2$
H_2SO_4	$CH_2{=}CH{-}O{-}n\text{-}C_4H_9$
BF_3	$CH_2{=}CH{-}Cl$
$n\text{-}C_4H_9Li$	$CH_2{=}C(CH_3){-}CO_2CH_3$
	$CH_2{=}O$
	$CF_2{=}S$

What is the initiating species from each of these catalysts? Show equations. Which catalyst(s) can be used to polymerize each of the various monomers? Explain your answers. What general reaction conditions (e.g., temperature, solvent) are required for each of these polymerizations?

5-2. Consider the cationic polymerization of isobutylene in benzene solution using $TiCl_4$ catalyst and H_2O cocatalyst. Under a particular set of reaction conditions, it was found that the experimental polymerization rate is given by

$$R_p = k[TiCl_4][\text{isobutylene}][H_2O]^0$$

Termination occurs by rearrangement of the propagating species to give a polymer with an unsaturated end-group plus the catalyst-cocatalyst complex. Show the mechanism for this polymerization and derive the expressions for the rate and degree of polymerization.

Under what reaction conditions might the rate of polymerization show

a. First order dependence on $[H_2O]$
b. No dependence on $[TiCl_4]$
c. Second order dependence on [isobutylene]
d. Second order dependence on $[H_2O]$

5-3. A particular polymerization increases in rate with an increase in temperature. Is polymerization proceeding by a radical or ionic mechanism? What other experimental techniques besides the effect of temperature could be used to determine the type of initiation?

5-4. The sodium naphthalene polymerization of methyl methacrylate is carried out in benzene, tetrahydrofuran, and nitrobenzene solutions. Which solvent will yield the highest polymerization rate? Discuss the effect of solvent on the concentrations and identities of the propagating species.

5-5. A 1.5 molar solution of styrene in tetrahydrofuran is polymerized at 25°C by sodium naphthalene at a concentration of 3.2×10^{-5}. Calculate the initial rate of polymerization using the data in Table 5-7. Calculate the degree of polymerization at complete conversion. Compare the value of R_p with that calculated from Eq. 5-60 with data from Table 5-8.

5-6. A 2.0 molar solution of styrene in ethylene dichloride is polymerized at 25°C using 4.0×10^{-4} molar sulfuric acid. Calculate the initial degree of polymerization. What would be the degree of polymerization if the monomer solution contains isopropylbenzene at a concentration of 8.0×10^{-5} molar? Use the appropriate data from Tables 5-1 and 5-4 for your calculations.

6

CHAIN COPOLYMERIZATION

For most step polymerizations, e.g., in the synthesis of poly(hexamethylene adipamide) or poly(ethylene terephthalate), two reactants or monomers must be used in the process and the polymer obtained contains two different kinds of structures in the chain. This is not the case for chain polymerizations where only one monomer need be used to produce a polymer. However, chain polymerizations can be carried out with mixtures of two monomers to form polymeric products with two different structures in the polymer chain. This type of chain polymerization process in which two monomers are simultaneously polymerized is termed a *copolymerization* and the product is a *copolymer*. It is important to stress that the copolymer is not an alloy of two homopolymers but contains units of both monomers incorporated into each copolymer molecule. The process can be depicted as

$$M_1 + M_2 \longrightarrow$$
$$\sim\sim M_1M_2M_2M_1M_2M_2M_2M_1M_1M_2M_2M_1M_1M_2M_1M_1M_1M_2M_2M_1M_1\sim\sim \quad (6\text{-}1)$$

The two monomers enter into the copolymer in a relatively random manner in overall amounts determined by their relative concentrations and reactivities. The simultaneous chain polymerization of different monomers can also be carried out with mixtures of three or more monomers. Such polymerizations are generally referred to as *multi-component copolymerizations*; the term *terpolymerization* is specifically used for systems of three monomers.

6-1 GENERAL CONSIDERATIONS

6-1a Importance of Chain Copolymerization

Chain copolymerization is important from several considerations. Much of our knowledge of the reactivities of monomers, radicals, carbonium ions, and carbanions in chain polymerization arise from copolymerization studies. The behavior of monomers in copolymerization reactions is especially useful for studying the effect of chemical structure on reactivity. Copolymerization is also very important from the technological viewpoint. It greatly increases the ability of the polymer scientist to tailor-make a polymer product with specifically desired properties. Polymerization of a single monomer is relatively limited as to the number of different products that are possible. The term *homopolymerization* is often used to distinguish the polymerization of a single monomer from the copolymerization process.

Copolymerization allows the synthesis of an almost unlimited number of different products by variations in the nature and relative amounts of the two monomer units in the copolymer product. A prime example of the versatility of the copolymerization process is the case of polystyrene. Polystyrene is a brittle plastic with poor impact strength and poor solvent resistance and, as such, has relatively limited practical utility. Copolymerization and terpolymerization of styrene greatly increase the usefulness of polystyrene and have been responsible in large part for the annual production of over 3 ,billion pounds of polymer products containing styrene. Styrene copolymers and terpolymers are useful not only as plastics but also as elastomers. Thus, copolymerization of styrene with acrylonitrile leads to increased impact and solvent resistance while copolymerization with butadiene leads to elastomeric properties. Terpolymerization of styrene with both acrylonitrile and butadiene improves all three properties simultaneously. Another example of the utility of copolymerization is the case of the most common plastic—polyethylene. Small amounts of a monomer, such as 1-butene, vinyl acetate, or an acrylate, can be copolymerized with ethylene to produce ethylene copolymers which are more flexible than polyethylene. Copolymerization with larger amounts of monomers can change the polyethylene from a plastic to an elastomer as in the newly developed ethylene-propylene copolymers. Numerous other examples of the technological utility of the copolymerization process exist.

6-1b Types of Copolymers

The copolymer described by Eq. 6-1 has a relatively random structural distribution of the two monomer units along the copolymer chain. This type of structure is referred to as a *random copolymer.* There are three other copolymer structures which are known. These are the *alternating, block,* and *graft* copolymer structures. The alternating copolymer contains the two monomer units in equimolar amounts in a regular alternating distribution

$$\sim\sim M_1M_2M_1M_2M_1M_2M_1M_2M_1M_2M_1M_2M_1M_2M_1M_2M_1M_2M_1M_2M_1M_2M_1M_2M_1\sim\sim$$

I

The block and graft copolymers differ from random and alternating copolymers in that there are long sequences of each monomer in the copolymer chain. A block copolymer is a linear copolymer with one or more long uninterrupted sequences of each polymeric species

$$\sim\sim M_1M_1M_1M_1M_1M_1M_1M_1M_1M_1M_1M_1M_2M_2M_2M_2M_2M_2M_2M_2M_2M_2\sim\sim$$

II

while a graft copolymer is a branched copolymer with a backbone of one monomer to which are attached one or more side chains of another monomer

$$\sim\!\sim M_1M_1M_1M_1M_1M_1M_1M_1M_1M_1M_1M_1M_1M_1M_1M_1M_1M_1M_1M_1M_1M_1M_1M_1M_1 \sim\!\sim$$

$$M_2M_2M_2M_2M_2M_2M_2M_2M_2M_2M_2M_2M_2M_2M_2M_2M_2 \sim\!\sim$$

III

This chapter is primarily concerned with the simultaneous polymerization of two monomers to produce random and alternating copolymers. Graft copolymers and, to a large extent, block copolymers are not synthesized by the simultaneous polymerization of two monomers. These are generally obtained by other types of reactions. Block copolymers are considered to some extent in this chapter but more completely in Chap. 9. The synthesis of graft copolymers is also discussed in Chap. 9.

There is no accepted nomenclature system for copolymers at the present time [1]. A copolymer of styrene and methyl methacrylate, for example, would generally be named poly(methyl methacrylate-*co*-styrene) or simply methyl methacrylate-styrene copolymer. Nomenclature distinctions between random, alternating, block, and graft copolymers can be made by using *-co-*, *-alt-*, *-b-*, and *-g-*, respectively, as in poly(methyl methacrylate-*co*-styrene), poly(methyl methacrylate-*alt*-styrene) poly(methyl methacrylate-*b*-styrene), and poly(methyl methacrylate-*g*-styrene).

6-2 COPOLYMER COMPOSITION

6-2a Copolymerization Equation; Monomer Reactivity Ratios

The composition of a copolymer in most instances is found to be different than that of the comonomer feed from which it is produced. In other words, different monomers have differing tendencies to undergo copolymerization. It was observed early that the relative copolymerization tendencies of monomers bore little resemblance to their relative rates of homopolymerization [2]. Some monomers are more reactive in copolymerization than indicated by their rates of homopolymerization; other monomers are less reactive. Further, and most dramatically, a few monomers, such as maleic anhydride, stilbene, and fumaric esters, undergo facile copolymerization with radical initiation although they have little or no tendency to undergo homopolymerization.

The composition of a copolymer, thus, cannot be determined from a knowledge of the homopolymerization rates of the two monomers. The determinants of copolymer composition have been elucidated by several workers [3–5] by assuming the chemical reactivity of the propagating chain (which may be a free radical, a carbonium ion, or a carbanion) in a copolymerization to be dependent only on the monomer unit at the growing end and independent of the chain composition preceding the last monomer unit. Consider the case for the copolymerization of the two monomers M_1 and M_2. Although radical copolymerization has been more extensively studied [6, 7] and is more important than ionic copolymerizations, we will consider the general case without specification as to whether the mode of initiation is by a radical, anionic, or cationic species. Copolymerization of the two monomers leads to two types of propagating species–one with M_1 at the propagating end and the other with M_2. These can be represented by M_1^* and M_2^* where the asterisk represents either a radical, a carbonium ion, or a carbanion as the propagating species depending on the particular case. If it is assumed that the reactivity of the propagating species is dependent only on the monomer unit at the end of the chain, four propagation reactions are then possible. Monomers M_1 and M_2 can each add either to a propagating chain ending in M_1 or to one ending in M_2, that is

$$M_1^* + M_1 \xrightarrow{k_{11}} M_1^* \tag{6-2}$$

$$M_1^* + M_2 \xrightarrow{k_{12}} M_2^* \tag{6-3}$$

$$M_2^* + M_1 \xrightarrow{k_{21}} M_1^* \tag{6-4}$$

$$M_2^* + M_2 \xrightarrow{k_{22}} M_2^* \tag{6-5}$$

where k_{11} is the rate constant for a propagating chain ending in M_1 adding to monomer M_1, k_{12} that for a propagating chain ending in M_1 adding to monomer M_2, and so on. The propagation of a reactive center by addition of the same monomer (i.e., Reactions 6-2 and 6-5) is often referred to as *homopropagation* or *self-propagation*; propagation of a reactive center by addition of the other monomer (Reactions 6-3 and 6-4) is referred to as *cross-propagation* or a *cross-over* reaction.

Monomer M_1 disappears by Reactions 6-2 and 6-4 while monomer M_2 disappears by Reactions 6-3 and 6-5. The rates of disappearance of the two monomers, which are synonymous with their rates of entry into the copolymer, are given by

$$-\frac{d[M_1]}{dt} = k_{11}[M_1^*][M_1] + k_{21}[M_2^*][M_1] \tag{6-6}$$

$$-\frac{d[M_2]}{dt} = k_{12}[M_1^*][M_2] + k_{22}[M_2^*][M_2] \tag{6-7}$$

Dividing Eq. 6-6 by Eq. 6-7 yields the ratio of the rates at which the two monomers enter the copolymer, i.e., the copolymer composition, as

$$\frac{d[M_1]}{d[M_2]} = \frac{k_{11}[M_1^*][M_1] + k_{12}[M_2^*][M_1]}{k_{12}[M_1^*][M_2] + k_{22}[M_2^*][M_2]} \tag{6-8}$$

In order to remove the concentration terms in M_1^* and M_2^* from Eq. 6-8, a steady-state concentration is assumed for each of the reactive species M_1^* and M_2^* separately. For the concentrations of M_1^* and M_2^* to remain constant, their rates of interconversion must be equal. In other words, the rates of Reactions 6-3 and 6-4 are equal

$$k_{21}[M_2^*][M_1] = k_{12}[M_1^*][M_2] \tag{6-9}$$

Equation 6-9 can be rearranged and combined with Eq. 6-8 to yield

$$\frac{d[M_1]}{d[M_2]} = \frac{\dfrac{k_{11}k_{21}[M_2^*][M_1]^2}{k_{12}[M_2]} + k_{21}[M_2^*][M_1]}{k_{22}[M_2^*][M_2] + k_{21}[M_2^*][M_1]} \tag{6-10}$$

Dividing the top and bottom of the right side of Eq. 6-10 by $k_{21}[M_2^*][M_2]$ and combining the result with the parameters r_1 and r_2 which are defined by

$$r_1 = \frac{k_{11}}{k_{12}} \text{ and } r_2 = \frac{k_{22}}{k_{21}} \tag{6-11}$$

one finally obtains

$$\frac{d[M_1]}{d[M_2]} = \frac{[M_1](r_1[M_1] + [M_2])}{[M_2]([M_1] + r_2[M_2])} \tag{6-12}$$

Equation 6-12 is known as the *copolymerization equation* or the *copolymer composition equation*. Although its derivation involves the use of steady-state assumptions, several workers [8, 9] have shown that the same expression can be obtained by a statistical method without resorting to any steady-state assumptions. The copolymer composition, $d[M_1]/d[M_2]$, is the molar ratio of the two monomer units in the copolymer. $d[M_1]/d[M_2]$ is expressed by Eq. 6-12 as being related to the concentrations of the two monomers in the feed, $[M_1]$ and $[M_2]$, and the parameters r_1 and r_2. The parameters r_1 and r_2 are termed the *monomer reactivity ratios*. Each r as defined above in Eq. 6-11 is the ratio of the rate constant for a reactive propagating species adding its own type of monomer to the rate constant for its addition of the other monomer. The tendency of two monomers to copolymerize is noted by r values between zero and unity. An r_1 value greater than unity means that M_1^* preferentially adds M_1 instead of M_2 while an r_1 value less than unity means that M_1^* preferentially adds M_2. An r_1 value of zero would mean that M_1 is incapable of undergoing homopolymerization.

The copolymerization equation can also be expressed in terms of mole fractions instead of concentrations. If f_1 and f_2 are the mole fractions of monomers M_1 and M_2 in the feed, and F_1 and F_2 are the mole fractions of M_1 and M_2 in the copolymer, then

$$f_1 = 1 - f_2 = \frac{[M_1]}{[M_1] + [M_2]} \tag{6-13}$$

and

$$F_1 = 1 - F_2 = \frac{d[M_1]}{d[M_1] + d[M_2]} \tag{6-14}$$

Combining Eqs. 6-13 and 6-14 with Eq. 6-12 yields

$$F_1 = \frac{r_1 f_1^2 + f_1 f_2}{r_1 f_1^2 + 2 f_1 f_2 + r_2 f_2^2} \tag{6-15}$$

Equation 6-15 gives the copolymer composition as the mole fraction of monomer M_1 in the copolymer and is often more convenient to use than the previous form (Eq. 6-12) of the copolymerization equation.

6-2b Range of Applicability of Copolymerization Equation

The copolymerization equation has been experimentally verified in innumerable comonomer systems. The copolymerization equation is equally applicable to radical, cationic, and anionic chain copolymerizations although the r_1 and r_2 values for any particular comonomer pair can be drastically different depending on the mode of initiation. Thus, the r_1 and r_2 values for the comonomer pair of styrene (M_1) and methyl methacrylate (M_2) are 0.52 and 0.46 in radical copolymerization, 10 and 0.1 in cationic copolymerization and 0.1 and 6 in anionic copolymerization [10, 11]. Figure 6-1 shows that these different r_1 and r_2 values give rise to large differences in the copolymer composition depending on the mode of initiation [11]. The ionic copolymerizations are predictably much more selective than radical copolymerization. Methyl methacrylate as expected shows increased reactivity in anionic copolymerization and decreased reactivity in cationic copolymerization while the opposite is observed for styrene. Thus, for an equimolar styrene-methyl methacrylate feed, the copolymer is approximately a 1:1 copolymer in the radical case but is mostly styrene in the cationic copolymerization and mostly methyl methacrylate in the anionic copolymerization. The high selectivity of ionic copolymerization limits its practical use. Since only a small number of monomers undergo ionic

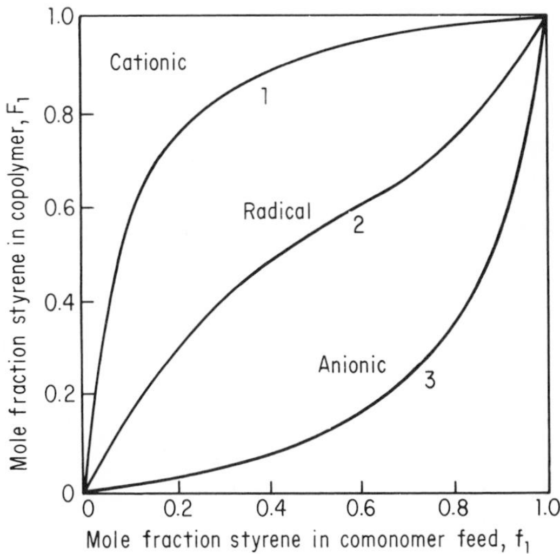

FIG. 6-1 *Dependence of the instantaneous copolymer composition* F_1 *on the comonomer feed composition* f_1 *for styrene-methyl methacrylate in cationic (Curve 1), radical (Curve 2), and anionic (Curve 3) copolymerizations initiated by* $SnCl_4$*, benzoyl peroxide, and Na/liquid* NH_3*, respectively. After [11] (by permission of The Chemical Society, Burlington House, London) from data in [10] (by permission of Gauthier-Villars, Paris).*

copolymerization, the range of copolymer products which can be obtained is limited. On the other hand, almost all monomers undergo radical copolymerization and a wide range of products can be synthesized.

For any specific type of initiation (i.e., radical, cationic, or anionic), the monomer reactivity ratios and therefore, the copolymer composition equation are independent of many reaction parameters. Since termination and initiation rate constants are not involved, the copolymer composition is independent of differences in the rates of initiation and termination or of the absence or presence of inhibitors or chain transfer agents. Under a wide range of conditions, the copolymer composition is independent of the degree of polymerization. The only limitation on this generalization is that the copolymer be a high polymer. Further, the particular initiation system used in a copolymerization has no effect on copolymer composition as long as the type of initiation is the same. Thus, the same copolymer composition is obtained in radical copolymerization irrespective of whether initiation occurs by the thermal homolysis of catalysts such as AIBN or peroxides, photolysis, radiolysis, or redox systems.

6-2c Types of Copolymerization Behavior

Different types of copolymerization behavior are observed depending on the values of the monomer reactivity ratios. Copolymerizations can be classified into three types based on whether the product of the two monomer reactivity ratios r_1r_2 is unity, less than unity, or greater than unity.

6-2c-1 Ideal Copolymerization: $r_1r_2 = 1$. A copolymerization is termed *ideal* when the r_1r_2 product is unity. Ideal copolymerization occurs when the two types of propagating species M_1^* and M_2^* show the same preference for adding one or the other of the two monomers. Under these conditions

$$\frac{k_{22}}{k_{21}} = \frac{k_{12}}{k_{11}} \quad \text{or} \quad r_2 = \frac{1}{r_1} \tag{6-16}$$

and the relative rates of incorporation of the two monomers into the copolymer are independent of the identity of the unit at the end of the propagating species. For an ideal copolymerization, Eq. 6-16 is combined with Eq. 6-12 or 6-15 to yield the copolymerization equation as

$$\frac{d[M_1]}{d[M_2]} = \frac{r_1[M_1]}{[M_2]} \tag{6-17}$$

or

$$F_1 = \frac{r_1f_1}{r_1f_1 + f_2} \tag{6-18}$$

Most ionic copolymerizations (both anionic and cationic) are characterized by the ideal type of behavior.

When $r_1 = r_2 = 1$, the two monomers show equal reactivities toward both propagating species. The copolymer composition is the same as the comonomer feed with a random placement of the two monomers along the copolymer chain. For the case where the two monomer reactivity ratios are different, that is, $r_1 > 1$ and $r_2 < 1$ or $r_1 < 1$ and $r_2 > 1$, one of the monomers is more reactive than the other toward both propagating species. The copolymer will contain a larger proportion of the more reactive monomer in random placement.

Figure 6-2 shows [12] the variation in the copolymer composition as a function of the comonomer feed composition for different values of r_1. The term ideal copolymerization was introduced by Wall [5] to show the analogy between the curves in Fig. 6-2 and those for vapor-liquid equilibria in ideal liquid mixtures. The copolymer is richer in M_1 when $r_1 > 1$ and is poorer in M_2 when $r_1 < 1$. A very important practical consequence of ideal copolymerizations is that it becomes progressively more difficult to produce copolymers containing appreciable amounts of both monomers as the difference in reactivities of the two monomers increases. This is one of the reasons for the fact that ionic copolymerization is of little practical

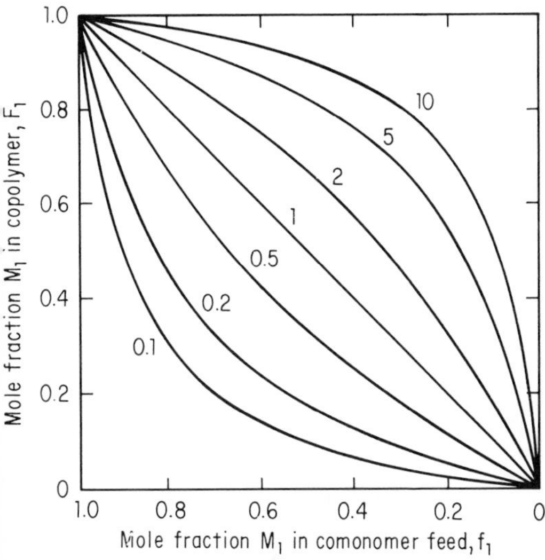

FIG. 6-2 *Dependence of the instantaneous copolymer composition* F_1 *on the comonomer feed composition* f_1 *for the indicated values of* r_1 *where* $r_1 r_2 = 1$. *After [6] (by permission of John Wiley & Sons, Inc., New York) from plot in [12] (by permission of American Chemical Society, Washington).*

significance. When, for example, $r_1 = 10$ and $r_2 = 0.1$, copolymers containing appreciable amounts of M_2 cannot be obtained. Thus, a comonomer feed composition of 80 mole percent M_2 ($f_2 = 0.8$) would yield a copolymer containing only 18.5 mole percent M_2 ($F_1 = 0.185$). It is only when r_1 and r_2 do not differ markedly (for example, $r_1 = 0.5$-2) that there will exist a large range of comonomer feed compositions which yield copolymers containing appreciable amounts of both monomers.

6-2c-2 Alternating Copolymerization: $r_1 = r_2 = 0$. When $r_1 = r_2 = 0$ (and $r_1 r_2 = 0$), the two monomers enter into the copolymer in equimolar amounts in a non-random, alternating arrangement along the copolymer chain. This type of copolymerization is referred to as *alternating copolymerization*. Each of the two types of propagating species preferentially adds the other monomer, that is, M_1^* adds only M_2 and M_2^* adds only M_1. The copolymerization equation reduces to

$$\frac{d[M_1]}{d[M_2]} = 1 \tag{6-19}$$

or

$$F_1 = 0.5 \tag{6-20}$$

The copolymer has the alternating structure I irrespective of the comonomer feed composition. Many radical copolymerizations show a tendency toward the alternation behavior.

The behavior of most comonomer systems lies between the two extremes of ideal and alternating copolymerization. As the $r_1 r_2$ product decreases from unity toward zero, there is an increasing *tendency toward alternation*. Perfect alternation occurs when r_1 and r_2 are both zero. The tendency toward alternation and the tendency away from ideal behavior increases as r_1 and r_2 become progressively less than unity. The range of behaviors can be seen by considering the situation where r_2 remains constant at 0.5 and r_1 varies between 2 and 0. Figure 6-3 shows the copolymer composition as a function of the feed composition in these cases. The curve for $r_1 = 2$ shows the ideal type of behavior described previously. As r_1 decreases below 2, there is an increasing tendency toward the alternating behavior with

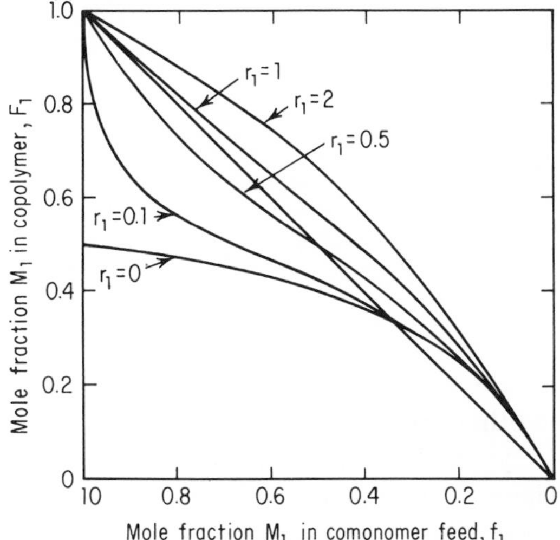

FIG. 6-3 *Dependence of the instantaneous copolymer composition* F_1 *on the comonomer feed composition* f_1 *for the indicated values of* r_1 *with* r_2 *being constant at 0.5. After [6] (by permission of John Wiley & Sons, Inc., New York) from plot in [12] (by permission of American Chemical Society, Washington).*

each type of propagating species preferring to add the other monomer. The increasing alternation tendency is measured by the tendency of the product r_1r_2 to approach zero. Of great practical significance is the fact that a larger range of feed compositions will yield copolymers containing sizable amounts of both monomers. However, when r_1r_2 is very small or zero, the alternation tendency is too great and the range of copolymer compositions which can be obtained is again limited. In the extreme case where both r_1 and r_2 are zero, only the 1:1 alternating copolymer can be produced.

The curves in Fig. 6-3 illustrate an interesting characteristic of copolymerizations with a tendency toward alternation. For values of r_1 and r_2 both less than unity, the F_1 versus f_1 curves cross the line representing $F_1 = f_1$. At these intersections or *crossover points*, the copolymer and feed compositions are the same and copolymerization occurs without a change in the feed composition. Such copolymerizations are termed *azeotropic copolymerizations*. The condition under which azeotropic copolymerization occurs, obtained by combination of Eq. 6-12 with $d[M_1]/d[M_2] = [M_1]/[M_2]$, is

$$\frac{[M_1]}{[M_2]} = \frac{(r_2 - 1)}{(r_1 - 1)} \tag{6-21}$$

or, in terms of mole fractions

$$f_1 = \frac{(1 - r_2)}{(2 - r_1 - r_2)} \tag{6-22}$$

A special situation arises when one of the monomer reactivity ratios is much larger than the other. For the case of $r_1 \gg r_2$ (that is, $r_1 \gg 1$ and $r_2 \ll 1$), both types of propagating species preferentially add monomer M_1. There is a tendency toward *consecutive homopolymerization* of the two monomers. Monomer M_1 tends to homopolymerize until it is consumed; monomer M_2 will subsequently homopolymerize. An extreme example of this type of behavior is shown by the radical polymerization of styrene-vinyl acetate with monomer reactivity ratios of 55 and 0.01. (See Secs. 6-3b-1 and 6-3c-1 for a further discussion of this comonomer system.)

6-2c-3 Block Copolymerization: $r_1 > 1$, $r_2 > 1$. If both r_1 and r_2 are greater than unity (and therefore, also $r_1 r_2 > 1$), there is a tendency to form a block copolymer (Structure II) in which there are blocks of both monomers in the chain. This type of behavior has been encountered only in a few copolymerizations initiated by coordination catalysts (Sec. 8-4d-2). The extreme case of both r_1 and r_2 being much larger than unity—corresponding to the simultaneous and independent homopolymerizations of the two monomers—has not been observed except in one or two systems [13].

6-2d Variation of Copolymer Composition with Conversion

The various forms of the copolymerization equation (Eqs. 6-12 and 6-15) give the *instantaneous copolymer composition*—the composition of the copolymer formed from a particular feed composition at very low degrees of conversion (approximately < 5%) such that the composition of the comonomer feed is relatively unchanged from its initial value. For all copolymerizations except azeotropic copolymerizations the comonomer feed and copolymer compositions are different. The comonomer feed changes in composition as one of the monomers preferentially enters the copolymer. Thus, there is a drift in the comonomer composition toward the less reactive monomer as the degree of conversion increases. This results in a similar variation of copolymer composition with conversion. In order to determine the instantaneous copolymer composition as a function of conversion for any given comonomer feed, one must resort to an integrated form of the copolymerization equation. Various attempts to directly integrate Eq. 6-12 have not been too fruitful [4, 5]. The integrated form of Eq. 6-12 due to Mayo and Lewis [4] has recently been rearranged to yield a useful result [14].

The most generally useful method is that developed by Skeist [15] and its recent variations [16, 17]. Consider a system initially containing a total of M moles of the two monomers and in which the copolymer formed is richer in monomer M_1 than is the feed (that is, $F_1 > f_1$). When dM moles of monomers have been copolymerized, the polymer will contain $F_1 dM$ moles of monomer 1 and the feed will contain $(M - dM)(f_1 - df_1)$ moles of monomer 1. A material balance for monomer 1 requires that the moles of M_1 copolymerized equal the difference in the moles of M_1 in the feed before and after reaction, or

$$Mf_1 - (M - dM)(f_1 - df_1) = F_1\, dM \tag{6-23}$$

Equation 6-23 can be rearranged (neglecting the $df_1 dM$ term which is small) and converted to the integral form

$$\int_{M_0}^{M} \frac{dM}{M} = \ln \frac{M}{M_0} = \int_{(f_1)_0}^{f_1} \frac{df_1}{(F_1 - f_1)} \tag{6-24}$$

where M_0 and $(f_1)_0$ are the initial values of M and f_1.

Equation 6-15 allows the calculation of F_1 as a function of f_1 for a given set of r_1 and r_2 values. These can then be employed as $(F_1 - f_1)$ to allow the graphical or numerical integration of Eq. 6-24 between the limits of $(f_1)_0$ and f_1. In this manner one can obtain the variations in the feed and copolymer compositions with the degree of conversion (defined as $1 - M/M_0$).

Equation 6-24 has been recently [16, 17] integrated to the very useful closed form

$$1 - \frac{M}{M_0} = 1 - \left[\frac{f_1}{(f_1)_0}\right]^{\alpha} \left[\frac{f_2}{(f_2)_0}\right]^{\beta} \left[\frac{(f_1)_0 - \delta}{f_1 - \delta}\right]^{\gamma} \tag{6-25}$$

which relates the degree of conversion to changes in the feed composition. The zero subscripts indicate initial quantities and the other symbols are given by

$$\alpha = \frac{r_2}{(1 - r_2)} \qquad \beta = \frac{r_1}{(1 - r_1)}$$
$$\gamma = \frac{(1 - r_1 r_2)}{(1 - r_1)(1 - r_2)} \qquad \delta = \frac{(1 - r_2)}{(2 - r_1 - r_2)} \tag{6-26}$$

Equation 6-25 has been used to calculate the drift in the feed and copolymer compositions with conversion. The calculations can be conveniently performed by means of an appropriate computer program which may even be set up to directly yield the results in a graphical manner [17].

A few examples will illustrate the utility of Eqs. 6-24 and 6-25. Figure 6-4 shows the behavior observed in the radical copolymerization of styrene and methyl methacrylate. The copolymer produced is slightly richer in methyl methacrylate than the feed because methyl methacrylate has a slightly larger monomer reactivity ratio than styrene. The feed becomes richer in styrene with conversion—leading to an increase in the styrene content of the copolymer with conversion. Figure 6-4 also shows the average composition of all the copolymer formed up to some degree of conversion as a function of conversion. The average copolymer composition becomes richer in styrene than methyl methacrylate but less so than the instantaneous copolymer composition.

One can show the drift of copolymer composition with conversion for various comonomer feed compositions by a three-dimensional plot such as that in Fig. 6-5 for the radical copolymerization of styrene (M_1)-2-vinylthiophene(M_2). This is an ideal copolymerization with $r_1 = 0.35$ and $r_2 = 3.10$. The greater reactivity of the 2-vinylthiophene results in its being incorporated preferentially into the first formed copolymer. As the reaction proceeds, the feed and, therefore, the copolymer become progressively enriched in styrene. This is shown

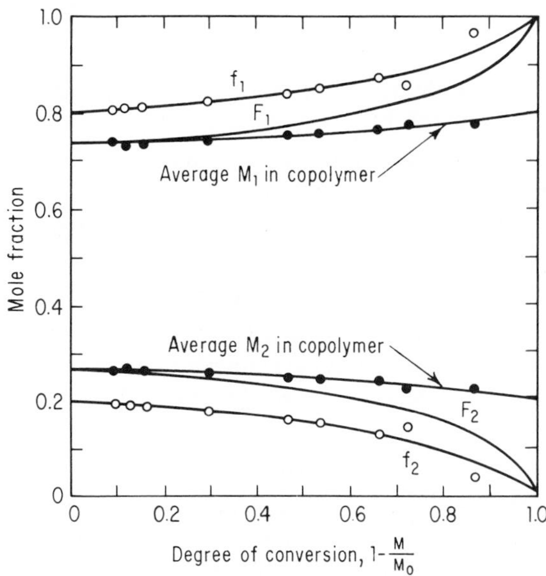

FIG. 6-4 *Variations in feed and copolymer compositions with conversion for styrene*(M_1)*-methyl methacrylate*(M_2) *with* $(f_1)_0 = 0.80$, $(f_2)_0 = 0.20$, *and* $r_1 = 0.53$, $r_2 = 0.56$. *After [17] (by permission of Division of Polymer Chemistry, American Chemical Society, Washington).*

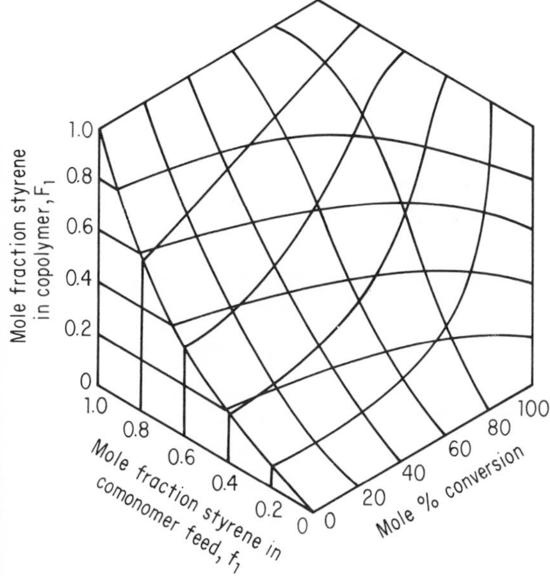

FIG. 6-5 *Dependence of instantaneous copolymer composition* F_1 *on the initial comonomer feed composition* f_1 *and the % conversion for styrene*(M_1)*-2-vinylthiophene* (M_2) *with* $r_1 = 0.35$ *and* $r_2 = 3.10$. *After [6] (by permission of John Wiley & Sons, Inc., New York) from plot in [12] (by permission of American Chemical Society, Washington).*

by Fig. 6-6 which describes the distribution of copolymer compositions at 100% conversion for several different initial feeds.

Corresponding data for the alternating radical copolymerization of styrene (M_1)-diethyl fumarate (M_2) (r_1 = 0.30 and r_2 = 0.07) are shown in Figs. 6-7 and 6-8. This system undergoes azeotropic copolymerization at 57 mole percent styrene. Feed compositions near the azeotrope yield narrow distributions of copolymer composition except at high conversion where there is a drift to pure styrene or pure fumarate depending on whether the initial feed contains more or less than 57 mole percent styrene. The distribution of copolymer compositions becomes progressively wider as the initial feed composition differs more from the azeotropic composition.

In the commercial use of copolymerization it is usually desirable to obtain a copolymer with as narrow a distribution of compositions as possible. Two general methods are employed for this purpose. One involves stopping the copolymerization before 100% conversion and the second involves maintaining the feed composition constant by

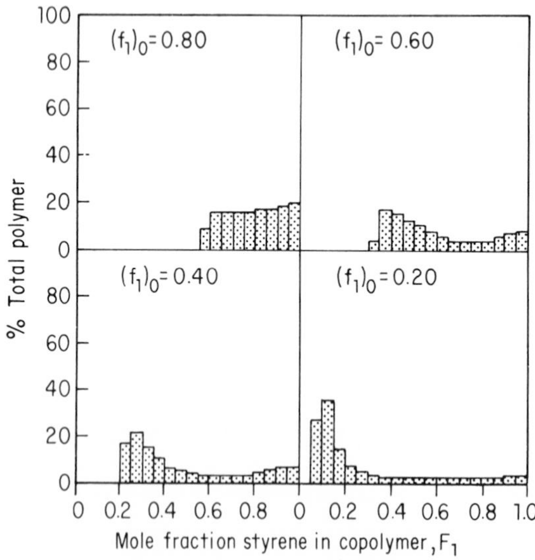

FIG. 6-6 *Distribution of copolymer composition at 100% conversion for styrene-2-vinylthiophene at the indicated values of mole fraction styrene in the initial comonomer feed. After [7] (by permission of Interscience Publishers, John Wiley & Sons, Inc., New York) from plot in [12] (by permission of American Chemical Society, Washington).*

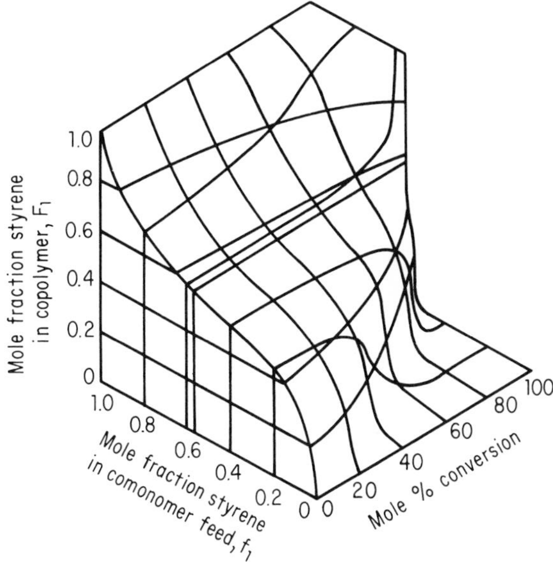

FIG. 6-7 *Dependence of instantaneous copolymer composition* F_1 *on the initial comonomer feed composition* f_1 *and the % conversion for styrene* (M_1)*-diethyl fumarate* (M_2) *with* $r_1 = 0.30$ *and* $r_2 = 0.07$. *After [6] (by permission of John Wiley & Sons, Inc., New York) from plot in [12] (by permission of American Chemical Society, Washington).*

the continuous addition of the more reactive monomer. The precise application of these techniques involves a consideration of the pertinent copolymer composition distribution (e.g., Fig. 6-6 or 6-8) in relation to the desired copolymer product.

6-2e Experimental Evaluation of Monomer Reactivity Ratios

All procedures for the evaluation of r_1 and r_2 involve the experimental determination of the copolymer composition formed from several different comonomer feed compositions. The techniques used for copolymer analysis include elemental analysis, radioisotopic tagging, and ultraviolet, infrared, and nuclear magnetic spectroscopy. The older, more established procedures involve copolymerizations carried out to low degrees of conversion (approximately $< 5\%$). The experimental data can be analyzed in several ways. One method involves plotting the instantaneous copolymer composition versus the comonomer feed composition and then determining which

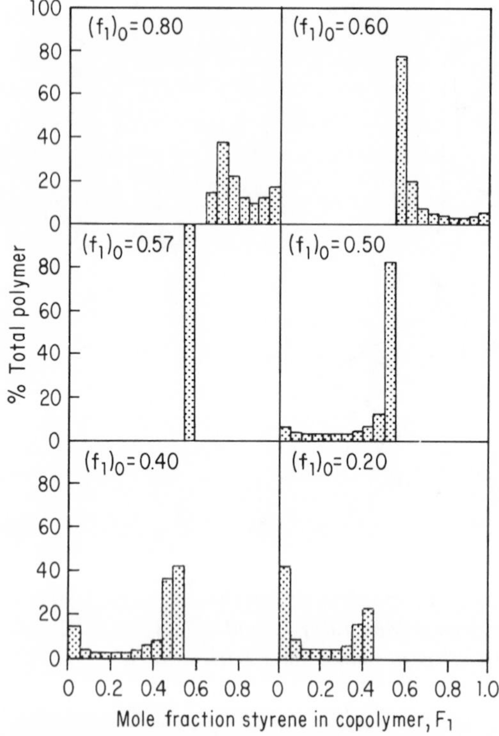

FIG. 6-8 *Distribution of copolymer composition at 100% conversion for styrene-diethyl fumarate at the indicated values of mole fraction styrene in the initial comonomer feed. After [7] (by permission of Interscience Publishers, John Wiley & Sons, Inc., New York) from plot in [12] (by permission of American Chemical Society, Washington).*

theoretical curve would best fit the data by trial and error selections of r_1 and r_2. This is a tedious procedure and it is usually easier to solve either of Eqs. 6-12 or 6-15 simultaneously for the different sets of data. The accuracy of the r_1 and r_2 values obtained will depend on using data for feed compositions for which the copolymer compositions are most sensitive to variations in the r values.

A second procedure [4] involves the following rearranged form of Eq. 6-12

$$r_2 = \frac{[M_1]}{[M_2]}\left[\frac{d[M_2]}{d[M_1]}\left\{1 + \frac{r_1[M_1]}{[M_2]}\right\} - 1\right] \tag{6-27}$$

Data for the feed and copolymer compositions for each experiment with a given feed are substituted into Eq. 6-27 and r_2 is plotted as a function of various assumed values of r_1. Each experiment yields a straight line and the intersection of the lines for different feeds gives the best values of r_1 and r_2. Any variations observed in the points of intersection of various lines are a measure of the experimental errors in the composition data.

Another very useful method [18] involves Eq. 6-15 rearranged in the form

$$\frac{f_1(1 - 2F_1)}{F_1(1 - f_1)} = r_2 + \left[\frac{f_1^2(F_1 - 1)}{F_1(1 - f_1)^2}\right] r_1 \tag{6-28}$$

The left side of this equation is plotted against the coefficient of r_1 to yield a straight line with slope r_1 and intercept r_2. The relative merits of the different methods for analyzing feed-copolymer data to determine r_1 and r_2 have been recently discussed as has the use of computational methods for improved data analysis [19].

Values of r_1 and r_2 have recently been determined from analysis of copolymer composition-conversion data. One method [20] uses the previously discussed Eq. 6-25. Experimental data on the variation of copolymer composition with conversion are plotted as f_1 or f_2 versus $1-M/M_0$ to yield curves like those in Fig. 6-4. Using computational procedures, one then determines the best values of r_1 and r_2 which must be used with Eq. 6-25 to yield the same curve.

6-2f Microstructure of Copolymers

The copolymerization equation describes the copolymer composition on a macroscopic scale, i.e., the overall composition of a copolymer sample produced from a comonomer feed. This leaves unanswered two details concerning the microscopic composition of the copolymer. The first concerns the exact arrangement of the two monomers along the polymer chain. Any particular overall copolymer composition would be consistent with many different microscopic compositions. Thus, for example, a copolymer with a composition of $f_1 = 0.6$, $f_2 = 0.4$ could have the regular copolymer structure

$$\sim\sim M_1M_1M_1M_2M_2M_1M_1M_1M_2M_2M_1M_1M_1M_2M_2M_1M_1M_1M_2M_2\sim\sim$$

or the random copolymer structure

$$\sim\sim M_1M_2M_1M_2M_2M_1M_1M_1M_1M_2M_2M_1M_1M_2M_1M_1M_2M_1M_1M_2\sim\sim$$

or the block copolymer structure

$$\sim\sim M_1M_1M_1M_1M_1M_1M_1M_1M_1M_1M_1M_1M_2M_2M_2M_2M_2M_2M_2M_2\sim\sim$$

Statistical analysis of the copolymerization equation predicts that copolymerizations will usually proceed to yield the random copolymer structure. A tendency toward alternation occurs for comonomer pairs whose r_1r_2 products approach zero. The block copolymer structure is obtained only under special conditions (Sec. 6-2c-3). (There is an appreciable probability of producing long blocks of one monomer in a copolymer when one has feeds containing large proportions of a reactive monomer.)

Although these theoretical conclusions are generally accepted, verification of the random nature of copolymerization is experimentally difficult. This generally involves the experimental determination of the relative amounts of the three possible types of inter-monomer linkages in the copolymer (that is, $M_1{-}M_1$, $M_2{-}M_2$, $M_1{-}M_2$) and comparison with the relative amounts calculated on the basis of a statistically random distribution. Chemical methods have been successful in some comonomer systems. These include lactone formation in hydrolyzed copolymers of vinyl acetate with acrylic acid or maleic anhydride, the dechlorination of vinyl chloride-vinyl acetate copolymers with zinc, and the periodate oxidation of hydrolyzed vinyl acetate-vinylene carbonate copolymers. The latter reaction yields aldehydic moieties and formic acid

$$\sim\sim CH_2{-}\underset{\displaystyle OH}{\underset{|}{CH}}{+}\underset{\displaystyle OH}{\underset{|}{CH}}{-}\underset{\displaystyle OH}{\underset{|}{CH}}{)_m}CH_2{-}\underset{\displaystyle OH}{\underset{|}{CH}}\sim\sim \xrightarrow{HIO_4}$$

$$\sim\sim CH_2{-}\underset{\displaystyle O}{\underset{\|}{CH}} + (2m - 1)HCO_2H + H\underset{\displaystyle O}{\underset{\|}{C}}{-}CH_2{-}\underset{\displaystyle OH}{\underset{|}{CH}}\sim\sim \qquad (6\text{-}29)$$

Thus, the number of vinylene carbonate units which are followed by another vinylene carbonate unit (that is, M_1—M_1 linkages) is determined by analysis for formic acid [21]. More recently, high-resolution nuclear magnetic resonance (NMR) has been used to verify the random distribution of monomer units in copolymerization [22, 23]. Thus, NMR has been used to determine the relative amounts of M_1—M_1, M_2—M_2, and M_1—M_2 linkages in poly(ethylene-vinyl chloride) by analysis of the different types of methylene protons indicative of each linkage. In all instances, the experimental data verify the random distribution of monomers in copolymerization.

Another uncertainty concerning copolymer composition is the distribution of composition from one copolymer molecule to another in a sample produced at any given degree of conversion. Stockmayer [24] has indicated that the distribution of copolymer composition due to statistical fluctuations generally follows a very sharp Gaussian curve. Although the distribution is wider for low molecular weight copolymers and for ideal copolymerizations compared to alternating copolymerizations, it is essentially nil in all practical cases. Thus, it is calculated that for an ideal copolymer containing an average of 50 mole percent of each component, only 12 percent of the copolymer molecules contain less than 43 percent of either monomer for $\bar{X}_n$ = 100 while only 12 percent contain less than 49 percent of either monomer at $\bar{X}_n$ = 10,000. These theoretical conclusions of Stockmayer have been experimentally verified in a limited manner [25].

6-2g Multi-Component Copolymerization

Terpolymerization, the simultaneous polymerization of three monomers, has become increasingly important from the commercial viewpoint. The improvements that are obtained by copolymerizing styrene with acrylonitrile or butadiene have been previously mentioned. The radical terpolymerization of styrene with acrylonitrile and butadiene increases even further the degree of variation in properties that can be built into the final product. Many other commercial uses of terpolymerization exist. In most of these, the terpolymer has two of the monomers present in major amounts, to obtain the gross properties desired, with the third monomer in a minor amount for modification of a special property. Thus, the newly developed ethylene-propylene elastomers are terpolymerized with minor amounts of a diene in order to allow the product to be subsequently crosslinked.

The quantitative treatment of terpolymerization is quite complex since nine propagation reactions

$$
\begin{array}{ll}
\textit{Reaction} & \textit{Rate} \\
M_1\cdot + M_1 \longrightarrow M_1\cdot & R_{11} = k_{11}[M_1\cdot][M_1] \\
M_1\cdot + M_2 \longrightarrow M_2\cdot & R_{12} = k_{12}[M_1\cdot][M_2] \\
M_1\cdot + M_3 \longrightarrow M_3\cdot & R_{13} = k_{13}[M_1\cdot][M_3] \\
M_2\cdot + M_1 \longrightarrow M_1\cdot & R_{21} = k_{21}[M_2\cdot][M_1] \\
M_2\cdot + M_2 \longrightarrow M_2\cdot & R_{22} = k_{22}[M_2\cdot][M_2] \\
M_2\cdot + M_3 \longrightarrow M_3\cdot & R_{23} = k_{23}[M_2\cdot][M_3] \\
M_3\cdot + M_1 \longrightarrow M_1\cdot & R_{31} = k_{31}[M_3\cdot][M_1] \\
M_3\cdot + M_2 \longrightarrow M_2\cdot & R_{32} = k_{32}[M_3\cdot][M_2] \\
M_3\cdot + M_3 \longrightarrow M_3\cdot & R_{33} = k_{33}[M_3\cdot][M_3]
\end{array}
\tag{6-30}
$$

and six monomer reactivity ratios

$$
\begin{array}{lll}
r_{12} = \dfrac{k_{11}}{k_{12}}, & r_{13} = \dfrac{k_{11}}{k_{13}}, & r_{21} = \dfrac{k_{22}}{k_{21}}, \\[2ex]
r_{23} = \dfrac{k_{22}}{k_{23}}, & r_{31} = \dfrac{k_{33}}{k_{31}}, & r_{32} = \dfrac{k_{33}}{k_{32}}
\end{array}
\tag{6-31}
$$

are involved (as well as six termination reactions). The expression for the rate R of each of the propagation reactions is shown above. An expression for the terpolymer composition can be obtained by a treatment similar to that used in copolymerization [27]. The rates of disappearance of the three monomers are given by

$$
-\frac{d[M_1]}{dt} = R_{11} + R_{21} + R_{31} \tag{6-32a}
$$

$$
-\frac{d[M_2]}{dt} = R_{12} + R_{22} + R_{32} \tag{6-32b}
$$

$$-\frac{d[M_3]}{dt} = R_{13} + R_{23} + R_{33} \qquad (6\text{-}32c)$$

The assumption of steady-state concentrations for $M_1\cdot$, $M_2\cdot$, and $M_3\cdot$ radicals can be expressed as

$$R_{12} + R_{13} = R_{21} + R_{31} \qquad (6\text{-}33a)$$

$$R_{21} + R_{23} = R_{12} + R_{32} \qquad (6\text{-}33b)$$

$$R_{31} + R_{32} = R_{13} + R_{23} \qquad (6\text{-}33c)$$

Combination of Eqs. 6-32 with 6-33, and the use of the appropriate rate expressions from Eq. 6-30 for each of the R terms, yields the terpolymer composition as

$$d[M_1]:d[M_2]:d[M_3] =$$

$$[M_1]\left\{\frac{[M_1]}{r_{31}r_{21}} + \frac{[M_2]}{r_{21}r_{32}} + \frac{[M_3]}{r_{31}r_{23}}\right\}\left\{[M_1] + \frac{[M_2]}{r_{12}} + \frac{[M_3]}{r_{13}}\right\}$$

$$:[M_2]\left\{\frac{[M_1]}{r_{12}r_{31}} + \frac{[M_2]}{r_{12}r_{32}} + \frac{[M_3]}{r_{32}r_{13}}\right\}\left\{[M_2] + \frac{[M_1]}{r_{21}} + \frac{[M_3]}{r_{23}}\right\}$$

$$:[M_3]\left\{\frac{[M_1]}{r_{13}r_{21}} + \frac{[M_2]}{r_{23}r_{12}} + \frac{[M_3]}{r_{13}r_{23}}\right\}\left\{[M_3] + \frac{[M_1]}{r_{31}} + \frac{[M_2]}{r_{32}}\right\} \qquad (6\text{-}34)$$

A simpler expression for the terpolymer composition has been obtained [28] by expressing the steady-state with the relationships

$$R_{12} = R_{21} \qquad (6\text{-}35a)$$

$$R_{23} = R_{32} \qquad (6\text{-}35b)$$

$$R_{31} = R_{13} \qquad (6\text{-}35c)$$

instead of those in Eq. 6-33. The combination of Eqs. 6-35 and 6-32 yields the terpolymer composition as

$$d[M_1]:d[M_2]:d[M_3] = [M_1]\left\{[M_1] + \frac{[M_2]}{r_{12}} + \frac{[M_3]}{r_{13}}\right\}$$

$$:[M_2]\frac{r_{21}}{r_{12}}\left\{\frac{[M_1]}{r_{21}} + [M_2] + \frac{[M_3]}{r_{23}}\right\}$$

$$:[M_3]\frac{r_{31}}{r_{13}}\left\{\frac{[M_1]}{r_{31}} + \frac{[M_2]}{r_{32}} + [M_3]\right\} \tag{6-36}$$

Ham [29, 30] has treated the problem of terpolymer composition by making the simple assumption that the probability of producing a certain sequence of monomers is the same as producing the exact reverse sequence (or of producing the same sequence in the reverse direction). This can be expressed as the equality of two product probabilities, for example

$$P_{21}P_{13}P_{32} = P_{23}P_{31}P_{12} \tag{6-37}$$

for the production of $M_2M_1M_3M_2$ and $M_2M_3M_1M_2$ sequences. The P terms are the probabilities that a certain growing chain will add a certain monomer. Thus, P_{12} is the probability that a growing chain ending in M_1 adds a monomer unit of M_2 and is given by

$$P_{12} = \frac{R_{12}}{R_{11} + R_{12} + R_{13}} \tag{6-38}$$

The conventional terpolymerization equation (Eq. 6-34) can be written in terms of probabilities

$$\frac{d[M_1]}{d[M_2]} = \frac{P_{21}P_{31} + P_{32}P_{21} + P_{23}P_{31}}{P_{12}P_{32} + P_{31}P_{12} + P_{13}P_{32}} \tag{6-39a}$$

$$\frac{d[\mathrm{M}_1]}{d[\mathrm{M}_3]} = \frac{P_{21}P_{31} + P_{32}P_{21} + P_{23}P_{31}}{P_{13}P_{23} + P_{21}P_{13} + P_{12}P_{23}} \tag{6-39b}$$

and then appropriately manipulated to yield

$$\frac{d[\mathrm{M}_1]}{d[\mathrm{M}_2]} = \frac{\dfrac{[\mathrm{M}_1]}{r_{21}}\left\{[\mathrm{M}_1] + \dfrac{[\mathrm{M}_2]}{r_{12}} + \dfrac{[\mathrm{M}_3]}{r_{13}}\right\}}{\dfrac{[\mathrm{M}_2]}{r_{12}}\left\{\dfrac{[\mathrm{M}_2]}{r_{21}} + [\mathrm{M}_2] + \dfrac{[\mathrm{M}_3]}{r_{23}}\right\}} \tag{6-40a}$$

$$\frac{d[\mathrm{M}_1]}{d[\mathrm{M}_3]} = \frac{\dfrac{[\mathrm{M}_1]}{r_{31}}\left\{[\mathrm{M}_1] + \dfrac{[\mathrm{M}_2]}{r_{12}} + \dfrac{[\mathrm{M}_3]}{r_{13}}\right\}}{\dfrac{[\mathrm{M}_3]}{r_{13}}\left\{\dfrac{[\mathrm{M}_1]}{r_{31}} + \dfrac{[\mathrm{M}_2]}{r_{32}} + [\mathrm{M}_3]\right\}} \tag{6-40b}$$

A consideration of Eqs. 6-36 and 6-40 shows them to be completely equivalent.

The conventional (Eq. 6-34) and simplified (Eq. 6-36 or 6-40) terpolymerization equations can be used to predict the composition of a terpolymer from the reactivity ratios in the two component systems M_1/M_2, M_1/M_3, and M_2/M_3. Table 6-1 shows the predicted and experimental terpolymer compositions in several systems of three monomers. The compositions calculated by either of the terpolymerization equations show good agreement with the experimentally observed [31] compositions. Neither one is superior to the other in predicting terpolymer composition. Both equations have been successfully extended to multi-component copolymerizations of four or more monomers [28, 31–33]. The general agreement of the calculated and experimental compositions for a system of four monomers is also shown in Table 6-1. (Ham's treatment also allows the prediction of the copolymerization behavior of the system M_1/M_3 from data on the systems M_1/M_2 and M_2/M_3 –see Sec. 6-3b-5.)

The terpolymerization and multi-component composition equations are generally valid only when all of the reactivity ratios have

Table 6-1 Predicted and Experimental Compositions in Radical Terpolymerization[a]

Feed composition			Terpolymer (mole percent)		
				Calculated from	
System	Monomer	Mole percent	Found	Eq. 6-34	Eqs. 6-36/6-40
1	Styrene	31.24	43.4	44.3	44.3
	Methyl methacrylate	31.12	39.4	41.2	42.7
	Vinylidene chloride	37.64	17.2	14.5	13.0
2	Methyl methacrylate	35.10	50.8	54.3	56.6
	Acrylonitrile	28.24	28.3	29.7	23.5
	Vinylidene chloride	36.66	20.9	16.0	19.9
3	Styrene	34.03	52.8	52.4	53.8
	Acrylonitrile	34.49	36.7	40.5	36.6
	Vinylidene chloride	31.48	10.5	7.1	9.6
4	Styrene	35.92	44.7	43.6	45.2
	Methyl methacrylate	36.03	26.1	29.2	33.8
	Acrylonitrile	28.05	29.2	26.2	21.0
5	Styrene	20.00	55.2	55.8	55.8
	Acrylonitrile	20.00	40.3	41.3	41.4
	Vinyl chloride	60.00	4.5	2.9	2.8
6	Styrene	25.21	40.7	41.0	41.0
	Methyl methacrylate	25.48	25.5	27.3	29.3
	Acrylonitrile	25.40	25.8	24.8	22.8
	Vinylidene chloride	23.91	8.0	6.9	6.9

[a]Data and calculations from [28] and [31].

finite values. When one or more of the monomers is incapable of homopolymerization, the equations generally become indeterminate. Various modified expressions based on both the conventional and simplified equations have been derived for these and other special cases.

6-3 RADICAL COPOLYMERIZATION

The discussions thus far have been quite general without any specification as to whether copolymerization occurs by radical or ionic propagation. Consider now some of the specific characteristics of radical copolymerization.

6-3a Effect of Reaction Conditions

In addition to their independence of the initiation and termination steps, monomer reactivity ratios have also been shown to be almost completely independent of the reaction medium in radical copolymerization. Thus, the r values and the copolymer compositions for the styrene-methyl methacrylate system are the same for copolymerization in bulk, emulsion, and in solvents of different dielectric constants such as benzene and acetonitrile, or even methanol, in which the copolymer is insoluble [6]. Emulsion [26] and suspension polymerizations occasionally show copolymer compositions which are different from those in bulk or solution polymerization when the comonomer composition at the reaction site (monomer droplet in suspension polymerization and micelle in emulsion polymerization) is different from that in the bulk of the reaction system. This can occur if one of the two monomers has appreciable solubility in the suspending medium or is preferentially adsorbed by the initially formed copolymer or, in emulsion copolymerization, if diffusion of one of the monomers into the micelles is too slow. The monomer reactivity ratios are unchanged in these systems and the apparent discrepancies in copolymer composition are simply due to altered $[M_1]$ and $[M_2]$ values at the reaction sites. These effects are ones which have to be taken into account from the practical viewpoint of producing a copolymer of a desired composition.

The effect of temperature on monomer reactivity ratios is relatively small [34]. Thus, the r_1 and r_2 values for styrene-methyl methacrylate are 0.52 and 0.46 at 60°C, and 0.59 and 0.54 at 131°C. The monomer reactivity ratio is the ratio between two propagation rate constants and the variation of r with temperature will, therefore, depend on the difference between the activation energies of the two rate constants. The effect will not be large since activation energies for radical propagation reactions are relatively low and appreciable differences are not usually found between two different ones. An increase in temperature results in a less selective copolymerization as the two monomer reactivity ratios of a comonomer pair each tend toward unity (that is, $r_1 = r_2 = 1$) with decreasing preference of either radical for either monomer. Temperature has the greatest effect on those systems for which the r values deviate markedly from unity.

Although high pressure polymerizations and copolymerizations are of industrial importance, little data are reported in the literature concerning the effect of pressure on monomer reactivity ratios. Increasing pressure tends to decrease the selectivity of the copolymerization by altering the r values in the direction of ideal copolymerization behavior [35]. The effect of pressure is in the same direction as that of temperature. Thus, methyl methacrylate-acrylonitrile shows r_1r_2 values of 0.16 at 1 atm., 0.54 at 100 atm., and 0.91 at 1,000 atm. The effect has been ascribed to an enhancement of radical reactivity without alteration of monomer reactivity. High pressure copolymerization in several other systems, including ethylene copolymerization, also indicates a definite tendency toward the ideal copolymerization behavior [36]. Data [37] in other systems, however, show r_1r_2 values of 2–3.

6-3b Reactivity

The monomer reactivity ratios for many of the more common monomers in radical copolymerization are shown in Table 6-2. These data [38] are useful for a study of the relation between structure and reactivity in radical addition reactions. The reactivity of a monomer toward a radical depends on the reactivities of both the monomer and the radical. The relative reactivities of monomers and their corresponding radicals can be obtained from an analysis of the monomer reactivity ratio data. The reactivity of a monomer can be seen by considering the inverse of the monomer reactivity ratio ($1/r$). The inverse of the monomer reactivity ratio gives the ratio of the rate of reaction of a radical with another monomer to its rate of reaction with its own monomer

$$\frac{1}{r_1} = \frac{k_{12}}{k_{11}} \tag{6-41}$$

Table 6-3 shows $1/r$ values calculated from the data in Table 6-2. The data in each vertical column show the *monomer reactivities* of a series of different monomers toward the same reference polymer radical. Thus, the first column shows the reactivities of the monomers toward the butadiene radical, the second column shows the monomer reactivities toward the styrene radical, and so on. It is important to note that the data in each horizontal row in Table 6-3

Table 6-2 Monomer Reactivity Ratios in Radical Copolymerization[a]

M_1	r_1	M_2	r_2	T (°C)
Acrylic acid	1.15	Acrylonitrile	0.35	50
	0.25±0.02	Styrene	0.15±0.01	60
	2	Vinyl acetate	0.1	70
Acrylonitrile	0.35	Acrylic acid	1.15	50
	0.02	1,3-Butadiene	0.3	40
	0.14±0.04	t-Butyl vinyl ether	0.0032±0.0002	60
	0.7±0.2	Ethyl vinyl ether	0.03±0.02	80
	0.02±0.02	Isobutylene	1.8±0.2	50
	1.5±0.1	Methyl acrylate	0.84±0.05	50
	0.150±0.080	Methyl methacrylate	1.224±0.100	80
	0.61±0.04	Methyl vinyl ketone	1.78±0.22	60
	0.04±0.04	Styrene	0.40±0.05	60
	4.2	Vinyl acetate	0.05	50
	2.7±0.7	Vinyl chloride	0.04±0.03	60
	0.91±0.10	Vinylidene chloride	0.37±0.10	60
	0.113±0.002	2-Vinylpyridine	0.47±0.03	60
Allyl acetate	0	Methyl methacrylate	23	60
	0.00	Styrene	90±10	60
	0.7	Vinyl acetate	1.0	60
1,3-Butadiene	0.3	Acrylonitrile	0.2	40
	0.75±0.05	Methyl methacrylate	0.25±0.03	90
	1.35±0.12	Styrene	0.58±0.15	50
	8.8	Vinyl chloride	0.035	50
Diethyl fumarate	0	Acrylonitrile	8	60
	0.070±0.007	Styrene	0.30±0.02	60
	0.444±0.003	Vinyl acetate	0.011±0.001	60
	0.12±0.01	Vinyl chloride	0.47±0.05	60
Diethyl maleate	0	Acrylonitrile	12	60
	0	Methyl methacrylate	20	60
	0.0±0.1	Styrene	5±1.5	70
	0.043±0.005	Vinyl acetate	0.17±0.01	60
	0.009±0.003	Vinyl chloride	0.77±0.03	60

Table 6-2 Monomer Reactivity Ratios in Radical Copolymerization *(Continued)*

M_1	r_1	M_2	r_2	T (°C)
Fumaronitrile	0.01±0.01	Methyl methacrylate	3.5±0.5	79
	0.01±0.01	Styrene	0.23±0.01	60
	0.00	Vinyl acetate	0.14	–
Maleic anhydride	0.046±0.052	Dodecyl vinyl ether	−0.046±0.054	50
	0.02	Methyl acrylate	2.8±0.05	75
	0.02	Methyl methacrylate	6.7±0.2	75
	0.015	Styrene	0.040	50
	0.003	Vinyl acetate	0.055±0.015	75
	0.008	Vinyl chloride	0.296±0.07	75
Methacrylic acid	0.526	Butadiene	0.201	50
	0.7±0.05	Styrene	0.15±0.1	60
	20	Vinyl acetate	0.01	70
	0.58±0.05	2-Vinyl pyridine	1.55±0.10	70
Methyl acrylate	0.05±0.05	Acrylamide	1.30±0.05	60
	0.67±0.1	Acrylonitrile	1.26±0.1	60
	0.05±0.02	1,3-Butadiene[b]	0.76±0.04	5
	3.3	Ethyl vinyl ether	0	60
	0.504	Methyl methacrylate	1.91	130
	0.15±0.05	Styrene	0.7±0.1	60
	9	Vinyl acetate	0.1	60
	4	Vinyl chloride	0.06	45
	0.20±0.09	2-Vinyl pyridine	2.03±0.49	60
Methyl methacrylate	0.46±0.026	Styrene	0.52±0.026	60
	20±3	Vinyl acetate	0.015±0.015	60
	10	Vinyl chloride	0.1	68
	2.53±0.01	Vinylidene chloride	0.24±0.03	60
α-Methylstyrene	0.1±0.02	Acrylonitrile	0.06±0.02	75
	0.010±0.01	1,3-Butadiene	1.6±0.5	12.8
	0.038±0.003	Maleic anhydride	0.08±0.03	60
	0.14±0.01	Methyl methacrylate	0.50±0.03	60
	0.38	Styrene	2.3	–

Table 6-2 Monomer Reactivity Ratios in Radical Copolymerization *(Continued)*

M_1	r_1	M_2	r_2	T (°C)
Methyl vinyl ketone	0.35±0.02	Styrene	0.29±0.04	60
	7.00	Vinyl acetate	0.05	70
	8.3	Vinyl chloride	0.10	70
	1.8	Vinylidene chloride	0.55	70
Stilbene	0.03±0.03	Maleic anhydride	0.03±0.03	60
	0	Styrene	11.2±1.2	60
Styrene	80±40	Ethyl vinyl ether	0	80
	1.38±0.54	Isoprene	2.05±0.45	50
	55±10	Vinyl acetate	0.01±0.01	60
	17±3	Vinyl chloride	0.02	60
	1.85±0.05	Vinylidene chloride	0.085±0.010	60
	0.55	2-Vinyl pyridine	1.14	60
Tetrafluoro-ethylene	1.0	Chlorotrifluoroethy-lene[b]	1.0	60
	0.85	Ethylene[b]	0.15	80
	<0.3	Isobutylene[b]	0.0	–
Vinyl acetate	3.0±0.1	Ethyl vinyl ether	0	60
	0.23±0.02	Vinyl chloride	1.68±0.08	60
	0.1	Vinylidene chloride	6	68

[a]Data are typical values taken from [38] (pp. II-141 and II-291).
[b]Emulsion polymerization.

cannot be compared; the data can only be compared in each vertical column.

6-3b-1 Resonance Effects. The monomers have been arranged in Table 6-3 in their general order of reactivity. The order of monomer reactivities is approximately the same in each vertical column irrespective of the reference radical. The exceptions which occur are due to the strong alternating tendency of certain comonomer pairs. Table 6-3 and other similar data [6] show that substituents increase the reactivity of a monomer toward radical attack in the general order

Table 6-3 Relative Reactivities $(1/r)$ of Monomers with Various Polymer Radicals[a]

Monomer	Polymer radical						
	Butadiene	Styrene	Vinyl acetate	Vinyl chloride	Methyl methacrylate	Methyl acrylate	Acrylo-nitrile
Butadiene		1.7		29	4	20	50
Styrene	0.4		100	50	2.2	6.7	25
Methyl methacrylate	1.3	1.9	67	10		2	6.7
Methyl vinyl ketone		3.4	20	10			1.7
Acrylonitrile	3.3	2.5	20	25	0.82	1.2	
Methyl acrylate	1.3	1.4	10	17	0.52		0.67
Vinylidene chloride		5.4	10		0.39		1.1
Vinyl chloride	0.11	0.059	4.4		0.10	0.25	0.37
Vinyl acetate		0.019		0.59	0.050	0.11	0.24

[a] $1/r$ values calculated from data of Table 6-2.

$$-\phi, -CH{=}CH_2 > -CN, -COR > -COOH, -COOR >$$

$$-Cl > -OCOR, -R > -OR, -H$$

The order of monomer reactivities corresponds to the order of increased resonance stabilization by the particular substituent of the radical formed from the monomer. Substituents composed of unsaturated linkages are most effective in stabilizing the radicals because of the loosely held π-electrons which are available for resonance stabilization. Substituents such as halogen, acetoxy, and ether are increasingly ineffective in stabilizing the radicals since only the non-bonding electrons on halogen or oxygen are available for interaction with a radical. The spread in the effectiveness of the various substituents in enhancing monomer reactivity is about 50–200 fold depending on the reactivity of the radical. The less reactive the attacking radical, the greater is the spread in reactivities of the different monomers. The effect of a second substituent in the 1-position as in vinylidene chloride is approximately additive.

The order of *radical reactivities* can be obtained by multiplying the $1/r$ values by the appropriate propagation rate constants for homopolymerization (k_{11}). This yields the values of k_{12} for the reactions of various radical-monomer combinations (Table 6-4). The

Table 6-4 Rate Constants (k_{12}) for Radical-Monomer Reactions[a]

Monomer (M_1)	Polymer radical								
	Butadiene	Styrene	Methyl methacrylate	Acrylo-nitrile	Methyl acrylate	Vinyl acetate	Vinyl chloride	Q_1	e_1
Butadiene	100	246	2,820	98,000	41,800		357,000	2.39	–1.05
Styrene	40	145	1,550	49,000	14,000	230,000	615,000	1.00	–0.80
Methyl methacrylate	130	276	705	13,100	4,180	154,000	123,000	0.74	0.40
Acrylonitrile	330	435	578	1,960	2,510	46,000	178,000	0.60	1.20
Methyl acrylate	130	203	367	1,310	2,090	23,000	209,000	0.42	0.60
Vinyl chloride	11	8.7	71	720	520	10,100	12,300	0.044	0.20
Vinyl acetate		2.9	35	230	230	2,300	7,760	0.026	–0.22

[a] k_{12} values calculated from data in Tables 3-9 and 6-3.

k_{12} values in any vertical column in Table 6-4 give the order of monomer reactivities—as was the case for the data in Table 6-3. The data in any horizontal row give the order of radical reactivities toward a reference monomer. (The Q_1 and e_1 values in the last two vertical columns should be ignored at this point; they will be considered in Sec. 6-3b-4.)

As with monomer reactivities, it is seen that the order of radical reactivities is essentially the same irrespective of the monomer used as reference. The order of substituents in enhancing radical reactivity is the opposite of their order in enhancing monomer reactivity. A substituent which increases monomer reactivity does so because it stabilizes and decreases the reactivity of the corresponding radical. A consideration of Table 6-4 shows that the effect of a substituent on radical reactivity is considerably larger than its effect on monomer reactivity. Thus, vinyl acetate radical is about 100–1,000 times more reactive than styrene radical toward a given monomer while styrene monomer is only 50–100 times more reactive than vinyl acetate monomer toward a given radical. A comparison of the self-propagation rate constants (k_p) for vinyl acetate and styrene shows that these two effects very nearly compensate each other. The k_p for vinyl acetate is only sixteen times that of styrene (Table 3-9).

The interaction of radical reactivity and monomer reactivity in determining the rate of a radical-monomer reaction can be more clearly seen by the use of the reaction coordinate diagram [39] in Fig. 6-9. Figure 6-9 shows the potential energy changes accompanying the radical-monomer reaction as a function of the separation between the atoms forming the new bond. These energy changes are shown for the four possible reactions between resonance stabilized and non-stabilized monomers and radicals

$$\mathrm{R}\cdot + \mathrm{M} \longrightarrow \mathrm{R}\cdot \tag{6-42}$$

$$\mathrm{R}\cdot + \mathrm{M}_s \longrightarrow \mathrm{R}_s\cdot \tag{6-43}$$

$$\mathrm{R}_s\cdot + \mathrm{M}_s \longrightarrow \mathrm{R}_s\cdot \tag{6-44}$$

$$\mathrm{R}_s\cdot + \mathrm{M} \longrightarrow \mathrm{R}\cdot \tag{6-45}$$

where the presence or absence of the subscript s indicates the presence or absence, respectively, of a substituent which is capable of resonance stabilization. Vinyl acetate and styrene monomers are

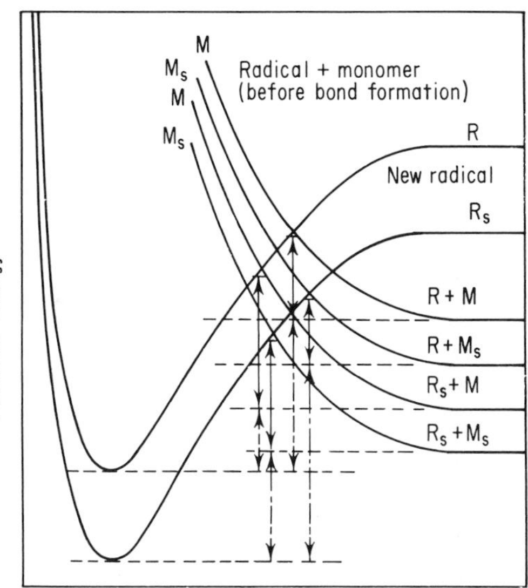

FIG. 6-9 *Reaction coordinate diagram for the reaction of a polymer radical with a monomer. The dependence of the potential energy of the system (radical + monomer) on the separation between the radical and the unsaturated carbon atom of the monomer is shown. The subscript s indicates the presence of a substituent which is capable of resonance stabilization. Activation energies are represented by the solid-lined arrows; heats of reaction by the broken-lined arrows. After [6] (by permission of John Wiley & Sons, Inc., New York).*

examples of M and M_s, respectively; vinyl acetate and styrene radicals are examples of R· and R_s·, respectively.

There are two sets of potential energy curves in Fig. 6-9. One set of four repulsion curves represents the energetics of the approach of a radical to a monomer; the other set of two Morse curves represents the stability of the bond (or of the polymer radical) finally formed. The intersections of the curves represent the transition states for the monomer-radical reactions (Eqs. 6-42 to 6-45) where the unbonded and bonded states have the same energies. The various activation energies and heats of reaction are represented by the solid-lined and broken-lined arrows, respectively. The separation between the two

Morse curves is significantly larger than that between either the top or bottom two repulsion curves since substituents are much more effective in decreasing radical reactivity than in increasing monomer reactivity.

Figure 6-9 shows that the order of reaction rate constants for the various monomer-radical reactions is

$$\underset{(6\text{-}45)}{R_s\cdot + M} < \underset{(6\text{-}44)}{R_s\cdot + M_s} < \underset{(6\text{-}42)}{R\cdot + M} < \underset{(6\text{-}43)}{R\cdot + M_s}$$

since the order of activation energies is the exact opposite. (This assumes that there are no appreciable differences in the entropies of activation—a reasonable assumption for sterically unhindered monomers.) This order of reactivity concisely summarizes the data in Tables 6-3 and 6-4 as well as many homopolymerization data. It is clear that monomers without stabilizing substituents (e.g., vinyl chloride or vinyl acetate) will self-propagate faster than those with stabilizing substituents (e.g., styrene) (Reaction 6-42 versus 6-44). Copolymerization, on the other hand, will occur primarily between two monomers with stabilizing substituents or between two monomers without stabilizing substituents. The combination of a monomer with a stabilizing substituent and one without (e.g., styrene-vinyl acetate) yields a system in which a combination of Reactions 6-43 and 6-45 is required to have facile copolymerization. This does not occur since Reaction 6-45 is very slow. Thus, in the styrene-vinyl acetate system, copolymerization is not efficient since styrene radical is too unreactive to add the unreactive vinyl acetate monomer.

6-3b-2 Steric Effects. The rates of radical-monomer reactions are also dependent on considerations of steric hindrance. This is easily observed by considering the reactivities of di-, tri-, and tetra-substituted ethylenes in copolymerization. Table 6-5 shows the k_{12} values for the reactions of various chloroethylenes with vinyl acetate, styrene, and acrylonitrile radicals. The effect of a second substituent on monomer reactivity is approximately additive when both substituents are in the 1- or α-position. However, a second substituent when in the 2- or β-position of the monomer results in a decrease in reactivity due to steric hindrance between it and the radical to which it is adding. Thus, 2–10 fold increases and 2–20 fold decreases in the reactivities of vinylidene chloride and 1,2-dichloroethylene, respectively, are observed compared to vinyl chloride.

Table 6-5 Rate Constants (k_{12}) for Radical-Monomer Reactions[a]

Monomer	Polymer radical		
	Vinyl acetate	Styrene	Acrylonitrile
Vinyl chloride	10,100	8.7	720
Vinylidene chloride	23,000	78	2,200
cis-1,2-Dichloroethylene	370	0.60	
trans-1,2-Dichloroethylene	2,300	3.9	
Trichloroethylene	3,450	8.6	29
Tetrachloroethylene	460	0.70	4.1

[a]k_{12} values calculated from data in Tables 3-9 and 6-2 and [38] (p. II-14).

Although the reactivity of 1,2-disubstituted ethylenes in copolymerization is low, it is still much greater than their reactivity in homopolymerization. It was observed in Sec. 3-9b-3 that the steric hindrance between a β-substituent on the attacking radical and a substituent on the monomer is responsible for the inability of 1,2-disubstituted ethylenes to homopolymerize. The reactivity of 1,2-disubstituted ethylenes toward copolymerization is due to the lack of β-substituents on the attacking radicals (e.g., the styrene, acrylonitrile, and vinyl acetate radicals).

A comparison of the *cis*- and *trans*-1,2-dichloroethylenes shows the trans isomer to be the more reactive by a factor of 6 [40]. This is a general phenomenon observed in comparing the reactivities of cis and trans-1,2-disubstituted ethylenes. The cis isomer, which is usually also the less stable isomer, is the less reactive one toward reaction with a radical. The difference in reactivity has been attributed to the inability of the cis isomer to achieve a completely coplanar conformation in the transition state—a requirement for resonance stabilization of the newly formed radical by the substituent [6].

The data on the reactivities of trichloroethylene and tetrachloroethylene further illustrate the competitive effects of substitutions on the 1- and 2-positions of ethylene. Trichloroethylene is more reactive than either of the 1,2-dichloroethylenes but less reactive than vinylidene chloride. Tetrachloroethylene is less reactive than trichloroethylene—analogous to the difference in reactivities between vinyl chloride and 1,2-dichloroethylene. The case of polyfluoroethylenes is an exception to the generally observed large decrease in reactivity with polysubstitution. Tetrafluoroethylene and chlorotrifluoroethylene show enhanced reactivity due apparently to the small size of the fluorine atoms.

6-3b-3 Alternation; Polar Effects. It was noted earlier that the exact quantitative order of monomer reactivities is not the same when different reference radicals are considered (Tables 6-3 and 6-4). Analogously, the exact order of radical reactivities varies depending on the reference monomer. Monomer reactivity cannot be considered independent of radical reactivity and vice versa. One observes enhanced reactivities in certain pairs of monomers due apparently to subtle radical-monomer interactions. This effect is a very general one in radical copolymerization and corresponds to the alternating tendency of the comonomer pairs. The deviation of the r_1r_2 product from unity and its approach to zero is a measure of the alternating tendency. One can list monomers in order of their r_1r_2 values with other monomers in such a manner that the further apart two monomers are, the greater is their tendency toward alternation (Table 6-6). (Ignore the e values until Sec. 6-3b-4.) Thus, acrylonitrile undergoes ideal copolymerization with methyl vinyl ketone (r_1r_2 = 1.1) and alternating copolymerization with butadiene (r_1r_2 = 0.006).

The order of monomers in Table 6-6 is one based on the polarity of the double bond. Monomers with electron-pushing substituents are located at the top (left) of the table and those with electron-pulling substituents at the bottom (right). The r_1r_2 value decreases progressively as one considers two monomers further apart in the table. The significant conclusion is that the tendency toward alternation increases as the difference in polarity between the two monomers increases. The occurrence of polar effects between electron donor and electron acceptor species in radical reactions was noted in the discussion on chain transfer (Sec. 3-9b-3). A most dramatic illustration of this polar effect is the facile copolymerization of monomers which show little or no tendency to homopolymerize. Maleic anhydride and diethyl fumarate do not homopolymerize but will readily form (very strongly) alternating copolymers with electron donor monomers such as styrene and vinyl ethers [41]. The copolymerization of maleic anhydride (electron acceptor) and stilbene (electron donor)

Table 6-6 Values of $r_1 r_2$ in Radical Copolymerization[a]

Vinyl ethers[b] (-1.3)[c]									
	Butadiene (-1.05)[c]								
	0.98	Styrene (-0.80)[c]							
		0.55	Vinyl acetate (-0.22)[c]						
	0.31	0.34	0.39	Vinyl chloride (0.20)[c]					
	0.19	0.24	0.30	1.0	Methyl methacrylate (0.40)[c]				
	<0.1	0.16	0.6	0.96	0.61	Vinylidene chloride (0.36)[c]			
		0.10	0.35	0.83		0.99	Methyl vinyl ketone (0.68)[c]		
0.0004	0.0006	0.016	0.21	0.11	0.18	0.34	1.1	Acrylonitrile (1.20)[c]	
~ 0		0.021	0.0049	0.056		0.56			Diethyl fumarate (1.25)[c]
~ 0.002		0.006	0.00017	0.0024	0.11					Maleic anhydride (2.25)[c]

[a] $r_1 r_2$ values calculated from data in Table 6-2, [38] (pp. II-141 and II-291) and [41].
[b] Ethyl, *i*-butyl, or dodecyl vinyl ethers.
[c] e value.

$$\underset{\phi}{\text{CH}}{=}\underset{\phi}{\text{CH}} + \text{CH}{=}\text{CH}\ (\text{CO–O–CO ring}) \longrightarrow \left[\underset{\phi}{\text{CH}}-\underset{\phi}{\text{CH}}-\text{CH}-\text{CH}\ (\text{CO–O–CO ring})\right]_n \tag{6-46}$$

takes place even though neither monomer undergoes appreciable homopolymerization.

That polarity does not completely account for the exact order of the alternating tendency of monomers is evident from some of the data in Table 6-6. For example, vinyl acetate alternates less than styrene with acrylonitrile but more than styrene with diethyl fumarate. Steric considerations are probably the cause of such deviations from the strict correlation of alternating tendency with monomer polarity.

The enhancement of reactivity in radical reactions by polar effects has been explained by considering the interaction between an electron acceptor radical and an electron donor monomer or an electron donor radical and an electron acceptor monomer to lead to a decrease in the activation energy for the radical-monomer reaction. The general lack of any effect of solvent on monomer reactivity ratios in radical copolymerization indicates that the polar interactions between radical and monomer occur, not in the ground state as suggested by Price [42], but in the transition state at very close to actual bonding distances in such a way that solvent would be excluded from the transition state. (However, recent data [43] in the styrene-methyl methacrylate system show that r_1 and r_2 vary somewhat with solvent polarity.)

It has been suggested [6, 44] that the lowering of the energy of the transition state occurs by electron transfer between the electron donor and electron acceptor species, e.g., between a styrene monomer and maleic anhydride radical

$$\sim\text{CH}-\overset{\text{H}}{\text{C}}\cdot\ (\text{CO–O–CO ring})\quad \text{CH}_2{=}\text{CH}-\text{C}_6\text{H}_5 \longleftrightarrow \sim\text{CH}-\overset{\text{H}}{\text{C}}{=}\text{C}(\text{O}^-)\ (\text{CO–O ring})\quad \overset{+}{\text{CH}_2}-\text{CH}{=}\text{C}_6\text{H}_5\cdot \tag{6-47}$$

and similarly between styrene radical and maleic anhydride monomer

$$\sim\!\sim CH_2-\overset{H}{\underset{C_6H_5}{C}}\cdot \quad \underset{CO-O-CO}{CH{=}CH} \longleftrightarrow \sim\!\sim CH_2-\overset{H}{C}{=}(\text{ring})^{+} \quad \underset{{}^{-}O-C-O-CO}{CH-\dot{C}H}$$

$$(6\text{-}48)$$

More recently [45], it has been suggested that alternating copolymers result from the homopolymerization of 1:1 complexes formed between electron donor and electron acceptor monomers rather than from the addition of donor and acceptor monomers to a propagating chain. If so, one would expect that the formation of such complexes could be catalyzed by increasing the electron accepting ability of an acceptor monomer through complexation with an appropriately added compound. This has indeed been observed, e.g., the addition of ethylaluminum sesquichloride to styrene-methyl methacrylate results in a distinctly greater tendency toward alternation. Further, the copolymerization rate is increased.

6-3b-4 ***Q-e* Scheme.** Various attempts have been made to place the radical-monomer reaction on a quantitative basis in terms of correlating structure and reactivity. Success in this area is desirable since it would allow the prediction of the monomer reactivity ratios for comonomer pairs which have not yet been copolymerized. The Hammett sigma-rho approach has been used fairly successfully with meta and para substituted styrenes [6]. A more generally useful correlation is the *Q-e scheme* of Alfrey and Price [46, 47]. These authors proposed that the rate constant for a radical-monomer reaction, e.g., for the reaction of $M_1\cdot$ radical with M_2 monomer, be written as

$$k_{12} = P_1 Q_2 \exp(-e_1 e_2) \qquad (6\text{-}49)$$

where P_1 is a measure of the general reactivity of the radical, Q_2 is a measure of the general reactivity of the monomer, and e_1 and e_2 are measures of the polarities of the radical and monomer, respectively. The P and Q terms primarily define the resonance effects in the radical and monomer. By assuming that the same e value applies to both a monomer and its radical (that is, e_1 defines the polarities of M_1

and $M_1\cdot$ while e_2 defines the polarities of M_2 and $M_2\cdot$), one can write expressions for k_{11}, k_{22}, and k_{21} analogous to Eq. 6–49. These can be appropriately combined to yield the monomer reactivity ratios in the forms

$$r_1 = \frac{Q_1}{Q_2}\exp[-e_1(e_1 - e_2)] \tag{6-50}$$

$$r_2 = \frac{Q_2}{Q_1}\exp[-e_2(e_2 - e_1)] \tag{6-51}$$

which correlate monomer-radical reactivity with the parameters Q_1, Q_2, e_1, and e_2.

The basis of the Q-e scheme (Eqs. 6-50 and 6-51) is the theoretically unsatisfactory suggestion of Price [42] that the alternating tendency is due to ground state electrostatic interactions between permanent charges in the monomer and radical. Attempts have been made to place the Q-e scheme on a solid theoretical basis [48]. Thus, for example, molecular orbital treatments have shown the P and Q values to be related to the localization energy of a monomer and the e value of a monomer has been related to its electron affinity. However, none of these theoretical approaches has as yet been quantitatively successful. The Q-e scheme is at present best considered as an empirical approach to placing monomer reactivity on a quantitative basis. Monomer reactivity is separated into the parameter Q which describes the resonance factor (and to some slight extent the steric factor) present in the monomer and the parameter e which describes the polar factor.

Consider now the use of the Q-e scheme to predict monomer reactivity ratios. Values of Q and e have been assigned to monomers based on their r values and the arbitrarily chosen reference values of $Q = 1$ and $e = -0.80$ for styrene. (Styrene was originally assigned an e value of -1.0 but this was revised to -0.80 to allow a better correlation of Q-e values with r values.) Q and e values for a large number of monomers have been calculated [38]. Table 6-7 shows the average Q and e values for some selected monomers. The practical success of the Q-e scheme in predicting the r_1 and r_2 values for comonomer pairs not previously copolymerized has been limited

Table 6-7 Q and e Values for Monomers[a]

Monomer	e	Q
t-Butyl vinyl ether	−1.58	0.15
Ethyl vinyl ether	−1.17	0.032
Butadiene	−1.05	2.39
Styrene	−0.80	1.00
Vinyl acetate	−0.22	0.026
Vinyl chloride	0.20	0.044
Vinylidene chloride	0.36	0.22
Methyl methacrylate	0.40	0.74
Methyl acrylate	0.60	0.42
Methyl vinyl ketone	0.68	0.69
Acrylonitrile	1.20	0.60
Diethyl fumarate	1.25	0.61
Maleic anhydride	2.25	0.23

[a]Data from [38] (p. II-341).

in its quantitative aspects. The reason for this is that the Q and e values for a monomer are not unique values for both experimental and theoretical reasons. The precision of the calculated Q and e values is often poor due to inaccuracies in the experimentally determined monomer reactivity ratios. This is seen in Table 6-8 which shows the different e values calculated for acrylonitrile from different sets of r_1 and r_2 data for the same comonomer pair (either acrylonitrile-vinyl acetate or acrylonitrile-vinyl chloride). Further,

Table 6-8 Variation in Q and e Values[a]

Monomer(M_1)	Comonomer	e_1	Q_1
Acrylonitrile	Styrene	1.20	0.44
	Vinyl acetate	0.90	0.37
	Vinyl acetate	1.0	0.67
	Vinyl chloride	1.3	0.37
	Vinyl chloride	1.6	0.75
Vinyl chloride	Styrene	0.2	0.024
	Methyl acrylate	0.0	0.035

[a]Data from [42].

the Q and e values for a monomer vary considerably depending on the monomer with which it is copolymerized (Table 6-8). This is due to inherent deficiencies of the Q-e scheme. It does not explicitly take into account steric factors which may affect monomer reactivity for certain radical-monomer combinations. In this respect, it is significant that Q-e values are often meaningless for copolymerizations involving 1,1-disubstituted monomers or, in general, monomers other than monosubstituted ethylenes. The assumption of the same e value for a monomer and its corresponding radical is also inadequate. Attempts to refine the Q-e treatment by using separate e values for monomer and radical have not been successful.

In spite of these deficiencies, the Q-e scheme is a reasonable, qualitative, and even semi-quantitative approach to the effect of structure on monomer reactivity. It can be used to give a general idea of the behavior to be expected from a comonomer pair which has not been studied and has been especially useful for predicting terpolymerization behavior. The Q-e values can be used to more quantitatively discuss reactivity data such as those in Tables 6-4 and 6-6. It is clear that the monomers in Table 6-6 are lined up in order of their e values. This order defines the polarities of the various monomers. The relative importance of resonance and polar factors in determining monomer reactivity can be discussed by considering the data in Table 6-4 in terms of the Q-e values of the monomers. The various reference radicals can be divided into two groups—one composed of the relatively unreactive radicals (styrene and butadiene) and the other composed of reactive radicals (all those other than styrene and butadiene). With the reactive radicals, the subtle polar effects do not come into play and monomer reactivity depends primarily on the resonance factor. The k_{12} values increase with increasing Q values for the monomer. The butadiene and styrene radicals are relatively unreactive and, therefore, are susceptible to the subtle polar factors. There is enhanced reactivity of these two radicals (possessing negative e values) toward monomers, such as methyl methacrylate and acrylonitrile, with relatively high positive e values. The resonance factor is, however, more important than the polar factor; the former determines the magnitude of monomer reactivity. Thus, monomer reactivities toward the butadiene and styrene radicals fall into two groups—one group of monomers with high Q values and high reactivities and another group with low Q values and low reactivities.

6-3b-5 Product Probability Approach to Reactivity. Ham [29, 30, 33, 49] has used Eq. 6-37, the equality of two product probabilities, to predict the copolymerization behavior of a comonomer pair from data on the copolymerization behavior of each of the monomers separately with some common monomer or, in other words, to predict the terpolymerization behavior of $M_1/M_2/M_3$ from data on the separate systems M_1/M_2 and M_2/M_3. For a terpolymerization involving equimolar amounts of the three monomers, Eq. 6-37 takes the form

$$\left(\frac{r_{13}}{r_{13}+r_{12}r_{13}+r_{12}}\right)\left(\frac{r_{21}}{r_{21}+r_{23}r_{21}+r_{23}}\right)\left(\frac{r_{32}}{r_{32}+r_{32}r_{31}+r_{31}}\right) =$$

$$\left(\frac{r_{12}}{r_{12}+r_{12}r_{13}+r_{13}}\right)\left(\frac{r_{31}}{r_{31}+r_{31}r_{32}+r_{32}}\right)\left(\frac{r_{23}}{r_{23}+r_{23}r_{21}+r_{21}}\right) \tag{6-52}$$

after the substitution of the appropriate expressions (Eq. 6-38) for each of the P terms. This reduces to the simpler relationship

$$r_{12}r_{23}r_{31} = r_{13}r_{32}r_{21} \tag{6-53a}$$

which can be rearranged to

$$\frac{r_{13}}{r_{31}} = \frac{r_{12}r_{23}}{r_{21}r_{32}} \tag{6-53b}$$

from which the ratio of the monomer reactivity ratios for the system M_1/M_3 can be calculated from data for the M_1/M_2 and M_2/M_3 systems.

This treatment has been further extended to allow calculation of the individual r_{13} and r_{31} values (instead of their ratio) as well as to attempt a basic understanding of monomer reactivity. From theoretical considerations and the observed behavior of many terpolymerization systems, Ham concluded that the product probabilities $P_{21}P_{13}P_{32}$ and $P_{23}P_{31}P_{12}$ should have one of two unique values—either 0.037 or 0.006. If all three monomers in the system are conjugated to some extent (as in monomers with phenyl, vinyl, nitrile, carbonyl, or carboxyl substituents), the product probabilities are approximately 0.037. This value is obtained by assuming the monomers to have equal reactivities with the various radicals such that the product probabilities would be $(1/3)^3$ or 0.037. If one or two of the monomers has a probability larger than 1/3, the other(s) must be small enough to yield the same overall product probability. When two of the three monomers are of the conjugated type and one is weakly conjugated (monomers with halogen, acetoxy, ether, or alkyl substituents), the product probabilities are 0.006. This value was derived by assuming $P_{13} = P_{23}$ with both values small, $P_{31} = P_{32}$ with both values large, and $r_{12} = r_{21} = 1$, $r_{32}r_{23} = 1$, and $r_{31}r_{13} = 1$ where M_3 is the weakly conjugated monomer.

Equation 6-37 can then be written in the form

$$P_{21}P_{13}P_{32} = P_{23}P_{31}P_{12} = \mathcal{P} \tag{6-54}$$

where $\mathcal{P}$ is the constant characteristic of the terpolymerization system with a value of either 0.037 or 0.006. The combination of Eqs. 6-52, 6-53, and 6-54 can be used to determine r_{13} and r_{31} from the monomer reactivity ratios for the M_1/M_2 and M_2/M_3 systems. The left (and also the right) side of Eq. 6-52 is equal to $\mathcal{P}$. This gives in combination with Eq. 6-53 two equations with the two unknowns r_{13} and r_{31}. Solving the two equations simultaneously yields the individual monomer reactivity ratios.

This treatment by Ham has been the subject of much discussion—both pro and con [50, 51]. The treatment does have its discrepancies. Complete quantitative verification of Eqs. 6-37 and 6-53 and of the values of $\mathcal{P}$ have not yet been experimentally obtained (Table 6-9). The accuracy of the available data does not appear to be high enough to allow unequivocal verification of the equality of the product probabilities (Eq. 6-37) or of the monomer reactivity ratio products (Eq. 6-53). This can be seen simply from the calculations of $\mathcal{P}$ in Table 6-9 from different sets of data for the ST/MA/AN, ST/AN/AA, and MM/MA/VCl systems. The two values of 0.006 and 0.037 for $\mathcal{P}$ are useful for qualitative or semi-quantitative predictions but leave much to be desired in terms of quantitative predictions of monomer reactivity. The assumptions made in the theoretical derivations of these values probably preclude their quantitative application. However, in spite of all these considerations, the product

Table 6-9 Product Probabilities for Various Monomer Combinations[a]

Monomers[b]	$P_{23}P_{31}P_{12}$	$P_{21}P_{13}P_{32}$
ST/MM/AN	0.053	0.0454
ST/MA/AN	0.00504	0.00435
	0.0157	0.00284
ST/MM/VCl_2	0.042	0.023
MM/AN/VCl_2	0.0262	0.0467
ST/MM/VP	0.051	0.0562
ST/MM/MA	0.0348	0.046
ST/AN/AA	0.0491	0.0199
	0.0164	0.085
MM/MA/VCl	0.00782	0.0055
	0.0131	0.00315
AN/MA/VCl	0.0168	0.0167

[a] Data from [49].
[b] AA = acrylic acid, AN = acrylonitrile, MA = methyl acrylate, MM = methyl methacrylate, ST = styrene, VCl = vinyl chloride, VCl_2 = vinylidene chloride, VP = 2-vinylpyridine.

probability treatment by Ham is quite useful, as is also the *Q-e* scheme, for approximating the reactivity of monomers for which data is not available. In this respect, it should be noted that the *Q-e* and product probability treatments are not unrelated. The relationship between the two has been discussed [49, 50]. The two treatments are quite consistent with each other. In fact, Eq. 6-53 can be obtained directly from the *Q-e* treatment as well as from the product probability treatment.

6-3c Rate of Copolymerization

The rate of copolymerization, unlike the copolymer composition, depends on the initiation and termination steps as well as on the propagation steps. In the usual case both monomers combine efficiently with the initiator radicals and the initiation rate is independent of the feed composition. Two different approaches have been used to derive expressions for the rate of copolymerization.

6-3c-1 Chemical-Controlled Termination. The approach found in the standard polymer texts (for example, [6] and [11]) assumes the termination reaction to be chemically-controlled [52]. Copolymerization consists of four propagation reactions (Eqs. 6-2 to 6-5) and the three termination steps

$$M_1\cdot + M_1\cdot \xrightarrow{k_{t11}} \tag{6-55}$$

$$M_2\cdot + M_2\cdot \xrightarrow{k_{t22}} \tag{6-56}$$

$$M_1\cdot + M_2\cdot \xrightarrow{k_{t12}} \tag{6-57}$$

corresponding to termination between like radicals (Eqs. 6-55 and 6-56) and cross-termination between unlike radicals (Eq. 6-57).

The overall rate of copolymerization is given by the sum of the four propagation rates

$$R_p = \frac{d[M_1] + d[M_2]}{dt} =$$

$$k_{11}[M_1\cdot][M_1] + k_{12}[M_1\cdot][M_2] + k_{22}[M_2\cdot][M_2] + k_{21}[M_2\cdot][M_1] \tag{6-58}$$

In order to eliminate radical concentrations from Eq. 6-58, two steady-state assumptions are made. A steady-state concentration is assumed for each type of radical

$$k_{21}[M_2\cdot][M_1] = k_{12}[M_1\cdot][M_2] \tag{6-59}$$

as was done via Eq. 6-9 in deriving the copolymer composition equation. Steady-state is also assumed for the total concentration of radicals

$$R_i = 2k_{t11}[M_1\cdot]^2 + 2k_{t12}[M_1\cdot][M_2\cdot] + 2k_{t22}[M_2\cdot]^2 \tag{6-60}$$

Eliminating radical concentrations from Eq. 6-58 by combining it with Eqs. 6-59 and 6-60 and then using the definitions of r_1 and r_2, one obtains for the copolymerization rate

$$R_p = \frac{(r_1[M_1]^2 + 2[M_1][M_2] + r_2[M_2]^2)R_i^{1/2}}{\left\{r_1^2\delta_1^2[M_1]^2 + 2\phi r_1 r_2 \delta_2 \delta_1 [M_1][M_2] + r_2^2\delta_2^2[M_2]^2\right\}^{1/2}} \tag{6-61}$$

where

$$\delta_1 = \left(\frac{2k_{t11}}{k_{11}^2}\right)^{1/2} \tag{6-62a}$$

$$\delta_2 = \left(\frac{2k_{t22}}{k_{22}^2}\right)^{1/2} \tag{6-62b}$$

$$\phi = \frac{k_{t12}}{2(k_{t11}k_{t22})^{1/2}} \tag{6-62c}$$

The δ terms are simply the reciprocals of the familiar $k_p/(2k_t)^{1/2}$ ratios for the homopolymerizations of the individual monomers. The ϕ term represents the ratio of half the cross-termination rate constant to the geometric mean of the rate constants for self-termination of like radicals. The 1/2 factor is present since cross-termination is statistically favored over termination by like radicals by a factor of 2. A $\phi < 1$ means that cross-termination is not favored while $\phi > 1$ means that cross-termination is favored.

The δ_1 and δ_2 values are obtained from homopolymerization and the r_1 and r_2 from copolymerization data. Experimental determination of the rate of copolymerization then allows the calculation of ϕ from Eq. 6-61. Values of ϕ for several monomer pairs are shown in Table 6-10 along with their r_1r_2 values. There is a general trend of ϕ values greater than unity indicating that cross-termination is favored. The tendency toward cross-termination parallels the tendency toward cross-propagation (i.e., toward alternation) in that the ϕ increases as r_1r_2 approaches zero. This has led to the conclusion that polar effects are responsible for the tendency toward cross-termination. The reaction between radicals of dissimilar polarity is enhanced due to electron transfer effects analogous to those used to describe the tendency toward alternation of dissimilar monomers.

Table 6-10 Values of ϕ and r_1r_2 in Radical Copolymerization[a]

Comonomer system	ϕ	r_1r_2
Styrene-butyl acrylate	150	0.07
Styrene-methyl acrylate	50	0.14
Methyl methacrylate-*p*-methoxystyrene	24	0.09
Styrene-methyl methacrylate	13	0.24
Styrene-*p*-methoxystyrene	1	0.95

[a] Taken from Table 4-11 of [6].

A consequence of the preference for cross-termination is a decrease in the rate of copolymerization compared to the mean of the rates of homopolymerization of the two monomers. The rapid cross-propagation rates in alternating copolymerization are offset by the large cross-termination rates and according to Eq. 6-61 yield decreased overall copolymerization rates. This can be seen in Fig. 6-10 which shows the calculated copolymerization rates for the styrene-methyl methacrylate system for ϕ values of 1 and 13.

It is difficult to predict the shape of the overall rate versus feed composition curve for strongly alternating copolymerizations because of the opposing effects of a large ϕ value and a small r_1r_2 value. Styrene-vinyl acetate presents an interesting case of an ideal type copolymerization (recall Sec. 6-2c-2) [52]. The value of r_2 is assumed very small and Eq. 6-61 approximates

$$R_p = \left([M_1] + \frac{2[M_2]}{r_1}\right)\frac{R_i^{1/2}}{\delta_1} \tag{6-63}$$

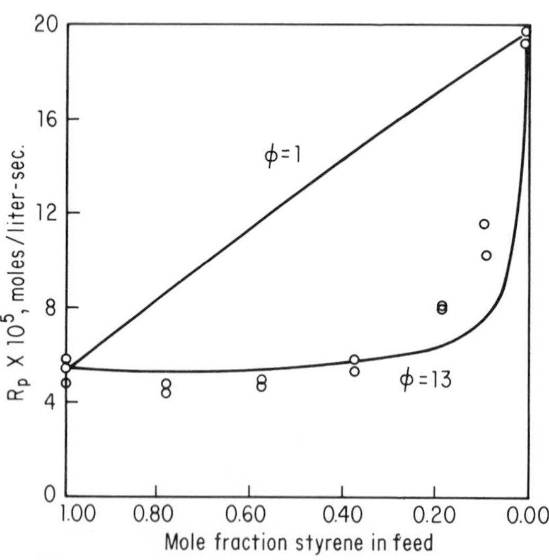

FIG. 6-10 *Dependence of the rate of radical copolymerization of styrene-methyl methacrylate (at 60°C with AIBN) on the comonomer feed composition. The two curves are the theoretical curves calculated for ϕ values of 1 and 13; the circles represent the experimental data. After [52] (by permission of American Chemical Society, Washington).*

from which it is observed that the addition of very small amounts of styrene to vinyl acetate results in very large decreases in the polymerization rate. Styrene essentially inhibits the polymerization of vinyl acetate. Vinyl acetate radicals are rapidly converted to styrene even at low styrene concentrations because of the high reactivity of both vinyl acetate radical and styrene monomer. The styrene radicals react very slowly with vinyl acetate monomer and are unable to react with styrene monomer because the latter is present in small amounts. The net effect is an almost complete cessation of polymerization.

6-3c-2 Diffusion-Controlled Termination. North and co-workers [53, 54] have pointed out that the usual treatment of copolymerization with the ϕ factor can be ambiguous since it is fairly well established that termination in radical polymerization is generally diffusion-controlled. ϕ cannot be interpreted primarily in terms of the chemical effects of the radical ends. The dependence of the rate of termination on the translational and segmental diffusion of the polymer chains was discussed in Sec. 3-10b. A ϕ value different from unity should then be interpreted in terms of the changes which occur in the translational and segmental diffusion of the chains due to their composition. The observation that ϕ in several systems varies with copolymer composition corroborates this interpretation and makes the use of Eq. 6-61 with a single value of ϕ of dubious value.

A more applicable kinetic expression for the rate of (diffusion-controlled) copolymerization is obtained [54] by considering the termination reaction as the reaction

$$\left.\begin{matrix} M_1\cdot + M_1\cdot \\ M_1\cdot + M_2\cdot \\ M_2\cdot + M_2\cdot \end{matrix}\right\} \xrightarrow{k_{t(12)}} \text{Dead copolymer} \tag{6-64}$$

where the termination rate constant $k_{t(12)}$ is a function of the copolymer composition. The condition for the steady-state for the total concentration of radicals then takes the form

$$R_i = 2k_{t(12)}([M_1\cdot] + [M_2\cdot])^2 \tag{6-65}$$

instead of Eq. 6-60. Combination of Eqs. 6-58, 6-59, and 6-65 with the definitions of r_1 and r_2 yields the rate of copolymerization as

$$R_p = \frac{(r_1[M_1]^2 + 2[M_1][M_2] + r_2[M]^2)R_i^{1/2}}{k_{t(12)}^{1/2}\left\{\left(\frac{r_1[M_1]}{k_{11}}\right) + \left(\frac{r_2[M_2]}{k_{22}}\right)\right\}} \tag{6-66}$$

One would expect the termination rate constant $k_{t(12)}$ to be a function of the termination rate constants for the corresponding two homopolymerizations. In an ideal situation, this dependence might take the form

$$k_{t(12)} = F_1 k_{t11} + F_2 k_{t22} \tag{6-67}$$

where $k_{t(12)}$ is the average of k_{t11} and k_{t22} each weighted on the basis of the copolymer composition in mole fractions (F_1 and F_2).

The utility of Eq. 6-66 in correlating data on the copolymerization rate, although not extensively studied, has been established in a few studies [54, 55]. Thus, Fig. 6-11 shows the experimentally determined $k_{t(12)}$ values (i.e., the values calculated from Eq. 6-66) for vinyl acetate-methyl methacrylate copolymerization (dotted curve). The expected variation of $k_{t(12)}$ with the comonomer (and copolymer) composition can be handled by Eq. 6-66 whereas Eq. 6-61 with a single ϕ value is not applicable. Figure 6-11 also shows the $k_{t(12)}$ values calculated via Eq. 6-67 from the copolymer composition and the termination rate constants for the two homopolymerizations (solid curve). Equation 6-67 appears to be qualitatively but not quantitatively valid. Evidently, the method of weighting the k_{t11} and k_{t22} values directly with the copolymer composition is not correct. A refinement of this treatment has been made in the styrene-methyl methacrylate system [55]. It was assumed that termination between chains containing two styrene units at the radical ends would be slower than termination between chains containing styrene as the last unit and methyl methacrylate as the next-to-last (or *penultimate*) unit. It was postulated that steric interactions between benzene rings on adjacent monomer units lead to slower segmental diffusion due to hindered rotation about the polymer chain axis. Modification of Eq. 6-67 to include the three types of terminating species (methyl methacrylate, styrene, and

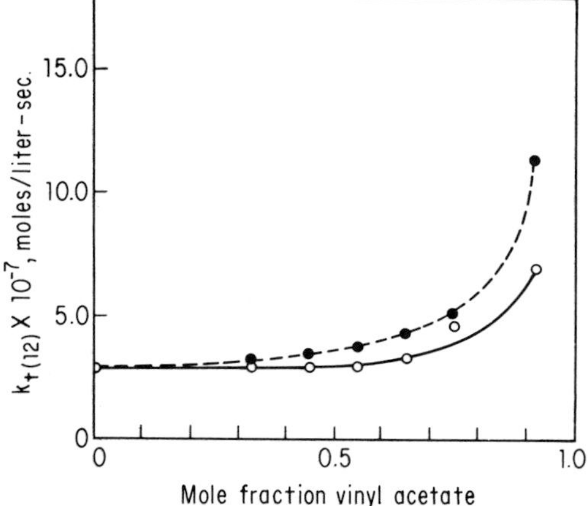

FIG. 6-11 *Dependence of the termination rate constant* $k_{t(12)}$ *on the mole fraction of vinyl acetate in the radical copolymerization of vinyl acetate-methyl methacrylate. The solid-lined curve and open circles represent calculations by Eq. 6-67; the broken-lined curve and solid circles represent calculations by Eq. 6-66. After [54] (by permission of The Faraday Society, London).*

styrene with methyl methacrylate as the penultimate unit) has been successful in allowing the prediction of $k_{t(12)}$ values.

6-4 IONIC COPOLYMERIZATION

Ionic copolymerizations are distinctively different from radical copolymerizations in several respects. Ionic copolymerizations are much more selective than radical copolymerizations. The number of comonomer pairs which undergo either cationic or anionic copolymerization is relatively limited due to the wider range of monomer reactivities in ionic copolymerization [56, 57]. Cationic copolymerization is limited to monomers with electron-pushing substituents and anionic copolymerization to monomers with electron-pulling substituents. For comonomer pairs which undergo ionic copolymerization, the general tendency is toward the ideal type of behavior (Sec. 6-2c-1), with the r_1r_2 product approaching unity, where the relative reactivities of the two monomers toward the two different ionic propagating centers are approximately the same. There is a general lack of any tendency toward alternation. Furthermore, quite a few copolymerizations proceed with r_1r_2 values greater than unity. Thus, there are relatively few monomer pairs which yield copolymers containing large proportions of both monomers.

Another characteristic feature of ionic copolymerizations is the sensitivity of the monomer reactivity ratios to changes in the initiator, reaction medium, or temperature. This is quite different than the behavior observed in radical copolymerization. Monomer reactivity ratios in radical copolymerization are essentially independent of reaction conditions.

6-4a Cationic Copolymerization

6-4a-1 Monomer Reactivity. The effect of a substituent on the reactivity of a monomer in cationic copolymerization depends on the extent to which it increases the electron density on the double bond and on its ability to resonance stabilize the carbonium ion which is formed. However, the order of monomer reactivities in cationic copolymerization (as in anionic copolymerization) is not nearly as well-defined as in radical copolymerization. Reactivity is often influenced to a larger degree by the reaction conditions (solvent, gegen-ion, and temperature) than by the structure of the monomer. There are relatively few reports in the literature in which monomer reactivity has been studied for a wide range of different monomers under conditions of the same solvent, gegen-ion, and reaction temperature.

The most extensive studies of monomer reactivity have been those involving the copolymerization of various meta and para-substituted styrenes with other styrene monomers (styrene, α-methylstyrene, and *p*-chlorostyrene) as the reference monomer [56, 58, 59]. The relative reactivities of the various substituted styrenes have been correlated by the Hammett sigma-rho treatment. Plots of log $1/r_1$ values against the sigma substituent constants yield straight lines as required by the Hammett treatment. The sigma value of a substituent is a quantitative measure of the sum of the resonance and polar effects of the substituent. Electron-pulling and electron-pushing substituents have positive and negative sigma constants, respectively. Substituents increase the reactivity of styrene in the approximate order

$$p\text{-OCH}_3 > p\text{-CH}_3 > p\text{-H} > p\text{-Cl} > m\text{-Cl} > m\text{-NO}_2$$

(−0.27) (−0.17) (0) (+0.23) (+0.37) (+0.71)

which follows the order of their electron-pushing power as indicated by the sigma values shown in parentheses.

Although the Hammett treatment is most useful for the quantitative correlation of monomer reactivity with structure, it is only applicable to substituted styrenes. One is, however, usually more interested in the relative reactivities of the commonly encountered monomers such as isoprene, acrylonitrile, propylene, isobutylene, etc. The appropriate quantitative data are relatively sparse for these monomers. The generally observed order of monomer reactivity is

vinyl ethers > isobutylene > styrene, isoprene

which is the order expected on the basis of the electron-pushing ability of the various substituents. Monomers with electron-pulling substituents such as acrylonitrile, methyl methacrylate, and vinyl chloride show negligible reactivity in cationic copolymerization.

Copolymerization studies have shown that steric effects, similar to those observed in radical polymerization, are also operative in cationic polymerization. Table 6-11 shows the effect of methyl substituents in the α- and β-positions of styrene [60–62]. Reactivity is increased by the α-methyl substituent due to its electron-pushing power. The decreased reactivity of the β-methylstyrene relative to styrene indicates that the steric effect of the β-substituent outweighs its polar effect of increasing the electron density on the double bond. Furthermore, the trans-β-methylstyrene appears to be more reactive than the cis-isomer although the difference is much less than in radical copolymerization (Sec. 6-3b-2). It is worth noting that 1,2-disubstituted alkenes have finite r values in cationic copolymeri-

Table 6-11 Steric Effects in Copolymerization of α- and β-Methylstyrenes (M_1) with *p*-Chlorostyrene (M_2)[a,b]

M_1	r_1	r_2
Styrene	2.50	0.30
α-Methylstyrene	15.0	0.35
trans-β-methylstyrene	0.32	0.74
cis-β-methylstyrene	0.32	1.0

[a] Data from [60–62].
[b] $SnCl_4$ in CCl_4 at 0°C.

zation compared to the values of zero in radical copolymerization (Table 6-2). There is a tendency for 1,2-disubstituted alkenes to self-propagate in cationic copolymerization although this tendency is nil in the radical reaction.

6-4a-2 Effect of Solvent and Gegen-Ion. It has previously been shown that large changes can occur in the rate of a cationic copolymerization by using different solvents or different gegen-ions (Sec. 5-2f). The monomer reactivity ratios can also be affected by changes in the solvent or gegen-ion although the effects can be quite complex. As many systems do not show an effect as do show an effect of solvent or gegen-ion on monomer reactivity. The reaction conditions can often have a very large effect on the monomer reactivities. The dramatic effect which solvents can have on monomer reactivity is illustrated by the data in Table 6-12 for the copolymerization of isobutylene-*p*-chlorostyrene [63]. The aluminum bromide catalyzed copolymerization shows $r_1 = 1.0$, $r_2 = 1.0$ in hexane, and $r_1 = 14.7$, $r_2 = 0.15$ in nitrobenzene. The variation in the monomer reactivity ratios has been explained by the preferential solvation or complexing of the propagating free ion and/or ion-pair, in the nonpolar medium (hexane), by the more polar monomer (*p*-chlorostyrene). The increased *p*-chlorostyrene concentration at the reaction site results in a larger calculated value of its monomer reactivity ratio. In the polar nitrobenzene, the propagating species is solvated completely by the solvent without participation by the *p*-chlorostyrene, and the more reactive isobutylene can exhibit its greater reactivity.

Table 6-12 Effect of Solvent and Gegen-Ion on Monomer Reactivity Ratios[a]

r_1 Isobutylene	r_2 p-Chlorostyrene	Solvent	Catalyst
1.0	1.0	Hexane (ϵ 1.8)	$AlBr_3$
14.7	0.15	Nitrobenzene (ϵ 36)	$AlBr_3$
8.6	1.2	Nitrobenzene (ϵ 36)	$SnCl_4$

[a]Data from [63].

The effect of solvents on monomer reactivity ratios cannot be considered independent of the gegen-ion employed. Here, as above, the situation is quite confusing with some comonomer systems showing altered r_1 and r_2 values for different catalysts and others showing no effects. Thus, the isobutylene-*p*-chlorostyrene (Table 6-12) system shows different r_1 and r_2 values for aluminum bromide and stannic chloride catalysts. The interdependence of the effects of solvent and gegen-ion are shown in Table 6-13 for the copolymerization of styrene-*p*-methylstyrene [64]. The catalysts are listed in order of their strength as measured by their effectiveness in homopolymerization studies. Antimony pentachloride is the strongest catalyst and iodine the weakest. This order is that based on the tightness of the ion-pair.

Table 6-13 Effects of Solvent and Gegen-Ion on Copolymer Composition in Styrene-*p*-Methylstyrene Copolymerization[a]

Catalyst	% Styrene in copolymer[b]		
	Toluene (ϵ 2.4)	1,2-Dichloroethane (ϵ 9.7)	Nitrobenzene (ϵ 36)
$SbCl_5$	46	25	28
AlX_3	34	34	28
$TiCl_4$, $SnCl_4$, $BF_3 \cdot OEt_2$, $SbCl_3$	28	27	27
Cl_3CCO_2H		27	30
I_2		17	

[a]Data from [64].
[b]Comonomer feed = 1:1 styrene-*p*-methylstyrene.

The data in Table 6-13 show the copolymer composition to be insensitive to the catalyst strength for solvents of high polarity (1,2-dichloroethane and nitrobenzene) and also insensitive to the solvent polarity for any catalyst except the strongest ($SbCl_5$). The styrene content of the copolymer decreases with increasing solvent polarity when $SbCl_5$ is the catalyst. The styrene content also decreases with decreasing catalyst strength for the low polarity solvent (toluene). These results can be interpreted in terms of the effects of solvent and gegen-ion on the ion-pair separation and on the selective complexing of the ion-pair by one of the monomers. In the styrene-*p*-methylstyrene system, *p*-methylstyrene is both the more polar and the more reactive of the two monomers. In the poor solvent (toluene), the monomers compete, against the solvent, with each other to complex with the ion-pair. The more polar *p*-methylstyrene complexes to the greater degree and is preferentially incorporated into the copolymer. The selectivity increases as the tightness of the ion-pair increases. For the better solvents, the gegen-ion does not appreciably influence the reaction since the monomers cannot compete with the solvent. In the case of the $SbCl_5$ catalyzed copolymerization, increasing the solvent power of the reaction medium also decreases the ability of the monomers to compete with the solvent to complex with the ion-pair. The copolymer composition is then determined primarily by the chemical reactivities of the monomers.

6-4a-3 Effect of Temperature. Temperature has a greater influence on the monomer reactivity ratios in cationic copolymerization than in radical copolymerization due to the greater spread of activation energies for the propagation reactions in the former. There is no general trend with regard to the variation of r with temperature as there was in radical copolymerization. Some r values increase with temperature and others decrease. Various combinations of effects have been observed for different comonomer pairs. Thus, for isobutylene-styrene, r_1 increased 1.5-fold and r_2 increased 3-fold in going from -90 to $-30°C$ [65]. On the other hand, for α-methylstyrene-*p*-chlorostyrene, r_1 decreased from 28 to 15 and r_2 increased from 0.12 to 0.35 in going from -78 to 0°C [61].

6-4b Anionic Copolymerization

6-4b-1 Reactivity. The reactivities of monomers in anionic copolymerization are the opposite of those in cationic copolymerization. Reactivity is enhanced by electron-pulling substituents which decrease the electron density on the double bond or resonance stabilize the carbanion formed. Although the available data is rather limited [57, 66], reactivity is generally increased by substituents in the order

$$-CN > -CO_2R > -\phi, -CH{=}CH_2 > -H$$

Monomers with electron-pushing substituents show negligible reactivity in anionic copolymerization.

The general characteristics of anionic copolymerization are very similar to those of cationic copolymerization. There is a definite tendency toward ideal behavior in most anionic copolymerization [67]. Steric effects give rise to an alternating tendency for certain comonomer pairs. Thus, the styrene-*p*-methylstyrene pair shows [67] ideal behavior with $r_1 = 5.3$, $r_2 = 0.18$, $r_1r_2 = 0.95$, while the styrene-α-methylstyrene pair shows [68] a definite alternating tendency with $r_1 = 35$, $r_2 = 0.003$, $r_1r_2 = 0.1$. The steric effect of the additional substituent in the α-position hinders the addition of α-methylstyrene to α-methylstyrene anion. The tendency toward alternation is essentially complete in the copolymerizations of the sterically hindered 1,1-diphenylethylene and *trans*-1,2-diphenylethylene with butadiene, isoprene, and 2,3-dimethylbutadiene [69].

6-4b-2 Effects of Solvent and Gegen-Ion. Monomer reactivity ratios and copolymer compositions in many anionic copolymerizations are altered by changes in the gegen-ion or solvent. Table 6-14 shows data for the styrene-isoprene system [70]. The solvents are arranged in the order of their solvating powers. As in the case of cationic copolymerization, it is clear that the effects of gegen-ion and solvent cannot be considered independently of each other. For the tightly bound lithium gegen-ion, there are large effects due to the solvent. In poor solvents, the copolymer is rich in the less reactive isoprene because isoprene is preferentially complexed with the lithium ion. (The complexing of 1,3-dienes with lithium is discussed further in Sec. 8-6b.) The quantitative effect of solvent is less for the less tightly bound sodium gegen-ion.

Table 6-14 Effect of Solvent and Gegen-Ion on Copolymer Composition in Styrene-Isoprene Copolymerization[a]

Solvent	% Styrene in copolymer for gegen-ion	
	Na^+	Li^+
None	66	15
Benzene	66	15
Triethylamine	77	59
Ethyl ether	75	68
Tetrahydrofuran	80	80

[a]Data from [70].

The anionic copolymerization of methyl methacrylate and styrene with lithium emulsion and butyllithium catalysts is an especially interesting case [71]. Bulk copolymerization of an equimolar mixture of the two monomers with a lithium emulsion yields a copolymer with a high percentage of styrene whereas in tetrahydrofuran solution the amount of styrene in the copolymer is decreased. When butyllithium is used as the catalyst in the bulk copolymerization, there is essentially no styrene in the copolymer. These results were explained by postulating initiation by electron-transfer in the case of lithium catalysis with the formation of radical-ions whose radical ends propagated to yield a 50–50 copolymer of styrene-methyl methacrylate while the anion ends propagated to yield a virtually styrene-free poly(methyl methacrylate). The effect of tetrahydrofuran in the lithium polymerization is due to its acceleration of the anionic polymerization without appreciably affecting the rate of the radical copolymerization. Butyllithium catalysis yields a pure anionic initiation and results in a copolymer which is almost pure methyl methacrylate.

In the anionic copolymerization, styrene enters into the copolymer only in so far as initiation occurs on styrene and then propagates with styrene [72]. There is no tendency for poly(methyl methacrylate) propagating anions to add styrene. Polystyrene anions do, however, add methyl methacrylate readily. The difference is due to the low basicity of the poly(methyl methacrylate) anion. When polystyrene anions are taken over by methyl methacrylate, styrene will no longer be added to those chains. The result is that in a short time after initiation all propagating chains are poly(methyl methacrylate) and there is no subsequent addition of styrene. This behavior corresponds to the case (Sec. 6-2c-2) of $r_1 \gg 1$ and $r_2 \ll 1$ and is observed in anionic copolymerization for comonomer pairs whose anions differ widely in basicity. The basicity of the anions parallels the e values of the monomers. Thus, monomers with similar e values, e.g., styrene ($e = -0.80$) and butadiene ($e = -1.05$), undergo copolymerization while those with dissimilar e values, e.g., styrene and methyl methacrylate ($e = 0.40$), primarily tend to yield the homopolymer of the more reactive monomer as the initial product.

More recent work [73] with the lithium-initiated reaction has shown that radical propagation does not occur in these copolymerizations since no random sequence of styrene and methyl methacrylate units is found in the copolymer. The copolymer consists of a block copolymer of the two monomers and possibly some homopolymer of methyl methacrylate. That the copolymer is rich in styrene when the copolymerization is carried out in bulk has been attributed to the insolubility of the lithium gegen-ion. The lithium ion is part of an insoluble lithium particle and propagation takes place on that particle surface. Styrene is more strongly absorbed than methyl methacrylate on these surfaces because of its dense π-electron system. The net result is that copolymerization takes place with a very high styrene concentration and the product obtained is rich in styrene. The overall styrene content of the copolymer decreases with conversion as the propagating chain end becomes soluble and the reaction takes place in solution where the styrene concentration is lower. The propagating polystyrene chains are taken over by methyl methacrylate and the result is a block copolymer. Since poly(methyl methacrylate) anions do not cross propagate with styrene, the methyl methacrylate content of the block copolymer increases with conversion. The styrene content of the copolymer is also slightly decreased when the reaction is carried out in a more polar solvent such as tetrahydrofuran in which the lithium gegen-ion is more soluble—but the effect is small. However, a very large decrease in the styrene content occurs when butyllithium is used as the catalyst. In this instance, there are no lithium particles and the propagation takes place in solution.

6-5 DEVIATIONS FROM COPOLYMER COMPOSITION EQUATION

The derivation of the copolymer composition equation (Eq. 6-12 or 6-15) rests on two important assumptions—one of a kinetic nature and the other of a thermodynamic nature. The first is that the reactivity of the propagating species is independent of the identity of the monomer unit which precedes the terminal unit. The second is the irreversibility of the various propagation reactions. Deviations from the quantitative behavior predicted by the copolymer composition equation under certain reaction conditions have been ascribed to the failure of one or the other of the two assumptions.

6-5a Kinetic Penultimate Effect

The behavior of some comonomer systems indicates that the reactivity of the propagating species is affected by the next-to-last or penultimate monomer unit. This effect, often referred to as the *penultimate effect*, manifests itself in a particular copolymerization by giving inconsistent values of the monomer reactivity ratios for different comonomer feed compositions. This has been observed in many radical copolymerizations where the monomers contain highly bulky or polar substituents. Thus, in the copolymerization of styrene (M_1) and fumaronitrile (M_2), Ham and Fordyce [74] reported that chains rich in fumaronitrile and having styrene as the last added unit showed greatly decreased reactivity with fumaronitrile monomer. The effect is due to the steric and polar repulsions between the penultimate fumaronitrile unit in the propagating chain and the incoming fumaronitrile monomer.

The mathematical treatment of the penultimate effect [75, 30] in such a copolymerization involves the use of the eight propagating reactions

$$\begin{aligned}
&\sim\!\!\sim M_1M_1\cdot + M_1 \xrightarrow{k_{111}} \sim\!\!\sim M_1M_1M_1\cdot \\
&\sim\!\!\sim M_1M_1\cdot + M_2 \xrightarrow{k_{112}} \sim\!\!\sim M_1M_1M_2\cdot \\
&\sim\!\!\sim M_2M_2\cdot + M_1 \xrightarrow{k_{221}} \sim\!\!\sim M_2M_2M_1\cdot \\
&\sim\!\!\sim M_2M_2\cdot + M_2 \xrightarrow{k_{222}} \sim\!\!\sim M_2M_2M_2\cdot \\
&\sim\!\!\sim M_2M_1\cdot + M_1 \xrightarrow{k_{211}} \sim\!\!\sim M_2M_1M_1\cdot \\
&\sim\!\!\sim M_2M_1\cdot + M_2 \xrightarrow{k_{212}} \sim\!\!\sim M_2M_1M_2\cdot \\
&\sim\!\!\sim M_1M_2\cdot + M_1 \xrightarrow{k_{121}} \sim\!\!\sim M_1M_2M_1\cdot \\
&\sim\!\!\sim M_1M_2\cdot + M_2 \xrightarrow{k_{122}} \sim\!\!\sim M_1M_2M_2\cdot
\end{aligned} \tag{6-68}$$

with the four reactivity ratios

$$\begin{aligned}
r_1 &= \frac{k_{111}}{k_{112}} \qquad r_1' = \frac{k_{211}}{k_{212}} \\
r_2 &= \frac{k_{222}}{k_{221}} \qquad r_2' = \frac{k_{122}}{k_{121}}
\end{aligned} \tag{6-69}$$

Each monomer is thus characterized by two monomer reactivity ratios. One monomer reactivity ratio represents the propagating species in which the penultimate and terminal monomer units are the same. The other represents the propagating species in which the penultimate and terminal units differ. The latter monomer reactivity ratios are signified by the prime notations (r_1' and r_2').

In a manner similar to that used in deriving Eq. 6-12, the copolymer composition with a kinetic penultimate effect present was obtained [75] as

$$\frac{d[M_1]}{d[M_2]} = \frac{1 + \dfrac{r_1'X(r_1X + 1)}{(r_1'X + 1)}}{1 + \dfrac{r_2'(r_2 + X)}{X(r_2' + X)}} \qquad (6\text{-}70)$$

where $X = [M_1]/[M_2]$. For the styrene-fumaronitrile system, fumaronitrile is incapable of self-propagation ($r_2 = r_2' = 0$) and Eq. 6-70 simplifies [76] to

$$\frac{d[M_1]}{d[M_2]} - 1 = \frac{r_1'X(r_1X + 1)}{(r_1'X + 1)} \qquad (6\text{-}71)$$

This equation gives a reasonable fit of the experimental copolymer composition data (Fig. 6-12) [77] with $r_1 = 0.072$ and $r_1' = 1.0$.

Penultimate effects have been observed in other systems. Among these are the radical copolymerizations of acrylonitrile-styrene, α-methylstyrene-acrylonitrile, and other comonomer pairs [30, 74, 78, 79]. Although ionic copolymerizations have not been as extensively studied, penultimate effects have been found in some cases. Thus, in the electron-transfer copolymerization of styrene-vinylpyridine, vinylpyridine adds faster to chains ending in vinylpyridine if the penultimate unit is styrene [80]. When vinylpyridine is the penultimate unit, it apparently acts as an electron sink and hinders bond formation with the approaching monomer. Whether or not a penultimate effect exists in a particular system cannot always be easily ascertained. The precision of the experimental data in many instances is not sufficiently high to allow the application of Eq. 6-70.

Data in the styrene-fumaronitrile system indicated that there are effects due to remote monomer units preceding the penultimate unit. Ham [77] treated this effect of remote units by further expansion of the copolymer composition equation by the use of greater numbers of monomer reactivity ratios for each monomer. For the styrene-(M_1)-fumaronitrile(M_2) copolymerization, the monomer reactivity ratios

$$r_1 = \frac{k_{111}}{k_{112}} \qquad r_1' = \frac{k_{11211}}{k_{11212}} \qquad r_1'' = \frac{k_{21211}}{k_{21212}} \tag{6-72}$$

appear to be important since the $M_2M_1M_1$ sequence tends to alternate with M_2M_1 as shown by the fact that it is impossible to produce copolymers containing more than 40 mole percent fumaronitrile. The copolymer composition is derived [77] as

$$\frac{d[M_1]}{d[M_2]} - 1 = \frac{\left[\dfrac{r_1''X(r_1'X + 1)}{r_1''X + 1}\right](r_1X + 1)}{\left[\dfrac{r_1''X(r_1'X + 1)}{(r_1''X + 1)}\right] + 1} \tag{6-73}$$

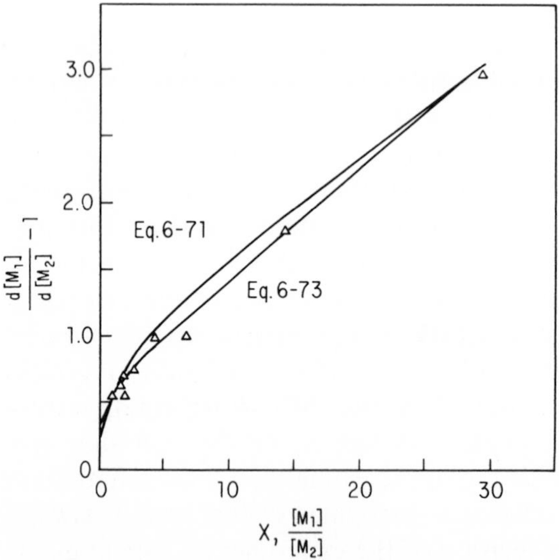

FIG. 6-12 *Kinetic penultimate effect in the radical copolymerization of styrene* (M_1)-*fumaronitrile*(M_2); *plot of copolymer composition as* $\{(d[M_1]/d[M_2]) - 1\}$ *versus the comonomer feed composition* X. *The two curves represent calculations using Eq. 6-71 (with* $r_1 = 0.072$, $r_1' = 1.0$*), and Eq. 6-73 (with* $r_1 = 0.08$, $r_1' = 0.3$, $r_1'' = 4.0$*), respectively. From [77] (by permission of Interscience Publishers, John Wiley & Sons, Inc., New York).*

Figure 6-12 shows that the experimental data in the styrene-fumaronitrile system fits Eq. 6-73 (with $r_1 = 0.08, r_1' = 0.3, r_1'' = 4.0$) more precisely than Eq. 6-71. This is especially evident at high fumaronitrile feed compositions where the fit of Eq. 6-71 is poor.

6-5b Depropagation during Copolymerization

In contrast to Ham's kinetic approach, Lowry [81] has treated the deviations from the copolymer composition equation from a thermodynamic viewpoint. Altered copolymer compositions in certain copolymerizations are accounted for in this treatment in terms of the tendency of one of the monomers (M_2) to depropagate. An essential difference between the kinetic and thermodynamic treatments is that the latter implies that the copolymer composition can vary with the concentrations of the monomers. If the concentration of monomer M_2 falls below its equilibrium value $[M]_c$ at the particular reaction temperature, terminal M_2 units will be prone to depropagate. The result would be a decrease in the amount of this monomer in the copolymer. The kinetic approach of Ham does not predict any dependence of the copolymer composition on the monomer concentration. Further, the thermodynamic approach differs from the kinetic approach in that the former emphasizes the temperature-dependence of the copolymer composition since the polymerization-depolymerization equilibrium is temperature-dependent.

The present discussion will be almost completely limited to copolymerizations in which only one of the monomers has a tendency to depropagate. Systems in which both monomers tend to depropagate are difficult to treat mathematically and also involve a large number of unknown parameters. Different types of copolymerization behavior can be considered depending on whether one assumes penultimate effects on the depropagation reaction. Thus, Lowry considers two different cases in which monomer M_1 has absolutely no tendency to depropagate irrespective of the preceding units in the chain while monomer M_2 has no tendency to depropagate if it is attached to an M_1 unit. The two cases differ in the different tendencies of monomer M_2 to depropagate. In Case I, M_2 tends to depropagate if it is attached to another M_2 unit

$$\sim\!\sim M_1M_2M_2^* \rightleftharpoons \sim\!\sim M_1M_2^* + M_2 \tag{6-74}$$

In Case II, M_2 tends to depropagate only when it is attached to a sequence of two or more M_2 units

$$\sim\sim M_1M_2M_2M_2^* \rightleftharpoons \sim\sim M_1M_2M_2^* + M_2 \tag{6-75}$$

Thus, $\sim\sim M_1M_2^*$ does not depropagate in Case I while neither $\sim\sim M_1M_2^*$ nor $\sim\sim M_1M_2M_2^*$ depropagate in Case II.

The copolymer compositions for copolymerizations involving depropagation according to these two cases have been derived by Lowry [81]. The copolymer composition for Case I is given by

$$\frac{d[M_1]}{d[M_2]} = \frac{(r_1[M_1] + [M_2])(1 - \alpha)}{[M_2]} \tag{6-76}$$

with α defined by

$$\alpha = \frac{\left(\left\{1 + K[M_2] + \left(\frac{K[M_1]}{r_2}\right)\right\} - \left[\left\{1 + K[M_2] + \left(\frac{K[M_1]}{r_2}\right)\right\}^2 - 4K[M_2]\right]^{1/2}\right)}{2} \tag{6-77}$$

where K is the equilibrium constant for the equilibrium in Eq. 6-74.

The copolymer composition for Case II is given by

$$\frac{d[M_1]}{d[M_2]} = \frac{\left\{\left(\frac{r_1[M_1]}{[M_2]}\right) + 1\right\}\left\{\alpha\gamma + \left[\frac{\alpha}{(1-\alpha)}\right]\right\}}{\alpha\gamma - 1 + \left\{\frac{1}{(1-\alpha)}\right\}^2} \tag{6-78}$$

with α defined by Eq. 6-77 and γ by

$$\gamma = \frac{\left\{K[M_2] + \frac{K[M_1]}{r_2} - \alpha\right\}}{K[M_2]} \tag{6-79}$$

where K is now the equilibrium constant for the equilibrium in Eq. 6-75.

Equations 6-76 and 6-78 have been experimentally tested recently in several copolymerizations [82, 83]. The systems studied included the radical copolymerizations of styrene-α-methylstyrene, styrene-methyl methacrylate, and acrylonitrile-α-methylstyrene, and the anionic copolymerization of vinylmesitylene-α-methylstyrene. (Vinylmesitylene is 2,4,6-trimethylstyrene.) These copolymerizations were generally studied over a range of comonomer feed compositions, reaction temperatures, and monomer concentrations. There is a transition from "normal" copolymerization behavior (i.e., behavior corresponding to Eq. 6-12) to "abnormal" behavior (i.e., behavior corresponding to Eqs. 6-76 and 6-78) as the reaction conditions are changed (increased temperature, decreased concentration of monomer M_2) to favor depropagation. Thus, in the radical copolymerization of styrene-α-methylstyrene [82], one observes a decrease in the α-methylstyrene content of the copolymer as the reaction temperature is increased from 0°C to 100°C. With increased temperature, there is increased depropagation of α-methylstyrene due to the effect of ceiling temperature (Sec. 3-9c). The effect is greatest for comonomer feed compositions rich in α-methylstyrene. The data in this system followed the quantitative behavior expected for Case II depropagation.

The anionic copolymerization of vinylmesitylene-α-methylstyrene is interesting [83]. The copolymerization was first studied at − 78°C at high monomer concentrations to determine the monomer reactivity ratios under conditions where depropagation was negligible. At the higher reaction temperature of 0°C, depropagation was still not important as long as the concentration of vinylmesitylene $[M_2]$ was sufficiently above the value of $[M_2]_c$ at that temperature. $[M_2]_c$ is 0.75 moles/liter at 0°C. When the vinylmesitylene concentration decreased below $[M_2]_c$ at constant $[M_1]/[M_2]$, depropagation became significant and the vinylmesitylene content of the copolymer decreased (see curved line in Fig. 6-13). The theoretical curves for this copolymerization for the Case I and Case II mechanisms were calculated from Eqs. 6-76 and 6-78 using the values of $[M_1]$, $[M_2]$, r_1, r_2, and K. The K value used in such calculations is, by necessity, that obtained from the polymerization-depolymerization equilibrium data for the homopolymerization of monomer M_2. The results are shown as the broken curves in Fig. 6-13. It is seen that

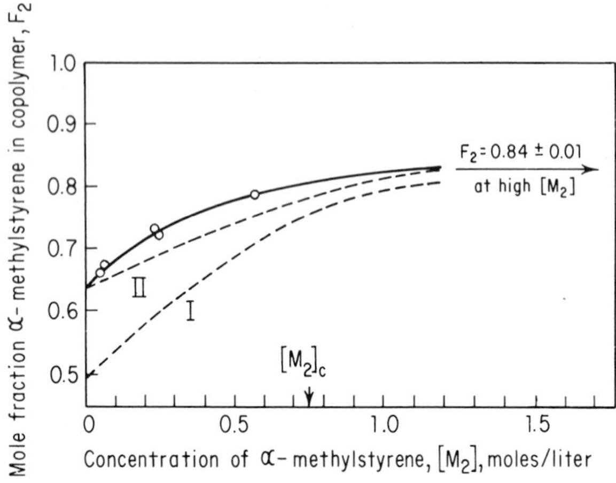

FIG. 6-13 *Effect of depropagation on copolymer composition in the anionic copolymerization of vinylmesitylene-*(M_1)*-α-methylstyrene*(M_2)*at 0°C for* f_2 *constant at 0.91. The broken-lined curves are the calculated curves for Lowry's Cases I and II (with* r_1 = *0.20 and* r_2 = *0.72); the experimental data follow the solid-lined curve. After [83] (by permission of Marcel Dekker, Inc., New York).*

the Case II mechanism fits the experimental data much more closely than the Case I mechanism. This is the general behavior which has been observed for most of the systems studied. It has been noted that the theoretical curve would fit the data even more closely if one assumed that monomer M_1 also tends to depropagate. Lowry [81] has treated this situation but the result is difficult to apply quantitatively at the present time.

6-6 COPOLYMERIZATIONS OF DIENES

6-6a Crosslinking

Diene monomers are often used in copolymerizations in order to obtain a crosslinked structure in the final product. The reaction is generally analogous to step polymerizations involving trifunctional reagents (Sec. 2-8). Crosslinking can occur in these copolymerizations either during the copolymerization or subsequently depending on the relative reactivities of the two double bonds of the diene monomer. The extent of crosslinking will depend on the latter and on the amount of the diene present relative to the other monomer. The point at which crosslinking occurs has been treated mathematically for several different types of dienes [84, 85]. In all instances, it is assumed that the diene is present at low concentrations since this is the case encountered in most practical instances.

The first case which can be considered is the copolymerization of a monomer A with diene monomer BB where all of the double bonds (i.e., the A double bond and both B double bonds) have the same reactivity. Methyl methacrylate-ethylene glycol dimethacrylate (EGDM), vinyl acetate-divinyl adipate (DVA), and styrene-divinylbenzene (DVB) are examples of this type of copolymerization system. The critical extent of reaction (i.e., the fraction of A groups reacted) p_c for the onset of gelation to occur is given in this case by

$$p_c = \frac{[A] + [B]}{[B]\overline{X}_w} \tag{6-80}$$

where [A] and [B] are the concentrations of the A and B double bonds (not the concentrations of the monomers) and $\overline{X}_w$ is the weight-average degree of polymerization of the linear polymer chains. $\overline{X}_w$ is usually considered to be the weight-average degree of polymerization which would be observed in the polymerization of monomer A in the absence of diene BB. Equation 6-80 predicts that extensive crosslinking occurs during this type of copolymerization. Thus, gelation is observed [86] at 12.5 percent reaction in the methyl methacrylate-ethylene glycol dimethacrylate system containing 0.05 mole percent EGDM [86]. Equation 6-80 has been found to be generally useful in predicting the gel points for various copolymerizations [86, 87]. Data for the styrene-divinylbenzene system are shown in Table 6-15. The equation holds best for systems containing low concentrations of the diene monomer; its utility decreases as the concentration of diene increases. With increasing diene concentration, Eq. 6-80 predicts gel points at conversions which are increasingly lower than those found experimentally. This general behavior has been attributed to the wastage of the diene monomer due to intramolecular cyclization reactions (Sec. 6-6b).

A second case is the copolymerization of A and BB in which the reactivities of the two groups are not equal but are, instead, r_1 and r_2, respectively. In this case the critical extent of reaction at gelation is given by

Table 6-15 Crosslinking in the Copolymerization of Styrene-Divinylbenzene

Mole fraction DVB	Gel point (p_c)	
	Calculated from Eq. 6-80	Observed[a]
0.004	0.21	0.16
0.008	0.10	0.14
0.02	0.042	0.076
0.032	0.026	0.074
0.082	0.010	0.052
0.30	0.0042	0.045

[a]Data from [87].

$$p_c = \frac{(r_1[A]^2 + 2[A][B] + r_2[B]^2)^2}{\bar{X}_w[B]([A] + [B])(r_2[B] + [A])^2} \tag{6-81}$$

which reduces to

$$p_c = \frac{[A]r_1^2}{[B]\bar{X}_w} \tag{6-82}$$

for $[A] \gg [B]$. When the double bonds of the diene are more reactive than that of the other monomer ($r_2 > r_1$), crosslinking occurs in the early stages of the copolymerization. Crosslinking is delayed until the later stages if $r_1 > r_2$. For the system where $r_1 > r_2$ and $r_1 > 1$, crosslinking is not as extensive at a given extent of reaction as that taking place in copolymerizations of the type governed by Eq. 6-80 where $r_1 = r_2$.

The third case is the copolymerization of a monomer A with the diene BC where the groups A and B have equal reactivity but group C has a much lower reactivity. An example of such a case would be methyl methacrylate-allyl methacrylate where A and B are the two methacrylate groups and C is the allyl group. If r is the reactivity ratio between the C and B groups, then the following hold for the radicals derived from the A and B groups

$$r = \frac{k_{AC}}{k_{AA}} = \frac{k_{AC}}{k_{AB}} = \frac{k_{BC}}{k_{BA}} = \frac{k_{BC}}{k_{BB}} \tag{6-83}$$

For such a system, the copolymer will consist of copolymerized A and B groups with pendant, unreacted C groups until the later stages of reaction. Crosslinking does not occur until relatively late in the reaction due to the low reactivity of the C group. The critical extent of reaction at gelation in this case is given by

$$p_c = 1 - \exp\left(\frac{-1}{2q\bar{X}_w r}\right) \tag{6-84}$$

where q is the mole fraction of the diene in the initial comonomer feed.

In selecting the make-up of a crosslinking system, one has a number of variables which can be used to control the process. Thus, gelation can be delayed with the production of a high conversion uncrosslinked product which is amenable to subsequent crosslinking. Gelation can be delayed by reducing the amount of the diene, the degree of polymerization by using chain transfer agents, or the reactivity of one of the double bonds of the diene monomer by proper choice of the diene. The extent of crosslinking in the final product is also controlled by these variables. Thus, extensive crosslinking, with the formation of "tight" network structures, is obtained by avoiding chain transfer agents and using increased amounts of dienes whose double bonds have similar reactivities.

A special situation which is often encountered is that where the reaction of one of the double bonds of the diene results in a decrease in the reactivity of the remaining double bond. If the decrease in reactivity is large, the effect is to markedly delay the crosslinking reaction. This case then becomes very similar to the last one where the C group had a much lower reactivity than the A and B groups. The most notable case in which there is a large drop in reactivity of one group upon reaction of the other is in the copolymerization of 1,3-dienes where 1,4-polymerization leads to residual 2,3-double bonds which have lowered reactivity. These are subsequently used to bring about crosslinking by reactions discussed in Sec. 9-2.

Crosslinking can also occur during the homopolymerization of a diene monomer. This has sometimes been a troublesome and undesirable occurrence in the homopolymerization of 1,3-dienes. As the reaction proceeds there is the possibility of crosslinking due to copolymerization between unreacted monomer and the newly formed 2,3-double bonds of reacted monomer. The number of crosslinks ρ formed per monomer unit in the primary linear polymer chain depends on the extent of reaction according [88] to

$$\rho = -\left(\frac{2}{r}\right)\left[1 + \left(\frac{1}{p}\right)\ln(1 - p)\right] \tag{6-85}$$

where r, the monomer reactivity ratio for the 1,3-diene, is the ratio of the rate constants for the addition of the propagating radical to the 1,3-diene monomer relative to its addition to the 2,3-double bond in the polymer. Since the gel point occurs when ρ reaches $1/\bar{X}_w$, Eq. 6-85 becomes

$$\frac{1}{\bar{X}_w} = -\left(\frac{2}{r}\right)\left[1 + \left(\frac{1}{p_c}\right)\ln(1 - p_c)\right] \tag{6-86}$$

for the critical extent of reaction at gelation. 1,3-Butadiene has been found [89] to have an r value of 7.4×10^3 at 50°C indicating that crosslinking will not be appreciable in this case until the later stages of reaction.

6-6b Alternating Intra-Intermolecular Polymerization

The polymerization of unconjugated dienes (e.g., diallyl phthalate, diethylene glycol bis(allyl carbonate), diallyl maleate) and trienes (e.g., triallyl cyanurate) to form highly crosslinked thermosetting products is a commerically important process. This is also true of the use of such monomers to bring about crosslinking in copolymerization systems (Sec. 6-6a). (The mathematical treatment [90] of crosslinking in unconjugated dienes is similar to that previously discussed for conjugated dienes.) The crosslinking reaction is almost always found to be somewhat inefficient in that the experimental gel points occur at higher extents of reaction than those predicted by theory. There is a wastage of the diene or triene monomer which has been ascribed to intramolecular cyclization of the diene or triene [91, 92]. This phenomenon is encountered not only in homo and copolymerizations involving dienes and trienes but also in step polymerizations with trifunctional reactants (Sec. 2-8c).

The competition between the intermolecular and intramolecular reactions in the polymerization of a diene can be depicted as

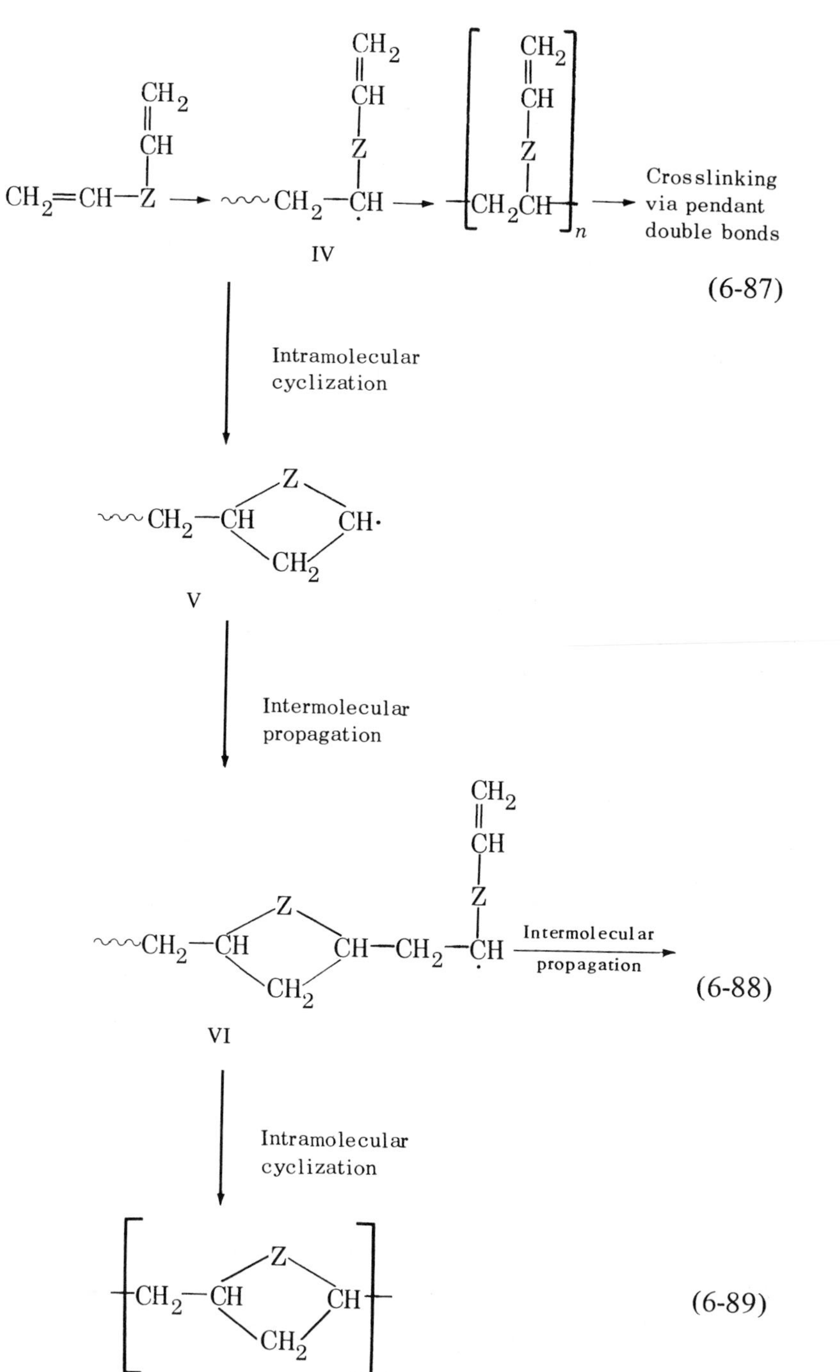
CH2=CH—Z
IV
Crosslinking via pendant double bonds
(6-87)
Intramolecular cyclization
V
Intermolecular propagation
VI
Intermolecular propagation
(6-88)
Intramolecular cyclization
(6-89)

where Z is a structural group such as the benzene ring in divinylbenzene or the trimethylene group in 1,6-heptadiene. Intermolecular polymerization proceeds according to the horizontal set of reactions (Eq. 6-87) to produce a linear polymer with pendant double bonds. The pendant double bonds of a propagating chain give rise to a crosslinked final product by copolymerizing (either with unreacted monomer or the pendant double bonds of other chains). The extent of crosslinking depends on factors discussed in Sec. 6-6a. Cyclization occurs when the propagating species IV reacts with its own pendant double bond in preference to intermolecular propagation. (Similar reaction sequences would apply to the occurrence of intramolecular crosslinking in polymerizations involving trienes or copolymerizations in which one of the monomers is a diene or triene.)

The importance of the intramolecular cyclization reaction was emphasized when Butler and co-workers [93, 94] found that the radical polymerization of diallyl quaternary ammonium salts gave soluble, uncrosslinked polymers with little or no residual unsaturation. In this case, there is essentially no tendency for the radical VI to propagate intermolecularly; the exclusive reaction is intramolecular cyclization. The reaction proceeds by the vertical sequence in Eq. 6-89 without any tendency toward the sequence in Eq. 6-88. The product is a completely linear polymer with cyclic structures in the backbone

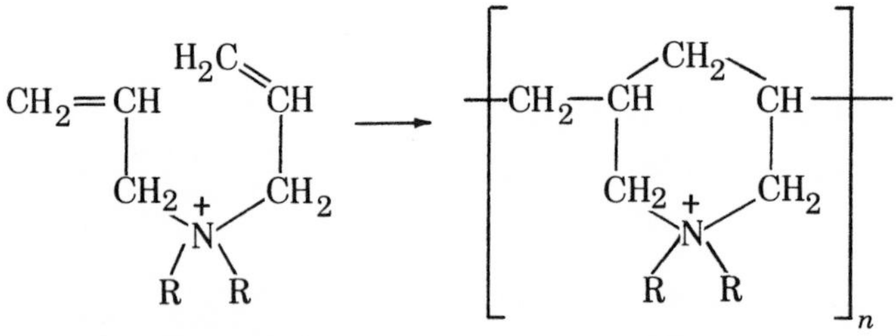

$$CH_2{=}CH-CH_2-\overset{+}{N}R_2-CH_2-CH{=}CH_2 \longrightarrow \left[-CH_2-CH\overset{CH_2}{\frown}CH- \;(\text{ring: } CH-CH_2-\overset{+}{N}R_2-CH_2-CH) \right]_n \qquad (6\text{-}90)$$

This type of polymerization has been referred to as *alternating intra-intermolecular polymerization* or *cyclopolymerization*. It can be considered as an alternating copolymerization between intra- and intermolecular propagations.

Extensive work by Butler and Marvel and their co-workers as well as others [91–98] have helped to show that the size of the ring structure which can be formed determines whether intermolecular polymerization or intramolecular cyclization is the predominant reaction for a particular monomer. The extent of cyclization generally increases with ring size in the order: 5- and 6-membered rings appreciably greater than 7-membered rings and the latter somewhat greater than larger sized rings. When 5- or 6-membered rings can be formed, the polymerization proceeds almost exclusively by the alternating intra-intermolecular route. This has been observed for a large number of monomers including 2,6-dimethylenepimelic acid and derivatives, acrylic anhydride, substituted 1,5-hexadienes and substituted 1,6-heptadienes, and 1,6-heptadiyne. Similar results have been observed for radical, anionic, and cationic polymerizations.

The extent of cyclization decreases quite sharply as one goes to ring sizes of seven or more atoms. However, contrary to expectations, the extent of cyclization is still quite appreciable for monomers which can form such rings. Thus, the extent of cyclization (measured as the percent of monomer units which are cyclized) is 15–20 percent for diallyl esters which give rise to ring structures containing up to 17 atoms [91]. Even more unexpectedly, the radical polymerization of *o*-diallyl phthalate gives a polymer with approximately 40 percent cyclization. The cyclic structure in this case is an eleven-membered ring

$$C_6H_4(COOCH_2CH{=}CH_2)_2 \longrightarrow \text{(ring: } C_6H_4\text{–CO–O–}CH_2\text{–}CH(\text{–}CH_2\sim)\text{–}CH_2\text{–}CH(\sim)\text{–}CH_2\text{–O–CO–)} \qquad (6\text{-}91)$$

Similar observations have been made in studies with other monomers.

It has been further observed that the polymerizations of 1,4-dienes such as divinyl ether and some methyl-substituted 1,4-diene-3-one monomers also lead to products which have little residual unsaturation and are not appreciably crosslinked [98]. Intramolecular cyclization occurs in these cases but not by the mechanism described above since unstable four-membered rings would be formed. The reaction proceeds according to the scheme

Monomer

VII

(6-92)

Secondary cyclization

Monomer

VIII

(6-93)

where Z is a group such as CH_2, O, S, or CO. Cyclization occurs in the sequence of reactions in Eq. 6-92 with the dimer radical (or ion in ionic polymerization) VII. Secondary cyclization via Eq. 6-93 may also take place to form the bicyclic structure VIII.

It is well at this point to recall the discussion in Sec. 2-3 concerning the competition between linear polymerization and cyclization in step polymerizations. Cyclization is not competitive with linear polymerization to any extent for ring sizes greater than seven atoms. Further, even for most of the reactants which would yield rings of 6–7 atoms if they cyclized, linear polymerization could be made to predominate due to the interconvertibility of the cyclic and linear structures. The difference in behavior between the chain and step polymerizations arises in part from the fact that the cyclic structures in chain polymerization do not depropagate under the reaction conditions, i.e., the cyclic structure is not interconvertible with the linear structure. But the prime difference between the two is that the radicals IV and VII (or the corresponding ionic species in an ionic cyclopolymerization) are much more reactive toward cyclization than the corresponding reactant in step polymerization. The reason for this is not established but it may simply be due to steric hindrance between the $-ZCH{=}CH_2$ group of the propagating species IV and an approaching monomer molecule.

6-7 OTHER COPOLYMERIZATIONS

6-7a Miscellaneous Copolymerizations of Alkenes

A variety of compounds including sulfur dioxide, carbon monoxide, phosphines, nitroso compounds, oxygen, and quinones, which do not homopolymerize due to polar and/or steric considerations, have been found to undergo radical copolymerization with alkenes to form polymeric sulfones [99, 100], ketones [101], phosphines [102], amine-oxides [103, 104], peroxides [105], and ethers [106]

$$CH_2{=}CHR + SO_2 \longrightarrow \left(CH_2CHR{-}SO_2 \right)_n \tag{6-94}$$

$$CH_2{=}CHR + CO \longrightarrow \left(CH_2CHR{-}CO \right)_n \tag{6-95}$$

$$CH_2{=}CHR + R_3'P \longrightarrow \left(CH_2CHR{-}PR_3' \right)_n \tag{6-96}$$

$$CH_2{=}CHR + R'{-}NO \longrightarrow \left[CH_2CHR{-}\underset{}{\overset{R'}{\overset{|}{N}}}{-}O \right]_n \tag{6-97}$$

$$CH_2{=}CHR + O_2 \longrightarrow \left(CH_2CHR{-}O{-}O \right)_n \tag{6-98}$$

$$CH_2{=}CHR + O{=}C_6H_4{=}O \longrightarrow \left[CH_2CHR{-}O{-}C_6H_4{-}O \right]_n \tag{6-99}$$

The sulfur dioxide reaction is probably the most studied copolymerization. Alkenes which are relatively electronegative, such as ethylene, α-olefins, 1,2-disubstituted olefins, allyl ethers, vinyl chloride, and styrene undergo facile copolymerization with sulfur dioxide. Monomers such as methyl acrylate, with electron withdrawing substituents, do not form such copolymers due to polar repulsions with the electropositive sulfur dioxide. Many of the simple olefins form 1:1 alternating polysulfones [99, 107] due to the polar effect between the electronegative alkene and the electropositive sulfur dioxide. An alternate explanation for the alternating tendency is that SO_2 forms a 1:1 complex with the olefin and the complex then reacts as a unit.

Monomers containing bulky substituents, such as styrene and vinyl chloride, yield polysulfones containing less SO_2 than the alkene monomer. This is probably due to the steric hindrance between the substituent of the alkene and the bulky sulfur dioxide. The kinetics and copolymer compositions in these copolymerizations are complicated by the occurrence of depropagation during the reaction [107] (Sec. 6-5b). The effect of depropagation is increasingly important as the alkene monomer becomes more substituted and as the substituents become bulkier; the sulfur dioxide content of the copolymers decreases accordingly. In the case of monomers with two bulky substituents on the same carbon atom, such as in 2-methyl-2-butene, copolymerization does not occur.

There appears to be a definite tendency toward alternation in the other copolymerizations also, although extensive data is not available. Thus, the reaction of CF_3NO and C_2F_4 leads to a 1:1 alternating copolymer [104] and the monomer reactivity ratios in the copolymerization of ethylene and carbon monoxide are 0.04 and 0, respectively [100]. The reactions of alkenes with quinones and peroxides are not well defined in terms of the stoichiometry of the products. These two reactions are better classified as retardation or inhibition reactions because of the very slow copolymerization rates (Sec. 3-7a).

6-7b Copolymerization of Carbonyl Monomers

Although the homopolymerization of carbonyl monomers has been studied fairly extensively (Sec. 5-5), there are only a few reported studies on the copolymerization of these monomers

$$\text{RCHO} + \text{R}'\text{CHO} \longrightarrow \left(\text{CHR—O—CHR}'\text{—O} \right)_n \qquad (6\text{-}100)$$

The cationic copolymerization of acetaldehyde with formaldehyde and a number of other aliphatic aldehydes has been carried out [108,

109]. Anionic copolymerizations have been reported with formaldehyde, acetaldehyde, and various chloro-substituted acetaldehydes [110, 111]. Many of these studies are fragmentary or not precise enough to give a clear picture of the reaction. In some cases, it is not clear whether block or random copolymers were obtained. The identity of the specific catalyst appeared to be important in other instances. Depending on the catalyst used, a comonomer pair might yield homopolymer, block copolymer, or random copolymer. The general tendency in the copolymerization of carbonyl monomers is toward ideal behavior. However, there is a very definite tendency toward alternation for comonomer pairs in which one of the monomers has a bulky substituent. Thus, the anionic copolymerization of acetaldehyde and chloral at $-78°C$ shows [110] a strong alternating tendency with $r_1 = 0.18$ and $r_2 = 0.00$.

The copolymerization of carbonyl monomers with alkenes has been even less studied than that between different carbonyl monomers. The radiation-induced copolymerization of styrene with formaldehyde has been studied in some detail [112]. The reaction appears to proceed via cationic propagation as determined by the fact that the rate of copolymerization of formaldehyde with several alkenes decreased in the order α-methylstyrene > styrene > methyl methacrylate > acrylonitrile. The formaldehyde(M_1)-styrene(M_2) system showed ideal behavior with $r_1 = 52$, $r_2 = 0$ for the reaction at $-78°C$. The product, consisting mostly of formaldehyde, was interesting in terms of the decreased tendency toward the thermal unzipping reaction compared to pure polyformaldehyde. The few styrene units in the copolymer chain apparently act as stopping points for the depolymerization process.

REFERENCES

1. R. B. Fox et al., *Polymer Preprints,* **8(1)**, e(1967); **8(2)**, e(1967).
2. H. Staudinger and J. Schneiders, *Ann.,* **541**:151 (1939).
3. T. Alfrey, Jr. and G. Goldfinger, *J. Chem. Phys.,* **12**:205 (1944).
4. F. R. Mayo and F. M. Lewis, *J. Am. Chem. Soc.,* **66**:1594 (1944).
5. F. T. Wall, *ibid.,* **66**:2050 (1944).
6. C. Walling, "Free Radicals in Solution," chap. 4, John Wiley & Sons, Inc., New York, 1957.
7. F. W. Billmeyer, Jr., "Textbook of Polymer Science," chap. 11, Interscience Publishers, John Wiley & Sons, Inc., New York, 1962.
8. H. W. Melville, B. Noble, and W. F. Watson, *J. Polymer Sci.,* **2**:229 (1947).

9. G. Goldfinger and T. Kane, *ibid.*, **3**:462 (1948).
10. Y. Landler, *Compt. rend.*, **230**:539 (1950).
11. D. C. Pepper, *Quart. Rev.* (London), 8:88 (1954).
12. F. R. Mayo and C. Walling, *Chem. Rev.*, **46**:191 (1950).
13. R. Gumbs, S. Penczek, J. Jagur-Grodzinski, and M. Szwarc, *Macromolecules*, 2:77 (1969).
14. R. L. Kruse, *J. Polymer Sci.*, **B5**:437 (1967).
15. I. Skeist, *J. Am. Chem. Soc.*, **68**:1781 (1946).
16. V. E. Meyer and G. G. Lowry, *J. Polymer Sci.*, **A3**:2843 (1965).
17. V. E. Meyer and R. K. S. Chan, *Polymer Preprints*, **8(1)**:209 (1967).
18. M. Fineman and S. D. Ross, *J. Polymer Sci.*, **5**:259 (1950).
19. P. W. Tidwell and G. A. Mortimer, *ibid.*, **A3**:369 (1965).
20. V. E. Meyer, *ibid.*, **A-1(4)**:2819 (1966).
21. H. L. Marder and C. Schuerch, *ibid.*, **44**:129 (1960).
22. Y. Yamashita, K. Ito, S. Ikuma, and H. Kida, *ibid.*, **B6**:219 (1968).
23. C. E. Wilkes, J. C. Westfahl, and R. H. Backderf, *Polymer Preprints*, **8(1)**:386 (1967).
24. W. H. Stockmayer, *J. Chem. Phys.*, **13**:199 (1945).
25. G. Phillips and W. Carrick, *J. Am. Chem. Soc.*, **84**:920 (1962); *J. Polymer Sci.*, **59**:401 (1962).
26. L. H. Peebles, in G. E. Ham (ed.), "Copolymerization," pp. 564–573, Interscience Publishers, John Wiley & Sons, Inc., New York, 1964.
27. T. Alfrey, Jr. and G. Goldfinger, *J. Chem. Phys.*, **12**:332 (1944).
28. A. Valvassori and G. Sartori, *Fortschr. Hochpolymer.-Forsch. (Advan. Polymer Sci.)*, **5**:28 (1967).
29. G. E. Ham, *J. Polymer Sci.*, **A2**:2735 (1964); *J. Macromol. Chem.*, **1**:403 (1966).
30. G. E. Ham, Theory of Copolymerization, in G. E. Ham (ed.), "Copolymerization," chap. 1, Interscience Publishers, John Wiley & Sons, Inc., New York, 1964.
31. C. Walling and E. R. Briggs, *J. Am. Chem. Soc.*, **67**:1774 (1945).
32. T. Alfrey, Jr. and G. Goldfinger, *J. Chem. Phys.*, **14**:115 (1946).
33. G. E. Ham, *J. Polymer Sci.*, **A2**:4191 (1964).
34. F. M. Lewis, C. Walling, W. Cummings, E. Briggs, and F. R. Mayo, *J. Am. Chem. Soc.*, **70**:1519 (1948).
35. R. D. Burkhart and N. L. Zutty, *J. Polymer Sci.*, **57**:593 (1962); **A1**:1137 (1963).
36. B. R. Thompson and R. H. Raines, *ibid.*, **41**:265 (1959).
37. F. E. Brown and G. E. Ham, *ibid.*, **A2**:3623 (1964).
38. J. Brandup and E. H. Immergut (eds.), "Polymer Handbook," Interscience Publishers, John Wiley & Sons, Inc., New York, 1966.
39. M. G. Evans, *Discussions Faraday Soc.*, **2**:271 (1947).
40. T. L. Dawson, R. D. Lundberg, and F. J. Welch, *J. Polymer Sci.*, **A-1(7)**: 173 (1969).

41. M. G. Baldwin, *ibid.,* **A3**:703 (1965).
42. C. C. Price, *ibid.,* **3**:772 (1948).
43. T. Ito and T. Otsu, *J. Macromol. Sci. (Chem.),* **A3**:197 (1969).
44. C. Walling et al., *J. Am. Chem. Soc.,* **70**:1537, 1544 (1948).
45. N. Gaylord et al., *J. Polymer Sci.,* **B6**:743, 749 (1968) and **B7**:145 (1969); *Polymer Preprints,* **10(2)**:546, 554 (1969).
46. T. Alfrey, Jr. and C. C. Price, *J. Polymer Sci.,* **2**:101 (1947).
47. T. Alfrey, Jr. and L. J. Young, The Q-e Scheme, in G. E. Ham (ed.), "Copolymerization," chap. II, Interscience Publishers, John Wiley & Sons, Inc., New York, 1964.
48. K. F. O'Driscoll and T. Yonezawa, *J. Macromol. Sci.–Revs. Macromol. Chem.,* **1(1)**:1 (1966).
49. G. E. Ham, General Aspects of Free Radical Polymerization, in G. E. Ham (ed.), "Vinyl Polymerization," vol. 1, part I, chap. 1, Marcel Dekker, Inc., New York, 1967.
50. F. R. Mayo, *J. Polymer Sci.,* **A-2**:4207 (1964).
51. K. F. O'Driscoll, *ibid.,* **B-3**:305 (1965).
52. C. Walling, *J. Am. Chem. Soc.,* **71**:1930 (1949).
53. A. M. North, *Polymer,* **4**:134 (1963).
54. J. N. Atherton and A. M. North, *Trans. Faraday Soc.,* **58**:2049 (1962).
55. K. F. O'Driscoll, W. Wertz, and A. Husar, *Polymer Preprints,* **8(1)**:380 (1967).
56. J. P. Kennedy, Cationic Copolymerizations, in G. E. Ham (ed.), "Copolymerization," chap. V, Interscience Publishers, John Wiley & Sons, Inc., New York, 1964.
57. M. Morton, Anionic Copolymerization, in G. E. Ham (ed.), "Copolymerization," chap. VII, Interscience Publishers, John Wiley & Sons, Inc., New York, 1964.
58. J. F. Dunphy and C. S. Marvel, *J. Polymer Sci.,* **47**:1 (1960).
59. R. B. Cundall, Copolymerization, in P. H. Plesch (ed.), "The Chemistry of Cationic Polymerization," chap. 15, Macmillan Company, New York, 1963.
60. C. G. Overberger, R. J. Ehrig, and D. Tanner, *J. Am. Chem. Soc.,* **76**:772 (1954).
61. C. G. Overberger, D. H. Tanner, and E. M. Pearce, *ibid.,* **80**:4566 (1958).
62. C. G. Overberger, L. H. Arnold, and J. J. Taylor, *ibid.,* **73**:5541 (1951).
63. C. G. Overberger and V. G. Kamath, *ibid.,* **81**:2910 (1959).
64. K. F. O'Driscoll, T. Yonezawa, and T. Higashimura, *J. Macromol. Chem.,* **1**:17 (1966).
65. J. Rehner, R. L. Zapp, and W. J. Sparks, *J. Polymer Sci.,* **9**:21 (1953).
66. M. Szwarc and J. Smid, Kinetics of Propagation of Anionic Polymerization and Copolymerization, in G. Porter (ed.), "Progress in Reaction Kinetics," vol. 2, chap. 5, Macmillan Company, New York, 1964.

67. M. Shima, D. N. Bhattacharyya, J. Smid, and M. Szwarc, *J. Am. Chem. Soc.,* **85**:1306 (1962).
68. D. N. Bhattacharyya, C. L. Lee, J. Smid, and M. Szwarc, *ibid.,* **85**:533 (1963).
69. H. Yuki, K. Kosai, S. Murahashi, and J. Hotta, *J. Polymer Sci.,* **B2**:1121 (1964).
70. D. J. Kelley and A. V. Tobolsky, *J. Am. Chem. Soc.,* **81**:1597 (1959).
71. K. F. O'Driscoll and A. V. Tobolsky, *J. Polymer Sci.,* **31**:115, 123 (1958).
72. K. F. O'Driscoll, *ibid.,* **57**:721 (1962); **B3**:43 (1965).
73. C. G. Overberger and N. Yamamoto, *Polymer Preprints,* **7(1)**:115 (1966).
74. R. G. Fordyce and G. E. Ham, *J. Am. Chem. Soc.,* **73**:1186 (1951).
75. E. Merz, T. Alfrey, Jr., and G. Goldfinger, *J. Polymer Sci.,* **1**:75 (1946).
76. W. G. Barb, *ibid.,* **11**:117 (1953).
77. G. E. Ham, *ibid.,* **45**:177 (1960).
78. A. Guyot and J. Guillot, *J. Macromol. Sci. (Chem.),* **A1(5)**:793 (1967).
79. J. K. Hecht and N. D. Ojha, *Macromolecules,* **2**:94 (1969).
80. C. Lee, J. Smid, and M. Szwarc, *Trans. Faraday Soc.,* **59**:1192 (1963).
81. G. G. Lowry, *J. Polymer Sci.,* **42**:463 (1960).
82. K. F. O'Driscoll and F. P. Gasparro, *J. Macromol. Sci. (Chem.),* **A1(4)**:643 (1967).
83. K. J. Ivin and R. H. Spensley, *ibid.,* **A1(4)**:653 (1967).
84. T. Alfrey, Jr., J. J. Bohrer, and H. Mark, "Copolymerization," chaps. IX, X, Interscience Publishers, New York, 1952.
85. F. W. Billmeyer, Jr., "Textbook of Polymer Science," pp. 348–353, Interscience Publishers, John Wiley & Sons, Inc., 1962.
86. C. Walling, *J. Am. Chem. Soc.,* **67**:441 (1945).
87. B. T. Storey, *J. Polymer Sci.,* **A3**:265 (1965).
88. P. J. Flory, *J. Am. Chem. Soc.,* **69**:2893 (1947); "Principles of Polymer Chemistry," chap. IX, Cornell University Press, Ithaca, 1953.
89. M. Morton and P. P. Salatiello, *J. Polymer Sci.,* **6**:225 (1951).
90. C. H. Bamford, W. G. Barb, A. D. Jenkins, and P. F. Onyon, "The Kinetics of Vinyl Polymerization by Radical Mechanisms," chap. 7, Butterworth and Co. (Publishers) Ltd., London, 1958.
91. T. Holt and W. Simpson, *Proc. Roy. Soc.* (London), **A238**:154 (1956).
92. M. Gordon and R. J. Roe, *J. Polymer Sci.,* **21**:57, 75 (1956).
93. G. B. Butler and F. L. Ingley, *J. Am. Chem. Soc.,* **73**:894 (1951).
94. G. B. Butler and R. J. Angelo, *ibid.,* **79**:3128 (1957).
95. G. B. Butler, *Pure and Appl. Chem.,* **4**:299 (1962); *Polymer Preprints,* **8(1)**: 35 (1967).
96. C. S. Marvel and R. D. Vest, *J. Am. Chem. Soc.,* **79**:5771 (1957); **81**:984 (1959).
97. C. S. Marvel and J. K. Stille, *ibid.,* **80**:1740 (1958).
98. W. E. Gibbs and J. M. Barton, The Mechanism of Cyclopolymerization of

Nonconjugated Diolefins, in G. E. Ham (ed.), "Vinyl Polymerization," vol. 1, part I, chap. 2, Marcel Dekker, Inc., New York, 1967.

99. F. S. Dainton and K. J. Ivin, *Quart. Rev.* (London), **12**:61 (1958).
100. M. Matsuda and M. Iino, *Macromolecules,* **2**:216 (1969).
101. P. Colombo, L. E. Kukacka, J. Fontana, R. N. Chapman, and M. Steinberg, *J. Polymer Sci.,* **A-1(4)**:29 (1966).
102. B. Laszkiewicz, *J. Appl. Polymer Sci.,* **8**:2117 (1964).
103. G. H. Crawford, D. E. Rice, and B. F. Landrum, *J. Polymer Sci.,* **1A**:565 (1963).
104. J. Green, N. Mayes, and E. Cottrill, *J. Macromol. Sci. (Chem.),* **A1(7)**:1387 (1967).
105. K. Griesbaum, A. A. Oswald, and W. Naegele, *J. Org. Chem.,* **29**:1887 (1964).
106. C. F. Hauser and N. L. Zutty, *Polymer Preprints,* **8(1)**:369 (1967).
107. J. E. Hazell and K. J. Ivin, *Trans. Faraday Soc.,* **58**:176, 342 (1962); **61**:2330 (1965).
108. O. Vogl, *J. Macromol. Sci. (Chem.),* **A1(2)**:243 (1967).
109. H. F. Mark and N. Ogata, *J. Polymer Sci.,* **A1**:3439 (1963).
110. T. Iwata, G. Wasai, T. Saegusa, and J. Furukawa, *Makromol. Chem.,* **77**:229 (1964).
111. I. Rosen, *J. Macromol. Sci. (Chem.),* **A1(2)**:243 (1967).
112. Y. P. Castille and V. Stannett, *J. Polymer Sci.,* **A-1(4)**:2063 (1966).

PROBLEMS

6-1. Discuss the differences in the structures of random, alternating, graft, and block copolymers.

6-2. What is the difference between the ideal and alternating behaviors in copolymerization?

6-3. Consider the following monomer reactivity ratios for the copolymerization of various pairs of monomers:

Case	r_1	r_2
1	0.1	0.2
2	0.1	10
3	0.1	3
4	0	0.3
5	0	0
6	0.8	2
7	1	15

What is the composition of the copolymer that would be formed at low conversion from equimolar mixtures of the two monomers in each case?

6-4. Using the r_1 and r_2 values from Table 6-2, construct plots showing the initial copolymer composition as a function of the comonomer feed composition for the radical copolymerizations of methyl acrylate-methyl methacrylate and styrene-maleic anhydride. Are these examples of ideal or alternating copolymerization?

6-5. Calculate the composition of the initial terpolymer which would be produced from the radical polymerization of a solution containing acrylonitrile, styrene, and 1,3-butadiene in molar concentrations of 0.47, 0.47, and 0.06, respectively.

6-6. Discuss the effects of monomer and radical reactivities on the observed reactivity of radical-monomer reactions. What is the general order of monomer reactivities for styrene, vinyl acetate, methyl methacrylate, and acrylonitrile? What is the order of radical reactivities for the radicals derived from these monomers?

6-7. List the following monomers in the order of their increasing tendency toward alternation with 1,3-butadiene in free radical copolymerization:

a. *n*-butyl vinyl ether
b. methyl methacrylate
c. methyl acrylate
d. styrene
e. maleic anhydride
f. vinyl acetate
g. acrylonitrile

Explain the relative alternating tendencies in these copolymerizations.

6-8. Using the Q and e values in Table 6-7, calculate the monomer reactivity ratios for the comonomer pairs styrene-butadiene and styrene-methyl methacrylate. Compare the results with the r_1 and r_2 values in Table 6-2.

6-9. Using the product probability treatment (Eqs. 6-52, 6-53, and 6-54), calculate the monomer reactivity ratios for styrene-butadiene. Compare the results with those obtained from Q-e treatment and with the values in Table 6-2.

6-10. If the copolymerizations in Problem 6-7 were carried out using cationic initiation, what would be expected qualitatively for the copolymer compositions? List the copolymers in order of their increasing butadiene content. Would copolymers be formed from each of the comonomer pairs? Explain. What would be observed if one used anionic initiation?

6-11. Discuss the general effects of temperature, solvent, and catalyst on the monomer reactivity ratios in ionic copolymerizations. How do these compare with the corresponding effects in radical copolymerizations?

6-12. What are the differences between the two treatments (kinetic penultimate effect and depropagation) used to account for the deviations observed in the copolymer composition equation?

6-13. Discuss qualitatively the course of the radical copolymerization for each of the following comonomer pairs in terms of the degree of reaction at which gelation would be expected to occur:

a. Styrene-divinylbenzene
b. Methyl methacrylate-allyl methacrylate
c. Vinyl acetate-ethylene glycol dimethacrylate
d. Methyl methacrylate-divinyl adipate
e. Styrene-butadiene

6-14. The product obtained in the polymerization of 4-methyl-1,6-heptadiene contains no residual unsaturation. What is its chemical structure?

7

RING–OPENING POLYMERIZATION

In addition to step and chain polymerizations, there is another mode of polymerization which has become important in recent years. This is the *ring-opening polymerization* of cyclic monomers such as cyclic ethers, acetals, esters, amides, and siloxanes. The ring-opening process is of commercial interest in a number of cases including the polymerizations of ethylene and propylene oxides ($R = —H$ and $—CH_3$, respectively)

$$n\,H_2C\overset{O}{\frown}CHR \longrightarrow -\!\!\left(CH_2-\underset{\substack{|\\R}}{CH}-O\right)\!\!-_n \tag{7-1}$$

ϵ-caprolactam

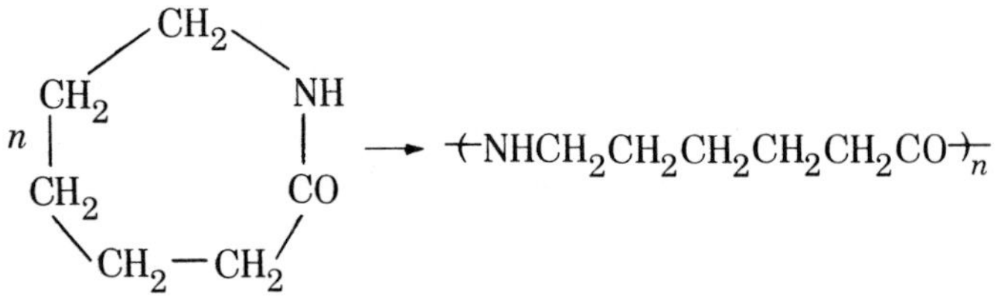

$$n\ \underset{\text{CH}_2\text{—CH}_2}{\overset{\text{CH}_2}{\text{CH}_2,\ \text{CH}_2,\ \text{NH},\ \text{CO}}} \longrightarrow -\!\!\left(\text{NHCH}_2\text{CH}_2\text{CH}_2\text{CH}_2\text{CH}_2\text{CO}\right)\!\!-_n \qquad (7\text{-}2)$$

and 3,3-bis(chloromethyl)oxetane

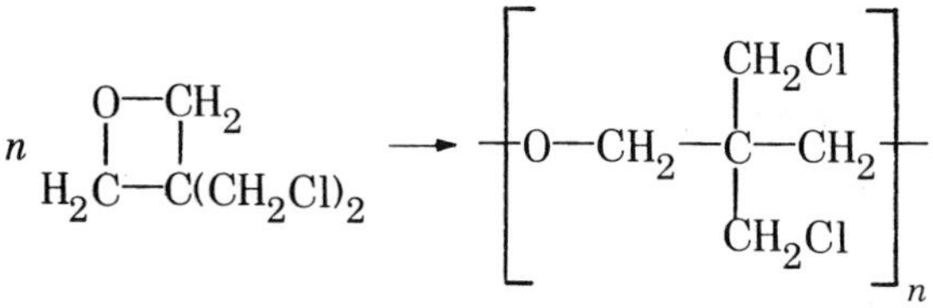

$$n\ \begin{array}{l}\text{O—CH}_2\\ |\quad\ \ |\\ \text{H}_2\text{C—C(CH}_2\text{Cl)}_2\end{array} \longrightarrow \left[\text{O—CH}_2\text{—}\underset{\text{CH}_2\text{Cl}}{\overset{\text{CH}_2\text{Cl}}{\text{C}}}\text{—CH}_2\right]_n \qquad (7\text{-}3)$$

(The term oxacyclobutane can also be used, instead of oxetane, to denote the four-membered cyclic ether structure.) Such polymers are usually named on the basis of the source of the polymer (i.e., the monomer), e.g., poly(ethylene oxide), poly(propylene oxide), poly(ϵ-caprolactam), and poly(3,3-bis(chloromethyl)oxetane). Polymers produced by ring-opening polymerizations are generally classified as condensation polymers based on the presence of functional groups, such as the ether and amide linkages, in the polymer chains (Sec. 1-1a).

7-1 GENERAL CHARACTERISTICS

7-1a Scope

A wide variety of cyclic monomers have been successfully polymerized by the ring-opening process [1]. This includes cyclic amines, sulfides, polysulfides, and even alkanes in addition to those classes of monomers mentioned above. The ease of polymerization of a given cyclic monomer depends on the reactivity of the functional group in the ring, the catalyst used, and the size of the ring. Although all three factors are discussed to varying extents throughout this chapter, it is worthwhile considering the last factor in general terms at this point. The effect of ring size on the polymerizability of a monomer generally depends on the factors previously discussed in Secs. 2-3. The reactivity of cyclic monomers generally follows the expected order with the effect of ring size being the opposite of that indicated in Fig. 2-3 for the ease of cyclization.

Polymerizability is high for rings of 3, 4, and 7 to 11 members and lower for rings of 5 and 6 members. In actual practice, ring-opening polymerizations are usually limited to monomers of less than 9 members due to the general unavailability of larger sized cyclic monomers.

7-1b Polymerization Mechanism and Kinetics

Ring-opening polymerizations have been initiated by ionic catalysts as well as catalysts which are molecular species. Initiation results in opening of the ring to form an initiator species M* which may be either an ion or neutral molecule depending on the catalyst. This can be generalized as

$$\overset{\frown}{\mathrm{R{-}Z}} + \mathrm{C} \longrightarrow \mathrm{M}^* \tag{7-4}$$

where Z is the functional group in the monomer and C is the ionic or molecular initiator. Ionic ring-opening polymerizations include those initiated by catalysts such as Na, RO^-, HO^-, H^+, and BF_3. The prime catalyst of the molecular type is water. Ionic initiators are usually more reactive than the molecular ones. Thus, it is usually only the more reactive cyclic monomers which undergo polymerization by initiators of the molecular type. Most monomers require the use of the stronger ionic initiators. Ionic ring-opening polymerizations show many of the general characteristics (e.g., effects of solvent and gegen-ion) of ionic chain polymerization.

The initiator species M* grows by successive ring-opening additions of many monomer molecules

$$\mathrm{M}^* + n\,\overset{\frown}{\mathrm{R{-}Z}} \longrightarrow \mathrm{M{\leftarrow}R{-}Z)}_n^* \tag{7-5}$$

The nature of the chain-growth process in ring-opening polymerization bears a superficial resemblance to that in chain polymerization. Only monomer adds to the growing chains in the propagation step. Species larger than monomer do not react with the growing chains. However, ring-opening polymerizations can have the characteristics of either chain or step polymerization or of both. The classification of a ring-opening polymerization as a chain or step polymerization can be made on two bases. One is the experimentally observed kinetic laws which describe the polymerization; the second is the time distribution in which high polymer is formed. The latter consideration is the prime characteristic which distinguishes chain and step polymerizations. High polymer is formed throughout the course of a chain polymerization in contrast to the slow buildup of polymer molecular weight in step polymerization. Most but not all ring-opening polymerizations behave as step polymerizations in that the polymer molecular weight increases slowly throughout the course of the polymerization. High polymer is not obtained until the later stages of reaction.

Irrespective of whether a particular ring-opening polymerization is a step or chain polymerization, its kinetics may follow expressions resembling those of either chain or step polymerizations. Many ring-opening polymerizations are complicated by the occurrence of polymerization-depolymerization equilibria. Various situations will be illustrated in this chapter by a detailed consideration of the kinetics of several typical ring-opening polymerizations.

7-2 CYCLIC ETHERS

The ether linkage is characteristically a strong one and is basic in the Lewis sense. The result is that the ring-opening polymerization of cyclic ethers is initiated only by cationic species. The epoxides (the 3-membered oxides) are the exception to this generalization. Epoxides are polymerized by both anionic and cationic initiators due to the high degree of strain in the small 3-membered ring. The initiation of cyclic ether polymerization by molecular species is essentially unknown due to the inherently low reactivity of the ether linkage.

The polymerization of simple cyclic ethers (i.e., those with a single ether linkage) has been, in practice, generally limited to those of 3, 4, and 5 members. The study of larger sized cyclic ethers has been carried out with cyclic acetals (Sec. 7-2b-4). The reactivity of different sized cyclic ethers follows the generally expected order. Cyclic ethers of less than 5 members or more than 6 members are relatively easily polymerized. The 5-membered cyclic ethers are polymerized with more difficulty. Substituted 5-membered cyclic ethers and acetals are usually unreactive, e.g., 2-methyltetrahydrofuran does not polymerize. The effect of substituents in increasing the stability and decreasing the reactivity of a cyclic compound is well known. The 6-membered cyclic ethers such as tetrahydropyran

(I) and 1,4-dioxane (II)

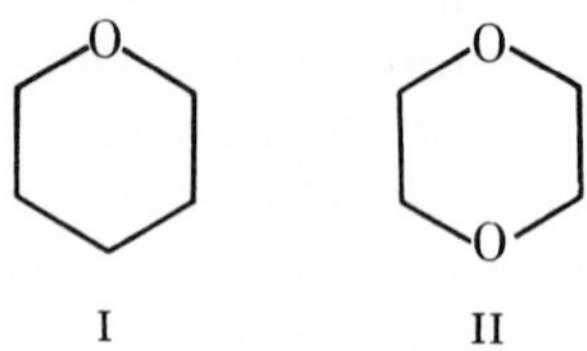

have been found to be completely unreactive. Polymerization does not take place under a wide range of reaction conditions.

7-2a Anionic Polymerization of Epoxides

7-2a-1 Reaction Characteristics. The anionic polymerization of epoxides such as ethylene and propylene oxides can be initiated by hydroxides, alkoxides, metal oxides, organometallic compounds and other bases [2, 3]. Thus, the polymerization of ethylene oxide by the catalyst M^+A^- involves initiation

$$\underset{\text{(epoxide ring: O bridging both C)}}{H_2C\!-\!CH_2} + M^+A^- \longrightarrow A\!-\!CH_2CH_2O^-M^+ \tag{7-6}$$

followed by propagation

$$A\!-\!CH_2CH_2O^-M^+ + \underset{\text{(O bridging)}}{H_2C\!-\!CH_2} \longrightarrow A\!-\!CH_2CH_2OCH_2CH_2O^-M^+ \tag{7-7a}$$

which may be generalized as

$$A\!\left(CH_2CH_2O\right)_n CH_2CH_2O^-M^+ + \underset{\text{(O bridging)}}{H_2C\!-\!CH_2} \longrightarrow$$

$$A\!\left(CH_2CH_2O\right)_{(n+1)} CH_2CH_2O^-M^+ \tag{7-7b}$$

Many epoxide polymerizations have the characteristics of living polymerizations in that there is often no termination in the absence of deliberately added terminating agents.

The polymerization of an unsymmetrical epoxide such as propylene oxide involves the possibility of two different sites (carbons 1 and 2) on the epoxide ring for the nucleophilic ring-opening reaction. Two different propagating species are then possible depending on the site at which reaction occurs

$$\underset{\text{(epoxide, O bridging CH and CH}_2)}{CH_3-CH-CH_2} \nearrow \quad \sim\!\sim\underset{CH_3}{\overset{|}{CH}}-CH_2-O^-K^+ \qquad (7\text{-}8)$$

$$\searrow \quad \sim\!\sim CH_2-\underset{CH_3}{\overset{|}{CH}}-O^-K^+ \qquad (7\text{-}9)$$

Although it might appear at first glance that the structure of the final polymer would be different depending on the reaction site, this is not the case. The polymer structure would be the same in both cases except for slight differences in the end-groups. However, nonpolymerization studies on the base catalyzed additions of small molecules such as water and alcohols across the epoxide ring (to form glycols or ether-alcohols, respectively) indicate that the attack is almost exclusively at carbon 2–the less sterically hindered site (Eq 7-9).

The anionic polymerization of epoxides is usually a step polymerization in that the polymer molecular weight increases slowly with conversion. However, the expressions for the rate and degree of polymerization bear a striking resemblance to those observed in living polymerizations. Thus, in the sodium methoxide catalyzed polymerization of ethylene oxide [4], the polymerization rate is given by

$$R_p = \frac{-d[C_2H_4O]}{dt} = k_p[CH_3O^-Na^+][C_2H_4O] \qquad (7\text{-}10)$$

However, not all anionic epoxide polymerizations are step polymerizations in terms of the relative rates of the initiation and propagation reactions. The potassium hydroxide catalyzed polymerization of propylene oxide appears to be a chain reaction [5]. The polymer molecular weight remains almost constant throughout the course of the reaction. This particular polymerization is complicated in that the reaction is probably a surface reaction–taking place on the potassium hydroxide surface.

For the usual case where the polymer molecular weight increases slowly with conversion throughout the course of the polymerization, the degree of polymerization of the polymer at time t in the reaction is given by the concentration of monomer which has reacted divided by the initial catalyst concentration, that is,

$$\overline{X}_n = \frac{[C_2H_4O]_0 - [C_2H_4O]_t}{[CH_3O^-Na^+]_0} \tag{7-11}$$

or, in general terms

$$\overline{X}_n = \frac{[M]_0 - [M]_t}{[C]} \tag{7-12}$$

where the 0 subscripts indicate initial concentrations and [C] is the catalyst concentration.

7-2a-2 Exchange Reactions. Many epoxide polymerizations such as the alkoxide and hydroxide catalyzed reactions are carried out in the presence of an alcohol (usually the alcohol whose alkoxide is used). The alcohol is usually used to produce a homogeneous system by solubilizing the catalyst. Under these conditions, the exchange reaction

$$R\text{+}OCH_2CH_2\text{+}_n O^-Na^+ + ROH \rightleftharpoons R\text{+}OCH_2CH_2\text{+}_n OH + RO^-Na^+ \tag{7-13}$$

between a propagating chain and the alcohol is possible. Similar exchange reactions are possible between the newly formed polymeric alcohol in Eq. 7-13 and other propagating chains

$$R\text{+}OCH_2CH_2\text{+}_n OH + R\text{+}OCH_2CH_2\text{+}_m O^-Na^+ \rightleftharpoons$$

$$R\text{+}OCH_2CH_2\text{+}_x O^-Na^+ + R\text{+}OCH_2CH_2\text{+}_y OH \tag{7-14}$$

where $(n + m) = (x + y)$. These exchange reactions, which are the equivalent of chain transfer reactions, will lower the polymer molecular weight. The degree of polymerization is then given by

$$\overline{X}_n = \frac{[M]_0 - [M]_t}{[C]_0 + [ROH]_0} \tag{7-15}$$

since each alcohol molecule is counted equally with a catalyst species as contributing to the number of propagating chains.

A number of somewhat different kinetic situations may arise depending on the relative rates of the initiation, exchange, and propagation reactions. When initiation is much faster than propagation, initiation is essentially complete before propagation starts and the polymerization follows Eq. 7-10 over the entire course of the reaction. All of the polymer chains start growing at the same time and the molecular weight distribution is very narrow as in living polymerizations. On the other hand, when initiation is slow, some chains are growing while others have not yet been initiated. The polymerization proceeds with an initial period in which the reaction rate shows an acceleration as the catalyst is being converted to the propagating species; thereafter, the rate will be constant. The molecular weight distribution will broaden since chains will grow for different periods of time. The effect of the exchange reaction depends on the relative acidities of the added alcohol and the polymeric alcohol. The exchange reaction will occur throughout the course of the polymerization if the acidities of the two alcohols are approximately the same. The polymerization rate will be unaffected while the degree of polymerization will decrease and the molecular weight distribution will broaden.

If the added alcohol ROH is much more acidic than the polymeric alcohol, all of it will undergo reaction with the first formed propagating species

$$ROCH_2CH_2O^-Na^+ + ROH \longrightarrow ROCH_2CH_2OH + RO^-Na^+ \qquad (7\text{-}16)$$

before any polymerization takes place. The polymer molecular weight distribution would be narrow here just as in the absence of alcohol; the difference is that a small amount of monomer is converted to the alcohol $ROCH_2CH_2OH$. The initial polymerization rate would probably be decreased since reinitiation by RO^-Na^+ would usually be slow since ROH is relatively acidic. The rate of polymerization would increase and then become constant as all of the alcohol is reacted by the exchange reaction (Eq. 7-16). The polymerization rate will be unaffected for the case in which ROH is less acidic than the polymeric alcohol. Exchange will occur in the later stages of polymerization with a broadening of the molecular weight distribution.

7-2a-3 Chain Transfer to Monomer. The polymer molecular weights obtained in epoxide polymerizations are quite low—usually being less than 5,000 and very rarely above 10,000. The reasons for this limitation are the relatively low reactivity of the epoxide ring toward anionic propagation and the presence of an undesirable chain transfer to monomer reaction. The latter is especially extensive in substituted ethylene oxides such as propylene oxide [6, 7]. The transfer reaction involves hydrogen abstraction from the alkyl substituent on the epoxide ring followed by very rapid ring cleavage to form an allyl ether anion

$$\sim\!\sim CH_2-\underset{}{\overset{CH_3}{\overset{|}{C}H}}-O^-Na^+ + CH_3-\overset{\overset{O}{\diagup\;\diagdown}}{CH-CH_2} \xrightarrow{k_{tr,M}}$$

$$\sim\!\sim CH_2-\overset{CH_3}{\overset{|}{C}H}-OH + H_2\overset{\overset{O}{\diagup\;\diagdown}}{C-CH}-CH_2^-Na^+ \tag{7-17}$$

$$H_2\overset{\overset{O}{\diagup\;\diagdown}}{C-CH}-CH_2^-Na^+ \xrightarrow{\text{very fast}} CH_2{=}CH-CH_2O^-Na^+ \tag{7-18}$$

The mathematical treatment of the effect of transfer to monomer on $\overline{X}_n$ is somewhat different than that previously described for transfer in radical and ionic chain polymerizations (Secs. 3-6 and 5-2e-1). For the case in which the exchange reaction (Eq. 7-13) is very rapid, the rate of monomer disappearance will be given by the sum of the rates of propagation and transfer reactions

$$\frac{-d[\mathrm{M}]}{dt} = (k_p + k_{tr,\mathrm{M}})[\mathrm{M}][\mathrm{C}]_0 \tag{7-19}$$

The increase in the concentration of polymer chains [N] is given by the rate of the transfer reaction

$$\frac{d[\mathrm{N}]}{dt} = k_{tr,\mathrm{M}}[\mathrm{M}][\mathrm{C}]_0 \tag{7-20}$$

Dividing Eq. 7-20 by Eq. 7-19, combining the result with $C_\mathrm{M} = k_{tr,\mathrm{M}}/k_p$ and integrating, one obtains

$$[N] = [N]_0 + \frac{C_M}{1 + C_M}([M]_0 - [M]) \tag{7-21}$$

where $[N]_0$ is the concentration of polymer chains in the absence of chain transfer to monomer.

The degrees of polymerization in the absence and presence of chain transfer, $(\bar{X}_n)_0$ and $\bar{X}_n$, respectively, are given by

$$(\bar{X}_n)_0 = \frac{[M]_0 - [M]}{[N]_0} \tag{7-22}$$

$$\bar{X}_n = \frac{[M]_0 - [M]}{[N]} \tag{7-23}$$

(Equation 7-22 is exactly the same as Eq. 7-12 since $[N]_0$ is equal to $[C]_0$.) Combination of Eqs. 7-21, 7-22, and 7-23 yields

$$\frac{1}{\bar{X}_n} = \frac{1}{(\bar{X}_n)_0} + \frac{C_M}{1 + C_M} \tag{7-24}$$

Equation 7-24 indicates that a plot of $1/\bar{X}_n$ versus $1/(\bar{X}_n)_0$ will be linear with an intercept of $C_M/(1 + C_M)$. Figure 7-1 shows such a plot for the polymerization of propylene oxide by sodium methoxide. Monomer chain transfer constants of 0.013 and 0.027 at 70°C and 93°C, respectively, were obtained. These values are larger by factors of 10^4–10^6 than the usual monomer transfer constants (Tables 3-3 and 5-3) and are responsible for drastically limiting the polymer molecular weights which can be achieved.

7-2b Cationic Polymerization

Propagation in the cationic polymerization of cyclic ethers is usually considered as proceeding via a tertiary *oxonium ion* (III), e.g., for the polymerization of 3,3-bis(chloromethyl)oxetane (R = CH_2Cl)

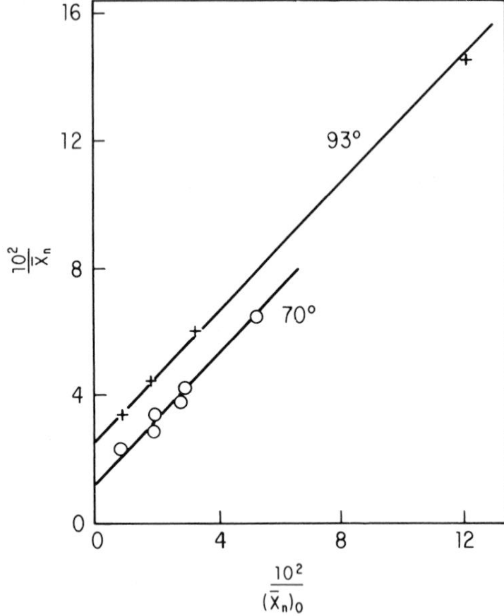

FIG. 7-1 *Effect of chain transfer to monomer in the polymerization of propylene oxide in dioxane by sodium methoxide at 70° and 93°C. After [6] (by permission of The Chemical Society, Burlington House, London).*

$$\sim\!\sim OCH_2CR_2CH_2-\overset{+}{\underset{\bar{A}}{O}}\boxed{}CR_2 + :O\boxed{}CR_2 \longrightarrow$$

$$\sim\!\sim OCH_2CR_2CH_2-O-CH_2CR_2CH_2-\overset{+}{\underset{\bar{A}}{O}}\boxed{}CR_2 \qquad \text{(7-25)}$$

III

where A^- is the gegen-ion. The propagation reaction is a nucleophilic attack by the oxygen of the monomer on the α-carbon of the oxonium ion. Many of the polymerizations are equilibrium polymerizations in which the polymer chains reach a limiting value corresponding to a propagation-depropagation equilibrium.

7-2b-1 Initiation. A variety of catalyst systems, of the types used in the cationic polymerization of alkenes (Sec. 5-2a), can be used to generate tertiary oxonium ion propagating species [1, 2, 8, 9].

7-2b-1-a Protonic Acids. Very strong protonic acids such as concentrated sulfuric, trifluoroacetic, or fluorosulfuric acids initiate polymerization via the initial formation of a secondary oxonium ion

$$H^+A^- + O\langle\rangle C R_2 \longrightarrow H\overset{+}{O}\langle\rangle C R_2 \quad \bar{A} \tag{7-26}$$

which reacts with a second monomer molecule to form the tertiary oxonium ion

$$H\overset{+}{O}\langle\rangle C R_2 \; \bar{A} + O\langle\rangle C R_2 \longrightarrow HOCH_2CR_2CH_2{-}\overset{+}{O}\langle\rangle C R_2 \; \bar{A} \tag{7-27}$$

This type of initiation is limited by the nucleophilicity of the anion A^- derived from the protonic acid. For acids other than the very strong acids, the anion is nucleophilic enough to compete with the monomer for either the proton or for the secondary oxonium ion. Thus, even concentrated sulfuric acid of 10 mole percent concentration is not strong enough to polymerize tetrahydrofuran [8]. The bisulfate ion is more nucleophilic than tetrahydrofuran; the protonated tetrahydrofuran reacts preferentially with the bisulfate gegen-ion

$$\overset{+}{O}H \; \bar{O}SO_3H \longrightarrow HO(CH_2)_4OSO_3H \tag{7-28}$$

instead of forming the tertiary oxonium ion. The presence of water in polymerizations initiated by strong acids can also directly disrupt the reaction since its nucleophilicity allows it to compete with monomer for the secondary oxonium ion.

7-2b-1-b Lewis Acids. Lewis acids such as BF_3 and $SnCl_4$ can be used to initiate polymerization. These catalysts almost always require water or some other compound with an acidic hydrogen as a cocatalyst. Interaction between the catalyst and cocatalyst yields a catalyst-cocatalyst complex, for example,

$$BF_3 + H_2O \longrightarrow H^+(BF_3OH)^- \tag{7-29}$$

which initiates polymerization by acting as a protonic acid as in the initiation sequence in Eqs. 7-26 and 7-27. A cocatalyst may not be an absolute requirement for a few catalysts. Thus, PF_5 and $SbCl_5$ have been reported to initiate the polymerization of tetrahydrofuran

[8, 9] although it is always difficult to experimentally ascertain the absence of trace amounts of water or other impurities which can act as cocatalysts. If initiation can indeed occur without the need for a cocatalyst, it may be due to disproportionation of the catalyst to yield a cationic species, for example,

$$2\,PF_5 \longrightarrow PF_4^+(PF_6)^- \tag{7-30a}$$

which initiates polymerization by the sequence

$$PF_4^+(PF_6)^- + O\!\!\bigcirc \longrightarrow PF_4\overset{+}{O}\!\!\bigcirc\ \bar{P}F_6 \xrightarrow{O\bigcirc} PF_4O(CH_2)_5\!-\!\overset{+}{O}\!\!\bigcirc\ \bar{P}F_6 \tag{7-30b}$$

Although a cocatalyst may not be necessary for initiation by a catalyst such as PF_5, it is known that added water significantly increases the polymerization rate [10] by acting as a cocatalyst. A plot of the polymerization rate versus the concentration of water for the PF_5 catalyzed polymerization of tetrahydrofuran is similar to Fig. 5-1 for the $SnCl_4$-H_2O catalyzed polymerization of styrene. The polymerization rate increases with increasing $[H_2O]$ up to a maximum and then decreases at higher $[H_2O]$. The decrease in the polymerization rate at high water concentrations has been attributed to catalyst destruction by water.

7-2b-1-c Carbonium Ions. Carbonium ions have also been used to initiate the polymerization of cyclic ethers. The initiation reaction generally consists of essentially the same sequence as in Eqs. 7-26 and 7-27 except that the catalyst is R^+A^- instead of H^+A^-. Carbonium ions formed from

$$HClO_4 + (CH_3\overset{O}{\overset{\|}{C}})_2O \longrightarrow CH_3\overset{O}{\overset{\|}{C}}{}^+(ClO_4)^- + CH_3CO_2H \tag{7-31}$$

$$CH_3\overset{O}{\overset{\|}{C}}Cl + SnCl_4 \longrightarrow CH_3\overset{O}{\overset{\|}{C}}{}^+(SnCl_5)^- \tag{7-32}$$

$$\phi CH_2Cl + FeCl_3 \longrightarrow \phi CH_2^+(FeCl_4)^- \tag{7-33}$$

$$ROSO_3R + BF_3 \longrightarrow R^+(ROSO_3BF_3)^- \tag{7-34}$$

and a variety of other reactions have been used [9, 11, 12].

The initiation step with some carbonium ions appears to involve hydride abstraction from monomer instead of addition to monomer [13]. Thus, for the polymerization of tetrahydrofuran by $\phi_3C^+(SbCl_6)^-$, the following initiation sequence

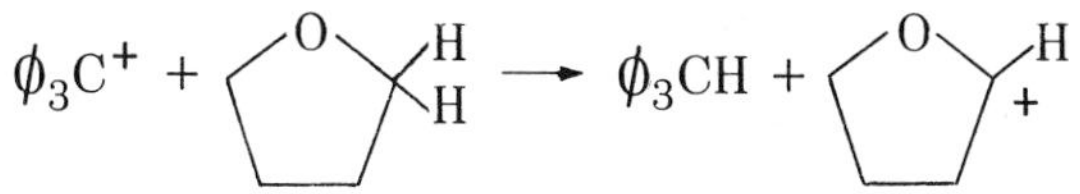

$$\phi_3C^+ + \text{(THF, }\alpha\text{-CH}_2\text{)} \longrightarrow \phi_3CH + \text{(THF, }\alpha\text{-CH}^+\text{)} \tag{7-35a}$$

$$\text{(THF, }\alpha\text{-CH}^+\text{)} + \text{THF} \longrightarrow \text{(THF-}\alpha\text{-CH)}-\overset{+}{O}\text{(C}_4\text{H}_8\text{)} \tag{7-35b}$$

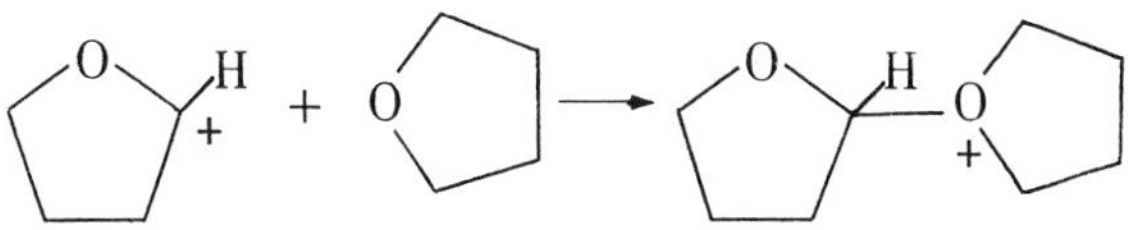

is supported by the rapid production of triphenylmethane in amounts equal to the catalyst. Propagation proceeds by the tertiary oxonium ion produced in Eq. 7-35b. A similar mechanism has been proposed for initiation by p-chlorophenyldiazonium hexafluorophosphate [14, 15].

7-2b-1-d Oxonium Ions. Since the tertiary oxonium ion is the actual propagating species, Meerwein and coworkers [9] used preformed tertiary oxonium ions such as triethyloxonium tetrafluoroborate, $(C_2H_5)_3O^+(BF_4)^-$, to initiate cyclic ether polymerizations. Initiation by an oxonium ion probably involves an alkyl exchange reaction with the monomer

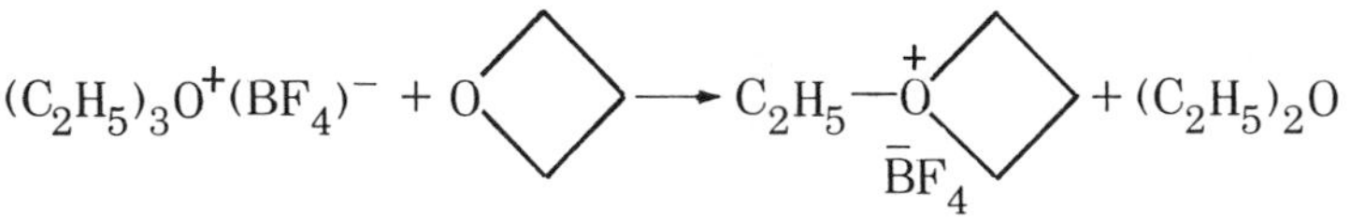

$$(C_2H_5)_3O^+(BF_4)^- + \text{O(C}_3\text{H}_6\text{)} \longrightarrow C_2H_5-\overset{+}{O}\text{(C}_3\text{H}_6\text{)}\ \overset{-}{B}F_4 + (C_2H_5)_2O \tag{7-36}$$

7-2b-1-e Promoters. Many combinations of a Lewis acid and a reactive cyclic ether (such as an epoxide or an oxacyclobutane), usually in combination with a cocatalyst, have been successfully used to initiate the polymerization of the relatively unreactive cyclic ethers such as tetrahydrofuran [8, 10, 13]. Initiation presumably occurs by formation of the secondary and tertiary oxonium ions of the reactive ether which then act as the actual initiating species, e.g., for the use of an epoxide in the polymerization of tetrahydrofuran (THF)

$$H_2C\overset{O}{\frown}CH_2 \longrightarrow H\overset{+}{O}\!\begin{matrix}CH_2\\|\\CH_2\end{matrix}\ \bar{A} \quad \text{and} \quad HOCH_2CH_2-\overset{+}{O}\!\begin{matrix}CH_2\\|\\CH_2\end{matrix}\ \bar{A}$$

$$\downarrow \text{THF} \qquad\qquad \downarrow \text{THF}$$

$$HOCH_2CH_2-\overset{+}{O}\bigcirc\ \bar{A} \qquad H(-OCH_2CH_2)_2-\overset{+}{O}\bigcirc\ \bar{A} \tag{7-37}$$

$$\downarrow \text{THF} \qquad\qquad \downarrow \text{THF}$$

$$\text{Propagation} \qquad\qquad \text{Propagation}$$

The reactive cyclic ether used as a component of the catalyst system is referred to as a *promoter* (or a cocatalyst). The promoter is, of course, used in small amounts relative to the cyclic ether being polymerized.

Epichlorohydrin is one of the most commonly used promoters. The mechanism of initiation for the case of epichlorohydrin with certain catalysts may be different from that described above. Thus, it was from the reaction of epichlorohydrin with boron trifluoride etherate that triethyloxonium tetrafluoroborate was formed by Meerwein. The overall reaction appears [9, 15] to be

$$6(C_2H_5)_2O{:}BF_3 + 3\,H_2C\overset{O}{\frown}CH{-}CH_2Cl \longrightarrow$$

$$3(C_2H_5)_3O^+(BF_4)^- + 2\,BF_3 + \left[C_2H_5OCH_2{-}\underset{\displaystyle CH_2Cl}{\underset{|}{CH}}{-}O\right]_3 B \tag{7-38}$$

7-2b-1-f Organometallic Catalysts. Organometallic compounds such as diethylzinc and triethylaluminium have also been used as catalysts [16–18]. These are usually used in the presence of water or an alcohol. Promoters such as epichlorohydrin may also be included in the catalyst system along with the water or alcohol. The nature of the initiating and propagating species differs considerably depending on the catalyst system and reaction conditions. The reaction appears to proceed by the usual oxonium ion mechanism in some cases. However, in most cases, polymerization appears to proceed by a coordination mechanism involving catalyst species such as $C_2H_5{-}ZnOZn{-}C_2H_5$ and $(C_2H_5)_2AlOAl(C_2H_5)_2$ formed by the reaction of water or alcohol with the organometallic compound. Coordination polymerization mechanisms are discussed in Chap. 8.

7-2b-2 Termination. Many cationic cyclic ether polymerizations have the characteristics of living polymerizations in that the propagating species are long-lived and narrow molecular weight distributions are often observed. Thus, the triisobutylaluminum polymerization of 3,3-bis(chloromethyl)oxetane yields [19] a product with a $\bar{M}_w/\bar{M}_n$ value of 1.09. However, termination does occur in many instances by a variety of different reactions, some of which are analogous to those in the cationic polymerization of alkenes (Sec. 5-2c). *Chain transfer to polymer via alkyl exchange* is a common mode by which a propagating chain is terminated although the kinetic chain is unaffected. The reaction involves an alkyl exchange between a propagating center (the oxonium ion) and an ether oxygen of a polymer chain

$$\sim\!\!\sim O(CH_2)_4{-}\overset{+}{O}\text{(ring, } (CH_2)_4\text{)}\ \bar{A} + O\begin{matrix}(CH_2)_4\sim\!\!\sim \\ (CH_2)_4\sim\!\!\sim\end{matrix} \longrightarrow$$

$$\sim\!\!\sim O(CH_2)_4{-}O(CH_2)_4{-}\overset{+}{O}\begin{matrix}(CH_2)_4\sim\!\!\sim \\ (CH_2)_4\sim\!\!\sim\end{matrix}\ \bar{A} \xrightarrow{\text{THF}}$$

$$\sim\!\!\sim O(CH_2)_4{-}O(CH_2)_4{-}O(CH_2)_4\sim\!\!\sim + \text{(ring)}\overset{+}{O}{-}(CH_2)_4\sim\!\!\sim\ \bar{A} \tag{7-39}$$

The transfer can occur both as an intramolecular reaction as well as an intermolecular one. In either case, the result is a broadening of the molecular weight distribution from the narrow distribution expected for a living polymerization [14].

The cationic polymerization of ethylene oxide is interesting in that it may involve two different equilibria. The presence of a polymer-cyclic dimer equilibrium in addition to, or instead of, a polymer-monomer equilibrium is indicated by the formation [1, 2] of 1,4-dioxane in polymerizations of ethylene oxide and depolymerizations of poly(ethylene oxide). The cyclic dimer dioxane is formed by an intramolecular *"back-biting," ring-expansion* reaction followed by a displacement step

$$\sim\sim OCH_2CH_2OCH_2CH_2-\overset{+}{\underset{\bar{A}}{O}}\!\!\triangleleft \longrightarrow \sim\sim OCH_2CH_2-\overset{+}{\underset{\bar{A}}{O}}\bigcirc O$$

$$\downarrow \overset{O}{\triangle}$$

$$\sim\sim OCH_2CH_2-\overset{+}{\underset{\bar{A}}{O}}\!\!\triangleleft + O\bigcirc O \qquad (7\text{-}40)$$

Oxacyclobutane undergoes a similar back-biting reaction. It is postulated that the reaction yields a stable 16-membered oxonium ion

$$\sim\sim(OCH_2CH_2CH_2)_4-\overset{+}{\underset{\bar{A}}{O}}\!\diamond \longrightarrow$$

$$\sim\sim OCH_2CH_2CH_2-\overset{+}{\underset{\bar{A}}{O}}\begin{matrix}(CH_2)_3O(CH_2)_3\\ (CH_2)_3O(CH_2)_3\end{matrix}O \qquad (7\text{-}41)$$

which is incapable of further propagation. Cyclic tetramer is isolated from the reaction mixture. It arises from a displacement reaction (similar to that in Eq. 7-40) brought about by a nucleophile such as monomer, gegen-ion, cocatalyst, or an added reagent. Substituted oxacyclobutanes, such as the 3,3-bis(chloromethyl) derivative, do not undergo this type of termination; there is excessive steric hindrance to cyclization due to the bulky substituents. The polymerization of 3,3-bis(chloromethyl)oxetane is complicated by the insolubility of the polymer in the reaction mixture. Termination has been considered as occurring by "burial" of the reactive oxonium ion center in the solid polymer with its inaccessibility to further propagation.

Termination may occur to varying degrees by combination of the propagating oxonium ion with either the gegen-ion or, more likely, an anionic fragment from the gegen-ion. Thus, it has previously been mentioned that the use of protonic acids as catalysts is limited by the nucleophilicity of the anion of the acid. Transfer of an anion from the gegen-ion, for example

$$\sim\!\!\sim OCH_2CH_2-\overset{+}{O}\triangleleft \;\; \overset{-}{B}F_3OH \longrightarrow \sim\!\!\sim OCH_2CH_2OCH_2CH_2OH + BF_3 \qquad (7\text{-}42)$$

occurs to varying degrees depending on the stability of the gegen-ion. Thus, gegen-ions such as $(PF_6)^-$ and $(SbCl_6)^-$ have little tendency to bring about termination by transfer of a halide ion while those of aluminum and tin have appreciable transfer tendencies; others such as $(BF_4)^-$ and $(FeCl_4)^-$ are intermediate in behavior [1, 2, 14, 20].

Termination may also occur by chain transfer with the cocatalyst (e.g., water or alcohol) or a deliberately added transfer agent. Acyclic ethers, for example, have been found [21] to act as transfer agents in the same manner as polymer acts as a transfer agent (Eq. 7-39)

$$\sim\!\!\sim \overset{+}{O}\diamond \;\; \overset{-}{A} + ROR \longrightarrow \sim\!\!\sim O(CH_2)_3\overset{+}{O}R_2 \;\; \overset{-}{A}$$

$$\downarrow \; O\diamond$$

$$\sim\!\!\sim O(CH_2)_3OR + R\overset{+}{O}\diamond \;\; \overset{-}{A} \qquad (7\text{-}43)$$

7-2b-3 Kinetics. *7-2b-3-a Similarity to Step Polymerization.* Cationic polymerization of cyclic ethers is similar to step polymerization with regard to the time distribution of high polymer production. Polymer size increases with conversion. However, the polymer molecular weight may not necessarily continue to increase throughout the whole course of polymerization as it does in step polymerization. Step polymerizations have no termination reaction if

Table 7-1 Reaction Parameters in Tetrahydrofuran Polymerization[a]

Parameter	Value
[M]	12.1 mole/liter
$[(C_2H_5)_3Al]$	0.179 mole/liter
$[H_2O]/[(C_2H_5)_3Al]$	0.500
[Epichlorohydrin]	0.159 mole/liter
[M*]	2.4-2.6 $\times 10^{-3}$ mole/liter
k_p	1.28 $\times 10^{-2}$ liter/mole-sec

[a]Data from [17].

stoichiometric amounts of functional groups are employed. Ring-opening polymerizations differ in that they may involve termination reactions. Thus, although polymer size increases with conversion, it may level off far before complete conversion.

The similarity between ring-opening and step polymerizations is even more apparent when one considers the values of the propagation rate constant for various cyclic ether polymerizations. Table 7-1 shows the values of some of the pertinent reaction parameters in the bulk polymerization of tetrahydrofuran at 0°C by a catalyst system composed of triethylaluminum, epichlorohydrin, and water [17]. These values can be compared to the corresponding data for step and chain reactions (Tables 2-1, 3-8, 5-1, and 5-7) to indicate the nature of cyclic ether polymerization. Thus, the k_p value for tetrahydrofuran is very close to that for esterification and much smaller than those for various chain polymerizations. Similar k_p values have been observed for a variety of polymerizations of epoxides, oxetanes, and tetrahydrofuran [2, 14, 15, 20].

7-2b-3-b Rate of Polymerization. The rate laws which describe the cationic ring-opening polymerizations of cyclic ethers take several forms. Many ether polymerizations can be described by kinetic expressions very similar to those used in alkene polymerizations (Sec. 5-2d-1), e.g., Eqs. 5-19, 5-20, 5-22, 5-23, 5-25, 5-26, and appropriate variations. In some polymerizations where there is little or no termination, one can employ kinetic expressions similar to those of living polymerization (Secs. 5-3b-2 and 5-3b-5), for example,

$$R_p = k_p[M^*][M] \tag{7-44}$$

where [M*] is the concentration of the propagating oxonium ion.

Ring-opening polymerizations which take place without termination and with a propagation-depropagation equilibrium are described in a different manner [17, 18, 22]. (The following treatment for reversible ring-opening polymerizations is also applicable to other reversible polymerizations such as those of alkenes or carbonyl monomers.) The propagation-depropagation equilibrium can be expressed by

$$M_n^* + M \underset{k_{dp}}{\overset{k_p}{\rightleftharpoons}} M_{n+1}^* \tag{7-45}$$

which is analogous to Eq. 3-169. The polymerization rate is given by the difference between the rates of the propagation and depropagation reactions

$$R_p = \frac{-d[M]}{dt} = k_p[M^*][M] - k_{dp}[M^*] \tag{7-46}$$

At equilibrium, the polymerization rate is zero and Eq. 7-46 becomes

$$k_p[M]_c = k_{dp} \tag{7-47}$$

where $[M]_c$ is the equilibrium monomer concentration (as in Eq. 3-173). Combination of Eqs. 7-46 and 7-47 gives the polymerization rate as

$$\frac{-d[M]}{dt} = k_p[M^*]([M] - [M]_c) \tag{7-48}$$

which can be integrated to yield

$$\ln\left(\frac{[M]_0 - [M]_c}{[M] - [M]_c}\right) = k_p[M^*]t \tag{7-49}$$

where $[M]_0$ is the initial monomer concentration. (A corresponding consideration of the degree of polymerization in an equilibrium polymerization is given in Sec. 7-3c-2.)

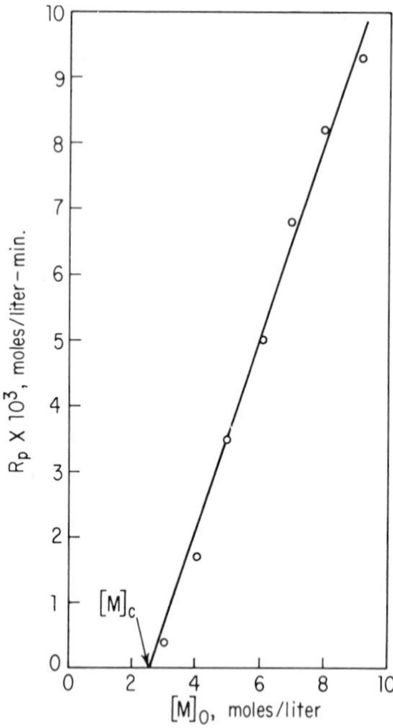

FIG. 7-2 *Determination of the equilibrium monomer concentration $[M]_c$ for the $(C_2H_5)_3O^+BF_4^-$ catalyzed polymerization of tetrahydrofuran in dichloroethane at 0°C. After [23] (by permission of Interscience Publishers, John Wiley & Sons, Inc., New York).*

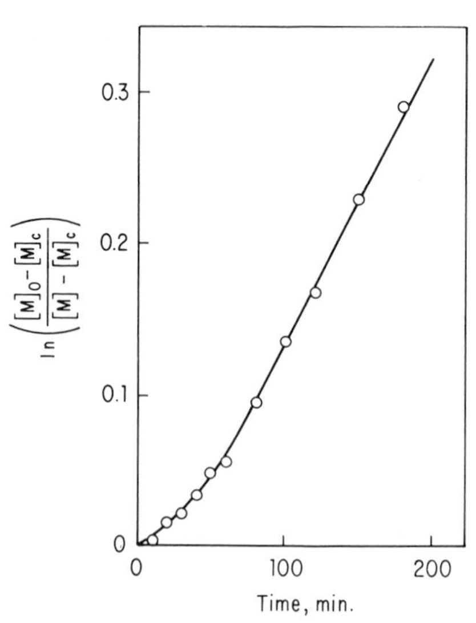

FIG. 7-3 *Disappearance of monomer in the polymerization of tetrahydrofuran by $(C_2H_5)_3Al$-H_2O at 0°C; plot of Eq. 7-49. After [17] (by permission of Hüthig and Wepf Verlag, Basel).*

Equations 7-48 and 7-49 can be used to determine the propagation rate constant. The equilibrium monomer concentration $[M]_c$ is evaluated by direct analysis or as the intercept of a plot of polymerization rate versus initial monomer concentration. Figure 7-2 shows such a plot for the polymerization of tetrahydrofuran in dichloroethane solution at 0°C using triethyloxonium tetrafluoroborate as the initiator [23]. The polymerization data can then be plotted in accordance with Eq. 7-49 as the left side of that equation versus time to yield a straight line (Fig. 7-3) whose slope is $k_p[M^*]$. The plot in Fig. 7-3 is linear except for an initial portion (below 5% conversion) corresponding to an induction period for the build-up of the concentration of the propagating species. Since $[M^*]$ for a living polymer can be obtained from measurements of the number-average molecular weight, one can easily evaluate the propagation rate constant. This is in fact the general procedure used to obtain the k_p value shown in Table 7-1. The concentration of the propagating species and polymerization rate in a polymerization initiated by a multi-component initiation system will generally depend on the concentrations of each of the components of the initiator system. Figures 7-4 and 7-5 show this effect in the dependence of [M*] on the concentrations of the catalyst and promoter in the polymerization of tetrahydrofuran by the triethylaluminum-water-epichlorohydrin system.

7-2b-4 Cyclic Acetals. *7-2b-4-a Trioxane.* Various cyclic acetals also undergo ring-opening cationic polymerization. Trioxane, the cyclic trimer of formaldehyde, undergoes facile polymerization to yield the same polymer, polyoxymethylene, as obtained by the polymerization of formaldehyde

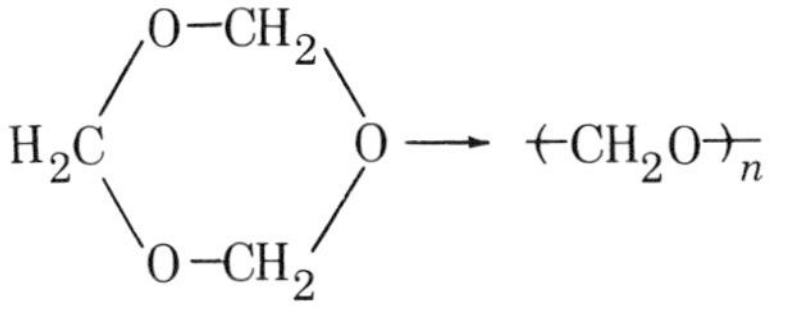

$$\text{cyclo-}(\mathrm{H_2C{-}O{-}CH_2{-}O{-}CH_2{-}O}) \longrightarrow \left(\mathrm{CH_2O}\right)_n \qquad (7\text{-}50)$$

The detailed mechanism of polymerization has not been elucidated. The unequivocal need for cocatalysts has not been clearly demonstrated although it appears that strong Lewis acids such as BF_3 and $TiCl_4$ do not require cocatalysts. The BF_3 initiation of trioxane polymerization can be pictured [24] as

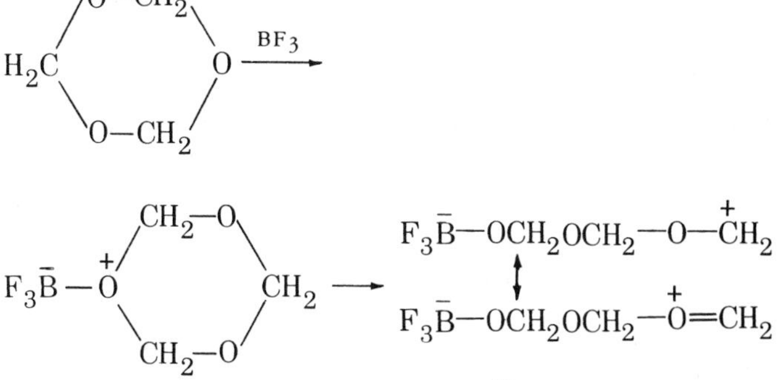

$$\text{cyclo-}(\mathrm{H_2C{-}O{-}CH_2{-}O{-}CH_2{-}O}) \xrightarrow{BF_3}$$

$$\underset{\text{IV}}{\mathrm{F_3\bar{B}{-}\overset{+}{O}}\text{(cyclo-}\mathrm{CH_2{-}O{-}CH_2{-}O{-}CH_2})} \longrightarrow \underset{\text{V}}{\mathrm{F_3\bar{B}{-}OCH_2OCH_2{-}O{-}\overset{+}{C}H_2} \longleftrightarrow \mathrm{F_3\bar{B}{-}OCH_2OCH_2{-}\overset{+}{O}{=}CH_2}} \qquad (7\text{-}51)$$

in which the oxonium ion IV undergoes ring opening to the carbonium ion V which is considered to be the propagating species. The carbonium ion is formed in trioxane polymerization (instead of only the oxonium ion as in the polymerization of cyclic ethers) due to resonance stabilization from the adjacent oxygen atom.

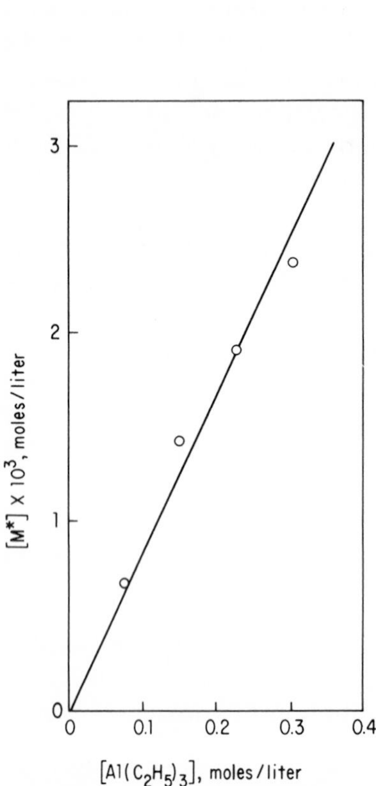

FIG. 7-4 *Dependence of the concentration of the propagating oxonium ion on the concentration of $Al(C_2H_5)_3$ in the $Al(C_2H_5)_3$-epichlorohydrin-H_2O catalyzed polymerization of tetrahydrofuran in cyclohexane at 0°C. The concentration of epichlorohydrin is constant at 0.185 molar and the $[H_2O]/[Al(C_2H_5)_3]$ is constant at 1/2. After [17] (by permission of Hüthig and Wepf Verlag, Basel).*

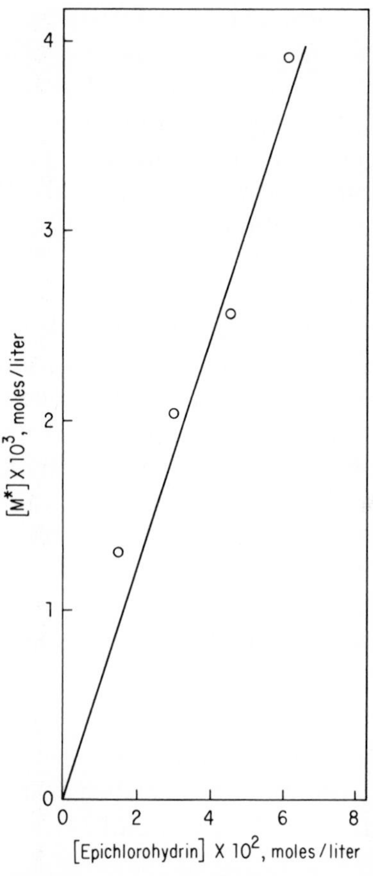

FIG. 7-5 *Dependence of the concentration of the propagating oxonium ion on the concentration of epichlorohydrin in the $Al(C_2H_5)_3$-epichlorohydrin-H_2O catalyzed polymerization of tetrahydrofuran in cyclohexane at 0°C. The concentration of $Al(C_2H_5)_3$ is constant at 0.924 molar and $[H_2O]/[Al(C_2H_5)_3]$ is constant at 1/2. After [17] (by permission of Hüthig and Wepf Verlag, Basel).*

Propagation consists in a repetition of the sequence consisting of reaction of the carbonium ion with monomer followed by ring-opening

$$F_3\bar{B}\!\leftarrow\!OCH_2OCH_2OCH_2\!\rightarrow_n\!OCH_2OCH_2\overset{+}{O}CH_2 + O\begin{matrix}CH_2-O\\ \\ CH_2-O\end{matrix}CH_2 \longrightarrow$$

$$F_3\bar{B}\!\leftarrow\!OCH_2OCH_2OCH_2\!\rightarrow_{(n+1)}\overset{+}{O}\begin{matrix}CH_2-O\\ \\ CH_2-O\end{matrix}CH_2 \longrightarrow$$

$$F_3\bar{B}\!\leftarrow\!OCH_2OCH_2OCH_2\!\rightarrow_{(n+1)}OCH_2OCH_2\overset{+}{O}CH_2 \qquad (7\text{-}52)$$

This mechanism suffers from the same deficiency as that previously described (Sec. 5-5b) for the $AlBr_3$ catalyzed polymerization of chloral. Propagation involves progressively increasing charge separation in the propagating species as its size increases. (Such species, which contain opposite charges at their two ends, are usually referred to as *zwitter-ions*.) This would require the two ends of the propagating carbonium ion to remain in relatively close proximity with each other. Alternately, a mechanism involving a second BF_3 molecule may be applicable (similar to that described by Eq. 5-83). This consideration is not applicable for those polymerizations involving a catalyst-cocatalyst combination. Those polymerizations do not involve zwitter-ion species, e.g., with H^+A^- as the initiator, the reaction is

$$H_2C\begin{matrix}O-CH_2\\ \\ O-CH_2\end{matrix}O \xrightarrow{H^+A^-} H_2C\begin{matrix}O-CH_2\\ \\ O-CH_2\end{matrix}\overset{H}{\underset{\bar{A}}{O^+}} \longrightarrow HOCH_2OCH_2O\underset{\bar{A}}{\overset{}{\underset{+}{C}}}H_2$$

$$\xrightarrow{\text{Monomer}} HOCH_2OCH_2OCH_2-\underset{\bar{A}}{\overset{+}{O}}\begin{matrix}CH_2-O\\ \\ CH_2-O\end{matrix}CH_2 \longrightarrow$$

$$HOCH_2OCH_2OCH_2OCH_2OCH_2O\underset{\bar{A}}{\underset{+}{C}}H_2 \qquad (7\text{-}53)$$

In addition to a polymer-monomer equilibrium which may be present, trioxane polymerization is complicated by the occurrence of a polymer-formaldehyde equilibrium

$$\sim\sim OCH_2OCH_2O\overset{}{\underset{+}{C}}H_2 \rightleftharpoons \sim\sim OCH_2O\underset{+}{C}H_2 + CH_2O \qquad (7\text{-}54)$$

Trioxane polymerizations usually proceed with long induction periods which correspond to the build-up of the equilibrium formaldehyde concentration. The induction periods can be reduced or eliminated by the initial addition of formaldehyde to the reaction mixture.

Termination occurs by the modes previously described (Sec. 7-2b-2). An additional complication in the polymerization of trioxane is termination by intramolecular hydride transfer

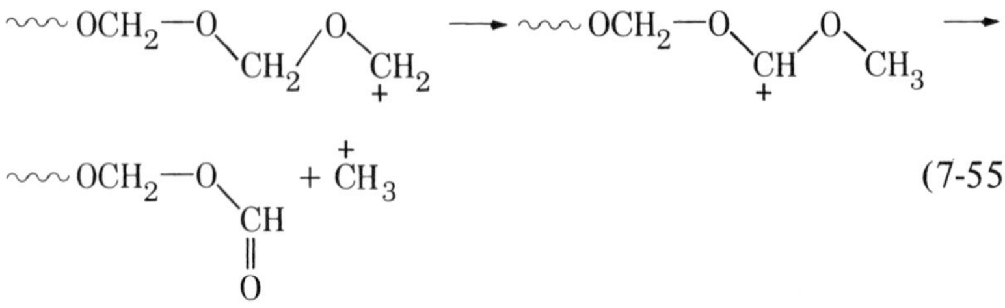

$$\sim\sim OCH_2{-}O{-}CH_2{-}O{-}\underset{+}{C}H_2 \longrightarrow \sim\sim OCH_2{-}O{-}\underset{+}{C}H{-}O{-}CH_3 \longrightarrow$$

$$\sim\sim OCH_2{-}O{-}CH{=}O + \overset{+}{C}H_3 \qquad (7\text{-}55)$$

resulting in methoxyl and formate end groups in the polymer. Some trioxane polymerizations give rise to tetraoxane [25] by a "back-biting" reaction

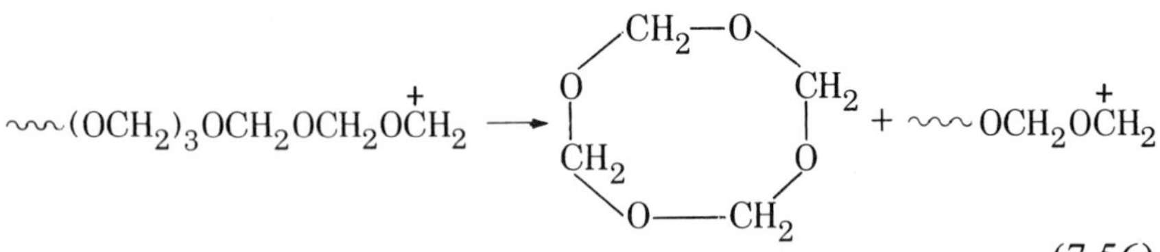

$$\sim\sim(OCH_2)_3OCH_2OCH_2O\overset{+}{C}H_2 \longrightarrow \text{cyclo-}[CH_2{-}O{-}CH_2{-}O{-}CH_2{-}O{-}CH_2{-}O] + \sim\sim OCH_2O\overset{+}{C}H_2 \qquad (7\text{-}56)$$

7-2b-4-b Cyclic Formals. Cyclic formals possess the structure VI

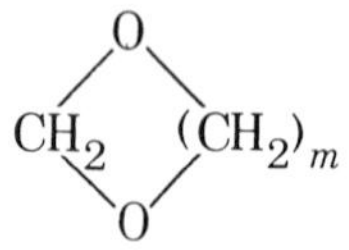

$$\text{cyclo-}[CH_2{-}O{-}(CH_2)_m{-}O]$$

VI

Various members of this group, such as 1,3-dioxolane ($m = 2$), 1,3-dioxepane ($m = 4$), and 1,3-dioxocane ($m = 5$), undergo facile polymerization. The reactions proceed in a manner similar to that for trioxane polymerization [26], e.g., for 1,3-dioxolane

$$\sim\!\sim OCH_2CH_2O\overset{+}{C}H_2 + \underset{CH_2-CH_2}{O \diagup^{CH_2} \diagdown O} \longrightarrow$$

$$\sim\!\sim OCH_2CH_2OCH_2-\overset{+}{O}\underset{CH_2-CH_2}{\diagup^{CH_2} \diagdown O} \longrightarrow$$

$$\sim\!\sim OCH_2CH_2OCH_2OCH_2CH_2O\overset{+}{C}H_2 \qquad (7\text{-}57)$$

7-2b-5 Energetic Characteristics. *7-2b-5-a Effect of Temperature.* The effects of temperature on the rate and degree of polymerization of cyclic ethers and acetals vary considerably depending on the specific reaction system. Variations due to different monomers, solvents, catalysts, cocatalysts, and promoters are generally analogous to those observed in the ionic polymerizations of alkenes (Secs. 5-2g and 5-3b-7). Increased temperature almost always results in an increase in the rate of polymerization (that is, E_{R_p} is positive). The overall activation energy for the polymerization rate is usually in the range of 5–15 kcal/mole although there is considerable variation depending on the reaction conditions. Thus, E_{R_p} for the BF_3-H_2O initiated polymerization of 3,3-bis(chloromethyl)oxacyclobutane in methyl chloride solution is 18.0 kcal/mole while the value is 3–4 kcal/mole for radiation-induced polymerization in the crystalline solid state [27, 28]. The difference may be due to the favorable orientation of the monomer in the solid-state polymerization. Similar effects have been observed in trioxane polymerizations although the differences between the E_{R_p} values for various catalyst-cocatalyst systems are often greater than the differences between the solution and solid-state values [29].

The effect of temperature on the degree of polymerization is more complex. For most polymerizations, increasing the temperature leads to a decrease in the polymer molecular weight due to increases in the rates of the termination reactions. Table 7-2 shows this effect for the BF_3-H_2O polymerization of oxacyclobutane [30]. (The intrinsic

Table 7-2 Effect of Temperature on Polymerization of Oxacyclobutane[a]

Temperature (°C)	Intrinsic viscosity of polymer (dl./g.)	Ultimate conversion of monomer (%)	Proportion of tetramer (%)
−80	2.9	95	4
0	2.1	94	10
50	1.3	64	66
100	1.1	62	62

[a]Data from [30].

viscosity, in deciliter/gram, is a measure of the polymer molecular weight.) The decrease in the polymer molecular weight in this polymerization corresponds to an increase in termination by the back-biting reaction (Eq. 7-41) as indicated by the increasing yield of tetramer. In other polymerizations, the termination reaction may not be appreciably affected by increasing temperature while the propagation reaction rate increases. The result is an increase in the polymer size with temperature. Figure 7-6 shows the interesting polymerization of tetrahydrofuran in which the polymer molecular weight increases initially with temperature at low temperatures and then decreases at higher temperatures [31]. Termination is relatively

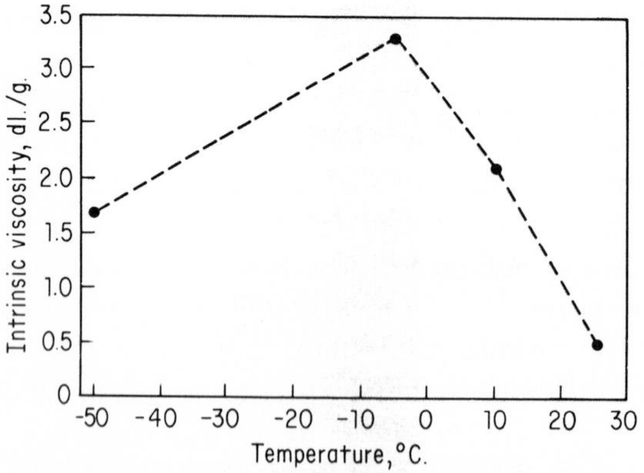

FIG. 7-6 *Effect of temperature on polymer molecular weight in the BF_3 catalyzed polymerization of tetrahydrofuran. The concentration of BF_3 is 10 percent. After [31] (by permission of Interscience Publishers, John Wiley & Sons, Inc., New York).*

unaffected at the lower temperatures but increases with temperature at the higher temperatures.

Table 7-2 shows a decrease in the ultimate conversion of monomer to polymer for the oxacyclobutane polymerization as the reaction temperature is increased. The effect appears to be due to the thermal destruction of the catalyst [30]. The same general trend is observed for the polymerization of most cyclic ethers and acetals but for a different reason. Increased temperature usually decreases the conversion of monomer to polymer by a ceiling temperature effect. The propagation-depropagation equilibrium (Eq. 7-45) is shifted to the left with increasing temperature. The equilibrium monomer concentration increases with increasing polymerization temperature in accord with Eq. 3-173b (bear in mind that ΔH° is negative). Figure 7-7 shows this effect for the polymerization of tetrahydrofuran in bulk using benzenediazonium hexafluorophosphate as the catalyst.

7-2b-5-b Thermodynamics of Polymerization. The enthalpies and entropies of polymerization for various cyclic monomers are shown in Table 7-3 [32–34]. (Some of the data are experimentally determined values; others have been calculated by semi-empirical methods.) Data for the polymerizations of formaldehyde and chloral are also included in Table 7-3. A limited comparison of the ΔH and ΔS values for alkenes, carbonyl monomers, and the cyclic monomers can be made from Tables 7-3 and 3-12. The ΔH values for the 3- and 4-membered cyclic monomers are comparable to those for alkenes and both are appreciably larger than the values for the two

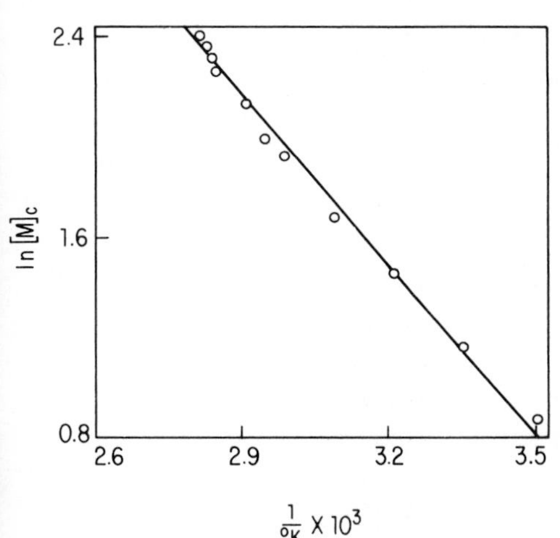

FIG. 7-7 *Temperature dependence of the equilibrium monomer concentration in the polymerization of tetrahydrofuran by* $\phi N_2^+ BF_4^-$. *After [14] (by permission of Interscience Publishers, John Wiley & Sons, Inc., New York).*

Table 7-3 Heats and Entropies of Polymerization for Cyclic Ethers and and Acetals[a]

Monomer	Ring size	$-\Delta H$ (kcal/mole)	$-\Delta S$ (cal/°K-mole)
Ethylene oxide	3	22.6	
Oxacyclobutane	4	16.1	
3,3-Bis(chloromethyl)oxacyclobutane	4	20.2	19.9
1,3-Dioxolane	5	6.2	
Tetrahydrofuran	5	5.3	18
Tetrahydropyran	6	0.4	
m-Dioxane	6	0.0	
1,3-Dioxepane	7	3.6	11.5
1,3-Dioxocane	8	12.8	
Formaldehyde		7.4	19
Chloral		9	23

[a]Data from [32–34].

carbonyl compounds. The conversion of a carbonyl π-bond to a σ-bond is not as exothermic as the corresponding conversion of an alkene π-bond. The entropy change, however, is similar in the two types of monomers. The cyclic monomers, being more ordered to begin with, have ΔS values indicating that the loss in disorder on polymerization is less than in the case of the non-cyclic monomers.

The ΔH values for the different cyclic ether and acetal monomers correspond very closely to the order expected, based on considerations of relative stability as a function of ring size (Sec. 2-3b and Fig. 2-3). The 3- and 4-membered cyclic monomers undergo the most exothermic polymerizations. There is a rapid decrease in ΔH for the 5- and 7-membered rings and then an increase for the 8-membered ring. The ΔH values of zero for the 6-membered cyclic monomers substantiate the observation that they have not yet been polymerized. As indicated in Sec. 2-3b, substituents on a ring structure tend to increase its stability relative to the unsubstituted compound. Thus, whereas tetrahydrofuran has been polymerized by a variety of catalysts, very few substituted tetrahydrofurans have been successfully polymerized.

7-3 CYCLIC AMIDES

The polymerization of cyclic amides

$$n\ \overline{\text{CO—NH—(CH}_2)_m} \longrightarrow \text{+NH—(CH}_2)_m\text{CO}\text{+}_n \qquad (7\text{-}58)$$

can be initiated by bases, cationic species, and water. The cyclic amides which have been studied are the lactams—those formed by the intramolecular amidation of amino acids. (The other type of cyclic amide is that formed by the intermolecular dimerization of an amino acid.) Lactams are referred to by trivial names such as β-propiolactam or 2-azetidinone for the 4-membered ring, γ-butyrolactam or 2-pyrrolidone for the 5-membered ring, δ-valerolactam or 2-piperidone for the 6-membered ring, 6-hexanolactam or ϵ-caprolactam for the 7-membered ring, 7-heptanolactam or enantholactam for the 8-membered ring, and 8-octanolactam or capryllactam for the 9-membered ring.

7-3a Anionic Polymerization

7-3a-1 Use of Strong Bases Alone. Strong bases such as alkali metals, metal hydrides, metal amides, and organometallic compounds initiate the polymerization of a lactam by forming the lactam anion [1]. e.g., for caprolactam with a metal

$$\overbrace{(\text{CH}_2)_5\text{—}\overset{\overset{\text{O}}{\|}}{\text{C}}\text{—NH}} + \text{M} \rightleftharpoons \overbrace{(\text{CH}_2)_5\text{—}\overset{\overset{\text{O}}{\|}}{\text{C}}\text{—N}^-\text{M}^+} + \tfrac{1}{2}\text{H}_2 \qquad (7\text{-}59\text{a})$$

or with a metal derivative

$$\overbrace{(\text{CH}_2)_5\text{—}\overset{\overset{\text{O}}{\|}}{\text{C}}\text{—NH}} + \text{B}^-\text{M}^+ \rightleftharpoons \underset{\text{VII}}{\overbrace{(\text{CH}_2)_5\text{—}\overset{\overset{\text{O}}{\|}}{\text{C}}\text{—N}^-\text{M}^+}} + \text{BH} \qquad (7\text{-}59\text{b})$$

The use of weaker bases such as hydroxides and alkoxides is not as satisfactory since a high concentration of the anion would generally be obtained only if the product BH is removed to push the equilibrium to the right.

The lactam anion VII reacts with monomer in the second step of the initiation process by a ring-opening transamidation

$$\overbrace{(CH_2)_5-N^-M^+}^{C=O} + \overbrace{HN-(CH_2)_5}^{C=O} \xrightarrow{\text{slow}} \underbrace{\overbrace{(CH_2)_5-N}^{C=O}-CO(CH_2)_5\overset{H}{N}{}^-M^+}_{\text{VIII}} \qquad (7\text{-}60)$$

The primary amine anion VIII, unlike the lactam anion VII, is not stabilized by conjugation with a carbonyl group. It is highly reactive and undergoes a rapid proton-abstraction reaction with monomer

$$\overbrace{(CH_2)_5-N}^{C=O}-CO(CH_2)_5\overset{H}{N}{}^-M^+ + \overbrace{(CH_2)_5-NH}^{C=O} \longrightarrow$$

$$\underbrace{\overbrace{(CH_2)_5-N}^{C=O}-CO(CH_2)_5NH_2}_{\text{IX}} + \underbrace{\overbrace{(CH_2)_5-N^-M^+}^{C=O}}_{\text{VII}} \qquad (7\text{-}61)$$

to form an imide dimer IX, *N*-caproylcaprolactam, and regenerate the lactam anion.

The imide dimer IX has been isolated [35] and is the actual initiating species necessary for the onset of propagation. Long induction periods are observed in lactam polymerization due to the slow reaction (Eq. 7-60) preceding its formation. The imide dimer is necessary for polymerization because the amide linkage is not sufficiently reactive (i.e., not sufficiently electron-deficient) toward transamidation by the lactam anion. The presence of the carbonyl group attached to the ring amide nitrogen in the imide dimer increases the electron-deficiency of the amide linkage. This increases the reactivity of the amide ring structure toward attack by the nucleophilic lactam anion. Propagation is considered as the reaction between a propagating imide species (X) and the lactam anion

$$\underset{\text{X}}{(CH_2)_5\overset{\overset{O}{\|}}{C}\!-\!N\!-\!CO(CH_2)_5NH\sim\sim} + (CH_2)_5\overset{\overset{O}{\|}}{C}\!-\!N^-M^+ \longrightarrow$$

$$(CH_2)_5\overset{\overset{O}{\|}}{C}\!-\!N\!-\!CO(CH_2)_5\!-\!\overset{M^+}{\bar{N}}\!-\!CO(CH_2)_5NH\sim\sim \qquad (7\text{-}62)$$

followed by fast proton-exchange with monomer

$$(CH_2)_5\overset{\overset{O}{\|}}{C}\!-\!N\!-\!CO(CH_2)_5\!-\!\overset{M^+}{\bar{N}}\!-\!CO(CH_2)_5NH\sim\sim + (CH_2)_5\overset{\overset{O}{\|}}{C}\!-\!NH \longrightarrow$$

$$\underset{\text{X}}{(CH_2)_5\overset{\overset{O}{\|}}{C}\!-\!N\!\left[CO(CH_2)_5NH\right]_2\!\sim} + (CH_2)_5\overset{\overset{O}{\|}}{C}\!-\!N^-M^+ \qquad (7\text{-}63)$$

to regenerate the lactam anion and the propagating imide X.

It is clear that the base-catalyzed polymerization of lactams is quite different from other polymerizations in two respects. First, the propagating center is not a radical, anion, or cation but is the cyclic amide linkage. Second, the monomer does not add to the propagating chain; it is the monomer anion, referred to as *activated monomer* [36], which adds to the propagating chain. This polymerization mechanism is exactly like that previously described for the anionic polymerization of acrylamide (Sec. 5-6b). For such a polymerization, the concentrations of both the propagating species and the activated monomer are determined by the concentration of base. A novel consequence of the reaction is that the growth rate of each propagating chain depends on the base concentration. Furthermore, if the proton-exchange equilibrium (Eqs. 7-61 and 7-63) lies far to the right, the growth rate of each chain will be completely independent of the monomer concentration. The growth rate of each chain will depend only on the concentration of the activated monomer as determined by the base concentration.

7-3a-2 Use of Acylating Agents. *7-3a-2-a Reaction Mechanism.* The use of a strong base alone for lactam polymerization is very limiting. There are the long induction periods previously noted and, more importantly, only the more reactive lactams such as caprolactam or enantholactam underdo polymerization. The less reactive lactams such as the 6-membered piperidone do not undergo polymerization by strong bases alone. These monomers are too unreactive to form the required imide dimer. Both limitations have been overcome by forming an imide by the reaction of monomer with acylating agents such as acid chlorides and anhydrides, isocyanates, inorganic anhydrides, and others [37–39]. Thus, caprolactam can be converted rapidly to an *N*-acylcaprolactam XI by reaction with an acid chloride

$$\overbrace{(\mathrm{CH_2})_5\!-\!\mathrm{NH}}^{\mathrm{C{=}O}} \xrightarrow{\mathrm{RCOCl}} \underset{\mathrm{XI}}{\overbrace{(\mathrm{CH_2})_5\!-\!\mathrm{N{-}CO{-}R}}^{\mathrm{C{=}O}}} \qquad (7\text{-}64)$$

The *N*-acyllactam can be synthesized in situ or preformed and then added to the reaction system.

Initiation consists of the reaction of the *N*-acylcaprolactam with activated monomer followed by a fast proton-exchange with monomer

$$\overbrace{(\mathrm{CH_2})_5\!-\!\mathrm{N{-}CO{-}R}}^{\mathrm{C{=}O}} + \overbrace{(\mathrm{CH_2})_5\!-\!\mathrm{N^-M^+}}^{\mathrm{C{=}O}} \longrightarrow$$

$$\underset{\mathrm{XII}}{\overbrace{(\mathrm{CH_2})_5\!-\!\mathrm{N{-}CO(CH_2)_5}}^{\mathrm{C{=}O}}\!-\!\overset{\mathrm{M^+}}{\bar{\mathrm{N}}}\!-\!\mathrm{CO{-}R}} \qquad (7\text{-}65)$$

$$\Big\downarrow \ \text{Monomer}$$

$$\underset{\mathrm{XIII}}{\overbrace{(\mathrm{CH_2})_5\!-\!\mathrm{N{-}CO(CH_2)_5}}^{\mathrm{C{=}O}}\!-\!\mathrm{NH{-}CO{-}R}} + \overbrace{(\mathrm{CH_2})_5\!-\!\mathrm{N^-M^+}}^{\mathrm{C{=}O}} \qquad (7\text{-}66)$$

The species XII and XIII correspond to species VIII and IX for polymerization in the absence of an acylating agent. The acylating agent brings about the facile polymerization of many lactams by substituting the fast initiation sequence in Eqs. 7-64 to 7-66 for the slower sequence in Eqs. 7-60 to 7-61. The use of acylating agents is the preferred method of polymerizing lactams. It is also advantageous for the more reactive lactams since the induction period will be absent and the polymerization rate increased.

Propagation follows in the same manner as for the propagation of species IX

$$\overbrace{(CH_2)_5-N}^{C=O}-CO(CH_2)_5NH\sim\sim CO-R + \overbrace{(CH_2)_5-N^-}^{C=O}M^+ \longrightarrow$$

$$\underset{\text{XIV}}{\overbrace{(CH_2)_5-N}^{C=O}-CO(CH_2)_5\overset{M^+}{\bar{N}}-CO(CH_2)_5NH\sim\sim CO-R} \tag{7-67}$$

$$\Big\downarrow \text{Monomer}$$

$$\overbrace{(CH_2)_5-N}^{C=O}\!\left[CO(CH_2)_5NH\right]_2\!\sim CO-R + \overbrace{(CH_2)_5-N^-}^{C=O}M^+ \tag{7-68}$$

In a lactam polymerization involving the use of a strong base and an acylating agent, initiation may involve contributions from both the imide dimer (IX) and the *N*-acyllactam (XI). However, in the usual case, the latter is by far the most important and one may ignore the former. For such a polymerization system, the terms used to describe the roles of the base and the acylating agent (or the *N*-acyllactam) are misnomers. The base is almost always referred to as the catalyst or initiator and the acylating agent as the cocatalyst or promoter. It is clear that the actual initiator is the acylating agent or the *N*-acyllactam. The base might be more precisely referred to as an activator [36] for its role is to form the activated monomer (lactam anion).

7-3a-2-b Rate of Polymerization. Detailed kinetic studies have not been made on these lactam polymerizations but one can note the main kinetic characteristics of the reaction. The polymerization rate may be expressed by an equation of the type

$$R_p = k[\mathrm{I}][\mathrm{M}^-] \tag{7-69}$$

where [I] and $[\mathrm{M}^-]$ are the concentrations of the propagating imide species and the activated monomer, respectively. The polymerization rate would, therefore, be expected to increase with increasing concentrations of base and *N*-acyllactam since $[\mathrm{M}^-]$ and [I], respectively would be increased. Figures 7-8 and 7-9 show these effects for the polymerizations of piperidone and pyrrolidone with potassium and *N*-acyllactams. The % conversion of monomer to polymer at a given reaction time is employed here as an indicator of the polymerization rate. The % conversion increases with increasing potassium concentration, reaches a maximum, and then decreases at higher potassium concentrations. The latter decrease may be due to hydrolysis of the *N*-acyllactam by the base.

7-3a-2-c Degree of Polymerization. The degree of polymerization increases with conversion as in a step polymerization. The dependence of $\overline{X}_n$ on the concentrations of the activated monomer and propagating species is similar to the case of living polymerization. The polymer size increases with increasing concentration of base and decreasing *N*-acyllactam concentration. Figures 7-8 and 7-9 show these effects for the piperidone and pyrrolidone polymerizations. A consideration of the degree of polymerization raises a question regarding the mode of termination. Many polymerizations contain no terminating agents and propagation continues until the monomer supply is exhausted. A compound with an active (acidic) hydrogen, present either as an impurity or deliberately added, brings about termination by reaction with the activated monomer or the propagating anion XIV.

The molecular weight distributions in these polymerizations are usually broad due to branching which occurs in the later stages of reaction [40]. As the monomer concentration decreases and the concentration of amide groups which are part of polymer chains increases, there is an increasing tendency for the propagating anion XIV to undergo a branching reaction with the terminal cyclic amide group of a polymer chain

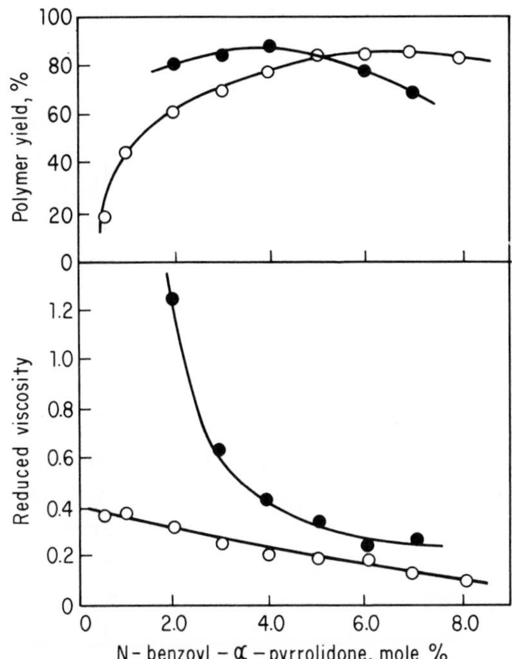

FIG. 7-8 *Dependence of the percent yield and polymer size of α-pyrrolidone polymerization at 40°C on the concentrations of N-benzoyl-α-pyrrolidone and potassium. The curves are for potassium concentrations of 0.61 (○) and 4.32 (●) mole percent. After [38] (by permission of Interscience Publishers, John Wiley & Sons, Inc., New York).*

$$\overbrace{(CH_2)_5-\overset{\overset{\displaystyle O}{\|}}{C}-N}^{\text{ring}}-CO(CH_2)_5\overset{M^+}{\bar{N}}-CO(CH_2)_5NH\sim\sim\sim CO-R + \overbrace{(CH_2)_5-\overset{\overset{\displaystyle O}{\|}}{C}-N}^{\text{ring}}\sim\sim\sim \longrightarrow$$

$$\overbrace{(CH_2)_5-\overset{\overset{\displaystyle O}{\|}}{C}-N}^{\text{ring}}-CO(CH_2)_5-\underset{\underset{\underset{\underset{\underset{\displaystyle \wr}{N^-M^+}}{|}}{(CH_2)_5}}{|}}{\underset{\displaystyle CO}{|}}}{N}-CO(CH_2)_5NH\sim\sim\sim CO-R \tag{7-70}$$

in preference to proton-transfer with monomer (Eq. 7-68). Amines have been found [40] to have a modifying effect on this molecular weight broadening. The effect may be due to reaction of the amine with the terminal cyclic amide structure to yield dead polymer chains (i.e., chains without the terminal cyclic structure) incapable of the reaction in Eq. 7-70.

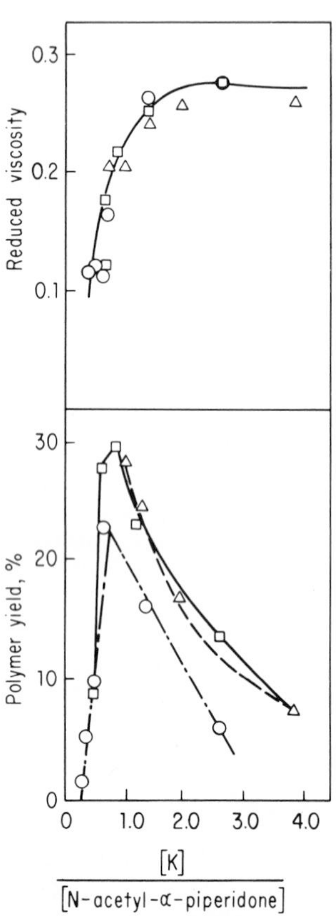

FIG. 7-9 *Dependence of the percent yield and polymer size of α-piperidone polymerization at 40°C on the molar ratio of potassium to N-acetyl-α-piperidone. The data are for potassium concentrations of 2.58 (○), 5.16 (□), and 7.74 (△) mole percent. After [38] (by permission of Interscience Publishers, John Wiley & Sons, Inc., New York).*

7-3b Cationic Polymerization

7-3b-1 Polymerization by Protonic Acids. Various protonic acids such as phosphoric, hydrochloric, hydrobromic, and carboxylic acids have been used to initiate the polymerization of lactams [41–43]. The polymerization proceeds according to the initiation sequence

$$\overbrace{(CH_2)_5\text{—}\overset{\overset{\displaystyle O}{\|}}{C}\text{—}NH}^{} + HA \rightleftharpoons \overbrace{(CH_2)_5\text{—}\overset{\overset{\displaystyle O}{\|}}{C}\text{—}\underset{\underset{\displaystyle Cl^-}{+}}{NH_2}}^{} \tag{7-71}$$

$$\overbrace{(CH_2)_5\text{—}\overset{\overset{\displaystyle O}{\|}}{C}\text{—}\underset{\underset{\displaystyle Cl^-}{+}}{NH_2}}^{} + \overbrace{H\ddot{N}\text{—}\overset{\overset{\displaystyle O}{\|}}{C}\text{—}(CH_2)_5}^{} \longrightarrow$$

$$\overbrace{(CH_2)_5\text{—}\overset{\overset{\displaystyle O}{\|}}{C}\text{—}\underset{\underset{\displaystyle Cl^-}{+}}{NH}}^{}\text{—}CO(CH_2)_5NH_2 \tag{7-72}$$

followed by propagation

$$\sim\!\sim NH(CH_2)_5CO-\overset{+}{N}H\underset{\displaystyle Cl^-}{}-(CH_2)_5\,\overset{O}{\overset{\|}{C}} + HN-(CH_2)_5\,\overset{O}{\overset{\|}{C}} \longrightarrow$$

$$\sim\!\sim\!\left[NH(CH_2)_5CO\right]_2 H\overset{+}{N}\underset{\displaystyle Cl^-}{}-(CH_2)_5\,\overset{O}{\overset{\|}{C}} \qquad (7\text{-}73)$$

The efficiency of an acid in initiating polymerization is directly dependent on its acidity [44]. Both the propagation and initiation reactions (Eqs. 7-72 and 7-73) involve a nucleophilic attack of the monomer nitrogen on the carbonyl of the lactam structure. The reaction is relatively similar to that for lactam polymerization by bases. In both types of polymerizations, the reactivity of the lactam carbonyl toward nucleophilic attack (by monomer or activated monomer) is increased by making it part of an imide structure. The nucleophilic agent (monomer) in the acid catalyzed polymerization is less nucleophilic than that (activated monomer) in the base reaction. This difference in nucleophilicity is compensated for by increasing the reactivity of the lactam carbonyl by protonation in the former polymerization.

A Lewis acid such as $SnCl_4$ has also been used to initiate the polymerization of lactams [45]. The reaction involves the formation of a 1:2 complex of $SnCl_4$ and monomer

$$2\ \text{Monomer} + SnCl_4 \longrightarrow [(\text{Monomer})_2SnCl_4] \longrightarrow HCl \qquad (7\text{-}74)$$

The complex, identified by infrared analysis, decomposes to yield HCl and an unidentified product. The polymerization is catalyzed by the HCl via the sequence in Eqs. 7-71 to 7-73.

7-3b-2 Polymerization by Amines. The polymerization of caprolactam by amines such as aniline or benzylamine is interesting [46]. The polymerization involves cationic initiation by an ammonium salt formed by reaction between the amine and the lactam. The overall reaction sequence is

$$\mathrm{RNH_2 + HA \rightleftharpoons RNH_3^+A^-} \tag{7-75}$$

$$\mathrm{RNH_3^+A^- + (CH_2)_5\text{—}\overset{\overset{\displaystyle O}{\|}}{C}\text{—}NH \longrightarrow RNHCO(CH_2)_5NH_3^+A^-} \tag{7-76}$$

$$\mathrm{RNH\sim\sim CO(CH_2)_5NH_3^+A^- + (CH_2)_5\text{—}\overset{\overset{\displaystyle O}{\|}}{C}\text{—}NH \longrightarrow}$$

$$\mathrm{RNH\sim\sim CO(CH_2)_5NHCO(CH_2)_5NH_3^+A^-} \tag{7-77}$$

where HA is the lactam. The mechanism is substantiated by the fact that the direct use of an amine hydrochloride results in polymerization without an induction period and with a first order dependence of R_p on the amine hydrochloride concentration. Polymerization with the amine, on the other hand, shows a one-half order dependence on the amine concentration since the reaction in Eq. 7-75 is an equilibrium and the ammonium concentration depends on the one-half power of the amine concentration. Further, in the amine catalyzed reaction, there is an induction period necessary for the buildup of the concentration of the ammonium salt.

The initiation and propagation reactions require the transfer of two protons from the ammonium salt to the lactam nitrogen simultaneously with the ring-opening of the lactam. This may proceed according to

$$\mathrm{RNH_3^+ + (CH_2)_5\text{—}\overset{\overset{\displaystyle O}{\|}}{C}\text{—}NH \longrightarrow (CH_2)_5\text{—}\overset{\overset{\displaystyle OH}{|}}{C}(\text{—}NHR)\text{—}\overset{+}{N}H_2 \longrightarrow}$$

$$\mathrm{RNH\text{—}CO(CH_2)_5\text{—}NH_3^+} \tag{7-78}$$

The necessity of transferring two protons explains why tertiary amines have been found to be completely ineffective in catalyzing lactam polymerizations. Primary and secondary amines are both effective but the secondary amines are less effective than the primary amines due to considerations of steric hindrance. For each class of amine, the initiation efficiency is directly dependent on the basicity of the amine [44, 46].

7-3c Catalysis by Water

7-3c-1 Reaction Mechanism. Water has been found to be a useful catalyst for the commercial polymerization of caprolactam. (Base catalysis is the other method of commercial significance.) The initial reaction is the hydrolysis of the lactam to the amino acid

$$\overbrace{(CH_2)_5-NH}^{\overset{O}{\overset{\|}{C}}} + H_2O \longrightarrow \underset{\text{XV}}{HO_2C(CH_2)_5NH_2} \tag{7-79a}$$

The subsequent reaction has previously [47, 48] been considered to be the ring-opening reaction between the amino acid and monomer

$$HO_2C(CH_2)_5NH_2 + \overbrace{(CH_2)_5-NH}^{\overset{O}{\overset{\|}{C}}} \longrightarrow \underset{\text{XVI}}{HO_2C(CH_2)_5NHCO(CH_2)_5NH_2} \tag{7-79b}$$

with propagation continuing in the same manner along with the propagation via step reactions between the amine and carboxyl endgroups of various species such as XV and XVI. The polymerization can often be more conveniently initiated by adding an amino acid directly at the beginning of the reaction.

More recently, a mechanism similar to that of the amine catalyzed lactam polymerization has been suggested for the water catalyzed reaction [44]. It is generally accepted that an amino acid such as XV would exist as the zwitter-ion $^{-}O_2C(CH_2)_5-NH_3^+$. Polymerization can then be considered as being initiated by electrophilic attack of the quarternary nitrogen of the zwitter-ion on monomer in exactly the same manner as the amine catalyzed reaction

$$\overbrace{(CH_2)_5-NH}^{\overset{O}{\overset{\|}{C}}} + H_2O \overset{K_i}{\rightleftharpoons} {}^{-}O_2C(CH_2)_5NH_3^+ \tag{7-80}$$

with propagation proceeding similarly

$$\sim\!\!\sim\!\!\sim CO(CH_2)_5NH_3^+ + HN\!-\!(CH_2)_5\!-\!C\!=\!O \;\overset{K_p}{\rightleftharpoons}\; \sim\!\!\sim\!\!\sim CO(CH_2)_5NHCO(CH_2)_5NH_3^+ \tag{7-81}$$

7-3c-2 Degree of Polymerization. This polymerization is an equilibrium reaction and its kinetics are handled in an appropriate manner, e.g., by Eq. 7-48 for the rate of polymerization. The quantitative dependence of the degree of (equilibrium) polymerization on various reaction parameters can be considered in the manner described by Tobolsky [49, 50]. This approach is generally applicable to many equilibrium polymerizations. For the water catalyzed polymerization of a lactam, K_i and K_p have different values and K_p is assumed to be independent of the size of the propagating species. (The latter is simply another instance of the concept of functional group reactivity independent of size.) The concentration $[M_n^+]$ of propagating chains of size n is given by

$$[M_n^+] = K_i[C]_c[M]_c(K_p[M]_c)^{n-1} \tag{7-82}$$

where C is the catalyst (water). The c subscripts refer to equilibrium concentrations. The total concentration of polymer molecules [N] is then the summation of Eq. 7-82 over all sizes of chains

$$[N] = \sum_{n=1}^{\infty} [M_n^+] = \frac{K_i[C]_c[M]_c}{1 - K_p[M]_c} \tag{7-83}$$

while the total concentration [W] of monomer segments incorporated in the polymer is given by

$$[W] = \sum_{n=1}^{\infty} n[M_n^+] = \frac{K_i[C]_c[M]_c}{(1 - K_p[M]_c)^2} \tag{7-84}$$

The degree of polymerization of the polymer is obtained by dividing Eq. 7-84 by Eq. 7-83

$$\overline{X}_n = \frac{[W]}{[N]} = \frac{1}{1 - K_p[M]_c} \tag{7-85}$$

Material balances on the monomer and catalyst are represented by

$$[M]_0 = [M]_c + [W] \tag{7-86}$$

$$[C]_0 = [C]_c + [N] \tag{7-87}$$

where the 0 subscripts refer to initial concentrations. Combinations of Eqs. 7-84 and 7-86 and of Eqs. 7-83 and 7-87 yield

$$[M]_0 = [M]_c(1 + K_i\overline{X}_n^2[C]_c) \tag{7-88}$$

$$[C]_0 = [C]_c(1 + K_i\overline{X}_n[M]_c) \tag{7-89}$$

Combination of Eqs. 7-85 to 7-87 also yields the obvious relationship

$$\overline{X}_n = \frac{[M]_0 - [M]_c}{[C]_0 - [C]_c} \tag{7-90}$$

The various relationships show the dependence of the degree of polymerization on the initial and equilibrium concentrations of monomer and catalyst and on the equilibrium constants for initiation (K_i) and propagation (K_p). The polymer molecular weight increases with decreasing K_i and $[C]_0$ and increasing K_p and $[M]_0$. Thus, Fig. 7-10 shows the variation of $\overline{X}_n$ with initial water concentration for the polymerization of ϵ-caprolactam [50, 51]. The dotted line represents the theoretical curve predicted from Eqs. 7-84, 7-88, 7-89, and 7-90 in the following manner. K_i and K_p can be obtained from one or more sets of experimental data for $\overline{X}_n$, $[C]_0$, $[M]_0$, and [M] using various combinations of the equations. Values of $[M]_c$ are then calculated from Eq. 7-85 for various assumed values $\overline{X}_n$. The corresponding values of $[C]_0$ are calculated from the expression

$$[C]_0 = \frac{[M]_0 - [M]}{\dfrac{K_i[M]_c\overline{X}_n^2}{1 + K_i[M]_c\overline{X}_n}} \tag{7-91}$$

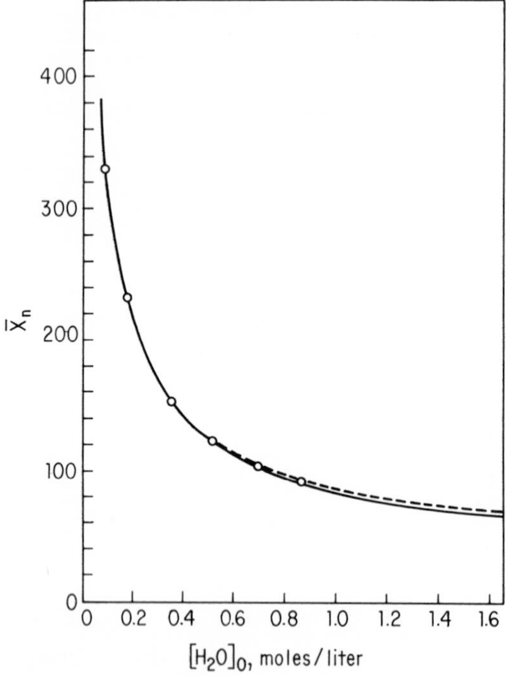

FIG. 7-10 *Dependence of the degree of polymerization of ε-caprolactam at 220°C on the initial concentration of water. The circles and solid-lined curve represent the experimental data; the broken-lined curve represents the theoretical curve. After [50] (by permission of American Chemical Society, Washington) from data in [51] (by permission of Akademische Verlagsgesellschaft, Frankfurt).*

obtained by combining Eqs. 7-89 and 7-90. The $\bar{X}_n$ and $[C]_0$ values are then used to draw the theoretical curve in Fig. 7-10. It is seen that the experimental curve fits the theoretical one extremely well.

7-3d Reactivity

The reactivity of a lactam toward polymerization depends primarily on the thermodynamic stability of the ring and on the type of initiation. The thermodynamic stability of different sized rings follows the same general order as for other cyclic compounds (Sec.

Table 7-4 Heats and Entropies of Polymerization for Lactams[a]

Monomer	Ring size	$-\Delta H$ (kcal/mole)	$-\Delta S$ (cal/°K-mole)
2-Pyrrolidone	5	1.3	7.3
2-Piperidone	6	1.1	6.0
Caprolactam	7	3.0	1.1
Enantholactam	8	5.7	4.0
Capryllactam	9	9.6	
12-Dodecanolactam	13	1.5	

[a]Data from [32] and [52].

2-3b). Table 7-4 shows the heats and entropies of polymerization for several lactams [32, 52]. The general order of ΔH values is similar to that for the cyclic ether polymerizations (Table 7-3) and the order of stability of cycloalkanes (Table 2-2). The net relative order of reactivity for the lactams varies somewhat depending on the type of initiation. There is a relatively scant amount of data available on reactivity as a function of ring size. Table 7-5 shows pertinent data which is available [47, 53, 54]. The orders of polymerization reactivities are close to what is expected (Sec. 2-3b) although there are some definite variations. Substituted cyclic amides show the expected lowered reactivity relative to unsubstituted monomers [47]. The effect of a substituent in lowering reactivity is greater, however, as the ring size decreases or if the substituent is on the nitrogen. The latter effect probably results from steric hindrance at the reaction site.

The unexpected low reactivities of the 9- and 11-membered lactams in the water and HCl polymerizations, respectively, may be

Table 7-5 Polymerization Reactivity of Lactams as a Function of Ring Size

Types of initiation	Order of reactivity of different sized rings	Ref.
Anionic with acylating agent	$7 \geq 5 > 6$	[53]
HCl	$8 > 7 > 11 \gg 5, 6$	[54]
Water	$7 > 8 \cong 9 \gg 5, 6$	[47]

due to their existence in the *trans* or *anti* conformation XVII as opposed to the *cis* or *syn* conformation XVIII

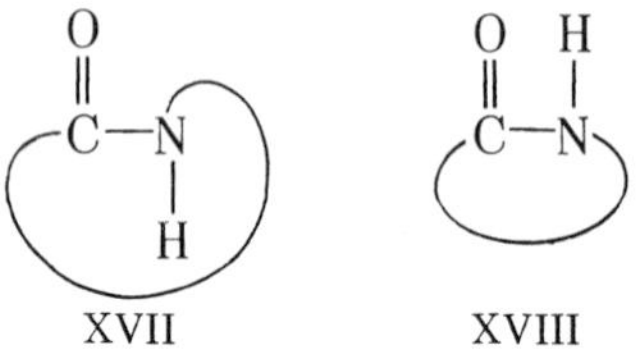

The anti conformation (in which the carbonyl oxygen and the amide hydrogen are on opposite sides of the amide carbon-nitrogen bond) is the more stable form for an amide. However, most rings of 7 or less members are able to exist only in the less stable syn conformation. As the ring size increases, the puckered ring structure can accommodate the amide linkage in the anti conformation to varying extents. Rings of 10 or more members essentially will be completely in the anti conformation while 8- and 9-membered rings will be partially in the syn and partially in the anti conformations. Thus, the somewhat altered order of reactivities of cyclic amides may be due to differences in reactivities of the syn and anti amide conformations.

It is interesting to note that the 5- and 6-membered lactams are much more reactive in anionic polymerization compared to either the HCl or water polymerizations. This is explainable in terms of the differences in the reaction mechanisms involved. Anionic polymerization involves attack on the lactam ring by a more nucleophilic agent than does the HCl polymerization. The water initiated polymerization, on the other hand, involves an electrophilic attack on the lactam ring. Due to the low electron density in the amide group, this is not as facile a reaction as that with the strong nucleophile. The net result is that the anionic polymerization is usually a faster and less selective reaction than either of the other two reactions. Lactams which are unreactive toward HCl or water initiated polymerization are polymerized fairly readily by the anionic route. These differences in reactivity are also observed in comparing the polymerization temperatures which are employed. Temperatures of close to 250°C are often required for the acid and water initiated polymerizations (as well as for the other cationic polymerizations). Lower temperatures can be successfully used for the corresponding anionic polymerizations.

7-4 CYCLOSILOXANES

Linear polysiloxanes, or silicones as they are often referred to, can be synthesized by the anionic or cationic polymerization of cyclic siloxanes. The most commonly encountered polymerization is that of the cyclic tetramer octamethylcyclotetrasiloxane

$$\text{cyclo-}\left[\text{Si(CH}_3)_2\text{—O}\right]_4 \longrightarrow \left[\begin{array}{c} CH_3 \\ | \\ \text{—Si—O—} \\ | \\ CH_3 \end{array} \right]_n \qquad (7\text{-}92)$$

7-4a Anionic Polymerization

The anionic polymerization of cyclic siloxanes can be initiated by alkali metal oxides and hydroxides, silanolates such as potassium trimethylsilanolate, $(CH_3)_2SiOK$, and other bases [1, 55]. Both initiation

$$A^- + \overset{\frown O}{\text{SiR}_2\text{+OSiR}_2\text{+}_3} \underset{k_2}{\overset{k_1}{\rightleftharpoons}} A\text{+SiR}_2\text{O+}_3\text{SiR}_2\text{O}^- \qquad (7\text{-}93)$$

and propagation

$$\sim\sim\text{SiR}_2\text{O}^- + \overset{\frown O}{\text{SiR}_2\text{+OSiR}_2\text{+}_3} \underset{k_4}{\overset{k_3}{\rightleftharpoons}} \sim\sim\text{+SiR}_2\text{O+}_4\text{SiR}_2\text{O}^- \qquad (7\text{-}94)$$

involve a nucleophilic attack of an anion on the cyclic monomer in a manner analogous to the anionic polymerization of epoxides. The propagation is terminated by the addition of a terminating agent.

An interesting aspect of this polymerization is the observation [56] that ΔH for the reaction is nearly zero and, amazingly, ΔS is positive by about 1.6 cal/mole-°K. The driving force in this polymerization is the increase in entropy (disorder) upon polymerization. A positive value of ΔS is a very rare occurrence for a polymerization. The only other reported instances of positive ΔS

values are those for the polymerizations of the cyclic octamers of sulfur and selenium [32]. All other polymerizations involve a decrease in entropy due to the decreased disorder for a polymer relative to its monomer. The positive ΔS for the polymerizations of the cyclic siloxane, S and Se, may be explained in terms of the high degree of flexibility of the linear polymer chains due to the large sized atoms comprising them. This flexibility leads to greater degrees of freedom in the linear polymer compared to the cyclic monomer.

7-4b Cationic Polymerization

Cationic polymerization of cyclic siloxanes has been carried out with protonic and Lewis acids [1, 57]. Both initiation

$$\underbrace{\mathrm{O}\!-\!\mathrm{SiR_2}\!\left(\mathrm{OSiR_2}\right)_3}_{\text{cyclic}} + \mathrm{H^+A^-} \rightleftharpoons \mathrm{HO^+(A^-)}\!-\!\mathrm{SiR_2}\!\left(\mathrm{OSiR_2}\right)_3 \rightleftharpoons \mathrm{H}\!\left(\mathrm{OSiR_2}\right)_3\!\mathrm{O}\!\!-\!\!\underset{\mathrm{R}}{\overset{\mathrm{R}}{\mathrm{Si}}}{}^{+}\mathrm{A^-} \tag{7-95}$$

and propagation

$$\sim\!\mathrm{O}\!-\!\underset{\mathrm{R}}{\overset{\mathrm{R}}{\mathrm{Si}}}{}^{+}\mathrm{A^-} + \underbrace{\mathrm{O}\!-\!\mathrm{SiR_2}\!\left(\mathrm{OSiR_2}\right)_3}_{\text{cyclic}} \rightleftharpoons \sim\!\mathrm{OSiR_2}\!-\!\mathrm{O^+(A^-)}\!-\!\mathrm{SiR_2}\!\left(\mathrm{OSiR_2}\right)_3 \rightleftharpoons \sim\!\left(\mathrm{OSiR_2}\right)_4\!\mathrm{O}\!\underset{\mathrm{R}}{\overset{\mathrm{R}}{\mathrm{Si}}}{}^{+}\mathrm{A^-} \tag{7-96}$$

proceed via a tertiary oxonium ion which rearranges to a transient siliconium ion.

No evidence exists for the actual existence of the siliconium ion in the above mechanism. The data available on this polymerization would be equally satisfied by a mechanism involving electrophilic attack of the tertiary oxonium ion on monomer (without rearrangement to the siliconium ion)

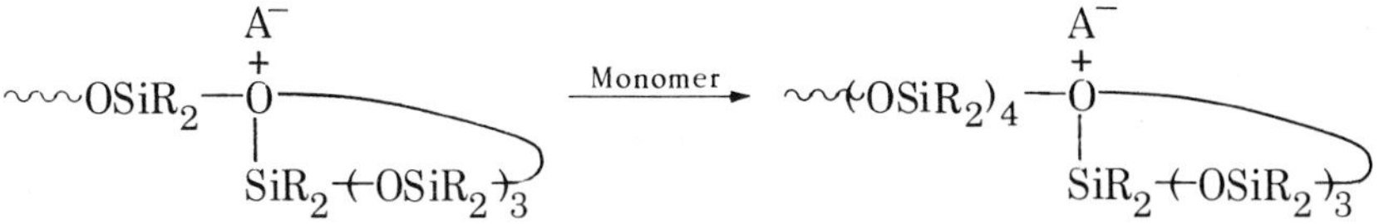

$$\sim\sim OSiR_2-\overset{\overset{A^-}{+}}{O}(-SiR_2(OSiR_2)_3-) \xrightarrow{\text{Monomer}} \sim\sim(OSiR_2)_4-\overset{\overset{A^-}{+}}{O}(-SiR_2(OSiR_2)_3-) \tag{7-97}$$

analogous to the polymerization of cyclic ethers. Interestingly, the siliconium ion has been postulated as an intermediate in another polymerization. The acid catalyzed polymerization of 1,1,3,3-tetramethyl-1,3-disilacyclobutane

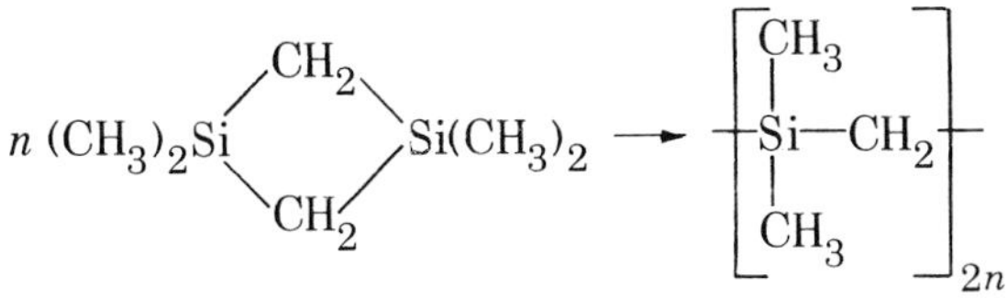

$$n\ (CH_3)_2Si\langle{}^{CH_2}_{CH_2}\rangle Si(CH_3)_2 \longrightarrow \left[\underset{CH_3}{\overset{CH_3}{Si}}-CH_2 \right]_{2n} \tag{7-98}$$

is considered [58] to proceed via the intermediate XIX

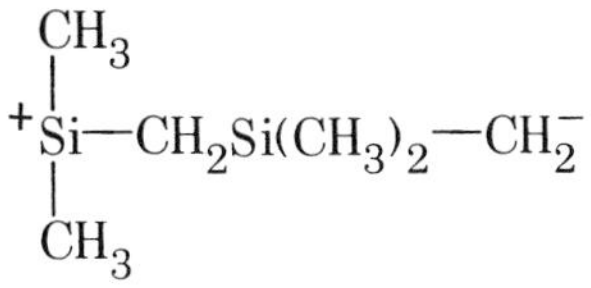

$$^{+}\underset{CH_3}{\overset{CH_3}{Si}}-CH_2Si(CH_3)_2-CH_2^-$$

XIX

7-5 OTHER CYCLIC MONOMERS

7-5a Cyclic Esters

Cyclic esters undergo ring-opening polymerization to polyesters with the use of a variety of cationic and anionic catalysts. Lactides (cyclic esters formed by intermolecular dimerization of a hydroxy acid) such as glycolide

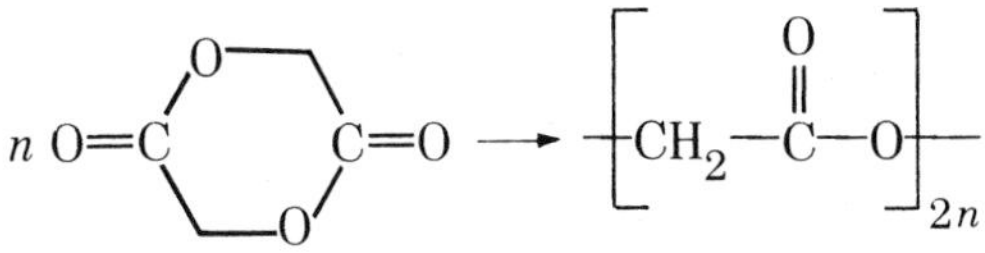

$$n\ O{=}C\langle{}^{O-CH_2}_{CH_2-O}\rangle C{=}O \longrightarrow \left[CH_2-\overset{O}{\overset{\|}{C}}-O \right]_{2n} \tag{7-99}$$

as well as lactones

$$n\ \overset{\overbrace{\quad O \quad}}{CO-R} \longrightarrow \left[R-\overset{\overset{\displaystyle O}{\|}}{C}-O \right]_n \tag{7-100}$$

have been studied [1, 59, 60]. The reactivity of different cyclic esters follows the same order as that of the lactams with one exception. The reactivities of the 5- and 6-membered lactones are just the opposite of the corresponding lactams. The 5-membered lactone (γ-butyrolactone) does not polymerize while the 6-membered δ-valerolactone does.

The cationic polymerization proceeds via attack on monomer by a propagating center which is either the oxonium ion XX or the acylium ion XXI formed by unimolecular

$$\sim\!\!\sim\overset{+}{O}\underset{\overbrace{\quad C(=O) \quad}}{-(CH_2)_m} \qquad\qquad \sim\!\!\sim O(CH_2)_m-\overset{\overset{\displaystyle O}{\|}}{C}{}^+$$

XX XXI

ring-opening of the oxonium ion. Anionic polymerization probably proceeds by

$$\sim\!\!\sim CO(CH_2)_mO^- + \underset{\overbrace{\quad C(=O) \quad}}{O-(CH_2)_m} \longrightarrow \sim\!\!\sim CO(CH_2)_mO\overset{\overset{\displaystyle O}{\|}}{C}(CH_2)_mO^- \tag{7-101}$$

This mechanism is consistent with the fact that the base saponification of esters generally proceeds by means of acyl oxygen cleavage, i.e., cleavage of the bond between the carbonyl carbon and the non-carbonyl oxygen. However, alkyl oxygen cleavage has been suggested for the reactions of some lactones and their polymerization may proceed [1] by way of the carboxylate anion as the propagating center

$$\sim\!\!\sim(CH_2)_m\overset{\overset{\displaystyle O}{\|}}{C}O^- + \underset{\overbrace{\quad C(=O) \quad}}{O-(CH_2)_5} \longrightarrow \sim\!\!\sim(CH_2)_mCO_2(CH_2)_5COO^- \tag{7-102}$$

7-5b Cyclic Amines

Cyclic amines, referred to as imines, are polymerized to polyamines by acid catalysts but not by bases [1, 61, 62]. The unreactivity toward base catalysis is due to instability of an amine anion (for example, $\sim\!\sim CH_2CH_2\bar{N}H$ for ethylenimine) as the propagating species. The 3-membered imines (or aziridines) are the only monomers in this class which are of significance. The high degree of strain in the 3-membered ring manifests itself by an extremely fast polymerization. Thus, the polymerization of ethylenimine at room temperature can be quite violent. A variety of cationic species including the mild benzyl carbonium ion (from benzyl chloride) are efficient catalysts for the polymerization.

The cationic polymerization of imines proceeds in a manner analogous to that of cyclic ethers. The propagating species is an immonium ion and propagation involves nucleophilic attack by monomer

$$\sim\!\sim\overset{A^-\,+}{\underset{H}{N}}\!\left<\begin{array}{c}CH_2\\|\\CH_2\end{array}\right. + \underset{H}{N}\!\left<\begin{array}{c}CH_2\\|\\CH_2\end{array}\right. \longrightarrow \sim\!\sim NHCH_2CH_2-\overset{A^-\,+}{\underset{H}{N}}\!\left<\begin{array}{c}CH_2\\|\\CH_2\end{array}\right. \qquad (7\text{-}103)$$

Branching occurs in imine polymerizations by either attack of the imine end-group of one polymer chain on the immonium center of a propagating species

$$\sim\!\sim\overset{+}{\underset{H}{N}}\!\left<\begin{array}{c}CH_2\\|\\CH_2\end{array}\right. + \begin{array}{c}CH_2-CH_2\\ \diagdown\;\diagup\\ N\end{array}\!\sim\!\sim\!\sim \longrightarrow \sim\!\sim NHCH_2CH_2\overset{\displaystyle CH_2-CH_2}{\underset{+}{N}}\!\sim\!\sim\!\sim \xrightarrow{\begin{array}{c}NH\\ CH_2-CH_2\end{array}}$$

$$\begin{array}{c}\sim\!\sim NHCH_2CH_2N\!\sim\!\sim\!\sim\\ |\\ CH_2\\ |\\ CH_2\\ |\\ \overset{+}{N}H\\ \diagup\;\diagdown\\ CH_2-CH_2\end{array} \qquad (7\text{-}104)$$

or attack of the secondary amine group of a polymer chain on an immonium center

$$\sim\!\!\sim\overset{+}{\underset{H}{N}}\!\!\left<\begin{matrix}CH_2\\ |\\ CH_2\end{matrix}\right. + \sim\!\!\sim CH_2CH_2NH\sim\!\!\sim \longrightarrow \sim\!\!\sim CH_2CH_2\overset{+}{N}H\sim\!\!\sim \quad (\text{with } -CH_2-CH_2-NH\sim \text{ on } N) \tag{7-105}$$

Termination can occur by proton abstraction from the immonium ion by the counterion or any nitrogen in the polymer chain or the monomer nitrogen. A back-biting, ring-expansion termination reaction (analogous to Eq. 7-40 for ethylene oxide)

$$\sim\!\!\sim NHCH_2CH_2\overset{+}{\underset{H}{N}}\!\!\left<\begin{matrix}CH_2\\ |\\ CH_2\end{matrix}\right. A^- \longrightarrow \sim\!\!\sim N\!\left<\begin{matrix}CH_2CH_2\\ CH_2CH_2\end{matrix}\right>\!NH + HA \tag{7-106}$$

with the formation of a relatively unreactive piperazine ring end-group has also been postulated [61].

7-5c Cyclic Sulfides

Cyclic sulfides are polymerized

$$n\ \overset{\frown}{R\text{—}S} \longrightarrow \text{+}R\text{—}S\text{+}_n \tag{7-107}$$

by acidic catalysts [1, 63]. By analogy to the polymerization of cyclic ethers, the propagating species is thought to be the cyclic sulfonium ion XXII

$$\underset{\text{XXII}}{\sim\!\!\sim\overset{\frown}{\underset{+}{S}\text{—}R}} \qquad \underset{\text{XXIII}}{\sim\!\!\sim R\text{—}S^-}$$

The three-membered cyclic sulfides have also been polymerized [64] by basic catalysts—apparently via the propagating sulfide ion XXIII. As was the case with the ethers, there do not appear to be any reported cases of the anionic polymerization of cyclic sulfides of greater than 4 members.

Other sulfide polymerizations include the cationic polymerization of trithiane, the cyclic trimer of thioformaldehyde,

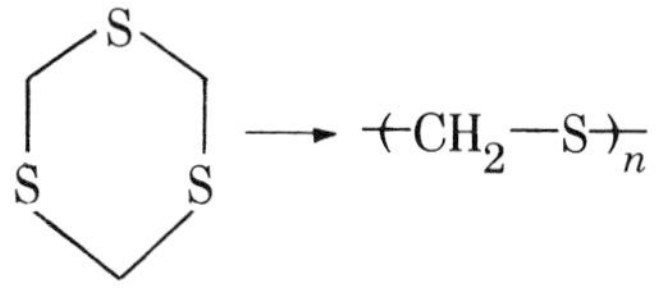

$$\text{trithiane} \longrightarrow -\!\!\left(\text{CH}_2\text{—S}\right)\!\!-_n \qquad (7\text{-}108)$$

and the radical polymerizations of cyclic disulfides and rhombic sulfur

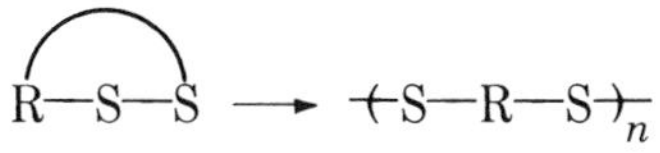

$$\text{R—S—S (cyclic)} \longrightarrow -\!\!\left(\text{S—R—S}\right)\!\!-_n \qquad (7\text{-}109)$$

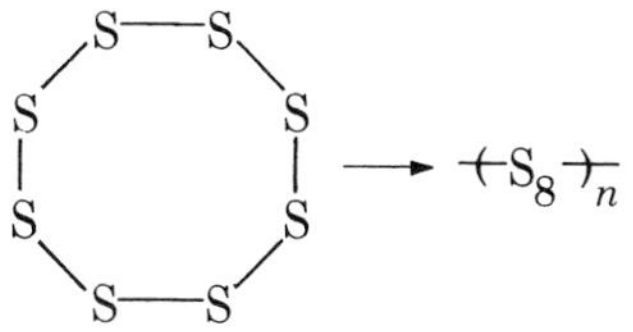

$$\text{S}_8 \text{ (ring)} \longrightarrow -\!\!\left(\text{S}_8\right)\!\!-_n \qquad (7\text{-}110)$$

by what are probably diradical intermediates.

7-5d *N*-Carboxy-α-Amino Acid Anhydrides

N-Carboxy-α-amino acid anhydrides, also referred to as oxazolidine-2,5-diones or Leuchs' anhydrides, are polymerized by various basic catalysts to polyamides

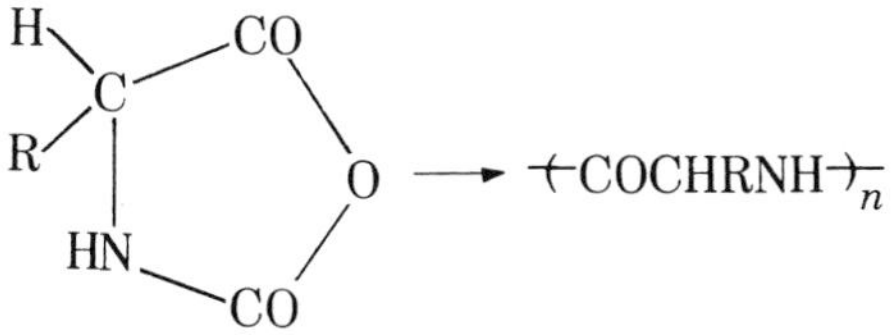

$$\text{HRC(CO—O—CO—NH) (ring)} \longrightarrow -\!\!\left(\text{COCHRNH}\right)\!\!-_n \qquad (7\text{-}111)$$

The propagation step, which involves a simultaneous decarboxylation, proceeds by way of the monomer anion

$$\sim\!\sim\text{NHCHRCO}-\overset{\text{CO}-\text{O}}{\underset{\text{C(H)(R)}-\text{CO}}{\text{N}}} + {}^{-}\overset{\text{CO}-\text{O}}{\underset{\text{C(H)(R)}-\text{CO}}{\text{N}}} \longrightarrow$$

$$\sim\!\sim\text{NHCHRCON}(\text{CO}_2^-)-\text{CHRCO}-\overset{\text{CO}-\text{O}}{\underset{\text{C(H)(R)}-\text{CO}}{\text{N}}} \xrightarrow[-\text{CO}_2]{\text{Monomer}}$$

$$\sim\!\sim\text{NHCHRCONHCHRCO}-\overset{\text{CO}-\text{O}}{\underset{\text{C(H)(R)}-\text{CO}}{\text{N}}} + {}^{-}\overset{\text{CO}-\text{O}}{\underset{\text{C(H)(R)}-\text{CO}}{\text{N}}} \qquad (7\text{-}112)$$

in a manner similar to the base catalyzed polymerization of lactams when strong bases are employed as catalysts [36, 65]. Polymerizations carried out with weak bases such as primary amines proceed [64, 65] by a different route—that involving nucleophilic attack by the amine group on the monomer

$$\text{RNH}_2 + \overset{\text{CO}-\text{NH}}{\underset{\text{CO}-\text{C(H)(R)}}{\text{O}}} \xrightarrow{-\text{CO}_2} \text{RNHCOCHRNH}_2 \qquad (7\text{-}113\text{a})$$

$$\text{RNH}\sim\!\sim\text{COCHRNH}_2 + \overset{\text{CO}-\text{NH}}{\underset{\text{CO}-\text{C(H)(R)}}{\text{O}}} \xrightarrow{-\text{CO}_2}$$

$$\text{RNH}\sim\!\sim\text{COCHRNHCOCHRNH}_2 \qquad (7\text{-}113\text{b})$$

7-5e Miscellaneous Polymerizations

Various exo-imino cyclic compounds have been polymerized by cationic catalysts [66]. The reaction

$$n\,\mathrm{R{-}N{=}C}\!\left<\begin{matrix}\mathrm{O}\\ \mathrm{Y}\end{matrix}\right]\longrightarrow \mathrm{+NR{-}CO{-}Y{-}CH_2CH_2+}_n \tag{7-114}$$

involves addition to the imino bond with a simultaneous ring-opening. The reaction has been observed with iminocarbonates (Y = O), 2-imino-1,3-oxazolidines (Y = NR) and 2-iminotetrahydrofurans (Y = CH_2). A similar polymerization is that of the endo-imino cyclic ethers [67]

$$n\,\mathrm{R{-}C}\!\left<\begin{matrix}\mathrm{N}\\ \mathrm{O}\end{matrix}\right>\!(\mathrm{CH_2})_m \longrightarrow \left[\begin{matrix}\mathrm{COR}\\ |\\ \mathrm{N{-}(CH_2)_m}\end{matrix}\right]_n \tag{7-115}$$

A few cycloalkanes such as cyclopropane derivatives and norbornene

$$n\,\mathrm{R{-}\underset{}{CH}{-}CH_2}\ (\text{ring closed by } \mathrm{CH_2}) \longrightarrow \mathrm{+CHRCH_2CH_2+}_n \tag{7-116}$$

$$\text{norbornene} \longrightarrow \left[\text{cyclopentane-1,3-diyl}{-}\mathrm{CH{=}CH}\right]_n \tag{7-117}$$

have also been polymerized [1, 8].

7-6 POLYMERIZATION OF INORGANIC OR SEMI-INORGANIC MONOMERS

As noted in Sec. 2-12c-9, there has been a considerable amount of interest in the synthesis of inorganic and semi-inorganic polymers. Some of the polymers studied have been obtained by ring-opening polymerizations [69].

7-6a Polyphosphazenes

The most thoroughly studied ring-opening polymerization of an inorganic monomer is probably that of the cyclic trimer of dichlorophosphazene (or phosphonitrilic chloride as it is more commonly referred to). An uncatalyzed polymerization takes place at temperatures of about 250°C while the use of catalysts such as carboxylic acids or acid salts, metals and alcohols allows polymerization to occur at lower temperatures [70, 71]. Depending upon the specific reaction conditions, varying amounts of branching and crosslinking take place. The uncatalyzed polymerization appears [70] to involve initiation by the thermal cleavage of an N—P bond in the monomer

$$(NPCl_2)_3 \text{ (ring)} \longrightarrow \text{ring-opened } Cl_2P^{+}{=}N{-}PCl_2{=}N{-}PCl_2{=}\bar{N}^{-} \tag{7-118}$$

followed by nucleophilic attack of the nitrogen anion on monomer

$$Cl_2\overset{+}{P}{=}NPCl_2N\underset{Cl}{\overset{Cl}{\underset{|}{\overset{|}{P}}}}{=}N^- + (NPCl_2)_3 \longrightarrow$$

$$Cl_2\overset{+}{P}{=}N{\leftarrow}PCl_2N{\rightarrow}_3PCl_2N\underset{Cl}{\overset{Cl}{\underset{|}{\overset{|}{P}}}}{=}N^- \tag{7-119}$$

Propagation follows in a similar manner

$$Cl_2\overset{+}{P}{=}N{\leftarrow}PCl_2N{\rightarrow}_n\underset{Cl}{\overset{Cl}{\underset{|}{\overset{|}{P}}}}{=}N^- + (NPCl_2)_3 \longrightarrow$$

$$\overset{+}{Cl_2P}{=}N{+}PCl_2N{\rightarrow}_{(n+3)}\underset{Cl}{\overset{Cl}{|}}P{=}N^- \tag{7-120}$$

Termination occurs by an intramolecular nucleophilic displacement of chloride ion followed by bonding of the chloride ion with the positive phosphorus end-group

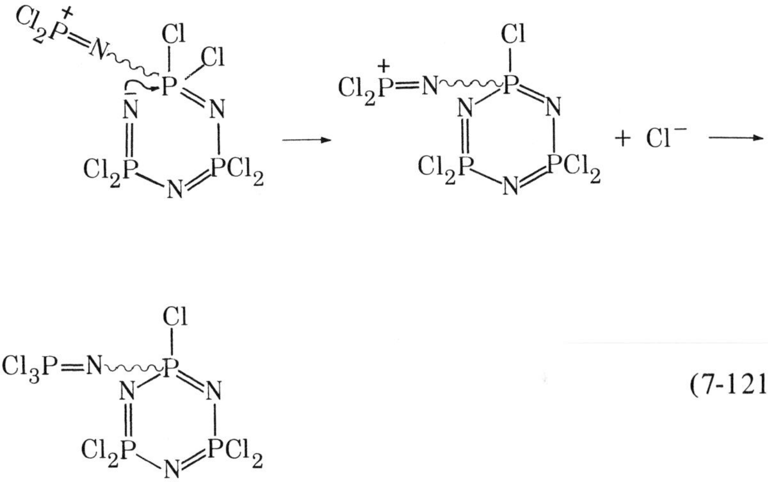

$$\overset{+}{Cl_2P}{=}N\sim\sim P(Cl)(Cl)\text{-ring}[N{=}PCl_2{-}N{=}PCl_2{-}N] \longrightarrow \overset{+}{Cl_2P}{=}N\sim\sim P(Cl)\text{-ring}[N{=}PCl_2{-}N{=}PCl_2{-}N] + Cl^- \longrightarrow$$

$$Cl_3P{=}N\sim\sim P(Cl)\text{-ring}[N{=}PCl_2{-}N{=}PCl_2{-}N] \tag{7-121}$$

Branching occurs by the corresponding intermolecular reaction between the nitrogen anion of one polymer chain and the P—Cl bond of another chain while crosslinking probably arises from a reaction of the type

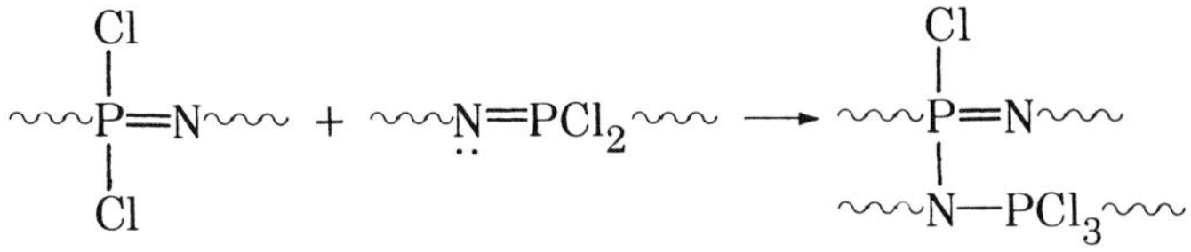

$$\sim\sim\underset{Cl}{\overset{Cl}{|}}P{=}N\sim\sim + \sim\sim\ddot{N}{=}PCl_2\sim\sim \longrightarrow \sim\sim\overset{Cl}{|}P{=}N\sim\sim \;\; (|\; \sim\sim N{-}PCl_3\sim\sim) \tag{7-122}$$

The catalyzed polymerization involves initiation by nucleophilic attack of the catalyst on monomer to form a nitrogen anion similar to the initiating species in the uncatalyzed reaction. For initiation by benzoate anion, this has been postulated as

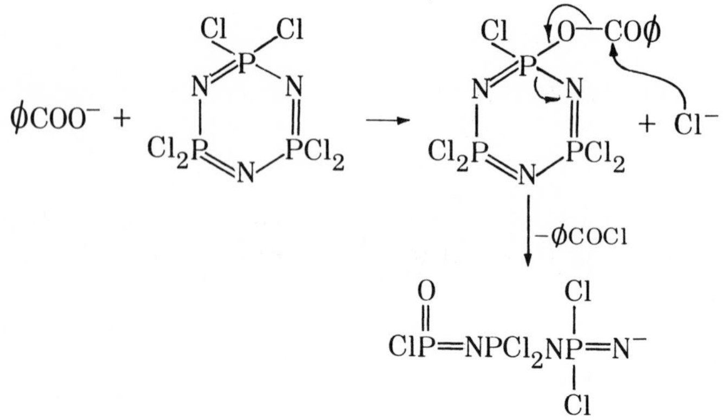

$$\phi COO^- + \text{(Cl}_2\text{PN)}_3 \text{ ring} \longrightarrow \text{ring-}P(Cl)(O\text{—}CO\phi) + Cl^- \xrightarrow{-\phi COCl} ClP(=O)\text{=NPCl}_2\text{NP(Cl)}_2\text{=N}^- \quad (7\text{-}123)$$

7-6b Other Polymerizations

The poly(phosphonitrilic chloride) polymers have shown some promise as useful materials from the practical viewpoint. They appear to have good elastomeric properties. Attempts have been made to polymerize other cyclic inorganic monomers but without any outstanding practical successes. Much of this lack of success can be ascribed to the poor understanding of the reaction mechanisms involved. At present, many systems yield only low molecular weight polymers with ill-defined structures. A clear understanding of the reactions should allow the synthesis of more useful materials in the future.

Cyclosilazanes, such as hexamethylcyclotrisilazane, $[(CH_3)_2SiNH]_3$, are polymerized [72] to low molecular weight products by the use of catalytic amounts of ammonium bromide at about 140°C. The polymer is not the linear structure $\text{+}Si(CH_3)_2NH\text{+}_n$ but contains large amounts of nitrogen atoms to which three silicon moities are attached. The polymer contains cyclic (XXIV) and branched (XXV) structures

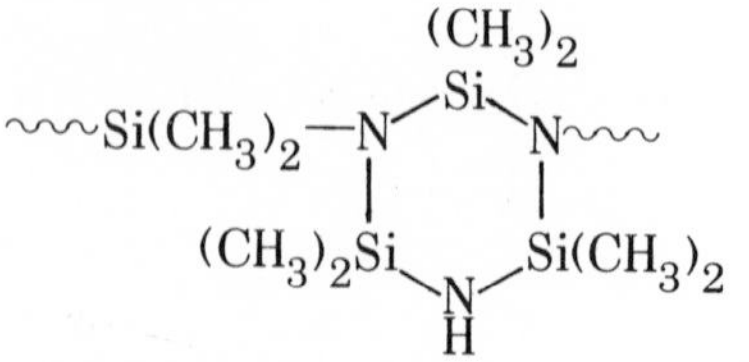

$$\sim\sim Si(CH_3)_2\text{—N} \text{ (ring: N–Si(CH}_3)_2\text{–N}\sim\sim\text{, Si(CH}_3)_2\text{–NH–Si(CH}_3)_2\text{)} \qquad \text{XXIV}$$

$$\sim\sim N(\text{—Si(CH}_3)_2\sim)\text{—Si(CH}_3)_2\text{—NH—Si(CH}_3)_2\text{—N}(\sim)\text{—Si(CH}_3)_2\sim\sim \qquad \text{XXV}$$

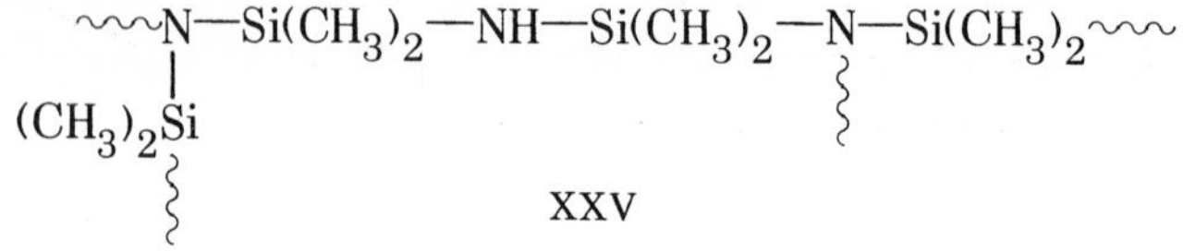

7-7 COPOLYMERIZATION

A sizable amount of work has been published on the copolymerizations of various cyclic monomers. These include the copolymerizations of pairs of cyclic monomers containing the same functional group (e.g., two cyclic ethers or two cyclic siloxanes) or containing different functional groups (e.g., the copolymerization of an ether with a lactone) and also the copolymerizations of cyclic monomers with alkenes. Very few of these copolymerizations are presently of commercial importance. An exception is the copolymerization of trioxane with small amounts of a cyclic ether to overcome the problem of the ceiling temperature effect in polyoxymethylene. The copolymer has been reported to be more stable toward thermal depolymerization than the end-capped homopolymer of trioxane [24]. Because the copolymer has monomer segments from the cyclic ether distributed randomly along the polyoxymethylene chain, a random thermal scission does not result in complete depolymerization.

The various copolymerizations of cyclic monomers are quite complicated due to a number of considerations. Most of the copolymerizations involve propagation-depropagation equilibria. This requires that the experimental data be handled in the appropriate manner (Sec. 6-5b) but this is often not done. The copolymer compositions are usually extremely sensitive to the reaction conditions. Changes in the gegen-ion, solvent, and temperature can have large effects on the observed copolymerization behavior. The initiation system employed is especially important for copolymerizations between monomers containing different polymerizing groups. Basic differences in the propagating centers (carbonium ion, oxonium ion, imide, carbanion, acylium ion, etc.) for different types of monomers precludes many copolymerizations.

7-7a Monomers Containing the Same Functional Group

Copolymerizations between pairs of cyclic ethers [73], lactams [74], lactones [75], and cyclic siloxanes [76] have been studied. The interpretation of data on monomer reactivity ratios is complicated by the range of behaviors observed depending on the particular comonomer pair and reaction conditions. Thus, for example, because of differences in reactivity, cyclic ethers of more than 4 members do not undergo anionic copolymerization but cationic polymerization occurs readily. When copolymerization is successful, the exact copolymerization behavior of monomers can often be considered from the viewpoint of the effect of ring size on their reactivity toward attack by the propagating species and toward ring-opening.

Table 7-6 shows some data on the cationic copolymerization of various cyclic ethers and acetals. The tendency of these cyclic monomers toward ring-opening would be expected to increase with ring size in the order $4 > 3 > 5 > 6$ based on the considerations previously discussed in Sec. 2-3b. On the other hand, monomer reactivity will also depend on the tendency toward oxonium ion formation since that is what occurs in the propagation step. Data on the basicity of the monomers [73] indicate that this will increase with ring size in the order $4 > 5 > 6 > 3$ with cyclic formals being less basic than the corresponding cyclic ethers. A consideration of the data in Table 7-6 as well as the corresponding $1/r_1$ values indicates that the two effects are of approximately equal importance. Monomer reactivity appears to increase with ring size in the order $4 > 5 > 3 > 6$ with cyclic formals being less reactive than the ethers. The marked effect of the catalyst system on copolymerization behavior is apparent from the monomer reactivity ratios in the copolymerizations of tetrahydrofuran with 3,3-bis(chloromethyl)oxetane and 1,3-dioxolane.

The ability of 2-methyltetrahydrofuran, tetrahydropyran, 1,3-dioxane and 1,4-dioxane to undergo copolymerization is interesting since these monomers do not homopolymerize under a variety of conditions. These monomers are formally similar in their unusual copolymerization behavior to the radical copolymerization behavior of monomers such as maleic anhydride, stilbene and diethyl fumarate (Sec. 6-3b-3) but not for the same reason. The copolymerizability of these cyclic monomers may be due to the highly reactive (unstable) nature of their propagating species. Consider the copolymerization sequence

$$\sim\sim \overset{+}{\text{O}}\text{—M}_1 \overset{M_2}{\rightleftharpoons} \sim\sim \text{M}_1\overset{+}{\text{O}}\text{—M}_2 \xrightarrow{M_1} \sim\sim \text{M}_1\text{M}_2\overset{+}{\text{O}}\text{—M}_1 \tag{7-124}$$

XXVI

in which M_2 is the cyclic monomer without a tendency to homopolymerize. In homopolymerization, the propagation-depropagation equilibrium for M_2 is completely to the left. However,

Table 7-6 Monomer Reactivity Ratios in Copolymerization of Cyclic Monomers[a,b]

M_1	M_2	r_1	r_2
3,3-Bis(chloromethyl)oxetane	Epichlorohydrin	3–2	0.3–0.5
	Tetrahydrofuran	0.82 ± 0.05	1.00 ± 0.05
	Tetrahydrofuran[c]	0.01 ∓ 0.01	1.80 ± 0.01
	2-Methyltetrahydrofuran	2.7 ± 0.25	0.05 ± 0.01
	Tetrahydropyran	1.66	0
	1,4-Dioxane	2.12	0
	1,3-Dioxane	13	0
	1,3-Dioxolane	1.5 ± 0.1	0.65 ± 0.05
1,3-Dioxolane	Epichlorohydrin	0.08	1.2
	Oxetane	0.0125	165
	Tetrahydrofuran	0.25 ± 0.05	28 ± 4
	Tetrahydrofuran[d]	0.24 ± 0.03	195 ± 10
	Trioxane[e]	1.75	0.57
Tetrahydrofuran	Epichlorohydrin	3.85 ± 0.05	0.00 ± 0.05
	1,3-Dioxolane	28 ± 4	0.25 ± 0.05

[a] Data from [73].
[b] Catalyst/temperature is $BF_3 \cdot (C_2H_5)_2O$/0 °C unless otherwise noted.
[c] $Al(C_2H_5)_3$ with epichlorohydrin as promoter.
[d] $SnCl_4$
[e] Siliconium ion/70°C.

with the second monomer M_1 present, the highly reactive species XXVI may add M_1 before depropagation can occur. The result is the copolymerization of M_1 and M_2. A similar situation exists in the triethylaluminum-water catalyzed copolymerization of β-propiolactone ($r_1 = 18 \pm 2$) with γ-butyrolactone ($r_2 = 0.36 \pm 0.10$) since the latter shows no homopolymerizability [75]. The copolymerizability of γ-butyrolactone is, however, highly dependent on the catalyst system. The use of potassium hydroxide, diethylzinc-water and aluminum isopropoxide does not result in copolymerization; only the homopolymer of β-propiolactone is obtained.

The anionic copolymerization (using an acetylated initiator) of ϵ-caprolactam (M_1) and α-pyrrolidone (M_2) shows the deficiencies involved in interpreting r_1 and r_2 values obtained by employing the standard copolymerization equation (Eq. 6-12). The monomer reactivity ratios have been calculated as $r_1 = 0.75$ and $r_2 = 5.0$ and it has been concluded that α-pyrrolidone is about eight times more reactive than ϵ-caprolactam [74]. However, a detailed study [77] of the system indicates that the copolymer composition is not determined by the rate constants k_{11}, k_{12}, k_{22}, and k_{21} for the various homo- and cross-propagation reactions. Transacylation,

$$\sim\!\sim\!\overset{\displaystyle O}{\overset{\|}{C}}-\widehat{N(CH_2)_3CO} + \widehat{\underline{N}(CH_2)_5CO} \overset{K_t}{\rightleftharpoons}$$

$$\sim\!\sim\!\overset{\displaystyle O}{\overset{\|}{C}}-\widehat{N(CH_2)_5CO} + \widehat{\underline{N}(CH_2)_3CO} \qquad (7\text{-}125)$$

involving an exchange of the monomer segments in the initiating and propagating imides, occurs at a much faster rate than any of the various propagation reactions. The copolymer composition is thus dependent on the transacylation equilibrium according to

$$\frac{d[M_1]}{d[M_2]} = \frac{K_t[M_1^-]}{[M_2^-]} \qquad (7\text{-}126)$$

where $[M_1^-]$ and $[M_2^-]$ represent the concentrations of the lactam anions. The ratio $[M_1^-]/[M_2^-]$ is determined by the relative acidities of the two monomers by the equilibrium

$$M_2^- + M_1 \overset{K_a}{\rightleftharpoons} M_2 + M_1^- \tag{7-127}$$

Combining the equilibrium expression for Eq. 7-126 with Eq. 7-127 yields

$$\frac{d[M_1]}{d[M_2]} = \frac{K_a K_t [M_1]}{[M_2]} \tag{7-128}$$

K_a and K_t have been independently determined as 0.4 and 0.3, respectively. The greater reactivity of α-pyrrolidone in the copolymerization with ϵ-caprolactam can then be attributed to the greater acidity of α-pyrrolidone (by a factor of about 2.5) and the greater nucleophilicity of the α-pyrrolidone anion in the transacylation equilibrium (by a factor of about 3.3).

7-7b Monomers Containing Different Functional Groups

Copolymerization between monomers containing different functional groups is highly selective. One of the cross-propagation steps in a contemplated copolymerization may easily be highly unfavorable because of the wide variations in the types of propagating centers involved and, often, in the energies of the bonds being broken during propagation. Copolymerization between certain types of monomers appears to be essentially impossible and that between others difficult to achieve while some copolymerizations would be expected to occur with relative ease. Thus, the combination of a lactam with another kind of monomer, such as a lactone, epoxide or alkene, is incompatible because of the differences in their propagation mechanisms. An anion derived from the second monomer would rapidly terminate by abstraction of a proton from the lactam monomer. Copolymerization would not occur; at most, the lactam homopolymer and/or homopolymer of the other monomer (of low molecular weight) would be produced.

Anionic copolymerizations between lactones and epoxides have been easily obtained [78]. These include the copolymerization of β-propiolactone(r_1 = 15.0)-styrene oxide (r_2 = 0.1), β-propiolactone (r_1 = 9.0)-epichlorohydrin(r_2 = 0.2), and δ-valerolactone (r_1 = 5.3)-propylene oxide(r_2 = 0.25). The copolymerizations show essentially ideal behavior ($r \sim 1$) with a tendency to have blocks of the lactone monomer. The ability of these two types of monomers to undergo anionic copolymerization is due to the fact that the propagating centers for both are the same—the alkoxide anion. The greater copolymerization reactivity of lactones is a consequence of the greater reactivity of the ester linkage toward nucleophilic attack compared to the ether linkage.

Copolymerization between cyclic oxides and lactones has been accomplished by using cationic initiation. Cross-propagation between the oxonium ion of the cyclic ether and oxonium (XX) or acylium (XXI) ion of the lactone occurs reasonably well. Thus, BF_3 etherate initiates [73] the copolymerizations of β-propiolactone (r_1 = 0.06)-3,3-bis(chloromethyl)oxetane (r_2 = 38) and β-propiolactone (r_1 = 0.4)-tetrahydrofuran (r_2 = 2.9). The greater reactivity of the cyclic ether is a consequence of its ease of oxonium ion formation (as measured by basicity) relative to the lactone. For the 4-membered cyclic ether, there is a large tendency toward its being incorporated in long blocks in the copolymer.

Copolymerization between alkenes and cyclic monomers requires a careful selection of the monomers and reaction conditions because there are often very large differences in the types of propagating centers for the two monomers [1]. Thus, cationic copolymerization of cyclic ethers with alkenes is unsuccessful because the oxonium ion is not electrophilic enough to attack an alkene double bond. Cationic copolymerization of an alkene is, however, possible with trioxane, tetraoxane, and cyclic formals such as 1,3-dioxolane [1, 73, 79]. Copolymerization occurs because the propagating centers for both monomers are the same—the carbonium ion. On the other hand, lactones such as β-propiolactones have not been cationically copolymerized with alkenes. This would indicate that the propagating center in lactone polymerization is not the acylium ion (XXI) but the oxonium ion (XX). Styrene has not been successfully copolymerized with either epoxides or lactones using basic catalysts although block copolymers with ethylene oxide have been obtained. The alkoxide ion (the propagating center for both epoxides and lactones) is, apparently, not sufficiently basic to react with the double bond of styrene.

A variety of other copolymerizations have been studied. Copolymerization has been accomplished in such comonomer pairs as ethyleneimine-β-propiolactone [80], trioxane-trithiane [81], ethylenimine-carbon monoxide [82], maleic anhydride-propylene oxide [83], and propylene oxide-sulfur dioxide [84]. The latter two copolymerizations are interesting in that they are ionic reactions

$$\underset{\text{CH=CH}}{\overset{\text{CO}\diagdown\text{O}\diagup\text{CO}}{}} + \overset{\text{O}}{\text{CH—CHCH}_3} \longrightarrow$$

$$\left[\text{CO—CH=CH—COO—}\overset{\text{CH}_3}{\overset{|}{\text{CH}}}\text{—CH}_2\text{O}\right]_n \qquad (7\text{-}129)$$

$$\overset{\text{O}}{\overset{\|}{\text{S}}}\text{=O} + \overset{\text{O}}{\text{CH—CHCH}_3} \longrightarrow \left[\overset{\text{O}}{\overset{\|}{\text{S}}}\text{—O—}\overset{\text{CH}_3}{\overset{|}{\text{CH}}}\text{—CH}_2\text{O}\right]_n \qquad (7\text{-}130)$$

involving propagations of maleic anhydride and sulfur dioxide which proceed differently from the radical propagations of these monomers (Chap. 3 and Sec. 6-7a). Although all of the copolymerizations discussed in this section are ionic reactions, a few radical copolymerizations have been reported [1]. There are very few comonomer pairs, however, which lend themselves to radical propagation. An exception is the reported radical terpolymerization of ethylenimine, carbon monoxide, and ethylene by AIBN and gamma radiation [85].

REFERENCES

1. R. A. Patsiga, *J. Macromol. Sci.–Revs. Macromol. Chem.*, **C1(2)**: 223 (1967).
2. J. Furukawa and T. Saegusa, "Polymerization of Aldehydes and Oxides," chaps. III–VII, Interscience Publishers, John Wiley & Sons, Inc., New York, 1963.
3. A. E. Gurgiolo, *J. Macromol. Sci.–Revs. Macromol. Chem.*, **1(1)**:39 (1966).
4. G. Gee, W. C. E. Higginson, and G. T. Merrall, *J. Chem. Soc.*, **1959**:1345.
5. E. C. Steiner, R. R. Pelletier, and R. O. Trucks, *J. Am. Chem. Soc.*, **86**:4678 (1964).
6. G. Gee, W. C. E. Higginson, K. J. Taylor, and M. W. Trenholme, *J. Chem. Soc.*, **1961**:4298.
7. W. H. Snyder and A. E. Meisinger, Jr., *Polymer Preprints*, **9(1)**:382 (1968).
8. R. C. Burrows, *ibid.*, **6(2)**:600 (1965).
9. H. Meerwein, D. Delfs, and H. Morshel, *Angew. Chem.*, **72**:927 (1960).
10. D. Sims, *Makromol. Chem.*, **98**:135, 245 (1966).

11. M. Okada, Y. Yamashita, and Y. Ishii, *ibid.*, **80**:196 (1964).
12. C. E. H. Bawn, R. M. Bell, and A. Ledwith, *Polymer,* **6**:95 (1965).
13. I. Kuntz, *J. Polymer Sci.,* **A-1(5)**:193 (1967); *Polymer Preprints,* **9(1)**:398 (1968).
14. M. P. Dreyfuss and P. Dreyfuss, *J. Polymer Sci.,* **A-1(4)**:2179 (1966).
15. A. M. Eastham, Epoxides, in P. H. Plesch (ed.), chap. 10, "The Chemistry of Cationic Polymerization," Pergamon Press Ltd., London, 1963.
16. T. Tsuruta, S. Inoue, and K. Tsubaki, *Makromol. Chem.,* **111**:236 (1968).
17. H. Imai, T. Saegusa, S. Matsumoto, T. Tadasa, and J. Furukawa, *ibid.,* **102**:222 (1967).
18. T. Saegusa, H. Imai, and S. Matsumoto, *J. Polymer Sci.,* **A-1(6)**:459 (1968).
19. P. Kubisa, J. Brzezinski, and S. Penczek, *Makromol. Chem.,* **100**:286 (1967).
20. A. M. Eastham, *Fortschr. Hochpolymer.-Forsch. (Advan. Polymer Sci.),* **2**:18 (1960).
21. I. Penczek, Y. N. Sazanov, and S. Penczek, *Makromol. Chem.,* **100**:156 (1967).
22. L. F. Beste and H. K. Hall, Jr., *J. Phys. Chem.,* **68**:269 (1964).
23. D. Vofsi and A. V. Tobolsky, *J. Polymer Sci.,* **A3**:3261 (1965).
24. M. B. Price and F. B. McAndrew, *J. Macromol. Sci.(Chem.),* **A1(2)**:231 (1967).
25. T. Miki, T. Higashimura, and S. Okamura, *J. Polymer Sci.,* **B5**:583 (1967).
26. Y. Yamashita, M. Okada, and K. Suyama, *Makromol. Chem.,* **111**:277 (1968).
27. I. Penczek and S. Penczek, *ibid.,* **67**:203 (1963).
28. A. Chapiro and S. Penczek, *J. chim. phys.,* **59**:696 (1962).
29. S. Okamura, E.Kobayashi, and T. Higashimura, *Makromol. Chem.,* **88**:1 (1965).
30. J. B. Rose, *J. Chem. Soc.,* **542**:547 (1956).
31. R. C. Burrows and B. F. Crowe, *J. Appl. Polymer Sci.,* **6**:467 (1962).
32. J. Brandrup and E. H. Immergut (eds.), "Polymer Handbook," pp. II-363, Interscience Publishers, John Wiley & Sons, Inc., New York, 1966.
33. R. M. Joshi and B. J. Zwolinski, Heats of Polymerization and Their Structural and Mechanistic Implications, in G. E. Ham (ed.), "Vinyl Polymerization," vol. 1, part I, chap. 8, Marcel Dekker, Inc., New York, 1967.
34. P. H. Plesch and P. H. Westermann, *Polymer,* **10**: 105 (1969).
35. V. M. Rothe, G. Reinisch, W. Jaeger, and I. Schopov, *Makromol. Chem.,* **54**:183 (1962).
36. M. Szwarc, *Pure and Appl. Chem.,* **12(1)**:127 (1966); *Fortschr. Hochpolymer.-Forsch. (Advan. Polymer Sci.),* **4**:1 (1965).
37. T. Yasumoto, *J. Polymer Sci.,* **A3**:3301 (1965).
38. H. Tani and T. Konomi, *ibid.,* **A-1(4)**:301 (1966).

39. R. P. Scelia, S. E. Schonfeld, and L. G. Donaruma, *J. Appl. Polymer Sci.*, **8**:1363 (1964).
40. E. H. Mottus, R. M. Hedrick, and J. M. Butler, *Polymer Preprints*, **9(1)**:390 (1968).
41. V. M. Rothe, G. Reinisch, W. Jaeger, and I. Schopov, *Makromol. Chem.*, **54**:183 (1962).
42. V. S. Doubravsky and F. Geleji, *ibid.*, **113**:270 (1968).
43. T. Kagiya, H. Kishimoto, S. Narisawa, and K. Fukui, *J. Polymer Sci.*, **A3**:145 (1965).
44. J. N. Hay, *ibid.*, **B5**:577 (1967).
45. A. J. Amass and J. N. Hay, *Makromol. Chem.*, **103**:244 (1967).
46. G. M. Burnett, J. N. Hay, and A. J. MacArthur, Polymerization of Caprolactam, in "The Chemistry of Polymerization Processes," pp. 139-156, Monograph 20, Society of Chemical Industry, London, 1966.
47. R. C. P. Cubbon, *Makromol. Chem.*, **80**:44 (1964).
48. P. H. Hermans and D. Heikens, *J. Polymer Sci.*, **44**:429, 437 (1960).
49. A. V. Tobolsky, *ibid.*, **25**:220 (1957).
50. A. V. Tobolsky and A. Eisenberg, *J. Am. Chem. Soc.*, **81**:2302 (1959); **82**:289 (1960).
51. F. Wiloth, *Z. Physik. Chem., N.F. (Frankfurt)*, **4**:66 (1955).
52. K. Dachs and E. Schwartz, *Angew. Chem. (Intern. Ed.)*, **1**:430 (1962).
53. N. Yoda and A. Miyake, *J. Polymer Sci.*, **43**:117 (1960).
54. N. Okata, *ibid.*, **A1**:3151 (1963).
55. A. J. Barry and H. N. Beck, Silicone Polymers, in F. G. A. Stone and W. A. G. Graham (eds.), "Inorganic Polymers," chap. 5, Academic Press, Inc., New York, 1962.
56. C. L. Lee and O. K. Johannson, *J. Polymer Sci.*, **A-1(4)**:3013 (1966).
57. T. C. Kendrick, *J. Chem. Soc.*, **1965**:2027.
58. G. Levin and J. B. Carmichael, *J. Polymer Sci.*, **A-1(6)**:1 (1968).
59. K. Chujo, H. Kobayashi, J. Suzuki, S. Tokuhara, and M. Tanabe, *Makromol. Chem.*, **100**:262 (1967).
60. V. H. Ohse and H. Cherdron, *ibid.*, **95**:283 (1966); **97**:139 (1966).
61. G. D. Jones, D. C. MacWilliams, and N. A. Braxtor, *J. Org. Chem.*, **30**:1994 (1965).
62. G. D. Jones, Nitrogen Compounds, in P. H. Plesch (ed.), "The Chemistry of Cationic Polymerization," chap. 14, Pergamon Press Ltd., Oxford, (1963).
63. J. K. Stille and J. A. Empen, *J. Polymer Sci.*, **A-1(5)**:273 (1967).
64. W. Cooper, D. R. Morgan, and R. T. Wragg, *Eur. Polym. J.*, **5(1)**:71 (1969).
65. M. Terbojevich, G. Pizziolo, E. Peggion, A. Cosani, and E. Scoffone, *J. Am. Chem. Soc.*, **89**:2733 (1967).
66. T. Mukaiyama, T. Fujisawa, H. Nohira, and T. Hijugaji, *J. Org. Chem.*, **27**:3337 (1962).
67. A. Levy and M. Litt, *J. Polymer Sci.*, **A-1(6)**:57 (1968).
68. F. W. Michelotti and W. P. Keaveney, *ibid.*, **A3**:895 (1965).

69. H. R. Allcock, "Heteroatom Ring Systems and Polymers," chaps. 6 and 8, Academic Press, Inc., New York, 1967.
70. J. R. MacCallum and A. Werninck, *J. Polymer Sci.,* **A-1(5)**:3061 (1967).
71. N. L. Paddock, *Quart. Rev. (London),* **18**:168 (1964).
72. C. R. Kruger and E. G. Rochow, *J. Polymer Sci.,* **A2**:3179 (1964).
73. Y. Yamashita, T. Tsuda, M. Okada, and S. Iwatsuki, *ibid,* **A-1(4)**:2121 (1966).
74. F. Kobayashi and K. Matsuya, *ibid.,* **A1**:111 (1963).
75. K. Tada, Y. Numata, T. Saegusa, and J. Furukawa, *Makromol. Chem.,* **77**:220 (1964).
76. R. L. Merker and M. J. Scott, *J. Polymer Sci.,* **43**:297 (1960).
77. S. Bar-Zakay, M. Levy and D. Vofsi, *ibid.,* **A-1(5)**:965 (1967).
78. V. H. Cherdron and H. Ohse, *Makromol. Chem.,* **92**:213 (1966).
79. T. Higashimura, A. Tanaka, T. Miki, and S. Okamura, *J. Polymer Sci.,* **A-1(5)**:1927, 1937 (1967).
80. T. Kagiya, S. Narisawa, K. Manabe, and K. Fukui, *ibid.,* **B3**:617 (1965).
81. J. B. Lando and P. Frayer, *ibid.,* **B6**:285 (1968).
82. T. Kagiya, S. Narisawa, T. Ichida, K. Fukui, H. Yokota, and M. Kondo, *ibid.,* **A-1(4)**:293 (1966).
83. R. J. Kern and J. Schaefer, *J. Am. Chem. Soc.,* **88**:3627 (1966).
84. J. Schaefer, R. J. Kern, and R. J. Katnik, *Macromolecules,* **1**:107 (1968).
85. T. Kagiya, I. Maruta, T. Ichida, S. Narisawa, and K. Fukui, *J. Polymer Sci.,* **A-1(5)**:1645 (1967).

PROBLEMS

7-1. Consider the following monomers and catalysts:

Catalysts	*Monomers*
n-C_4H_9Li	Propylene oxide
BF_3	ϵ-Pyrrolidone
H_2SO_4	δ-Valerolactam
$NaOC_2H_5$	Ethylenimine
H_2O	Octamethylcyclotetrasiloxane
	Propylene sulfide
	Trioxane
	Oxacyclobutane

Which catalyst(s) can be used to polymerize each of the various monomers? Discuss the need, if any, for cocatalysts or other species used in combination with the catalyst. Show the mechanism of each polymerization by means of chemical equations.

7-2. Discuss the effect of ring size on the tendency of a cyclic monomer toward ring-opening polymerization.

7-3. Anionic polymerization of propylene oxide is usually limited to producing a relatively low molecular weight polymer. Discuss the reasons for this occurrence.

7-4. Consider the polymerization of propylene oxide with sodium methoxide at 70°C. The propylene oxide and sodium methoxide concentrations are 0.80 molar and 2.0×10^{-4} molar, respectively. Calculate the number-average molecular weight of the polymer at 80% conversion taking into account the effect of chain transfer to monomer.

7-5. Describe by means of equations the role of a promoter in the cationic polymerization of a cyclic ether.

7-6. The tetrahydrofuran polymerization described in Table 7-1 is an equilibrium polymerization with $[M]_c = 1.7$ molar. Calculate the initial polymerization rate and the polymerization rate at 20% conversion.

7-7. What are the roles of an acylating agent and activated monomer in the anionic polymerization of lactams?

7-8. Consider the equilibrium polymerization of ϵ-caprolactam initiated by water at 220°C. For the case where $[C]_0 = 0.352$, $[M]_0 = 8.79$ and $[M]_c = 0.484$, the degree of polymerization at equilibrium is 152, calculate the values of K_i and K_p at equilibrium.

7-9. Discuss by means of equations the occurrence of back-biting, ring-expansion reactions in the polymerizations of cyclic ethers, acetals and amines.

8

STEREOCHEMISTRY OF POLYMERIZATION

Several types of *positional* or *substitutional isomerism* are encountered in polymers. These are polymers having the same overall chemical composition but different arrangements of atoms or groups of atoms. Such isomeric polymers can be obtained when isomeric monomers are used, e.g., poly(vinyl alcohol), polyacetaldehyde, and poly(ethylene oxide)

$$\left[CH_2-\underset{\displaystyle}{\overset{\displaystyle OH}{\overset{|}{C}H}} \right]_n \qquad \left[\overset{\displaystyle CH_3}{\overset{|}{C}H}-O \right]_n \qquad \left(CH_2CH_2-O \right)_n$$

Poly(vinyl alcohol) Polyacetaldehyde Poly(ethylene oxide)

are isomeric as are poly(methyl methacrylate) and poly(ethyl acrylate)

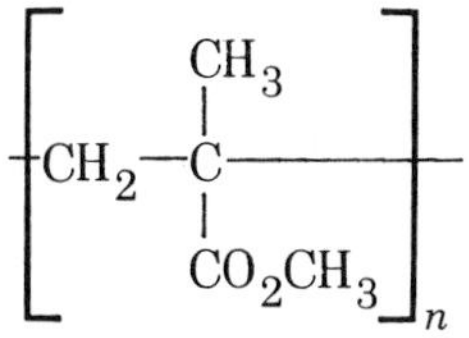

$$\left[\begin{array}{c} CH_3 \\ | \\ -CH_2-C- \\ | \\ CO_2CH_3 \end{array}\right]_n \qquad \left[-CH_2-\underset{\underset{CO_2C_2H_5}{|}}{CH}- \right]_n$$

Poly(methyl methacrylate) 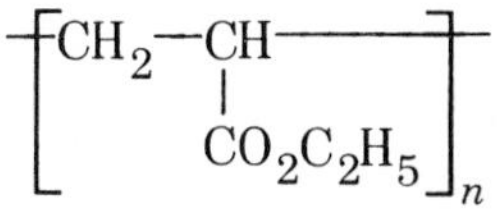 Poly(ethyl acrylate)

Poly(ϵ-caprolactam) and poly(hexamethylene adipamide)

$$-\!\!\left[CO(CH_2)_5NH\right]\!\!-_n \qquad -\!\!\left[NH(CH_2)_6NHCO(CH_2)_4CO\right]\!\!-_n$$

are isomeric even though the monomers are not directly isomeric. In this case, ϵ-caprolactam has the same overall composition as the combination of hexamethylene diamine and adipic acid. Similarly, the 1:1 copolymer of ethylene and 1-butene is isomeric with polypropylene.

Isomeric polymers can also be obtained from a single monomer if there is more than one polymerization route. The head-to-head placement which may occur in small amounts in the polymerization of an alkene is isomeric with the normal head-to-tail placement (see Structures III and IV in Sec. 3-2a). Monomers with two polymerizable groups can yield isomeric polymers by polymerization routes which favor one or the other of the two alternate polymerization routes. Examples of this type of isomerism are the 1,2- and 1,4-polymers from 1,3-dienes (Sec. 3-14 and 8-6), the separate polymerizations of the alkene and carbonyl linkages in ketenes and acrolein (Sec. 5-6a), and the synthesis of linear or cyclized polymers from unconjugated dienes (Sec. 6-6b). All of these different examples of positional isomerism are important to note from the practical viewpoint since the isomeric polymers often differ considerably in their properties.

This chapter will be primarily concerned with a different type of isomerism in polymers—namely, that which arises due to stereoisomerism in the structure of polymers as a consequence of the polymerization reaction. This is an important topic because of the significant effect that stereoisomerism has on many important polymer properties. Considerations of stereoisomerism in the chain polymerization reactions of alkenes were recognized as early as 1932 by Staudinger [1]. However, the possibility that each of the propagation steps in the growth of a polymer chain could give rise to stereoisomerism was not fully appreciated until the last decade or so. Further, the synthesis of polymers with ordered spatial configurations in which the stereoisomerism of repeating units in the chain would show a regular or ordered arrangement instead of a random one was essentially not considered. One of the major developments in the polymer field in the last decade has been the elucidation of the occurrence of stereoisomerism in polymers. More importantly, the pioneering works of Ziegler [2] and Natta [3, 4] have led to the convenient synthesis of polymers with highly stereoregular structures [5–11]. It is interesting to note in this last respect that we are beginning only now to do what nature has been doing for eons. Stereoregular polymers of different kinds are commonly found in nature; these include natural rubber, cellulose, starch, and various biological polymers.

8-1 TYPES OF STEREOISOMERISM IN POLYMERS

Stereoisomerism in polymers, as in all organic compounds, is of two types–*geometrical* and *optical isomerism*–and arises from different arrangements (configurations) of the atoms or substituents in a molecule [12]. Geometrical isomerism arises from different configurations of substituents on a carbon-carbon double bond or on a cyclic structure. Optical isomerism arises from different configurations of substituents on a saturated carbon atom. The term "configuration" should not be confused with the term "conformation." Conformation refers to the different arrangements of atoms and substituents in a molecule which come about from simple rotations around single bonds. Examples of different polymer conformations are the fully extended planar zigzag, randomly coiled, helical, and folded chain arrangements. The different arrangements are referred to as "conformational isomers." Conformational isomers may be interconverted one into the other by bond rotations. Configurational isomerism, on the other hand, involves different arrangements of the atoms and substituents in a molecule which can be interconverted only by the breakage and reformation of primary chemical bonds.

8-1a Monosubstituted Ethylenes

8-1a-1 Site of Steric Isomerism. Isomerism is observed in the polymerization of alkenes whenever one of the carbon atoms of the double bond is at least monosubstituted. The polymerization of a monosubstituted ethylene, $CH_2{=}CHR$, (where R is any substituent group) leads to polymers in which every other carbon atom in the polymer chain can theoretically be considered to be asymmetric. Each of these "asymmetric" carbon atoms, denoted by C*, can be depicted as

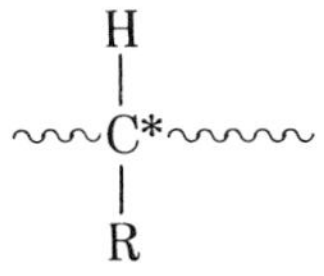

$$\begin{array}{c} \mathrm{H} \\ | \\ \sim\sim\mathrm{C}^*\sim\sim\sim\sim \\ | \\ \mathrm{R} \end{array}$$

I

where the asymmetry would be considered to reside in the fact that the carbon atom C* holds four different substituents–H, R, and two polymer chain segments, $\sim\sim$ and $\sim\sim\sim\sim$, of different lengths. Although this view has been prevalent for some time [6, 7], carbon atoms such as C* are no longer considered as being truly asymmetric [13, 14]. True asymmetry in an atom (or molecule) i.e., asymmetry which manifests itself in optical activity, is determined only by the first few atoms of any substituents attached to an apparently asymmetric atom. The first few atoms of the two chain segments attached to C* are the same and C* is therefore not an asymmetric atom. The result is that polymer structures such as I do not exhibit optical activity. Another way of saying the same thing is to consider that there is a plane of internal symmetry at C* because the two chain segments are equivalent; thus, internal compensation results in a net optical rotation of zero.

Although C* is not a true asymmetric site, it is a *site of steric isomerism* in the polymerization of $CH_2{=}CHR$. Each such site, which for convenience might be termed a pseudoasymmetric site or an "asymmetric" site, can exhibit either of two different configurations. Considering the main carbon-carbon polymer chain of the polymer $\left(CH_2CHR\right)_n$ to be stretched out in its fully extended planar zigzag conformation, two different configurations arise for each "asymmetric" carbon atom since the R group may be situated on either side of the plane of the carbon-carbon polymer chain. If the plane of the carbon-carbon chain is considered as being in the plane of this page, the R groups will then be located either above or below this plane. The two configurations are usually referred to as *D*- and *L*- configurations or *R*- and *S*- configurations although these designations are not strictly correct since true asymmetry is absent.

It has been recommended [13, 14] that the configurations at pseudoasymmetric sites be indicated by the small letters *r*- and *s*- but this designation has not as yet been generally adopted.

8-1a-2 Tacticity. The regularity with which successive "asymmetric" centers show the same configuration determines the overall order or *tacticity* of the polymer chain. (The term "tacticity" is often used in a practical sense to indicate the crystallinity of a polymer specimen.) If the R groups on successive "asymmetric" carbons are randomly distributed above and below the planar zigzag polymer main chain, the polymer does not have order and is termed *atactic*. Two types of ordered or *tactic* polymer structures may occur—*isotactic* and *syndiotactic*. An isotactic polymer structure occurs when the site of steric isomerism in each repeating unit in the polymer chain has the same configuration. All the R groups will be located on one side of the plane of the carbon-carbon polymer chain—either all above or all below the plane of the chain. A syndiotactic polymer structure occurs when the site of steric isomerism in each repeating unit in the polymer has the opposite configuration of that in the preceding repeating unit. The *R*- and *S*-configurations alternate along the polymer chain as the R groups are located alternately above and below the plane of the polymer chain. These different polymer structures are shown in Fig. 8-1. The various structures are described by two different pictorial representations. The ones on the left, drawn in the same manner as in Sec. 3-9b-2, show the carbon-carbon polymer chain in the plane of this page with the H and R substituents above and below that plane. The representations on the right are the corresponding Fisher projections [12]. Vertical lines in the Fisher projections correspond to bonds going behind the plane of this page; horizontal lines represent bonds coming in front of the plane. The configuration at each carbon atom in the polymer chain is drawn in the Fisher projection by imagining the rotation of each carbon-carbon bond in the polymer chain into an eclipsed conformation as opposed to the staggered conformation which actually exists.

Polymerizations which yield tactic structures (either isotactic or syndiotactic) are termed *stereospecific polymerizations;* the polymer structures are termed *stereoregular polymers*. (The terms stereospecific and stereoregular are often used interchangeably.) The naming of the different steric structures of polymers follows the rules recommended by the International Union of Pure and Applied

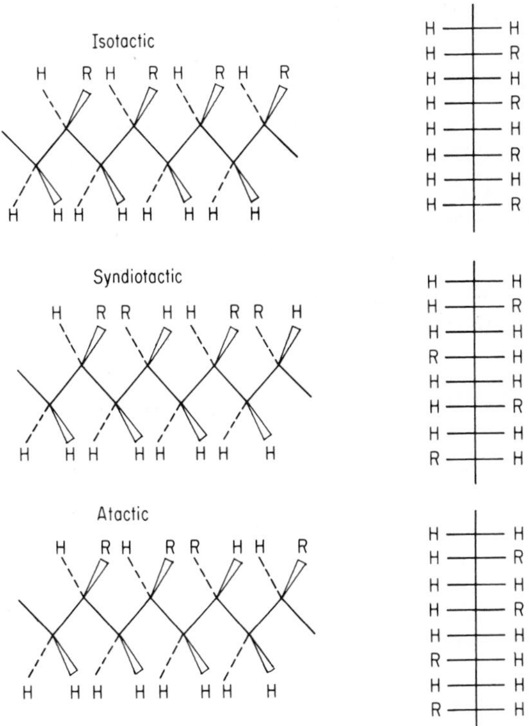

FIG. 8-1 *Different polymer structures from a monosubstituted ethylene,* $\lbrack CH_2-CHR \rbrack_n$. *The dotted and triangular lines represent bonds to substituents below and above the plane of the carbon-carbon chain, respectively.*

Chemistry [14]. The words *isotactic* and *syndiotactic* are placed before the name of the polymer to indicate the respective tactic structures, e.g., *isotactic* polypropylene and *syndiotactic* polypropylene. The prefixes *it*- and *st*- are used with the formula of the polymer for the same purpose, for example, *it*-$[CH_2CH(CH_3)]_n$ and *st*-$[CH_2CH(CH_3)]_n$. The absence of these terms and prefixes denote the atactic structure, i.e., polypropylene means *atactic* polypropylene.

8-1b Disubstituted Ethylenes

8-1b-1 1,1-Disubstituted Ethylenes. For disubstituted ethylenes, the presence and type of tacticity depends on the position of substitution and the identity of the substituents. In the polymerization of a 1,1-disubstituted ethylene ($CH_2{=}CRR'$), stereoisomerism does not exist if the R and R′ groups are the same as in isobutylene and vinylidene chloride. When R and R′ are different substituents (for example, $-CH_3$ and $-CO_2CH_3$ in methyl methacrylate), stereoisomerism occurs exactly analogously to the case of a monosubstituted ethylene. The methyl groups can be located all above or all below the main chain plane (isotactic), alternately above and below (syndiotactic), or randomly located (atactic). The presence of the second substituent has no effect on the situation since steric placement of the first substituent automatically fixes that of the second. The second substituent is isotactic if the first is isotactic, syndiotactic if the first is syndiotactic, and atactic if the first is atactic.

8-1b-2 1,2-Disubstituted Ethylenes. The polymerization of 1,2-disubstituted ethylenes, $RCH{=}CHR'$, such as 2-pentene ($R = -CH_3$, $R' = -C_2H_5$), presents a different situation. The polymerization of $RCH{=}CHR'$ yields a polymer structure (II)

```
    H   H
    |   |
~~~C---C~~~~~
    |   |
    R   R′
```

II

in which there are two sites of steric isomerism (two "asymmetric" carbons). Several possibilities of *di-tacticity* exist which involve different combinations of tacticity for the two sites [15]. Four different stereoregular structures can be defined as shown in Fig. 8-2. *Di-isotactic* structures occur when each of the two different sites of steric isomerism is isotactic; *di-syndiotactic* structures occur when each of the two different sites is syndiotactic. A *threo-di-isotactic* polymer is a di-isotactic polymer in which the two sites of steric isomerism are of opposite configuration. In the zigzag pictorial representation, both the R and R′ substituents are on the same side of the plane containing the carbon-carbon polymer chain. In the Fisher projection, R and R′ are on opposite sides of the line representing the polymer chain. An *erythro-di-isotactic* polymer is a di-isotactic polymer in which the configurations at the two sites of steric isomerism are the same. The difference between the erythro-

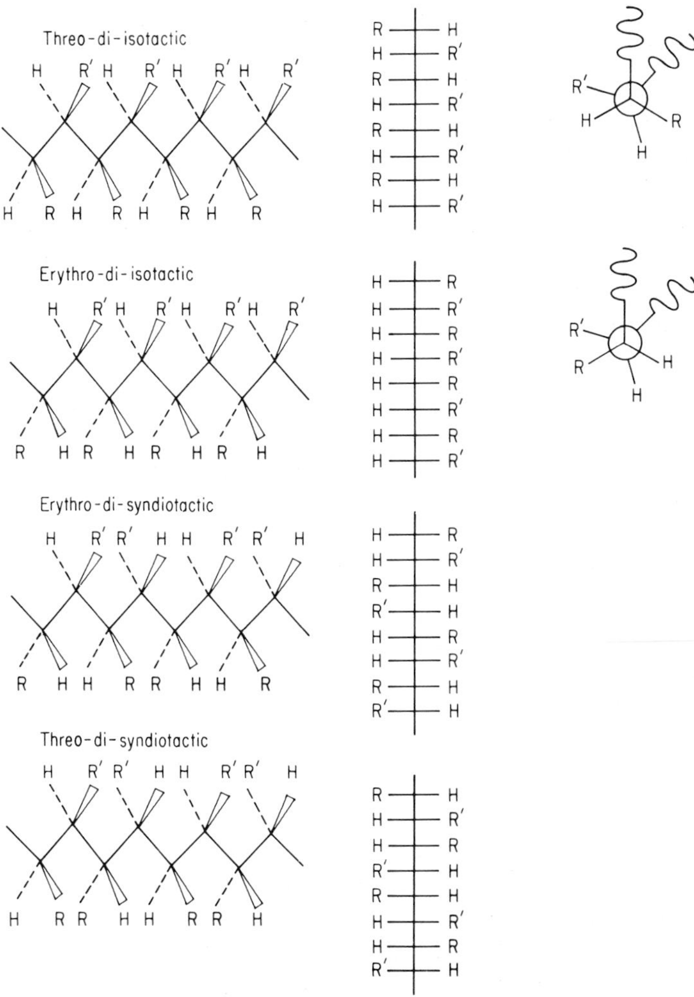

FIG. 8-2 *Stereoregular polymer structures from a 1,2-disubstituted ethylene, $\left(CHR-CHR'\right)_n$.*

and threo-di-isotactic structures can also be shown by Newman representations [12] of the eclipsed conformation of two consecutive carbon atoms in the polymer chain. These are shown in the far right-hand side of Fig. 8-2.

Threo-di-syndiotactic and *erythro-di-syndiotactic* polymers are di-syndiotactic polymers in which the configurations at the two sites are, respectively, the opposite and the same. A close examination of the two di-syndiotactic structures show that they would be identical except for difference in the end-groups. Thus, from the practical viewpoint, there is only one di-syndiotactic polymer. The nomenclature for di-tactic polymers [13, 14] follows in the same manner as for mono-tactic polymers. Thus, the various stereoregular poly(2-pentene) polymers would be *threo-di-isotactic* poly(2-pentene), *erythro-di-isotactic* poly(2-pentene), and *di-syndiotactic* poly(2-pentene) with the prefixes *tit-*, *eit-* and *st-*, respectively, used before the formula $[CH(CH_3)CH(C_2H_5)]_n$. It should be noted that other stereoregular structures from 1,2-disubstituted ethylene—those where one substituent is atactic while the other is isotactic or syndiotactic or those where one substituent is isotactic while the other is syndiotactic—can be postulated. However, these appear to be trivial possibilities at the present time since their syntheses have not been accomplished. The factors present during polymerization which lead to ordering or disordering of one substituent have the same effect on the other substituent.

8-1c Carbonyl and Ring-Opening Polymerizations

Several other types of polymer structures are capable of the same type of steric isomerism as the alkenes. Ordered structures are possible in the polymerization of carbonyl monomers (RCHO and RCOR′) and the ring-opening polymerizations of certain types of cyclic monomers. Thus, for example, the polymers from acetaldehyde and propylene oxide can have the isotactic and syndiotactic structures shown in Figs. 8-3 and 8-4.

Polyacetaldehyde, like all of the previously discussed alkene polymers, does not contain a truly asymmetric site (i.e., there is an internal plane of symmetry) and cannot, therefore, exhibit optical activity. Poly(propylene oxide), on the other hand, does not contain an internal plane of symmetry since the repeating unit, $—CH_2CH(CH_3)O—$, is unsymmetrical. It possesses a true asymmetric site—the carbon atom denoted by C* in structure III. The presence of the oxygen

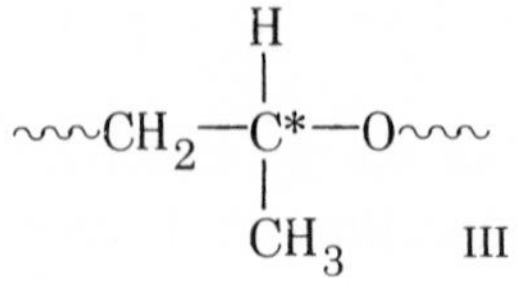

$$\sim\!\sim CH_2—\overset{\displaystyle H}{\underset{\displaystyle CH_3}{\overset{|}{\underset{|}{C^*}}}}—O\!\sim\!\sim \qquad \text{III}$$

attached to C* makes its near environment grossly dissimilar, unlike the situation in structures such as I and II. Because of this

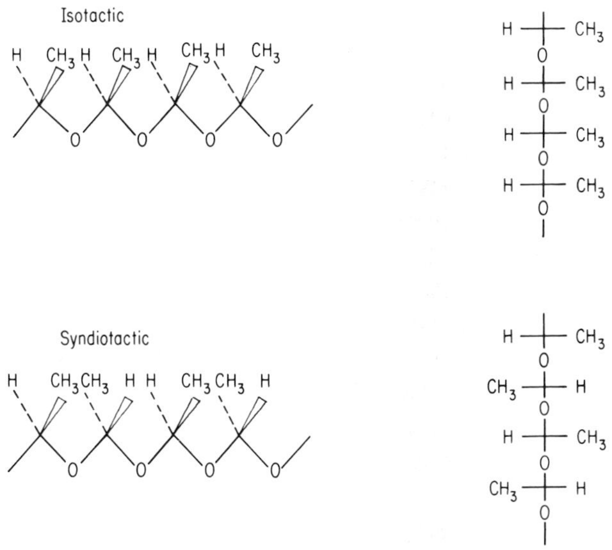

Isotactic

Syndiotactic

FIG. 8-3 *Stereoregular forms of polyacetaldehyde,* $+CH(CH_3)O+_n$.

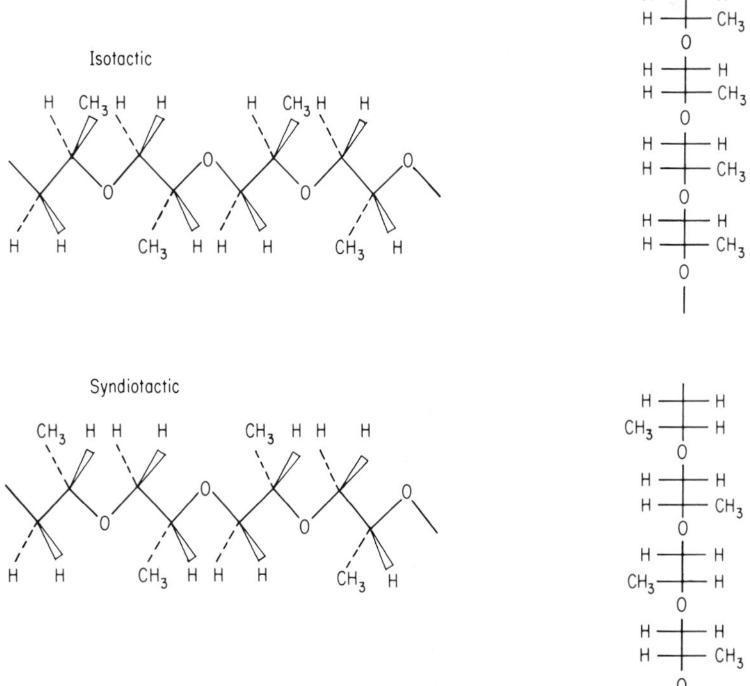

FIG. 8-4 *Stereoregular forms of poly(propylene oxide),* $+CH_2CH(CH_3)O+_n$.

asymmetry, the isotactic form of poly(propylene oxide) is capable of optical activity. *Syndiotactic* poly(propylene oxide) would not be expected to show a net optical activity; the alternation of configuration of successive asymmetric sites along the chain results in internal cancellation of optical activity. One should note that the stereoregularity in ring-opening polymerization does not arise from the formation of an asymmetric (or "asymmetric") site as a consequence of bond formation in the polymerization reaction as is the case in the polymerizations of alkenes and carbonyl monomers. In the case of ring-opening polymerization, the asymmetric site is present initially in the cyclic monomer (e.g., propylene oxide).

The stereochemistry of step polymerization should be considered at this point. Bond formation during step polymerization almost never results in the formation of an asymmetric or "asymmetric" site. Thus, neither the —O— and C=O in polysters nor the —NH— and C=O in polyamides represent sites of steric isomerism. Stereoregularity is possible in such polymers in the same manner that it is possible for the polymers produced by ring-opening polymerization—if there is a site of steric isomerism in one or the other of the monomers. Such monomers are usually not encountered in step polymerization. But, more importantly, even if such monomers were used, the reaction conditions employed in typical step polymerizations would not lead to stereoregularity.

8-1d 1,3-Butadiene and 2-Substituted 1,3-Butadienes

8-1d-1 1,2- and 3,4-Polymerizations. The polymerization of 1,3-dienes such as butadiene, isoprene, and chloroprene may exhibit

$$\underset{\text{1,3-Butadiene}}{CH_2{=}CH{-}CH{=}CH_2} \qquad \underset{\text{Isoprene}}{CH_2{=}\overset{\overset{\displaystyle CH_3}{|}}{C}{-}CH{=}CH_2} \qquad \underset{\text{Chloroprene}}{CH_2{=}\overset{\overset{\displaystyle Cl}{|}}{C}{-}CH{=}CH_2}$$

both optical and geometrical isomerism [6-8, 10, 11, 16]. Polymerization of these monomers through one or the other of the two double bonds leads to the possibility of optical isomerism. Thus, butadiene can yield isotactic, syndiotactic, and atactic structures when 1,2-polymerization occurs to yield 1,2-polybutadiene

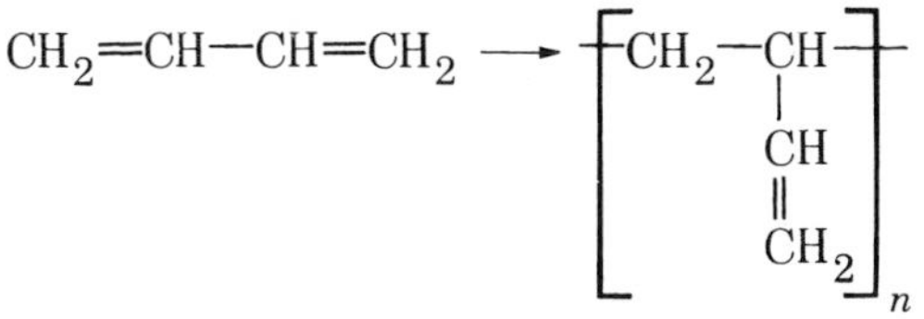

$$\mathrm{CH_2{=}CH{-}CH{=}CH_2} \longrightarrow \left[\mathrm{CH_2{-}\underset{\underset{\underset{CH_2}{\|}}{CH}}{\overset{|}{CH}}}\right]_n \qquad (8\text{-}1)$$

IV

The situation is exactly analogous to the polymerization of mono-substituted olefins; the various polymer structures would be those in Fig. 8-1 with R = $-CH{=}CH_2$. With chloroprene and isoprene, the possibilities are enlarged since the two double bonds are substituted differently. Polymerizations through the 1,2- and 3,4- double bonds do not yield the same products as they would in butadiene polymerization. There are, therefore, a total of six structures possible–corresponding to isotactic, syndiotactic, and atactic structures for both 1,2- and 3,4-polymerizations; e.g., for isoprene, one has

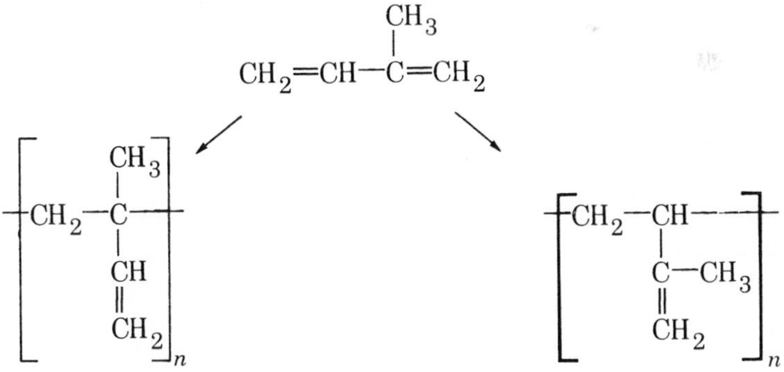

$$\mathrm{CH_2{=}CH{-}\overset{\overset{CH_3}{|}}{C}{=}CH_2}$$

$$\left[\mathrm{CH_2{-}\overset{\overset{CH_3}{|}}{\underset{\underset{\underset{CH_2}{\|}}{CH}}{\overset{}{C}}}}\right]_n \qquad\qquad \left[\mathrm{CH_2{-}\underset{\underset{\underset{CH_2}{\|}}{C{-}CH_3}}{\overset{|}{CH}}}\right]_n \qquad (8\text{-}2)$$

V — 1,2-Polymerization

VI — 3,4-Polymerization

with polymers V and VI capable of exhibiting the structures in Fig. 8-1 with R = $-CH{=}CH_2$ and $-C(CH_3){=}CH_2$, respectively.

8-1d-2 1,4-Polymerization. From the practical viewpoint, the more important products from 1,3-dienes are those which occur by 1,4-polymerization (Sec. 3-14) of the conjugated diene system, e.g., for isoprene

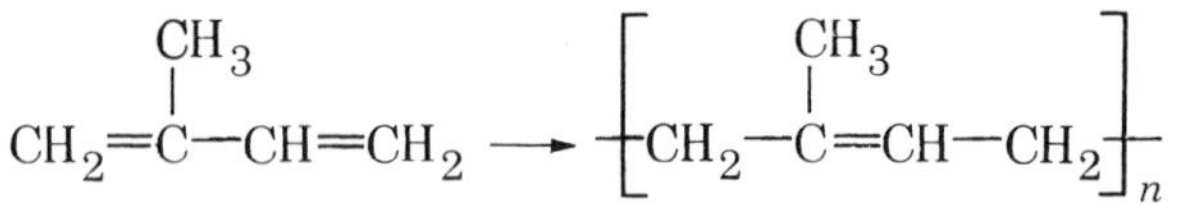

$$CH_2{=}\underset{\displaystyle CH_3}{\overset{}{C}}{-}CH{=}CH_2 \longrightarrow \left[CH_2{-}\underset{}{\overset{CH_3}{C}}{=}CH{-}CH_2 \right]_n \tag{8-3}$$

VII

1,4-Polymerization leads to a polymer structure (VII) with a repeating alkene double bond in the polymer chain. The double bond in each repeating unit of the polymer chain is a site of steric isomerism since it can have either a *cis* or a *trans* configuration. The polymer chain segments on each carbon atom of the double bond are located on the same side of the double bond in the cis configuration (VIII) and on opposite sides in the trans configuration (IX), e.g., for isoprene.

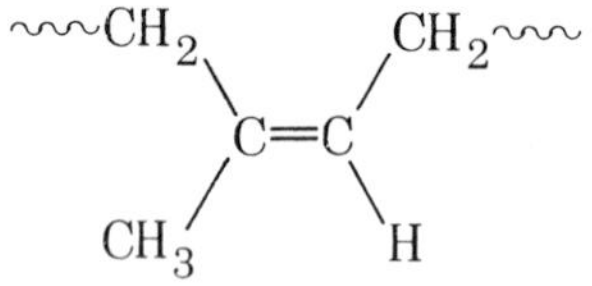

$$\begin{array}{ccc} \sim\!CH_2 & & CH_2\!\sim \\ & C{=}C & \\ CH_3 & & H \end{array} \qquad \begin{array}{ccc} \sim\!CH_2 & & H \\ & C{=}C & \\ CH_3 & & CH_2\!\sim \end{array}$$

Cis VIII   Trans IX

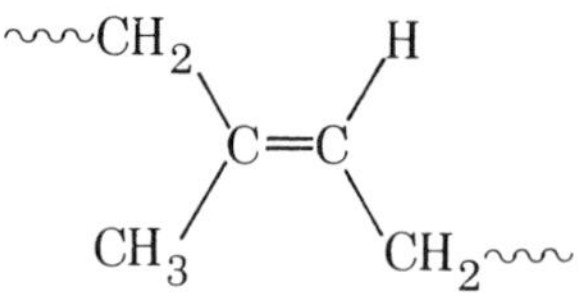

When all of the double bonds in the polymer molecule have the same configuration, the result is two different ordered (tactic) polymer structures due to geometrical isomerism. Figure 8-5 shows the structures of the completely cis and completely trans polymers of a 2-substituted butadiene. The stereochemistry of these polymers is indicated in naming them by using the prefixes *cis*-1,4 and *trans*-1,4, for example, *cis*-1,4-polyisoprene and *trans*-1,4-polyisoprene. If the trans configurations are placed randomly, the result is an atactic structure. The alternating placement of cis and trans configurations, analogous to the syndiotactic placement in the polymerization of alkenes, almost never occurs.

8-1e 4-Substituted and 1,4-Disubstituted 1,3-Butadienes

8-1e-1 1,2- and 3,4-Polymerizations. The polymerizations of 4-substituted (X) and 1,4-disubstituted (XI) 1,3-butadienes involve

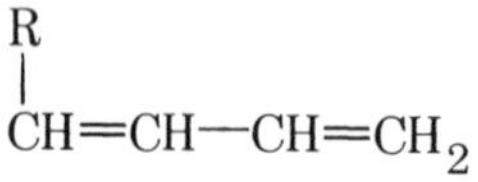

$$\overset{R}{\underset{}{CH}}{=}CH{-}CH{=}CH_2 \qquad \overset{R}{CH}{=}CH{-}CH{=}\overset{R'}{CH}$$

X 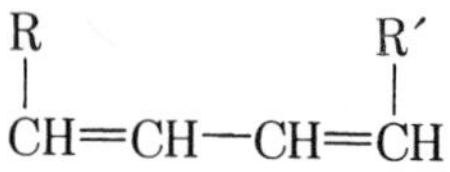   XI

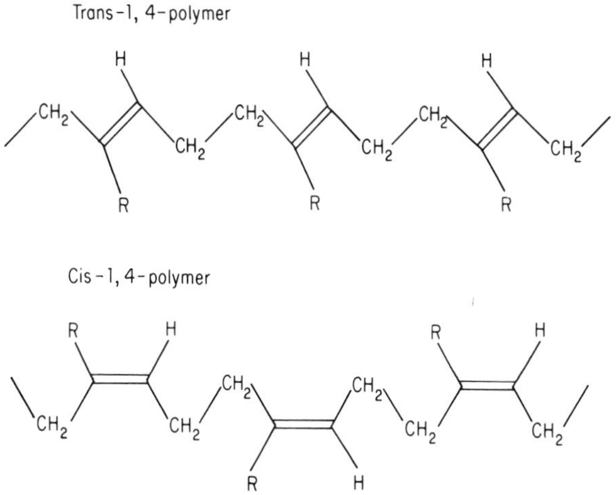

Trans-1, 4-polymer

Cis-1, 4-polymer

FIG. 8-5 *Cis- and trans-1,4-polymers from a 2-substituted 1,3-butadiene,* $+\!CH_2-CH{=}CR-CH_2\!+_n$.

a number of interesting possibilities [11, 16]. 1,2-Polymerization of either type of monomer (Eqs. 8-4 and 8-5) and also 3,4-polymerization of 1,4-disubstituted 1,3-dienes (Eq. 8-6) leads to polymers with

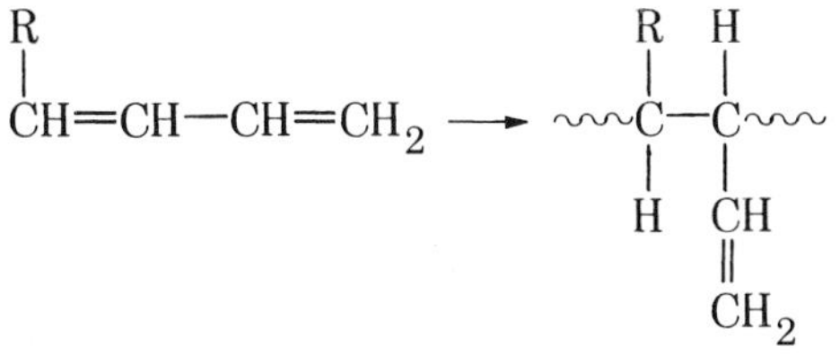

$$\mathrm{RCH{=}CH{-}CH{=}CH_2} \longrightarrow \sim\!\mathrm{C(R)(H)}{-}\mathrm{C(H)(CH{=}CH_2)}\!\sim \qquad (8\text{-}4)$$

$$\mathrm{RCH{=}CH{-}CH{=}CHR'} \longrightarrow \sim\!\mathrm{C(R)(H)}{-}\mathrm{C(H)(CH{=}CHR')}\!\sim \qquad (8\text{-}5)$$

$$\mathrm{RCH{=}CH{-}CH{=}CHR'} \longrightarrow \sim\!\mathrm{C(R')(H)}{-}\mathrm{C(H)(CH{=}CHR)}\!\sim \qquad (8\text{-}6)$$

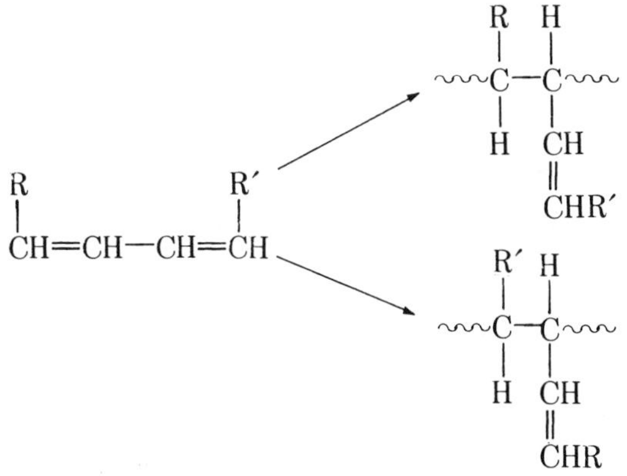

two "asymmetric" sites. Thus, each of the polymers is capable of exhibiting di-tacticity as in the case of the polymers derived from 1,2-disubstituted ethylenes.

8-1e-2 1,4-Polymerization. The 1,4-polymerization of these dienes is especially interesting since the polymers are simultaneously capable of both geometrical and optical isomerism [11, 16, 17]. 1,4-Polymerization of a 4-substituted 1,3-butadiene

$$CH_2{=}CH{-}CH{=}CHR \longrightarrow \sim\!\sim CH_2{-}CH{=}CH{-}\overset{\displaystyle R}{\underset{\displaystyle H}{\overset{|}{\underset{|}{C^*}}}}\sim\!\sim \qquad (8\text{-}7)$$

XII

can yield nine different di-tactic polymer structures involving various combinations of geometrical and optical isomerism. The double bonds can have cis, trans, or random configurations; each of these can be combined with isotactic, syndiotactic, or atactic configurations at the asymmetric carbon (C*). Thus, for example, the all isotactic-all trans and the all syndiotactic-all trans structures for the 1,4-polymerization of 1,3-pentadiene are shown in Fig. 8-6. In the naming of polymers with both optical and geometrical isomerism, the optical isomerism is denoted first, e.g., *iso-trans-tactic* 1,4-poly-1,3-pentadiene and *it*-[*trans*-$CH_2CH{=}CHCH(CH_3)]_n$ for the all isotactic-all trans structure, and *syndio-trans-tactic* 1,4-poly-1,3-pentadiene and *st*-[*trans*-$CH_2CH{=}CHCH(CH_3)]_n$ for the all syndiotactic-all trans structure of 1,4-poly-1,3-pentadiene.

The 1,4-polymerization of 1,4-disubstituted 1,3-butadienes

$$\overset{\displaystyle R}{\overset{|}{CH}}{=}CH{-}CH{=}\overset{\displaystyle R'}{\overset{|}{CH}} \longrightarrow \sim\!\sim\overset{\displaystyle R}{\overset{|}{CH}}{-}CH{=}CH{-}\overbrace{\overset{\displaystyle R'}{\underset{\displaystyle H}{\overset{|}{\underset{|}{C}}}}{-}\overset{\displaystyle R}{\underset{\displaystyle H}{\overset{|}{\underset{|}{C}}}}}^{\text{Threo-Erythro}}{-}\overbrace{CH{=}CH}^{\text{Cis-Trans}}{-}\overset{\displaystyle R'}{\overset{|}{CH}}\sim\!\sim \qquad (8\text{-}8)$$

XIII

leads to a polymer structure (XIII) which can exhibit tri-tacticity since the repeating unit has three sites of steric isomerism—one of

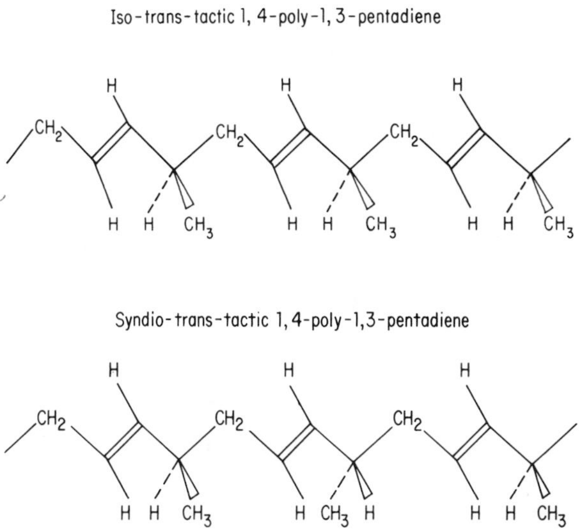

FIG. 8-6 *Two of the stereoregular structures of 1,4-poly-1,3-pentadiene,* $+CH_2-CH{=}CH-CH(CH_3)+_n$.

geometrical and two of optical isomerism [17]. The nomenclature in this case uses the *threo-erythro* system for the two asymmetric carbons which are in a 1,2-position in the polymer chain as in the polymer from a 1,2-disubstituted ethylene, as for example, *erythro-di-iso-trans-tactic* 1,4-poly(methyl sorbate) and *eit*-[*trans*-$CH(CH_3)CH{=}CHCH(CO_2CH_3)]_n$ for structure XIV

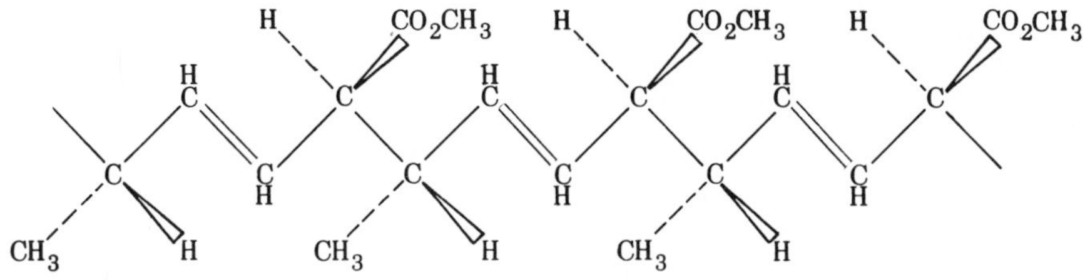

XIV

The 1,4-polymerization of 4-substituted and 1,4-disubstituted butadienes is also of interest since the optical isomerism in structures XII and XIII is a result of true asymmetry. The attachment of a double bond directly to the site of steric isomerism makes the site a truly asymmetric carbon atom. Optical activity is therefore possible in these polymers.

8-1f Cyclopolymers

Polymers containing rings incorporated into the main chain are also capable of exhibiting steric isomerism [10, 11, 14, 18]. Such polymers possess two sites of true asymmetry—the two points at which the polymer main chain enters and leaves each ring. Thus, the polymerization of cyclohexene to polycyclohexene

$$n \text{ (cyclohexene)} \longrightarrow \left[\text{(cyclohexane-1,2-diyl)} \right]_n \qquad (8\text{-}9)$$

is considered in the same manner as that of a 1,2-disubstituted alkene. Each carbon atom of the double bond gives rise to an asymmetric site upon polymerization. The four possible ordered structures are shown in Fig. 8-7. The *erythro* structures are those in which there is a cis configuration of the polymer chain bonds entering and leaving each ring; the *threo* structures have a trans configuration of the polymer chain bonds entering and leaving the ring.

8-2 PROPERTIES OF STEREOREGULAR POLYMERS

8-2a Significance of Stereoregularity in Polymers

The occurrence of isomerism in polymers plays a major role in the practical utilization of many polymers. There are very significant differences in the properties of unordered and ordered polymer structures as well as in ordered polymers of different types (i.e., syndiotactic vs. isotactic, and cis vs. trans). The ordered polymer structures are dramatically different from the corresponding unordered structures in terms of their physical properties. (This is especially interesting in terms of polymers which are ordered due to optical isomerism. Optical isomerism has a much greater effect on the properties of polymers than on those of small molecules. Optical isomers of small molecules do not generally differ in any property except the direction of rotation of plane polarized light and biological activity.)

8-2a-1 *Isotactic, Syndiotactic,* and *Atactic* Polypropylenes. The regularity or lack of regularity in polymers affects their properties by

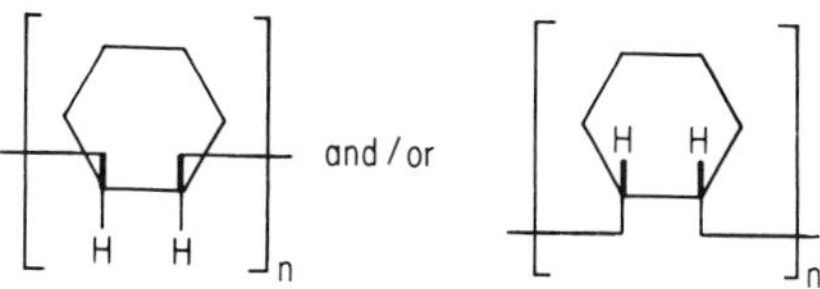

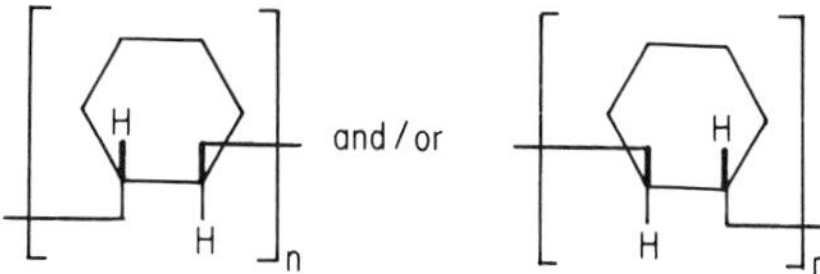

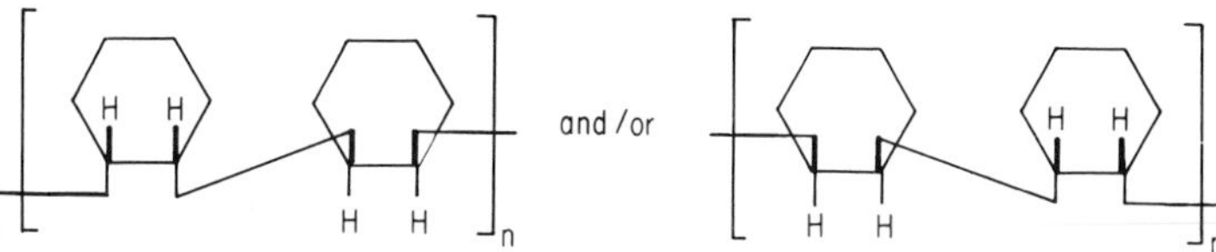

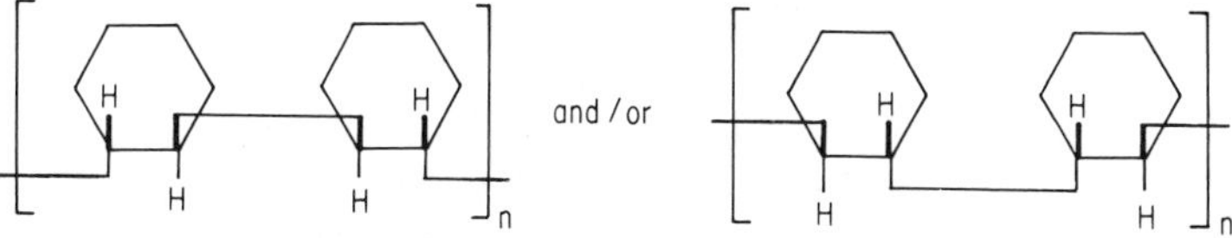

FIG. 8-7 *Stereoregular forms of polycyclohexene. The dark and light bonds at the 1- and 2-positions indicate bonds above and below the plane of the ring, respectively. Based on an illustration from* Pure and Applied Chemistry, **12**, *645 (1966), by permission of the International Union of Pure and Applied Chemistry and Butterworth and Co. (Publishers) Ltd., London.*

way of large differences in their abilities to crystallize. Atactic polymers are amorphous (non-crystalline), soft ("tacky") materials with little or no physical strength. On the other hand, the corresponding isotactic and syndiotactic polymers are usually obtained as highly crystalline materials. The ordered structures are capable of being packed into a crystal structure while unordered structures are not. Crystallinity leads to high physical strength and increased solvent and chemical resistance as well as differences in other properties which depend on crystallinity. A prime example of the commercial utility of stereoregular polymers is polypropylene. *Atactic* polypropylene is useless while *isotactic* polypropylene is a high melting, strong, crystalline plastic and fiber material of sizable commercial importance [19]. Isotactic forms of other polymers, such as poly(4-methyl-1-pentene) and poly(1-butene), are also presently beginning to receive commercial interest.

While the properties and utility of isotactic polymers have and are being extensively studied, those of syndiotactic polymers have received very little attention. The reason is the relative ease of formation of isotactic polymers; stereoregular polymerizations which yield syndiotactic structures are much less frequently encountered compared to those which yield isotactic structures. However, in the case of polypropylene, the properties of the syndiotactic polymer have been studied to some extent [20]. *Syndiotactic* polypropylene, like the isotactic structure, is easily crystallized. However, crystalline, *syndiotactic* polypropylene has a somewhat lower density, a lower T_m (by about 20°C) and is more soluble in ether and hydrocarbons than crystalline, *isotactic* polypropylene.

8-2a-2 *Cis-* and *Trans-*1,4-Poly-1,3-Dienes. Geometrical isomerism in 1,4-poly-1,3-dienes results in significant differences in the properties of cis and trans isomers. Table 8-1 shows the T_g and T_m values of the cis and trans stereoregular forms of 1,4-polybutadiene and 1,4-polyisoprene [21]. The higher values of T_m and T_g for the trans isomer follow the differences observed for the corresponding situation with small molecules such as 2-butene. The trans isomer is more symmetrical and packs more tightly than the cis isomer. The differences in the cis and trans polymers leads to major differences in their properties and utilization. For 1,4-polyisoprene, both the cis

Table 8-1 Crystalline and Glass Transition Temperatures[a]

Polymer	Isomer	T_g(°C)	T_m(°C)
1,4-Polybutadiene	cis	−108	1
	trans	− 18	141
1,4-Polyisoprene	cis	− 73	14
	trans	− 53	65

[a]Data from [21].

and trans isomers have rubbery properties at temperatures above their melting temperatures but are plastics at lower temperatures. Thus, *cis*-1,4-polyisoprene is used as an elastomer (rubber) at ambient temperatures while *trans*-1,4-polyisoprene can not be used because of the differences (Table 8-1) in their crystalline melting temperatures. It is of interest to note that 1,4-polyisoprene occurs in both the cis and trans forms in nature. Hevea rubber, obtained from the Hevea brasiliensis tree and a variety of other plants, contains more than 98 percent of the double bonds in the cis configuration. Other trees (mostly in Central America and Malaya) yield gutta percha or balata rubber which is predominantly the trans isomer.

8-2a-3 Cellulose and Amylose. The isomeric polysaccharides cellulose and amylose starch also show the significant effect of stereoisomerism on polymer properties. Cellulose and amylose starch have the structures shown in Fig. 8-8. Both are polymers of glucose in which the glucose units are joined together by glucoside linkages

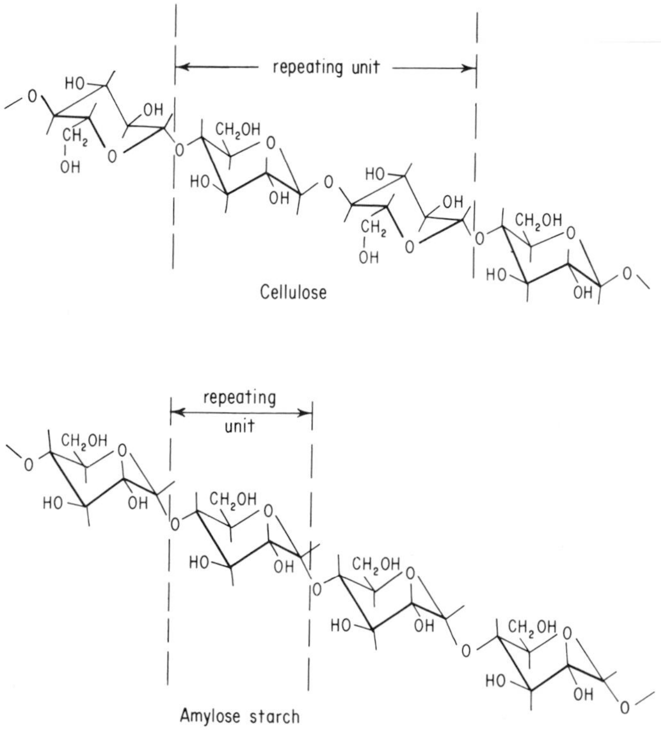

FIG. 8-8 *Structures of amylose starch and cellulose.*

at carbons 1 and 4. The structures are analogous to those in Fig. 8-7 except that the six-membered glucose rings are shown in the chair form. (The chair form is the actual conformation for a six-membered ring; the flat structure shown in Fig. 8-7 does not exist.) The two polysaccharides differ only in the configuration at carbon 1. The result is that two glucose units are required for the repeating unit of cellulose while starch has only one. In terms of the nomenclature used for stereoregular polymers, cellulose has a *threo*-di-syndiotactic structure while amylose starch is *erythro*-di-isotactic. In the nomenclature of carbohydrate chemistry, cellulose consists of β-1,4-linked *D*-glucopyranose chains and amylose of α-1,4-linked *D*-glucopyranose chains. The 1,4-linkage is trans(diequitorial) in cellulose and cis(equitorial-axial) in amylose. The difference in structure leads to a higher degree of crystallinity in cellulose. Cellulose compared to amylose, has good strength and mechanical properties, decreased solubility, and increased stability to hydrolysis. The result is that cellulose is used as a structural material both in nature (in plants) and by man. Although starch is not useful as a structural material, it does serve a very important function as a food source for both plants and animals. The utility of amylose for this purpose is due to its ease of hydrolysis which is a consequence of its structure.

8-2b Analysis of Stereoregularity

8-2b-1 Experimental Methods. Analysis of polymer structures for stereoregularity or tacticity is carried out by a number of methods [22]. Often, the methods involve a determination of the percent crystallinity in a sample as an indication of its stereoregularity. The equating of crystallinity and tacticity is a reasonable assumption but not necessarily quantitative. All of the stereoregular polymer molecules may not be in the crystalline portion of the sample. Some stereoregular chains may be of too low a molecular weight to crystallize. Short stereoregular sequences in an otherwise atactic polymer chain will escape detection. On the other hand, short atactic sequences in an otherwise tactic chain may be counted as tactic sequences. (Polymers containing sequences with different tacticities are referred to as *stereoblock* polymers if the sequences are long.) The most satisfactory analytical methods are those based on measurements of configuration. Infra-red absorption spectroscopy is an especially useful method for analyzing the products of 1,3-diene polymerizations. The various possible products

(1,2-, 3,4-, cis-1,4- and trans-1,4) have differently substituted double bonds which give rise to different infra-red absorption bands. The use of these spectral differences allows a direct quantitative measure of the amounts of 1,2-, 3,4- and cis-1,4- and trans-1,4-polymerizations. Infra-red spectroscopy can also be used for analysis of polymer tacticity due to optical isomerism; however, the method often determines crystallinity in lieu of tacticity. Nuclear magnetic resonance (NMR) is the most useful method for quantitatively analyzing the occurrence of optical isomerism in polymers [10, 22].

8-2b-2 Definition of Tacticity. Two ways are generally used to describe the degree of syndiotactic or isotactic regularity [20]. One is the *diad tacticity* defined by Natta [23] as the fractions of the adjacent monomer units (diads) which are placed isotactic or syndiotactic to one another. The isotactic and syndiotactic diads can be depicted as

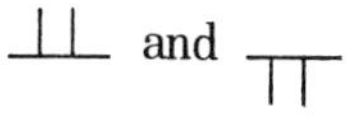

and

Isotactic

XVa

and

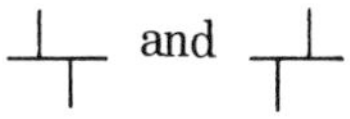

Syndiotactic

XVb

where the horizontal line represents a segment of the polymer chain and each vertical line represents the configuration at the site of steric isomerism in a monomer unit. The fractions of isotactic and syndiotactic diads are usually designated as i and s, respectively. (The reader is cautioned that I and S are also used in the literature to denote the diad tacticities.)

The second definition of tacticity is the *triad tacticity* suggested by Bovey and Tiers [24]. Isotactic, syndiotactic, and heterotactic triads are defined by

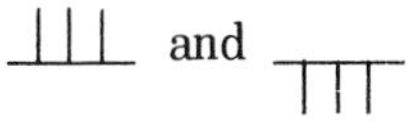

and

Isotactic

XVIa

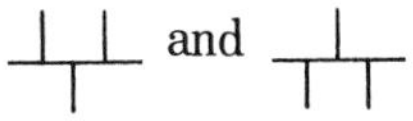

and

Syndiotactic

XVIb

, , , and

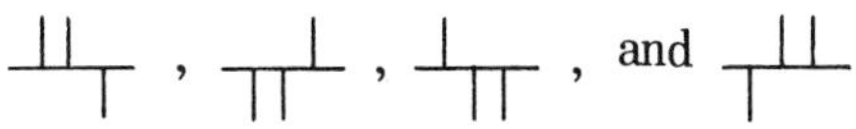

Heterotactic

XVIc

and designated as I, S, and H, respectively. The diad fractions i and s are not necessarily identical to the triad fractions I and S but they can be interrelated. The diad and triad fractions must total unity by definition, i.e.,

$$i + s = 1 \tag{8-10}$$

$$I + S + H = 1 \tag{8-11}$$

Combination of Eqs. 8-10 and 8-11 yields

$$i = I + \frac{1}{2}H \tag{8-12}$$

$$s = S + \frac{1}{2}H \tag{8-13}$$

Whether one determines the diad or triad tacticities by nuclear magnetic resonance depends on the particular polymer and on the sensitivity of the NMR instrument used. As the resolution of NMR instruments increases, tacticity of longer sequences than diads and triads can be analyzed [25]. Thus, the tetrad tacticity of poly-(methyl methacrylate) has been recently studied by high-resolution NMR [26].

It is clear that a determination of any two triad fractions allows a complete definition of both the triad and diad structures of a polymer from Eqs. 8-10 to 8-13. A knowledge of only the diad fractions, however, does not allow a definition of the triad structure. An atactic polymer is one in which $i = s = 0.5$ and the distribution of diads in the polymer chain is random. For a random distribution, the relationships

$$\begin{aligned} I &= i^2 \\ S &= s^2 \\ H &= 2is \end{aligned} \tag{8-14}$$

hold and $I = 0.25$, $S = 0.25$, $H = 0.50$ for the atactic case. The completely isotactic polymer has $i = I = 1$ with a completely non-random distribution, i.e., with all diads and triads placed isotactic. The completely syndiotactic polymer is analogously defined with $s = S = 1$. For random distributions with $i \neq s \neq 0.5$ ($I \neq S \neq 0.25$), one has different degrees of syndiotacticity or isotacticity. Isotacticity predominates when $i > 0.5$ and syndiotacticity when $s > 0.5$. These polymers can be referred to as *random tactic copolymers,* i.e., they are random copolymers of isotactic and syndiotactic diads or triads. When the distribution of diads or triads is more non-random than random, the polymer becomes a *tactic stereoblock polymer*—in which parts of polymer chains contain sufficient numbers of isotactic or syndiotactic diads joined together to allow crystallization. Such polymer chains contain syndiotactic or isotactic blocks connected to segments which may or may not have sufficient tacticity for crystallization.

8-3 FORCES OF STEREOREGULATION IN ALKENE POLYMERIZATIONS

Having discussed the types of stereoisomerism which are possible in polymers, one can consider the forces which are actually operating toward or against stereospecificity in a polymerization. The stereochemistry of alkene polymerizations will be considered first. The extent of stereospecificity in a polymerization is determined by the relative rate at which an incoming monomer molecule is added with the same configuration as the preceding monomer unit compared to its rate of addition with the opposite configuration. Different forces determine the relative rates of these two modes of addition depending on whether the active end of a propagating polymer chain is a free species or one which is coordinated (associated) with the catalyst. For freely propagating species which are not coordinated in any manner, both modes of addition are possible. The stereoregularity of the final polymer product is dependent primarily on the polymerization temperature which determines the relative rates of the two modes of addition. The situation is quite different when the propagation species is coordinated with the catalyst. One or the other of the modes of addition may be prevented from taking place by the configuration of the coordinated complex (usually consisting of the propagating chain end, initiator, and monomer). Under these circumstances, coordination directs the mode of monomer addition in a stereospecific manner.

8-3a Radical Polymerization

Radical polymerizations are generally considered to involve freely propagating species. The planar or nearly planar trigonal carbon atom does not have a specified configuration since there is free rotation about the terminal carbon-carbon bond (as indicated in Eq. 8-15 by the circular arrows). This would mean that the configuration of a monomer unit in the polymer chain is not determined during its addition to the radical center but only when the next monomer molecule adds to it. The situation can be depicted as

XVII $+ CH_2{=}CHR \xrightarrow{k_s}$ XVIII (8-15a)

XVII $+ CH_2{=}CHR \xrightarrow{k_i}$ XIX (8-15b)

where the two placements–syndiotactic (Eq. 8-15a) and isotactic (Eq. 8-15b)–take place with the rate constants k_s and k_i, respectively. Whether or not the same placement is propagated through the successive additions of monomer units determines the stereoregularity of the final polymer molecule. The amount and type of stereoregularity is specifically determined by the value of k_s/k_i. Isotactic polymer is produced if this ratio is zero, syndiotactic polymer if it is infinity, and atactic if unity. For k_s/k_i values between unity and infinity, one obtains a distribution of polymer molecules of varying degrees of atactic and syndiotactic placements.

8-3a-1 Energetics of Syndiotactic and Isotactic Placements. The value of k_s/k_i is determined by the difference F in the free energies of activation between the syndiotactic F_s and isotactic F_i placements according to

$$\frac{k_s}{k_i} = \exp\left\{\frac{-\Delta F^{\ddagger}}{RT}\right\} = \exp\left\{\frac{\Delta S^{\ddagger}}{R} - \frac{\Delta H^{\ddagger}}{RT}\right\} \tag{8-16}$$

with

$$\begin{aligned} \Delta F^{\ddagger} &= \Delta F_s^{\ddagger} - \Delta F_i^{\ddagger} \\ \Delta S^{\ddagger} &= \Delta S_s^{\ddagger} - \Delta S_i^{\ddagger} \\ \Delta H^{\ddagger} &= \Delta H_s^{\ddagger} - \Delta H_i^{\ddagger} \end{aligned} \tag{8-17}$$

where $\Delta F_s^{\ddagger}$, $\Delta H_s^{\ddagger}$, $\Delta S_s^{\ddagger}$ are the activation free energy, enthalpy, and entropy for syndiotactic placement and $\Delta F_i^{\ddagger}$, $\Delta H_i^{\ddagger}$, $\Delta S_i^{\ddagger}$ are the corresponding quantities for isotactic placement. Huggins [27] indicated this as early as 1944 by suggesting that stereoregularity should be temperature-dependent with ordered structures favored at low temperatures. This was mathematically confirmed by Fordham [28] who calculated the expected differences in the activation enthalpies $\Delta H^{\ddagger}$ and entropies $\Delta S^{\ddagger}$ between syndiotactic and isotactic placements from data on low molecular weight homologues of polymers. The energy differences are small; $\Delta H^{\ddagger}$ is about -1 to -2 kcal/mole and $\Delta S^{\ddagger}$ is 0 to -1 eu. Syndiotactic placement is favored over isotactic placement due primarily to the enthalpy difference. The small energy differences between syndiotactic and isotactic placements have been confirmed for a number of monomers by studies on the temperature dependence of tacticity. Thus, $\Delta H^{\ddagger}$ and $\Delta S^{\ddagger}$ have been reported as -1.07 and -0.99 for methyl methacrylate [29] and -0.31 and -0.6 for vinyl chloride [30].

The slight preference for syndiotactic placement over isotactic placement is a consequence of steric and/or electrostatic repulsions between substituents in the polymer chain. Repulsions between R substituent groups—more specifically, between the R groups on the terminal and penultimate units of the propagating chain—are minimized in the transition state of the propagation step (and also in the final polymer molecule) when they are located in the alternating arrangement of the syndiotactic placement. These steric and electrostatic repulsions between the R substituents are maximum for isotactic placement. There are some indications that the preference for syndiotactic placement may not always be due to repulsions between R groups on the terminal and penultimate units. Calculations [31] for poly(methyl methacrylate) show that the propagating radical end is not free to rotate as indicated previously; the energy barrier for rotation about the carbon-carbon bond is greater than 20 kcal/mole, while the activation energy for propagation is only 6.3 kcal/mole. In this case, the preference for syndiotactic placement is probably due to repulsions between the R group on the terminal monomer unit of the propagating chain and that on the incoming monomer molecule.

The difference in the activation enthalpies for syndiotactic and isotactic placements leads to an increasing tendency toward syndiotacticity with decreasing polymerization temperature. Figure 8-9 shows the increase in the syndiotactic fraction s of poly(vinyl chloride) from 0.51 to 0.67 as the temperature decreases from 120°C to −78°C [32]. (The low temperature polymerizations in this work were carried out using a trialkylboron initiator similar to that described in Sec. 5-5c.) Corresponding data [27] for poly(methyl methacrylate) are shown in Table 8-2. With decreasing temperatures, the energy difference between syndiotactic and isotactic placements exerts a progressively increasing influence on the stereospecificity of the polymerization; at high temperatures, their effects are progressively diminished.

Since radical polymerizations are generally carried out at moderately high temperatures, most of the resulting polymers are highly

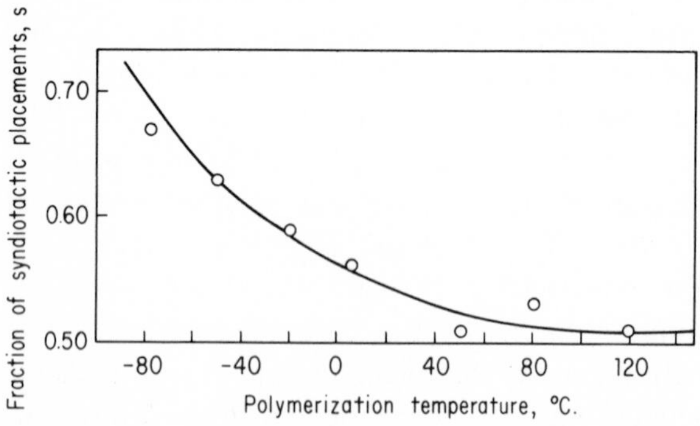

FIG. 8-9 *Dependence of syndiotacticity on temperature for the radical polymerization of vinyl chloride. After [32] (by permission of Hüthig and Wepf Verlag, Basel).*

Table 8-2 Effect of Temperature on Tacticity in Radical Polymerization of Methyl Methacrylate[a]

Temperature (°C)	Fraction of syndiotactic placements(s)
−40	0.86
60	0.76
100	0.73
150	0.67
250	0.64

[a]Data from [29].

atactic. This does not mean that there is a complete absence of syndiotacticity. There is a considerable difference in the extent of syndiotactic placement from one polymer to another. Thus, a comparison of Fig. 8-9 and Table 8-2 shows that there is a much greater tendency toward syndiotactic placement for methyl methacrylate than for vinyl chloride. The difference is a consequence, no doubt, of the greater degree of substitution of the former—leading to greater repulsions between substituent groups in adjacent monomer units. Whereas the poly(vinyl chloride) produced at the usual commercial polymerization temperatures of about 60°C is essentially completely atactic ($i = s = 0.5$), this is not the case for poly(methyl methacrylate). The polymerization of methyl methacrylate, which is typically carried out at temperatures of up to 100°C, yields polymers with appreciable syndiotacticity—Table 8-2 shows 73 percent syndiotactic placement at 100°C. In a similar comparison, poly(methyl acrylate) is essentially completely atactic while polyacrylonitrile is appreciably syndiotactic (approximately 70 percent at 100°C) [33, 34].

8-3a-2 Distribution of Stereoregular Sequence Lengths. Just as there is a distribution of molecular weights in a polymer sample, so there is a distribution of stereoregular sequence lengths in a sample. In other words, a polymer of syndiotacticity s contains an average length of sequences of monomer units having syndiotactic configurations with a distribution of syndiotactic sequences of different lengths. The ratio of the propagation rate constants k_s/k_i determines both the average sequence length and the sequence-length distribution [28]. The probability of having a syndiotactic sequence of n monomer units is the probability of having a sequence in which an initial syndiotactic placement is repeated $(n - 1)$ times followed by an isotactic placement. This probability P_s^n is given by

$$P_s^n = \beta^{n-1}\alpha \tag{8-18}$$

where

$$\beta = \frac{k_s}{k_s + k_i} \tag{8-19a}$$

$$\alpha = \frac{k_i}{k_s + k_i} = 1 - \beta \tag{8-19b}$$

The parameters α and β are the equivalent of i and s, respectively. The latter originate from experimental data while the former are more theoretical in origin.

The average length of the syndiotactic sequences $\bar{n}_s$ is given by

$$\bar{n}_s = \sum_{n=1}^{\infty} n\beta^{n-1}\alpha \tag{8-20a}$$

which yields

$$\bar{n}_s = \frac{\alpha}{(1 - \beta)^2} = \frac{1}{\alpha} \tag{8-20b}$$

on evaluation of the summation. The fraction of the total polymer sample F_s^n which has a sequence-length of n is given by

$$F_s^n = \frac{\beta n \beta^{n-1}\alpha}{\bar{n}_s} = n\alpha^2\beta^n \tag{8-21}$$

The distribution of syndiotactic sequence-lengths according to Eq. 8-21 is shown in Fig. 8-10 for k_s/k_i values of 1, 10, and 100. As the k_s/k_i value increases (i.e., as syndiotacticity increases), the syndiotactic sequences become longer with some of them being the length of the polymer molecule itself. The sequence-length distri-

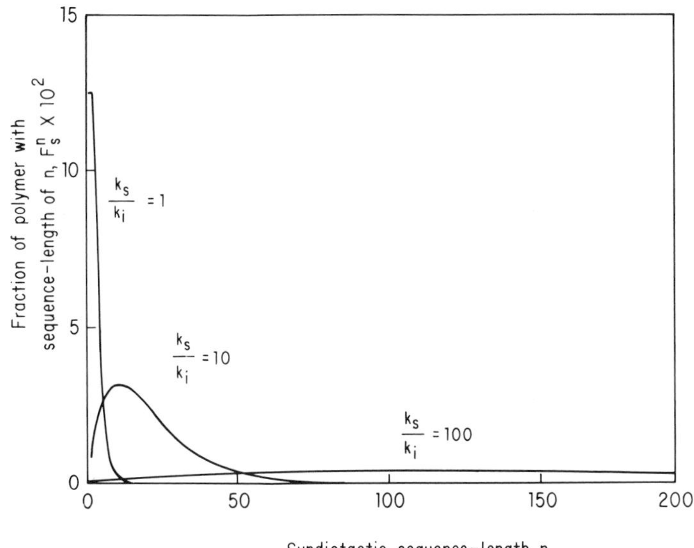

FIG. 8-10 *Distribution of syndiotactic sequence-lengths for* k_s/k_i *values of 1, 10, and 100. After [28] (by permission of Interscience Publishers, John Wiley & Sons, Inc., New York).*

bution is broad—even for the atactic polymer ($k_s/k_i = 1$). The atactic polymer has about half of the polymer with syndiotactic sequences of more than two monomer units; only about one-quarter of the polymer has syndiotactic sequences of unit length. The sequence-length distribution becomes increasingly broad as the syndiotacticity of the polymer increases. Polymers of high syndiotacticity have considerable amounts of short syndiotactic sequences. Unless the syndiotacticity is very high, there is some atactic polymer fraction. This explains clearly why even the moderately high degree of syndiotacticity present in a polymer such as poly(methyl methacrylate) is not enough to allow it to crystallize extensively.

8-3b Ionic and Coordination Polymerization

8-3b-1 Effect of Coordination. For ionic chain polymerizations involving free propagating species, the factors governing the stereochemistry of the reaction are similar to those for radical polymerization. Syndiotactic placement is increasingly favored as the polymerization temperature is lowered. When, however, extensive coordination is present between the initiator, propagating chain end, and monomer species, the situation is quite different. The configuration of the coordination complex (of propagating chain end, initiator, and monomer) may allow the entry of monomer molecules into the polymer chain only in a stereospecific manner. In the usual case, propagation is prevented from taking place by one or the other of the two placements (*R*- or *S*-) as coordination becomes the dominant driving force for stereospecificity in the polymerization. The k_s/k_i ratio tends toward a value of zero and stereospecific polymerization occurs with isotactic placement. Coordination can also lead to syndiotactic polymers in certain instances although the usual result is isotactic placement. Table 8-3 shows a few examples of various highly stereospecific polymerizations [26, 33, 35–38]. The polymer structures in most cases are greater than 90 percent stereospecific in terms of isotactic or syndiotactic diads; in some cases it is as high as 99 percent.

Table 8-3 Stereospecific Polymerizations

Monomer	Polymerization conditions	Polymer structure	Ref.
1-Butene	$TiCl_3$, $(C_2H_5)_2Zn$ in heptane at 50°C	Isotactic	[35]
Isobutyl vinyl ether	$BF_3 \cdot (C_2H_5)_2O$ in propane at −60° to −80°C	Isotactic	[36], [37]
Methyl acrylate	$\phi MgBr$ or n-C_4H_9Li in ϕCH_3 at −20°C	Isotactic	[33]
Methyl methacrylate	n-C_4H_9Li in ϕCH_3 at −78°C	Isotactic	[26]
Methyl methacrylate	$(C_2H_5)AlN\phi_2$ in ϕCH_3 at −78°C	Syndiotactic	[26]
Propylene	$TiCl_4$, $(C_2H_5)_3Al$ in heptane at 50°C	Isotactic	[35]
Propylene	VCl_4, $Al(i$-$C_4H_9)_2Cl$, anisole in ϕCH_3 at −78°C	Syndiotactic	[38]

The first reported instance of coordination-directed stereospecific polymerization was probably the cationic polymerization of isobutyl vinyl ether by Schildknecht [36] in 1947. He observed the formation of a highly crystalline polymer when the reaction was carried out at −60 to −80°C using boron trifluoride etherate as the catalyst. The full significance of the polymerization was not realized at the time as the crystallinity was attributed to a syndiotactic structure. X-ray diffraction studies in 1956 indicated that the polymer had an isotactic structure [37]. The field of stereospecific polymerization actually came into existence in 1954 when Ziegler in Germany and Natta in Italy developed new polymerization catalysts which showed unique stereoregulating powers [2–4]. The scientific and practical significance of their work earned Natta and Ziegler the joint award of the Nobel prize for chemistry in 1963. The Nobel prize addresses [5, 39] delivered by them are excellent introductions to the field of stereospecific polymerization.

The initial work of Natta and Ziegler has led to the development of a large number of catalyst systems obtained by the interaction of an organometallic compound or hydride of a Group I-III metal with a halide or other derivative of a Group IV-VIII transition metal. The polymerizations are carried out in hydrocarbon solvents such as heptane. Some of the compounds used as the Group I-III metal component are triethylaluminum, diethylaluminum chloride and diethylzinc; titanium trichloride, vanadium trichloride, cyclopentadienyltitanium dichloride, and chromium triacetylacetonate are examples of the transition metal component. These catalyst systems are referred to as Ziegler, Ziegler-Natta, Natta, or *coordination catalysts*. The last term is the most appropriate since it includes other catalysts which are not of the same chemical identity as described above but which bring about stereospecific polymerization by a common mechanism. Examples of coordination catalysts which are not of the Ziegler-Natta type are *n*-butylithium, phenylmagnesium bromide, and boron trifluoride etherate.

8-3b-2 Mechanism of Stereospecific Placement. Coordination catalysts perform two functions. First, they supply the species which initiates the polymerization. Second, the fragment of the catalyst aside from the initiator portion has unique coordinating powers. Coordination of this catalyst fragment (which may be considered as the gegen ion of the propagating species) with both the propagating chain end and the incoming monomer occurs so as to orient the monomer with respect to the growing chain end and bring about its stereospecific addition. Many different mechanisms have been advanced to explain the usual isotactic placement obtained with coordination catalysts [5-11]. Stereospecific polymerization is probably best considered as a concerted, multi-centered reaction. Figure 8-11 depicts the general situation for an *anionic coordinated polymerization* in which the polymer chain end can be considered as having a partial negative charge with the catalyst fragment G having a partial positive charge. (Cationic coordination polymerization would involve a similar mechanism except for reversal of the signs of the partial charges.) The catalyst fragment G is coordinated to both the propagating chain end and the incoming monomer molecule. The propagating chain end is considered to have a tetrahedral carbon in which the fourth substituent is the catalyst fragment.

The monomer is oriented and "held in position" by coordination during addition to the polymer chain. The coordination bond between the catalyst and the propagating chain is broken simultaneously with the formation of bonds between the chain end and the new monomer unit, and between the catalyst fragment and the new monomer unit. Propagation proceeds in the four-membered

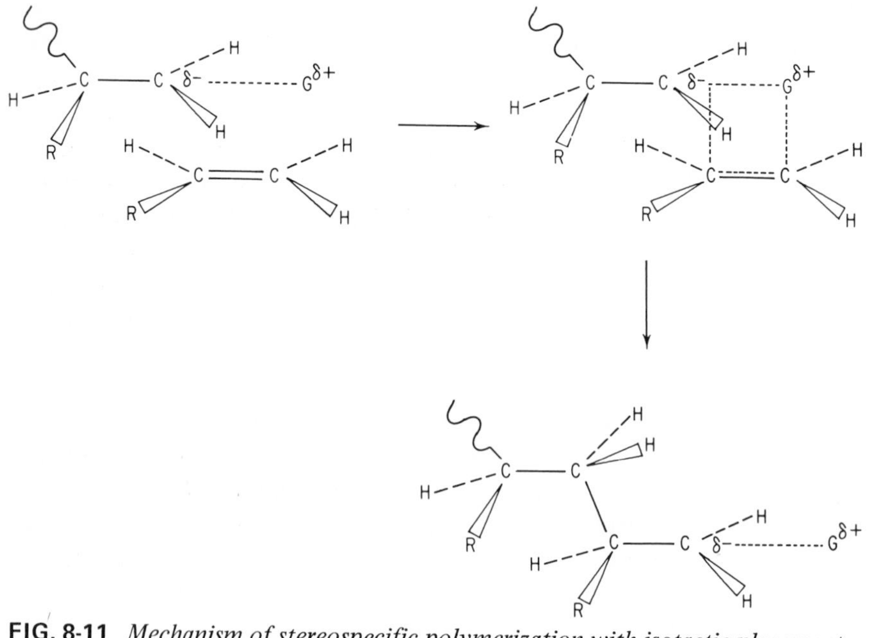

FIG. 8-11 *Mechanism of stereospecific polymerization with isotactic placement.*

cyclic transition state by the insertion of the monomer between the catalyst and the propagating chain end. The catalyst essentially acts as a template or mold for the successive orientations and isotactic placements of the incoming monomer units. The driving force for isotactic placement is the repulsive interactions of the catalyst fragment G with the substituent R of the incoming monomer. The monomer is forced to approach the reaction site in only one of the two possible orientations—that leading to isotactic placement.

Stereospecific polymerizations with syndiotactic placement occur in the relatively few instances when the catalyst can coordinate with the monomer in both of the two possible configurations (that is, *R*- and *S*-). In such cases, the driving force for syndiotactic placement is the same as that described previously for low temperature polymerizations—the repulsive interactions between substituent groups on adjacent monomer units. Coordination accentuates these interactions in the same manner as lowering the reaction temperature would.

The exact nature of the catalyst required to bring about stereospecific, isotactic polymerization differs considerably depending on the monomer. The ease of imposing steric requirements on the entry of a monomer molecule into a polymer chain increases with the ability of the monomer to coordinate with the catalyst. The coordinating power of a monomer depends primarily on its polarity. This is greatest for those monomers (e.g., acrylates, methacrylates, and vinyl ethers) with polar functional groups capable of taking an active and strong role in the coordination. Ethylene, α-olefins (e.g., propylene and 1-butene) and other alkenes without polar substituents, on the other hand, have poor coordinating powers. The result is that non-polar monomers require the use of catalysts with very strong stereoregulating powers in order to "hold them in place" and produce isotactic polymerization. This necessitates the use of heterogeneous Ziegler-Natta catalysts to impose the most severe hindrance on the approach of the monomer to the propagating chain end. The use of homogeneous (soluble) catalysts with non-polar monomers results in the production of atactic polymer except in the few instances when syndiotactic structures are obtained. For polar monomers, heterogeneity is not a requirement for isotactic polymerization. Soluble catalysts can be used to produce isotactic polymers; syndiotactic polymers are obtained only with soluble catalysts. Styrene and 1,3-diene monomers are intermediate in behavior between the polar and non-polar monomers since the phenyl and alkenyl groups are not strongly polar. These monomers are polymerized to isotactic structures with both homogeneous and heterogeneous catalysts.

8-4 ZIEGLER-NATTA POLYMERIZATION OF NON-POLAR ALKENES

The Ziegler-Natta catalysts are a remarkable group of catalysts. They are the only catalysts which can be used to polymerize α-olefins such as propylene and 1-butene. It should be recalled from Chaps. 3 and 5 that α-olefins are not polymerized by either radical or ionic catalysts. The Ziegler-Natta catalysts have become of practical importance due to the commercial production of isotactic polypropylene and high density or linear polyethylene. Although the phenomenon of optical isomerism is not applicable to the symmetrical ethylene, the use of stereospecific catalysts produces a polyethylene which is different from that produced by the free radical process. Polyethylene synthesized by these new catalyst systems contains far less branching because of the lower reaction temperatures and the relative absence of transfer reactions. The product crystallizes to a higher degree and has a higher density because the polymer chains are more linear. High density polyethylene is stronger and superior in other respects compared to the radical-produced, low density polyethylene.

Since the original discoveries of Ziegler and Natta, an ever increasing number of catalysts of the Ziegler-Natta type have been studied. These encompass literally hundreds and thousands of different combinations of a Group I-III organometallic compound (or hydride) and a compound of a Group IV-VIII transition metal. Table 8-4 shows some of the different catalyst components which have been reported in the literature. The catalysts exhibit a range of behaviors with different monomers in terms of activity and stereospecificity. The term *activity* as used in this chapter applies exclusively to the rate of polymerization; this usage of the term is not universally employed. The order of polymerization rates obtained with different Ziegler-Natta catalysts often differs from the order of their stereospecificities. Many catalysts with high activities (high polymerization rates) show poor stereospecificity. The Ziegler-Natta catalyst is extremely versatile in that changes in one or the other of its components can often be used to obtain a "tailor-made" catalyst

Table 8-4 Components of Ziegler-Natta Catalysts

Group I-III metal	Transition metal
$(C_2H_5)_3Al$	$TiCl_4$
$(C_2H_5)_2AlCl$	$TiCl_3$
$(C_2H_5)_2AlBr$	$TiBr_3$
$(C_2H_5)AlCl_2$	VCl_4
$(i\text{-}C_4H_9)_3Al$	VCl_3
$(C_2H_5)_2Be$	$(C_5H_5)_2TiCl_2$
$(C_2H_5)_2Mg$	$(CH_3COCHCOCH_3)_3V$
C_4H_9Li	$Ti(OC_4H_9)_4$
$(C_2H_5)_2Zn$	$Ti(OH)_4$
$(C_2H_5)_4Pb$	$VOCl_3$
$(\phi_2N)_3Al$	$MoCl_5$
$\phi MgBr$	$MoCl_4$
$(C_2H_5)_4AlLi$	$CrCl_3$
	$ZrCl_4$
	$CuCl$
	WCl_6
	$MnCl_2$
	NiO

to suit a particular set of requirements for a particular monomer. Very high stereospecificity can often be obtained along with reasonable polymerization rates by the proper choice of the catalyst components. Unfortunately, the choice of the catalyst components is often an empirical one due to the lack of knowledge of the detailed mechanism of stereoregulation with Ziegler-Natta catalysts.

8-4a Mechanism of Ziegler-Natta Polymerization

The number of mechanisms which have been proposed to explain the stereospecificity of Ziegler-Natta catalysts is large—surpassed only by the number of different catalysts which have been studied. Many of the proposed mechanisms include considerable detail which distinguish them from each other but which cannot be verified. All too often, the detailed mechanisms are not applicable to catalyst systems other than the particular ones for which they are proposed. In this section, the mechanistic features of Ziegler-Natta polymerizations will be considered with emphasis on those characteristics which hold for the large bulk of catalyst systems. The major interest will be on the titanium-aluminum catalysts, more specifically, the $(C_2H_5)_3Al$-$TiCl_3$ system which is one of the most thoroughly studied systems. Detailed information on a variety of other catalyst systems can be found in a number of excellent reviews [9, 11, 20, 40–42].

A number of general questions arise concerning the mechanism of Ziegler-Natta polymerizations. What is the chemical nature of the propagating species? Does propagation take place at a carbon-transition metal bond or at a carbon-Group I-III metal bond? What is the chemical and physical identity of the actual or active catalyst species which initiates polymerization, i.e., what is the identity of G in Fig. 8-11?

8-4a-1 Chemical Nature of Propagating Species. There has been considerable confusion in the literature concerning the nature of the propagating species. It has become increasingly apparent that the type of propagating center encountered in a polymerization using a Ziegler-Natta type catalyst depends on both the catalyst components and the monomer. Some of the polymerizations reported as Ziegler-Natta polymerizations are conventional free-radical, cationic, or anionic polymerizations which usually take place without stereospecificity. Ziegler-Natta catalysts often contain components which are capable of and are often used (Chap. 5) for initiating conventional ionic polymerizations. Thus, the use of butyllithium as the Group I-III metal component can result in anionic polymerization with monomers containing electron-poor double bonds, e.g., acrylates and methacrylates. Monomers with electron-rich double bonds, e.g., vinyl ethers, can undergo cationic polymerization when one uses a catalyst component which is a strong electron-acceptor, for example $TiCl_4$, VCl_4 and $RAlCl_2$. Some Ziegler-Natta catalyst components can react to yield free radicals, e.g., the interaction of $TiCl_4$ and R_3Al involves a complex set of reactions including

$$TiCl_4 + R_3Al \longrightarrow RTiCl_3 + R_2AlCl \tag{8-22}$$

$$TiCl_4 + R_2AlCl \longrightarrow RTiCl_3 + RAlCl_2 \tag{8-23}$$

$$TiCl_4 + RAlCl_2 \longrightarrow RTiCl_3 + AlCl_3 \tag{8-24}$$

$$RTiCl_3 \longrightarrow TiCl_3 + R\cdot \tag{8-25}$$

$$R\cdot + TiCl_4 \longrightarrow TiCl_3 + RCl \tag{8-26}$$

$$2\,R\cdot \longrightarrow \text{Combination and disproportionation} \tag{8-27}$$

Radicals produced in Eq. 8-25 or via other reactions are capable of initiating radical polymerizations with a number of monomers under certain conditions. The tendency toward radical polymerization is increased with many catalyst components when oxygen is present [9], e.g., recall the $R_3B\text{-}O_2$ catalyst system in Sec. 5-5c.

When one speaks of Ziegler-Natta polymerizations, one is almost always concerned with polymerizations which occur with stereospecificity. Stereospecificity occurs when the reaction takes place with a coordination mechanism. Anionic coordination, cationic coordination, and radical coordination polymerization mechanisms have been variously proposed to account for stereospecific polymerization by Ziegler-Natta catalysts. The experimental evidence is clearly against a coordinate-radical mechanism. One can cite a few of the arguments [9] which favor an ionic mechanism:

1) Radical chain transfer agents have no effect on polymer molecular weight.

2) The lifetime of the propagating species is much longer than that in a radical polymerization and, in fact, resembles that in living polymerizations.

3) Block copolymers can be produced by the alternate feeding of two different monomers.

4) Changes in the catalyst components result in changes in the monomer reactivity ratios of the two monomers in a copolymerization.

The generally accepted mechanism for the stereospecific Ziegler-Natta polymerization of α-olefins (and other non-polar alkenes) is a coordinate-anionic process similar to that described by Fig. 8-11. This can be shown in a more simplified manner as

$$\begin{array}{ccc} & \delta+ & \delta- \\ & \text{R—CH} \cdots\cdots & \text{CH}_2 \\ & \nwarrow 2 & \searrow 1 \\ \sim\sim\text{CHR—} & \text{CH}_2 \cdots\cdots & \text{G} \\ & \delta- & \delta+ \end{array}$$

XX

The polymerization has both cationic and anionic features [43]. The reaction consists of a nucleophilic attack by the incipient carbanion polymer chain end on the monomer double bond (Reaction 2 in XX) and an electrophilic attack by the catalyst cation on the alkene π-electrons (Reaction 1 in XX); the two steps are generally considered to occur in a concerted manner, i.e., essentially simultaneously.

The anionic character of the polymerization is noted from the observation that the polymerization rate for α-olefins increases in the order ethylene > propylene > 1-butene [44]. One would expect the reverse order for a polymerization involving the conversion of a monomer into the corresponding carbonium ion. For addition of a carbanion to the monomers, attack occurs at the α-carbon to form the less substituted (and more stable) carbanion. The effect of α-substituents is to sterically hinder the approach of a carbanion with the result that polymerization reactivity decreases with increasing substituent size. Evidence for the anionic nature of the growing polymer chain also comes from studies in which labeled methanol is used to terminate chain growth. The terminated polymer is radioactive when $CH_3O{-}H^3$ is used while termination by C^{14}-labeled methanol yields a non-radioactive polymer. One can observe the cationic nature of the anionic coordination mechanism with monomers in which the steric factor is constant. For a series of meta- and para-substituted styrenes, the reactivity toward polymerization increases with the electron-donating power of the substituents [45]. Thus, the anionic coordination mechanism involves insertion of a monomer molecule at a carbanion center with the electrophilic attack by the catalyst fragment (Reaction 1 in XX) being rate determining.

8-4a-2 Propagation at Carbon-Transition Metal Bond. Both the transition metal-carbon bond and the Group I-III metal-carbon bond have been proposed as the site at which propagation occurs. However, most individual pieces of data cited in favor of either proposal—usually consisting of the changes in isotacticity or polymerization rate observed when either one or the other of the two components of the Ziegler-Natta catalyst is changed—are inconclusive. An overall consideration of all the available evidence points rather overwhelmingly toward propagation at a carbon-transition metal bond. This is strongly supported by a large body of evidence involving catalyst systems free of the Group I-III metal component. A variety of catalysts containing only a transition metal have been found to be effective stereospecific catalysts [40]. These include [46–48] the polymerization of ethylene and propylene by:

1) Ball-milled (ground) $TiCl_2$
2) Ball-milled transition metals, for example, Ti, V, Nb
3) Mixtures of a ball-milled transition metal with an alkyl halide (Ti + C_2H_5Br), halogen (Ti + I_2), or hydrogen (Ti + H_2)
4) Mixtures of a transition metal with a transition metal compound, for example, Ti + $TiCl_3$ and $TiCl_3$ + CH_3TiCl_3

Polymerization with these Group I-III metal-free catalysts is similar to that with catalysts containing the Group I-III metal component except for the lowered activity of the former. The kinetic features of both polymerizations are the same. The transition metal catalysts yield isotactic polymers as do the catalysts containing both types of metals.

8-4a-3 Bimetallic versus Monometallic Mechanisms. A number of structures have been proposed for the active Ziegler-Natta initiator species. The diversity of the proposed species arises from the multitude of products which have been observed (e.g., Eqs. 8-22 to 8-26) or can be easily postulated in the interaction of the two components of the typical Ziegler-Natta catalyst. The proposed active species fall into either of two general categories—bimetallic and monometallic species—depending on the number of metal centers. The two types can be illustrated by the structures

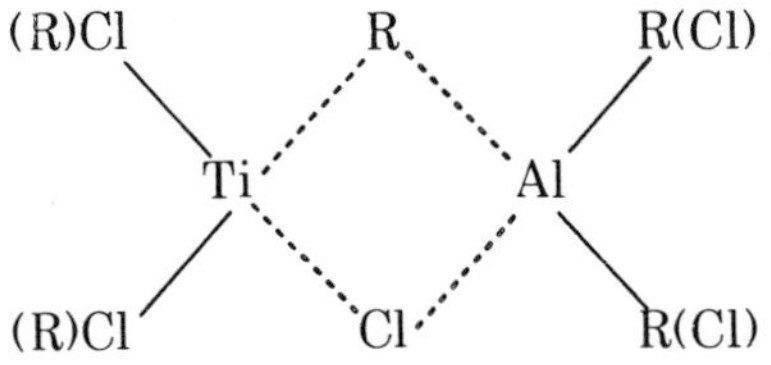

(R)Cl R R(Cl)
Ti Al
(R)Cl Cl R(Cl)

XXI

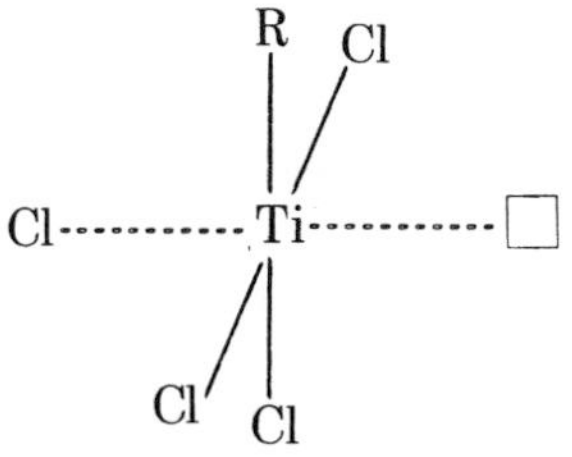

R Cl
Cl-----Ti-----□
Cl Cl

XXII

for the species formed by the interaction of a titanium chloride and an alkylaluminum compound such as $TiCl_4$ and $(C_2H_5)_3Al$. Structure XXII arises essentially from the alkylation of the titanium chloride by the organometallic compound. The □ in XXII designates an unoccupied or vacant octahedral titanium orbital. Structure XXI is the coordination complex of aluminum and titanium compounds arising from the interaction of the original catalyst components with exchange of R and Cl groups. The placing of R and Cl groups in parentheses in XXI indicates that the exact specification of the ligands on Al and Ti cannot be made. The identity and the number of ligands attached to each metal center may vary from one catalyst to another depending on the components and their relative amounts.

The two types of active species can be used to illustrate the two types of propagation mechanisms which have been proposed. Bimetallic mechanisms—involving propagations in which growth occurs at two metal centers—have been described by a number of workers [11, 40–42, 49–53]. Figure 8-12 shows a representation of the bimetallic mechanism. The mechanism is similar to that shown in Fig. 8-11 except for the detailing of the structure of catalyst fragment G. The monomer is coordinated with the catalyst and then inserted into the polarized titanium-carbon bond. Monometallic mechanisms—those involving propagation at a single metal center—

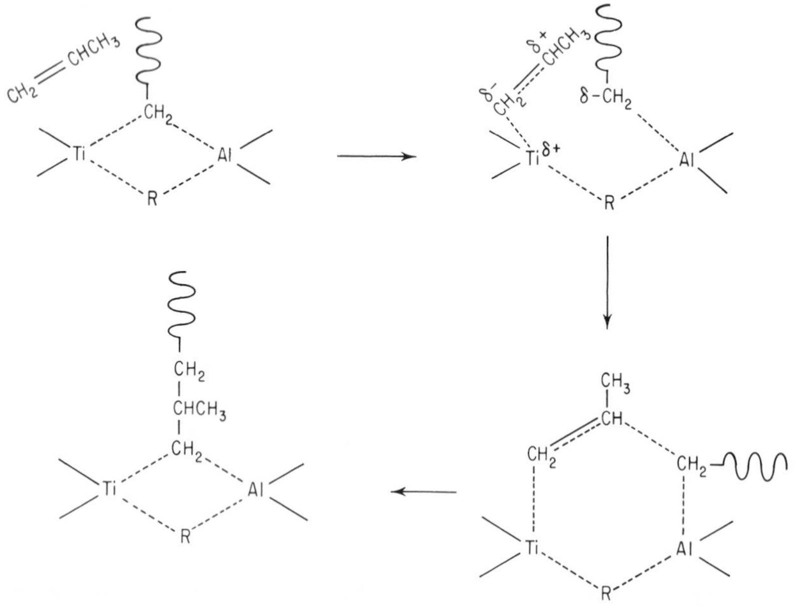

FIG. 8-12 *Bimetallic mechanism for stereospecific polymerization. After [49] (by permission of Interscience Publishers, John Wiley & Sons, Inc., New York) and [50] (by permission of Verlag Chemie GmbH, Weinheim).*

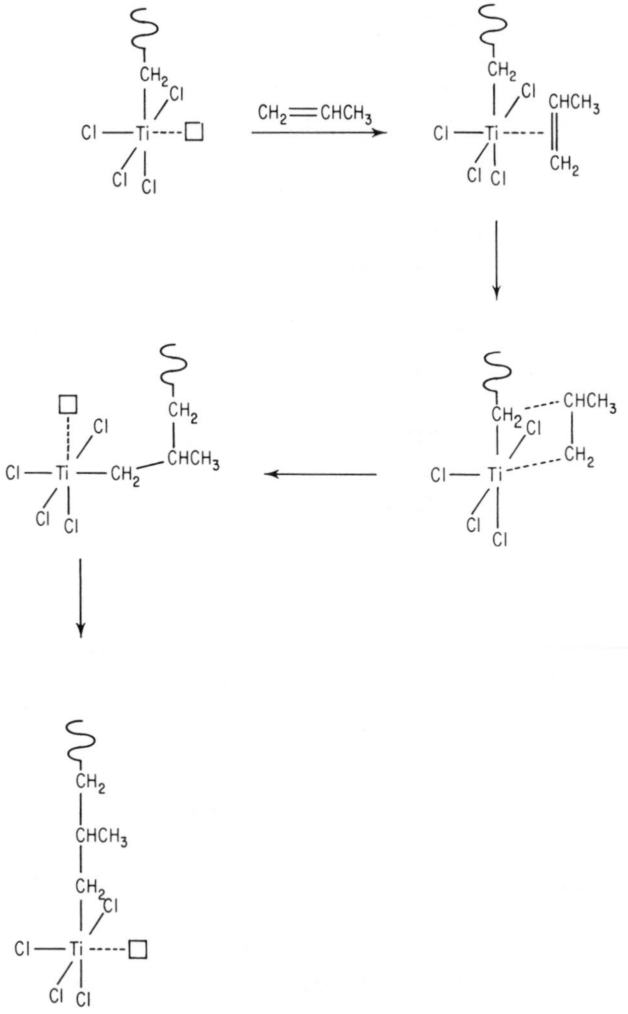

FIG. 8-13 *Monometallic mechanism for stereospecific polymerization. After [54] (by permission of Academic Press, Inc., New York).*

are illustrated in Fig. 8-13 by the mechanism proposed by Cossee [54]. The monomer is coordinated to the vacant orbital of the octahedral transition metal complex and then inserted into the polymer chain at the transition metal-carbon bond. This results in the regeneration of the vacant orbital with an orientation different from the original. If propagation continued with this species, the result would be syndiotactic polymerization [20]. Isotactic polymerization requires the migration of the polymer chain to its original site with the regeneration of the original vacant orbital.

At the present time it is not possible to experimentally verify either the bimetallic or monometallic mechanisms. The monometallic mechanism seems to be inherently simpler than the bimetallic mechanism except for the need of a migration step. Boor [40] suggested a monometallic mechanism which does not require the migration step. This involves the direct insertion of a monomer at the transition metal-carbon bond without coordination and with retention of the original catalyst geometry. The absence of a monomer-catalyst coordination in this mechanism, however, does not seem desirable in view of the generally accepted premise that coordination is necessary for stereospecificity. A large number of variations on both the bimetallic and monometallic mechanisms have been proposed [11, 40–42]. The distinction between the two mechanisms becomes obscured in some mechanisms, e.g., monometallic propagations have been proposed for some bimetallic catalysts with growth occurring solely at the transition metal-carbon bond [55]. Further, it is not impossible for both the bimetallic and monometallic mechanisms to be operative in Ziegler-Natta polymerizations. It may turn out that some catalyst systems involve propagation by the bimetallic mechanism while others involve the monometallic mechanism.

A word of caution should be given the reader at this point with regard to many of the mechanisms described in the literature. Most of these are highly detailed—often based only on conjecture and, all too frequently, on differences which are semantic or which become vague with time. An example of this situation can be seen by comparing the bimetallic mechanism of Natta [49] with that of Patat and Sinn [50] as described (interpreted) in [11] (Figs. 34 and 35) and [40] (Figs. 15 and 16). The Natta mechanism in [40] is amazingly similar to the Patat-Sinn mechanism in [11] whereas there are marked differences between the two mechanisms described in the original papers.

8-4a-4 Physical Nature of Catalyst. Ziegler-Natta catalysts are of both the heterogeneous and homogeneous types. As indicated previously, only heterogeneous Ziegler-Natta catalysts yield isotactic polymers from α-olefins and other non-polar monomers. The homogeneous catalysts usually yield atactic polymers although syndiotactic structures are obtained in a few instances.

8-4a-4-a Ligand-Monomer Interaction for Isotactic Polymerization. Propagation with heterogeneous catalysts is considered as taking place at active sites on the crystal surface of the insoluble transition metal compound (for example, $TiCl_3$). The active sites are formed by reaction of the soluble compound of the Group I-III metal (for example, $Al(C_2H_5)_3$ or $Al(C_2H_5)_2Cl$) with the $TiCl_3$ surface. The chemical identity of the active sites corresponds to the bimetallic or monometallic species described in Sec. 8-4a-3. The crystal structure of the catalyst along with its chemical structure determines the orientation(s) allowed to a monomer molecule as it is added to a propagating chain. The driving force for isotactic propagation results from steric and electrostatic interactions between the substituent of the incoming monomer and the ligands of the transition metal at the active site on the crystal surface. Monomer approaches the transition metal-carbon bond in only one configuration. Interactions between the incoming monomer and the terminal monomer unit of the polymer chain are minimized by rotation of the transition metal-carbon bond; this moves the substituent of the terminal monomer unit away from the vacant orbital of the metal. This model for isotactic placement has been referred to by Boor [40] as the *ligand-monomer interaction model.*

Several other models for isotactic placement have been proposed but none appear to be as generally applicable. Thus, helical growth of the polymer chain from the crystal surface has been considered to yield isotactic placement due to interaction of the monomer with the helix [56]. However, polymerization of propylene at temperatures high enough for polypropylene not to exist in the helical form can still result in highly isotactic polymer [57]; the helix is not a requirement for isotactic placement. Many workers have stressed the Group I-III metal component of the catalyst. Natta [44] suggested that bimetallic catalysts are asymmetric—they coordinate with monomers in only one configuration. Rodriguez and van Looy [55] attribute isotactic placement to the interactions between monomer and the Group I-III metallic portion of the bimetallic catalyst. Boor [40] rejected such models on the basis that the Group I-III metal component is not a requirement for isotactic polymerization (Sec. 8-4a-2). However, this model need not be in conflict with the ligand-monomer interaction model if both monometallic and bimetallic mechanisms are involved in Ziegler-Natta polymerization.

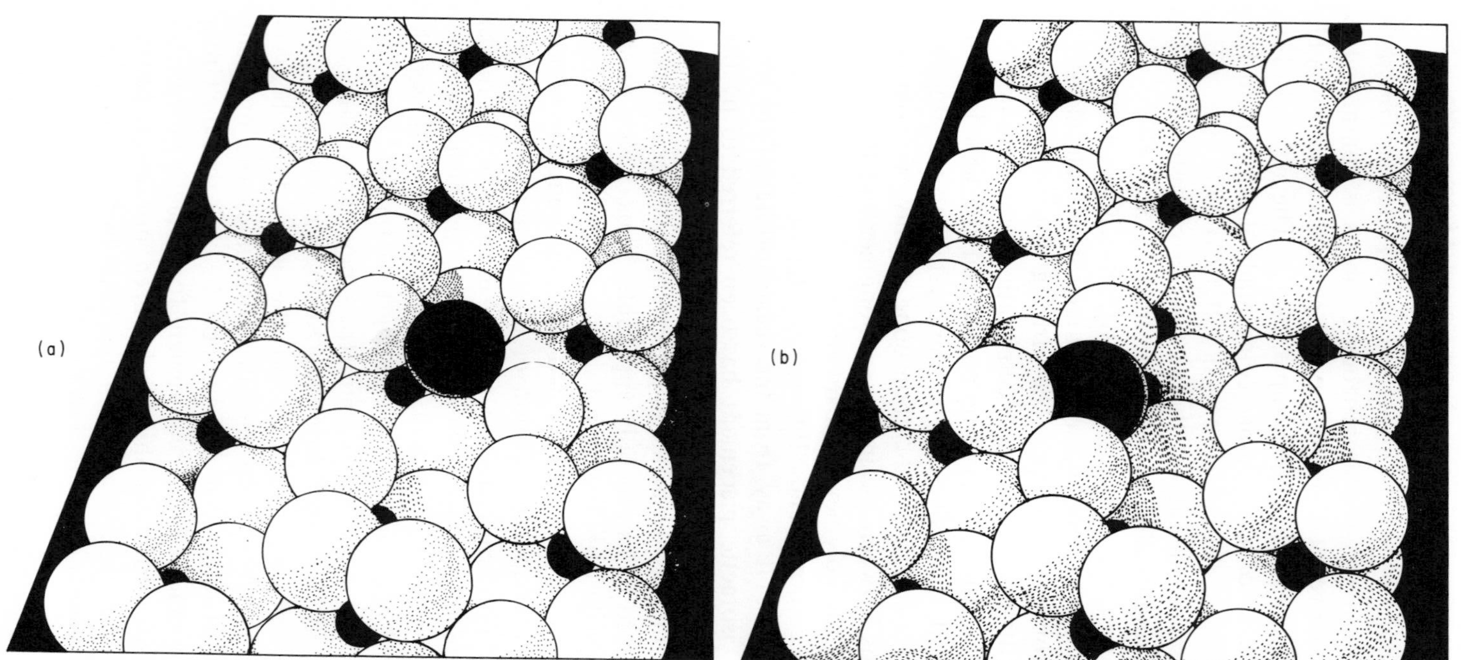

FIG. 8-14 *Crystal structure of $TiRCl_4\square$ for the Arlman-Cossee mechanism of isotactic placement. The structures shown in (a) and (b) differ in the geometry at the active titanium site; the positions of the propagating polymer chain and the orbital vacancy are interchanged After [60] (by permission of copyright holder, Academic Press, Inc., New York); original photographs from which this figure was drawn were kindly supplied by Dr. E. J. Arlman.*

8-4a-4-b Crystal Structure. Isotactic polymerization depends intimately on the crystal structure of the catalyst surface. For any coordination lattice, as opposed to molecular crystal lattices, the crystal will contain a number of ligand vacancies in order to achieve overall electrical neutrality of the crystal. α-$TiCl_3$ crystals are made up of elementary crystal sheets (XXIII) each containing

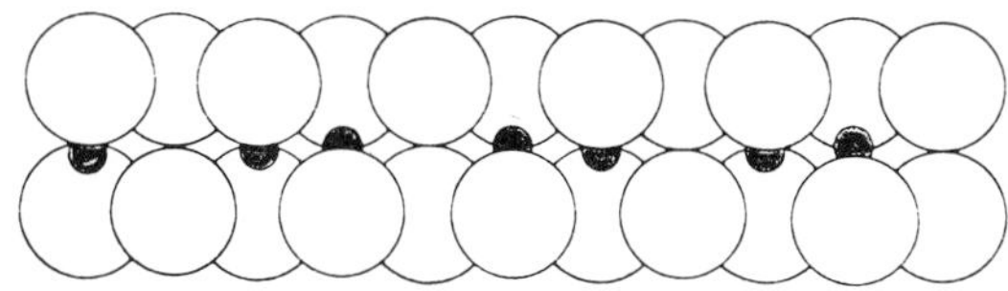

XXIII

a titanium layer in between two chloride layers [58]. (The structures XXIII, XXIV, and XXV are drawn after [58] by permission of Interscience Publishers, John Wiley & Sons, Inc., New York.) The titanium and chlorine atoms in XXIII are represented by small black and large white spheres, respectively. Two chloride layers alternate with a titanium layer along the principal crystal axis. The titaniums are at the octahedral interstices of the chloride lattice while chlorides are hexagonally close-packed. Every third titanium in the lattice is missing. These titanium sites, each of which contains a vacancy, are the active sites for Ziegler-Natta polymerization. The active sites ($TiRCl_4\square$) are formed at these titanium sites by alkylation which replaces a chloride with an R group. It is generally considered [42, 55, 59] that the active sites (titanium vacancies) are found on the edges of the elementary sheets and not in the basal planes of the crystal. This is supported by microscopic observations of polymer growth on the crystal edges [55].

Figure 8-14 shows some of the crystal structure details of the Arlman-Cossee [60] mechanism for the ligand-monomer interaction model of isotactic polymerization. This corresponds to the mechanism in Fig. 8-13 with the alkylated titanium species $TiRCl_4\square$ (XXII) as the active site in the surface of α-$TiCl_3$. One propagating polymer chain, represented by the large black sphere, is shown in Fig. 8-14. (The small black spheres are the titanium atoms and the white spheres are the chloride ligands.) Figures 8-14a and 8-14b differ in the geometry at the active titanium site. The sites are the same except that the positions of the propagating polymer chain and the orbital vacancy are interchanged. These correspond to the different geometries indicated in Fig. 8-13 for an active site before and after the addition of a monomer molecule to the propagating chain. The two sites are not equivalent; the polymer chain prefers the orientation in Fig. 8-14a where it protrudes much more from the polar $TiCl_3$ surface than in the other orientation. The overall extent of isotactic polymerization depends on the rate of polymer chain migration relative to the rate of monomer insertion into the chain. Isotactic polymerization occurs when the migration occurs at a faster rate than insertion. Whether this is the case or not depends on the particular monomer and catalyst system and the reaction temperature. Thus, for propylene with $(C_2H_5)_3Al$-α-$TiCl_3$ at the usual polymerization temperatures of 50–100°C, the overwhelming tendency is toward isotactic polymerization. The polymerization might be expected to show a syndiotactic tendency at low temperatures as the insertion step becomes more favored due to increased coordination between monomer and catalyst. In the propylene polymerization, a slight tendency toward syndiotacticity is noted—but only at very low temperatures of about −70°C [42]. At higher temperatures (that is, greater than 50–100°C), one would expect a tendency toward non-stereospecific (atactic) polymerization as coordination between monomer and catalyst is weakened.

The strong dependence of isotactic placement on the crystal structure of the catalyst is clearly seen by considering different crystalline forms of the same catalyst. Four different forms of $TiCl_3$ are known—the commonly used α-form described above and the β-, γ-, and δ-forms. (β-$TiCl_3$ is brown in color while the others are violet.) The α-, γ-, and δ-titanium trichlorides behave almost identically; catalysts derived from them yield isotactic polymerization [61]. This similarity is a consequence of the similar crystal structure of these $TiCl_3$ forms [61, 62]. γ-$TiCl_3$ contains a layer-type structure which is the same as that for α-$TiCl_3$ except that the chlorides are cubic close-packed instead of hexagonal close-packed. δ-$TiCl_3$ has a mixed hexagonal and cubic close-packed layered structure.

The behavior of β-$TiCl_3$ results from its different crystal structure. β-$TiCl_3$ consists of bundles of linear $TiCl_3$ chains. The chains can be represented [58] as

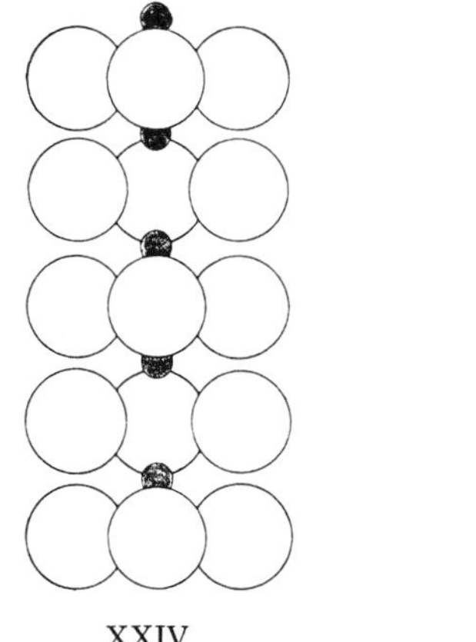

XXIV

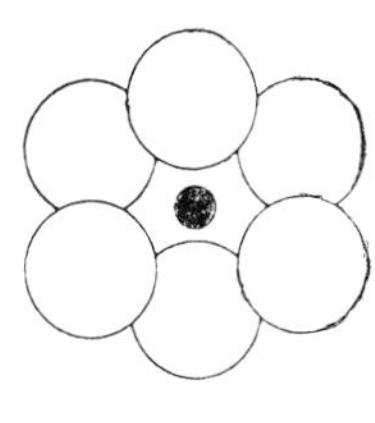

XXV

where XXIV and XXV are top and front views, respectively. This structure results in a surface in which half the titaniums have two vacancies and the other half have one vacancy. The titanium sites containing two vacancies each are responsible for the non-stereospecific properties of β-$TiCl_3$. The two vacancies yield a site with a loose configuration since one of the chlorides and/or the growing polymer chain will be loosely bound. This is exactly opposite to the situation with the other titanium trichlorides (one vacancy per active site) in which all chlorides and the polymer chain have fixed positions in a rigid configuration on the titanium site. That some isotactic polymer is formed with β-$TiCl_3$ is due, no doubt, to the titanium sites which have only one vacancy each.

8-4a-4-c Monomer-Monomer Interaction for Syndiotactic Polymerization. The synthesis of highly syndiotactic polymers by Ziegler-Natta catalysts has been successfully carried out only with propylene [20, 40]. Some syndiotactic fractions have also been obtained in various polymerizations of butadiene. Both homogeneous and heterogeneous catalysts have been used to obtain *syndiotactic* polypropylene. Only the soluble catalysts, however, yield highly *syndiotactic* polypropylene which is free of the isotactic polymer. The extent of syndiotacticity obtained in polymerizations with heterogeneous catalysts is small. Soluble Ziegler-Natta catalysts for producing *syndiotactic* polypropylene are almost entirely limited to those based on a vanadium compound as the transition metal. (A few soluble catalysts based on titanium compounds, e.g., biscyclopentadienyltitanium dichloride, have been used for the polymerization of ethylene and other monomers but these have not yielded syndiotactic polymer.)

The catalyst formed from VCl_4 and $(C_2H_5)_2AlCl$ in the presence of a third component (anisole) is one of the most efficient catalysts for producing *syndiotactic* polypropylene [63]. Other vanadium compounds such as vanadium acetylacetonate and various vanadates $(VO(OR)_xCl_{3-x}$ where $x = 1, 2, 3)$ can be used in place of VCl_4 but are more limited in their stereospecificity. The addition of anisole or other electron donors such as furan and diethyl ether to catalyst systems increases their syndiotactic specificity; the mechanism of this behavior is not clear. Syndiotacticity increases with decreasing temperature with most syndiotactic polymerizations being carried out below −40°C and usually at −78°C. The catalysts usually must also be prepared at the low temperatures since most of them become heterogeneous (and no longer produce syndiotactic polymer) when prepared at or warmed up to temperatures above about −40°C

The driving force for syndiotactic placement with Ziegler-Natta catalysts is the same as that (Sec. 8-3b-2) for low temperature radical and ionic, non-coordinated polymerizations—the repulsive interactions between substituents of the terminal and incoming monomer units. This is referred [40] to as the *monomer-monomer interaction model* for syndiotactic placement. Figure 8-15 shows this model for syndiotactic placement according to Boor and Youngman [20, 64]. The model is very similar to the Cossee model for isotactic placement (Fig. 8-13) except for a couple of important differences. The homogeneous catalyst allows coordination of the monomer (and insertion into the polymer chain) in either of the two possible configurations. The catalyst in a syndiotactic Ziegler-Natta polymerization accomplishes its stereospecificity in essentially the same manner as lowered reaction temperature would in a non-coordination polymerization. The environment around the vanadium center prevents rotation (Eq. 8-28) of the metal-growth bond (the bond between the metal and the growing polymer chain)

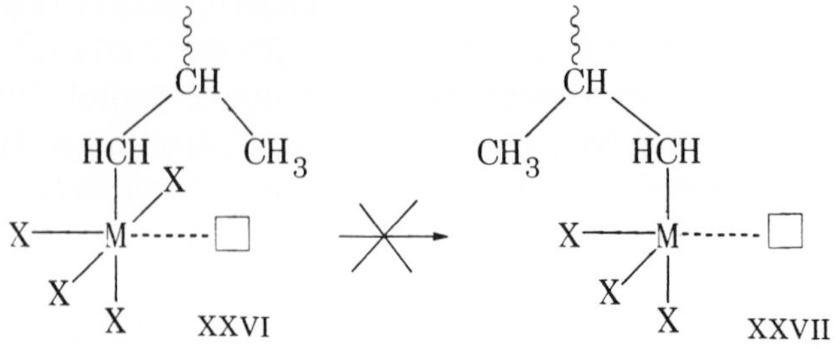

$$\underset{\text{XXVI}}{\text{(~CH(CH}_3\text{)–HCH–M(X)}_4\text{–}\square)} \;\not\longrightarrow\; \underset{\text{XXVII}}{\text{(~CH(CH}_3\text{)–HCH–M(X)}_3\text{–}\square)} \qquad (8\text{-}28)$$

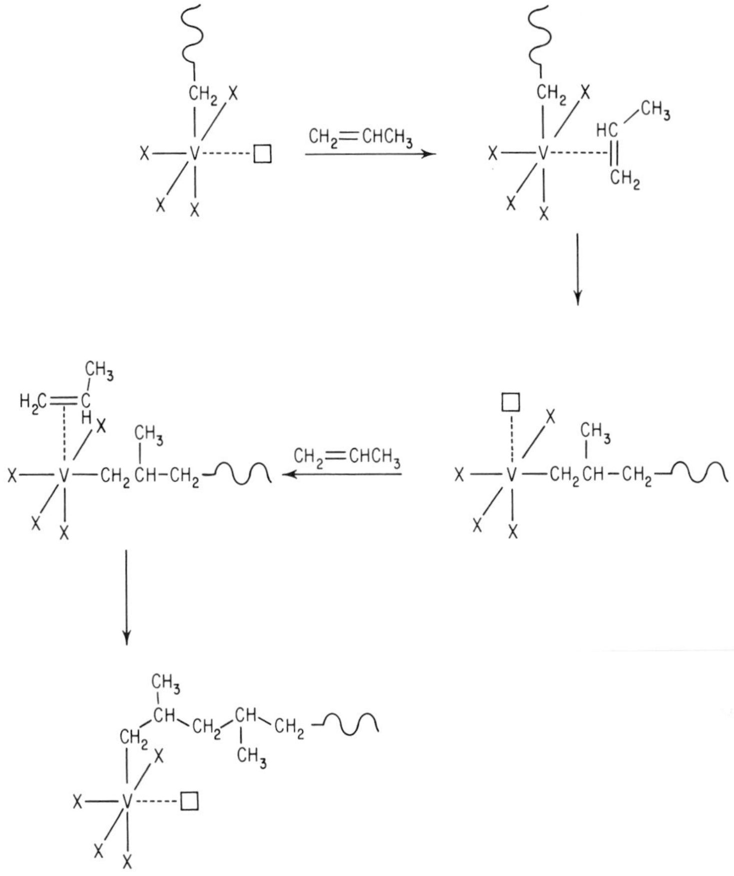

FIG. 8-15 *Monomer-monomer interaction model for syndiotactic placement. After [64] (by permission of Interscience Publishers, John Wiley & Sons, Inc., New York).*

and brings into play the interactions between incoming and terminal monomer units (in XXVI)—the result is syndiotactic placement. Monomer-monomer interactions are minimized with heterogeneous catalysts by rotation about the metal-growth bond. The chemical and crystal structure of the heterogeneous catalysts brings about isotactic placement by allowing only one configuration for the coordination and addition of monomer to XXVII. The isotactic and syndiotactic models also differ in that the former requires migration of the polymer chain to its original ligand position prior to the next propagation step. Syndiotactic propagation occurs at either of the ligand positions.

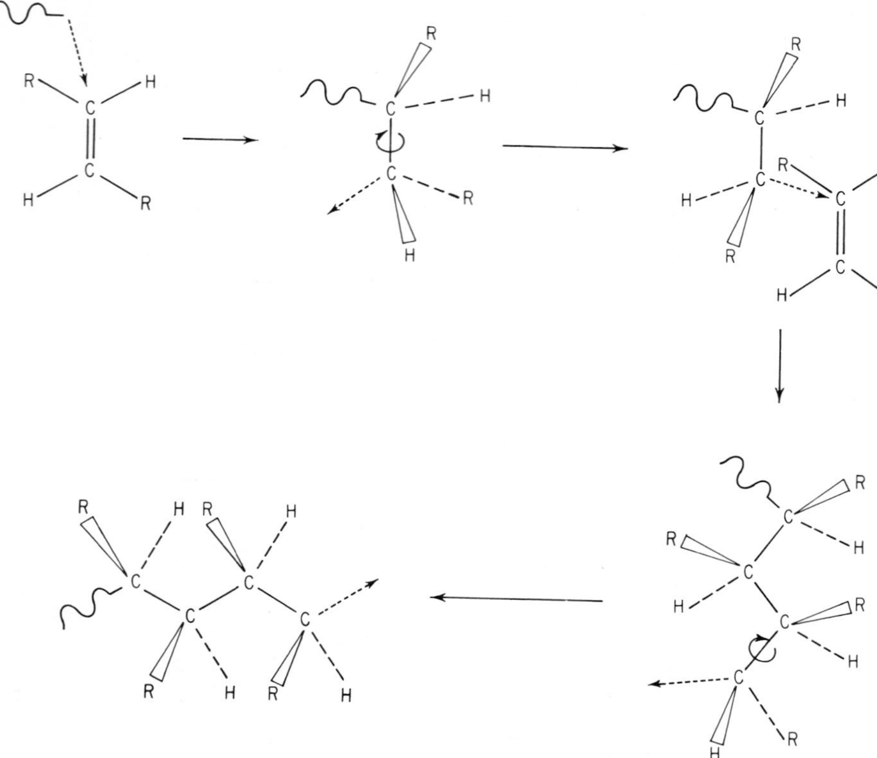

FIG. 8-16 *Cis-opening of a trans-1,2-disubstituted ethylene to yield the threo-di-isotactic polymer. After [11] (by permission of Interscience Publishers, John Wiley & Sons, Inc., New York).*

8-4a-5 Direction of Double Bond Opening. Although most addition reactions of the alkene double bond proceed with trans opening, a cis opening is usually implied in most Ziegler-Natta mechanisms. The direction of opening of the double bond has no effect on the stereochemical structure of the polymers from 1-monosubstituted ethylenes. However, the di-tacticity of polymers from 1,2-disubstituted ethylenes depends not only on the direction of double bond opening but also on whether the monomer is a cis or trans monomer. For di-isotactic polymerization, cis opening of a trans monomer would give the *threo*-di-isotactic structure. This is shown in Fig. 8-16 where it is proposed that the carbon-carbon bond in the monomer unit rotates after addition of the monomer to the polymer chain so as to avoid the 1,2-interactions in the fully eclipsed conformation [11]. In a corresponding manner, cis opening of the cis monomer would yield the *erythro*-di-isotactic polymer. Trans opening of the two monomers would give the opposite results. The cis opening of the double bond in isotactic polymerization has been confirmed by Natta [5] from studies with *cis*- and *trans*-1-deuteropropylenes. The cis and trans monomers gave *erythro* and *threo*-di-isotactic structures, respectively. More recently [65], it has been shown that syndiotactic polymerization also takes place with a cis opening. Copolymerizations of *cis*- and *trans*-1-deuteropropylenes with hexadeuteropropylene yield the trans and gauche syndiotactic structures XXVIII and XXIX, respectively

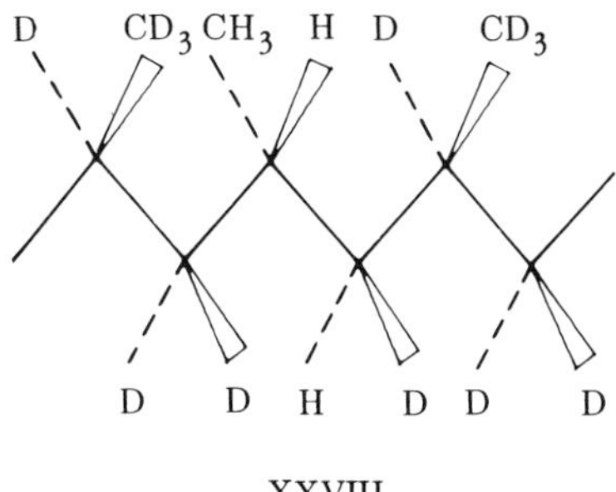

XXVIII

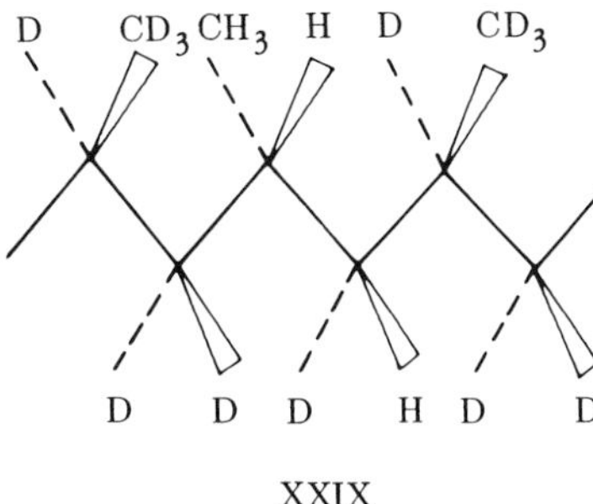

XXIX

8-4b Effect of Components of Ziegler-Natta Catalyst

The stereospecificity and activity of the Ziegler-Natta catalyst vary over a wide range depending on the identity of the catalyst components and their relative concentrations. Much of the available data are difficult to interpret mechanistically because the detailed identity of the active sites is not known. The situation is further complicated since changes in the catalyst components often affect catalyst activity and stereospecificity differently.

8-4b-1 Transition Metal Component. Valence states of +4, +3, and +2 have been proposed for the active site of titanium-based catalysts. Most of the evidence points to trivalent titanium as the active valence state. Catalysts based on titanium trihalides (except for β-$TiCl_3$) are much more (isotactic) stereospecific than those based on the tetrahalides or dihalides. $TiCl_2$ by itself is inactive as a catalyst but is activated by ball-milling due to disproportionation to $TiCl_3$ and Ti [47]. The valence state of the transition metal is dependent not only on the transition metal component but also on its relative amount compared to the Group I-III metal component. Analysis of the $TiCl_4$-$(C_2H_5)_3Al$ system shows that the catalyst activity varies directly with the concentration of the trivalent species which in turn depends on the aluminum-to-titanium ratio [66]. The aluminum alkyl reduces tetravalent titanium to the trivalent state and then to the divalent state depending on the aluminum-to-titanium ratio. For Al/Ti below approximately 3, there is very little reduction to divalent titanium over the temperature range −70 to +70°C; at higher Al/Ti ratios the reduction to divalent titanium is extensive and catalyst activity decreases [66]. Data [67] for the VCl_4-R_2AlCl system indicate that the trivalent valence state is also the active site for polymerization with vanadium catalysts. The situation for transition metals other than Ti and V may be different.

Changes in the ligands or transition metal of the transition metal component can greatly affect the stereospecificity and activity of the catalyst. For the polymerization of propylene at 75°C with various titanium compounds in combination with $(C_2H_5)_3Al$, the extent of isotacticity increases [58, 68] in the orders

$$\alpha\text{-}TiCl_3 > TiBr_3 > TiI_3$$

$$TiCl_4 \simeq TiBr_4 \simeq TiI_4 \tag{8-29}$$

$$TiCl_4 > TiCl_2(OC_4H_9)_2 \gg Ti(OC_4H_9)_4 \simeq Ti(OH)_4$$

Changes in the transition metal itself lead to the following differences in stereoregularity

$$\begin{aligned} &TiCl_4 \simeq VCl_4 \simeq ZrCl_4 \simeq MoCl_4 \\ &\alpha\text{-}TiCl_3 > VCl_3 > ZrCl_3 > CrCl_3 \end{aligned} \tag{8-30}$$

The order for different titanium chlorides in the same polymerization is

$$\alpha\text{-}, \gamma\text{- or } \delta\text{-}TiCl_3 > TiCl_2 > TiCl_4 \simeq \beta\text{-}TiCl_3 \tag{8-31}$$

Differences in catalyst activity and stereospecificity are observed only with the more stereospecific or active transition metal components. Thus, catalysts based on tetravalent transition metals are not appreciably affected by structural changes. The crystal structure, steric size, and electronegativity of the ligands and transition metal are all involved in determining catalyst stereospecificity and activity. Decreasing the electronegativity of the transition metal (leading to a more easily polarized metal-growth bond), by changes in the transition metal, or its valence state, or its ligands, increases the stereospecificity of the Ziegler-Natta catalyst. Increasing the size of the ligands decreases stereospecificity due probably to a decreased coordinating ability. The quantitative interrelationship of these and other factors with the crystal structure of the transition metal and the active sites in determining stereospecificity and activity is not clear at present.

8-4b-2 Group I-III Metal Component. Although the Group I-III metal component is not an absolute necessity for obtaining a Ziegler-Natta catalyst, its presence has a very significant effect on both catalyst activity and stereospecificity [40, 69]. In order to obtain high isotacticity and high rates in a polymerization, one almost always requires the use of the Group I-III metal component in combination with the transition metal component. The effect of changes in the Group I-III metal component varies somewhat depending on the particular transition metal component but some generalizations can be made. Table 8-5 shows the effect of changing the Group I-III metal on stereospecificity when $TiCl_3$ is the transition metal component [61, 69, 70]. Stereospecificity increases in the general order

$$Be > Al > Mg > Li \simeq Na \simeq Zn \tag{8-32}$$

Table 8-5 Effect of Group I-III Metal Component on Stereoregularity of Polypropylene[a]

Group I-III metal component	% Isotacticity in polymer[b]	Ref.
$(C_2H_5)_2Be$	93-95	[61]
$(C_2H_5)_3Al$	80-85	[61]
$(C_2H_5)_2Mg$	78-85	[70]
$(C_2H_5)_2Zn$	62	[69]
C_4H_9Li	58	[69]
$C_5H_{11}Na$	56	[69]

[a]Transition metal component = $TiCl_3$; polymerization temperature = 70°C.
[b]The percent of polymer insoluble in refluxing solvent. Butyl ether used for $(C_2H_5)_2Zn$; heptane for all others.

Catalysts based on Pb, Sn, Ge, Sb, Hg, and Cd show no activity.

For metal components in which the Group I-III metal is constant, the catalyst stereospecificity decreases as the size of organic groups increases, for example

$$(C_2H_5)_3Al > \phi_3Al > (i\text{-}C_4H_9)_3Al \tag{8-33}$$

The replacement of one of the organic groups by a halogen other than fluorine results in increased stereospecificity with the order

$$(C_2H_5)_2AlI > (C_2H_5)_2AlBr > (C_2H_5)_2AlCl > (C_2H_5)_3Al > (C_2H_5)_2AlF \tag{8-34}$$

The replacement of a second alkyl group by halogen leads to decreased stereospecificity.

The interpretation of these findings is difficult for the reasons described in the previous section. Attempts to interpret the effect of the Group I-III metal component on stereospecificity in terms of the monometallic polymerization mechanism is especially difficult. The order of stereospecificity for the different components does not follow the exact order expected for reduction or alkylation of the transition metal component. Many of the findings can be more easily explained using the bimetallic mechanism of Ziegler-Natta polymerization [69]. One would expect the strength of the bimetallic catalyst–species XXI–to be maximum when the Group I-III metal is similar to the transition metal in size and electronegativity as in the case of Be and Al. Increasing the size of the bridging alkyl group decreases the strength of the catalyst. A single halogen in the aluminum alkyl apparently alters the electronegativity of the aluminum to more closely match that of titanium; a second halogen makes the aluminum too electropositive. These interpretations leave much to be desired since the crystal structure of the catalyst is not considered.

8-4b-3 Third Component. A large variety of different compounds have been added as third components to Ziegler-Natta catalysts [40, 58, 69]. These include O_2, H_2, alcohols, H_2O, amines, inorganic halides (KCl, NaF), organic halides, CS_2, COS, phenols, ethers, phosphenes, aromatics (anisole, azulene), and hexamethylphosphoramide. (Some of these compounds may be present as unintentionally added trace impurities). The effect of these additives on catalyst activity and stereospecificity varies considerably depending on the additive and the other two components of the catalyst. Some additives increase catalyst activity and/or stereospecificity while others have the opposite effect. Some increase stereospecificity while decreasing catalyst activity. Still others may affect polymer molecular weight either exclusively or along with changes in catalyst activity and/or stereospecificity.

These third components manifest their effects by a variety of mechanisms which are usually poorly understood. Some of the third components react with either one or the other or both of the two metal components, for example

$$TiCl_3 + H_2O \longrightarrow Ti(OH)Cl_2 + HCl \tag{8-35}$$

$$AlR_3 + ROH \longrightarrow R_2AlOR + RH \tag{8-36}$$

to convert them into species with different catalyst activity and/or stereospecificity. The increased stereospecificity of α-$TiCl_3$-$Al(C_2H_5)Cl_2$ for propylene polymerization on addition of hexamethylphosphoramide (HMPA) has been attributed [71] to the dismutation of the inactive $Al(C_2H_5)Cl_2$ to the active $Al(C_2H_5)_2Cl$

$$2\ Al(C_2H_5)Cl_2 + HMPA \longrightarrow Al(C_2H_5)_2Cl + AlCl_3{\cdot}HMPA \quad (8\text{-}37)$$

However, this explanation is not entirely satisfactory since the α-$TiCl_3$-$Al(C_2H_5)Cl_2$-HMPA system is more stereospecific than α-$TiCl_3$-$Al(C_2H_5)_2Cl$ [72].

Most of the third components, including hexamethylphosphoramide, are electron-donors. Many explanations for the effects of third components on catalyst activity and stereospecificity have involved their coordination with either or both metal components. Why this results in enhanced catalyst activity and/or stereospecificity in some cases and the opposite behavior in other cases is unknown.

8-4c Kinetics

The kinetics of Ziegler-Natta polymerization, like all other aspects of the reaction, are extremely complicated. Homogeneous Ziegler-Natta polymerizations are almost always easier to treat than the heterogeneous polymerizations. The homogeneous reactions can be handled in a manner similar to that employed for non-coordination ionic polymerizations (Chap. 5) taking into account the termination reaction or reactions which are applicable. Although homogeneous kinetics have been successfully used for a few heterogeneous Ziegler-Natta polymerizations, this usually is not the case. The application of heterogeneous kinetics [73] is necessary in order to properly treat the heterogeneous polymerizations. The general features of this treatment [9, 58, 74, 75] will be briefly considered.

8-4c-1 Reaction Scheme. The polymerization can be considered as involving the adsorption from solution of the monomer M and Group I-III metal compound MeR on the surface of the transition metal compound (denoted by the heavy vertical line)

$$\Big| + MeR \underset{}{\overset{K_1}{\rightleftharpoons}} \Big|\!\!-MeR \quad (8\text{-}38)$$

$$\Big| + M \underset{}{\overset{K_2}{\rightleftharpoons}} \Big|\!\!-M \quad (8\text{-}39)$$

followed by initiation via reaction between the adsorbed species

$$\left[\begin{matrix}\text{—MeR} \\ \\ \text{—M}\end{matrix}\right. \xrightarrow{k_i} \left[\begin{matrix}\text{—Me—M—R} \\ \\ \\ \end{matrix}\right. \tag{8-40}$$

and propagation in a like manner

$$\left[\begin{matrix}\text{—Me—M}_n\text{—R} \\ \\ \text{—M}\end{matrix}\right. \xrightarrow{k_p} \left[\begin{matrix}\text{—Me—M}_{(n+1)}\text{—R} \\ \\ \\ \end{matrix}\right. \tag{8-41}$$

Termination can occur by chain transfer with monomer

$$\left[\begin{matrix}\text{—Me—M}_n\text{—R} \\ \\ \text{—M}\end{matrix}\right. \xrightarrow{k_{tr,\,\mathrm{M}}} \left[\begin{matrix}\text{—Me—M—R} \\ \\ \\ \end{matrix}\right. + \mathrm{P} \tag{8-42}$$

or by spontaneous internal hydride transfer

$$\left[\text{—Me—M}_n\text{—R}\right. \xrightarrow{k_s} \left[\text{—MeH}\right. + \mathrm{P} \tag{8-43}$$

or by transfer to Me—R

$$\left[\begin{matrix}\text{—Me—M}_n\text{—R} \\ \\ \text{—Me—R}\end{matrix}\right. \xrightarrow{k_{tr,\,\mathrm{C}}} \left[\begin{matrix}\text{—Me—R} \\ \\ \\ \end{matrix}\right. + \mathrm{P} \tag{8-44}$$

or by reaction with monomer to form an inactive site

$$\left[\begin{matrix}\text{—Me—M}_n\text{—R} \\ \\ \text{—M}\end{matrix}\right. \xrightarrow{k_{t\mathrm{M}}} \left[\begin{matrix}\text{—Me} \\ | \\ \text{—M}\end{matrix}\right. + \mathrm{P} \tag{8-45}$$

Other termination reactions may also be possible, e.g., transfer with the transition metal component of the catalyst or with compounds containing active hydrogens (H_2, H_2O, ROH, etc.).

8-4c-2 Rate Expressions. The derivation of a rate expression based on the above polymerization sequence (Eqs. 8-38 to 8-44) follows the Langmuir-Hinschelwood mechanism [73] in which reaction occurs between two adsorbed species (Me—R and M) which compete for the same active sites on the solid catalyst surface. In this treatment, it is assumed that the adsorptions (Eqs. 8-38 and 8-39) attain equilibrium rapidly and maintain it throughout the reaction. The fractions θ_A and θ_M of the catalyst surface covered by MeR and M, respectively, are given by the Langmuir isotherms

$$\theta_A = \frac{K_1[\text{MeR}]}{1 + K_1[\text{MeR}] + K_2[\text{M}]} \tag{8-46}$$

$$\theta_M = \frac{K_2[\text{M}]}{1 + K_1[\text{MeR}] + K_2[\text{M}]} \tag{8-47}$$

The rate of monomer disappearance per unit of active sites, neglecting the initiation step, is given by

$$\frac{-d[\text{M}]}{dt} = (k_p + k_{tr,\text{M}})\theta_M[\text{C}^*] \tag{8-48}$$

where [C*] is the concentration of growing polymer chains. Assuming a steady-state in [C*], one can equate the rate of the initiation with the sum of the rates of all the termination reactions to yield

$$k_i\theta_A\theta_M = k_s[\text{C}^*] + k_{tr,\text{C}}[\text{C}^*]\theta_A + k_{t\text{M}}[\text{C}^*]\theta_M \tag{8-49}$$

Combination of Eqs. 8-46 to 8-49 yields the rate of polymerization as

$$\frac{-d[\text{M}]}{dt} = \frac{(k_p + k_{tr,\text{M}})k_i[\text{MeR}]K_1K_2^2[\text{M}]^2}{(1 + K_2[\text{M}] + K_1[\text{MeR}])^3\left\{k_s + \dfrac{(k_{tr,\text{C}}K_1[\text{MeR}] + k_{t\text{M}}K_2[\text{M}])}{(1 + K_2[\text{M}] + K_1[\text{MeR}])}\right\}} \tag{8-50}$$

A corresponding expression for the degree of polymerization is obtained in the usual manner as the propagation rate divided by the sum of the rates of all termination reactions. Equation 8-50 takes a number of simpler forms for specific polymerization systems when one or more of the steps in the reaction scheme is negligible. Since MeR is more polar than the monomer, one can encounter the case where the adsorption of the latter is very weak ($K_1 \gg K_2$) and the terms in K_2 in Eq. 8-50 can be neglected. In many systems, one of the modes of termination predominates and terms for the other modes can be neglected.

8-4c-3 Observed Kinetic Behavior. The observed kinetics of Ziegler-Natta polymerizations often exhibit complicated behavior such as those shown in Fig. 8-17. The behavior described by curve 1 is usually obtained when the particle size of the transition metal component is relatively large. The catalyst particles are thought to consist of aggregates of smaller crystals. The mechanical pressure of the growing polymer chains cleaves the larger particles with the result that the surface area, number of active sites, and polymerization rate increase with time [76]. A steady-state value of R_p is reached which corresponds to cleavage to the smallest size crystals. When the initial catalyst particles are smaller (obtained by grinding), the time required to reach the steady-state is decreased (curve 2).

Some polymerizations show a rapid rise in R_p followed by a rapid decrease to the steady-state polymerization rate (curve 3). The latter behavior indicates that different types of polymerization centers exist in the Ziegler-Natta catalyst. Certain less active sites on the solid catalyst surface may become deactivated during the initial

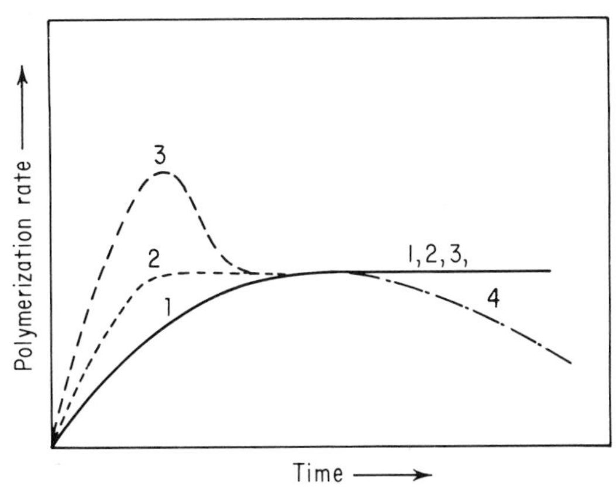

FIG. 8-17 *Typical types of kinetic behavior in Ziegler-Natta polymerizations.*

period [76]. The high initial rate may also be due to soluble, non-stereospecific species formed initially by reactions between the catalyst components. These decay with time (aging) to yield the rate corresponding to the steady-state rate for the heterogeneous polymerization sites [77]. Some polymerization systems may show a continuous rate decrease throughout the course of the reaction after the initial period (curve 4) due to catalyst destruction if the polymerization temperature is too high. This behavior may also be due to diffusion-control of the propagation step. Diffusion of the monomer through the formed polymer to the polymerization site may become the rate-determining step. This has been substantiated in some systems where the polymerization rate has been observed to increase with increased rates of stirring of the reaction mixture [78].

8-4c-4 Values of Kinetic Parameters. Table 8-6 shows the values of various kinetic parameters in a typical Ziegler-Natta polymerization [79]. The number of propagating centers is a small fraction (approximately 0.1–1 percent) of the total number of transition metal atoms present. The various rate constants have values which are generally similar to those in non-coordination ionic polymerizations (Tables 5-1 and 5-7). For the polymerization in Table 8-6, the most important mode of termination is by transfer with hydrogen (k_{tr,H_2}). Ziegler-Natta polymerizations bear a striking resemblance to anionic living polymerizations in terms of the lifetime of growing chains, which usually range from minutes up to hours. (The lifetimes of propagating chains in polymerizations with soluble catalysts are usually much shorter than those with heterogeneous catalysts. The lifetimes for the former rarely exceed 5–10 minutes.) The lifetime of the active sites is even longer—on the order of days in many instances.

Table 8-6 Kinetic Parameters in Polymerization of Ethylene by $(C_2H_5)_2AlCl$-γ-$TiCl_3$ at 40°C

[C*]	~10^{-2} mole/mole $TiCl_3$
k_p	~80 liter/mole-sec.
k_s	~3×10^{-4} sec.$^{-1}$
$k_{tr,M}$	~1×10^{-2} liter/mole-sec.
k_{tr,H_2}	~3 liter/mole-sec.

[a]Data from [79].

The molecular weight distributions obtained with heterogeneous Ziegler-Natta catalysts are quite broad. $\overline{M}_w/\overline{M}_n$ is usually in the range 5–20 for ethylene [79] and 5–15 for propylene [80]. The broad distribution may be due to a number of reasons—active sites with differing activities, long period before steady-state is attained, or diffusion-control in the later stages of polymerization. The size distribution is much narrower for homogeneous Ziegler-Natta polymerizations.

The activation energies for the rates of most Ziegler-Natta polymerizations fall in the range of 3–15 kcal/mole. The activation energy for a Ziegler-Natta polymerization is a composite of activation energies for the initiation, propagation and termination reactions, and the heats of the adsorption steps. Although the polymerization rates increase with temperature, reaction temperatures above 70–100°C usually cannot be employed. Higher temperatures result in loss of stereospecificity as well as lowered polymerization rates due to catalyst destruction.

8-4d Scope of the Ziegler-Natta Catalyst

The Ziegler-Natta catalyst polymerizes a variety of monomers [40] including ethylene, α-olefins such as propylene, 1-butene, 4-methyl-1-pentene and vinylcyclohexane, and styrene. 1,1-Disubstituted ethylenes such as isobutylene are polymerized but the reaction proceeds by a non-coordination ionic mechanism. Except for the 1-deuteropropylenes (Sec. 8-4a-5), 1,2-disubstituted ethylenes have not been polymerized due to steric hindrance. Polymers are obtained from some 1,2-disubstituted ethylenes but the reactions have involved isomerization of the monomer to a 1-substituted ethylene followed by polymerization, e.g., 2-butene yields poly(1-butene). The polymerization of dienes by Ziegler-Natta catalysts is discussed in Sec. 8-6. Some acetylenic monomers have also been polymerized by Ziegler-Natta catalysts.

Many polar monomers such as vinyl acetate, vinyl chloride, acrylates, and methacrylates have been polymerized by Ziegler-Natta catalysts but not by the anionic coordination mechanism. The reactions proceed by non-coordinated radical or ionic mechanisms. Many polar monomers, especially those containing electron-donor atoms such as nitrogen and oxygen, cannot be polymerized by Ziegler-Natta catalysts. These monomers inactivate the catalysts either by strongly complexing or irreversibly reacting with one or more of the catalyst components [81]. The stereoregular polymerization of some polar monomers by Ziegler-Natta catalysts has been successfully accomplished in a few instances. For those monomers which inactivate the catalyst by coordination, stereospecific polymerization can sometimes be achieved by using a solvent (e.g., dimethylformamide or tetrahydrofuran) which complexes with the catalyst but which can be displaced by the monomer. In other instances, one can use a less active form of the catalyst. Polar monomers can be polymerized by Ziegler-Natta catalysts if the polar atom or group is shielded by sterically bulky substituents. Thus, monomers with hydroxyl or amino groups can be polymerized by converting the groups to $-NR_2$ and $-O-SiR_2$, respectively [81].

8-4d-1 Cycloalkenes. Cycloalkenes undergo Ziegler-Natta polymerization, although they are 1,2-disubstituted ethylenes, due to the presence of ring-strain [40, 82]. Two modes of polymerization are possible—polymerization through the double bond or via a ring-opening reaction, e.g., for cyclobutene

$$\begin{array}{c} CH{=}CH \\ | \quad\;\; | \\ CH_2{-}CH_2 \end{array} \nearrow \left[\begin{array}{c} CH{-}CH \\ | \quad\;\; | \\ CH_2{-}CH_2 \end{array} \right]_n \quad \text{XXX} \tag{8-51}$$

$$\searrow \; \text{-(}CH_2{-}CH{=}CH{-}CH_2\text{)-}_n \quad \text{XXXI} \tag{8-52}$$

Each of the two modes of polymerization can yield two different stereoisomers. Structure XXX can exist as either the *erythro*-di-isotactic or *erythro*-di-syndiotactic isomer (Sec. 8-1b-2). Structure XXX has been named [14] as polycyclobutylenamer-2 although the name polycyclobutene is more often employed. Ring-opening polymerization of cyclobutene yields the same polymer as is obtained by the 1,4-polymerization of 1,3-butadiene; this can exist as either the cis or trans isomer. Each of the possible isomeric polymers has been observed in the polymerization of cyclobutene. Chromium, vanadium, and some rhodium catalysts yield polymerization exclusively through the double bond [18, 82-84]. Chromium-based catalysts yield the *erythro*-di-isotactic structure while *erythro*-di-syndiotactic polycyclobutylenamer-2 has been produced using a rhodium catalyst in an emulsion system [85]. The use of catalysts based on tungsten, titanium, and molybdenum result in polymerization predominantly via ring-opening with varying amounts of the cis and trans isomers. Polymerization with ruthenium catalysts proceeds exclusively by ring-opening.

The polymerizations of other cycloalkenes proceed in a similar manner although other modes of reaction can complicate the situation. Thus, the ring-opening polymerization of 3-methyl-1-cyclobutene proceeds by cleavage of the bond between carbons 1 and 4

$$\begin{array}{c} CH{=}CH \\ | \quad\;\; | \\ CH{-}CH_2 \\ | \\ CH_3 \end{array} \begin{array}{l} \nearrow \left[\begin{array}{l} CH{-}CH{=}CH{-}CH_2 \\ | \\ CH_3 \end{array} \right]_n \\ \\ \not\searrow \left[\begin{array}{c} CH_2{-}\underset{\displaystyle CH_3}{\underset{|}{C}}{=}CH{-}CH_2 \end{array} \right]_n \end{array} \qquad (8\text{-}53)$$

without any polyisoprene units being produced. The polymerization of monomers with two double bonds often takes place with simultaneous transannular migration depending on the particular catalyst system used, e.g., for 1,5-cyclooctadiene

$$\text{(1,5-cyclooctadiene)} \longrightarrow \left[\text{(fused bicyclo[3.3.0]octane unit)} \right]_n \qquad (8\text{-}54)$$

8-4d-2 Copolymerization. Several interesting types of behavior are observed when copolymerizations are carried out with Ziegler-Natta catalysts [40, 86, 87]. Random copolymerization occurs when one copolymerizes monomers which are capable of undergoing homopolymerization with Ziegler-Natta catalysts. The reactivities of monomers in copolymerization parallels their homopolymerization behavior–ethylene > propylene > 1-butene. As one might expect, the monomer reactivity ratios are often sensitive to the composition of the catalyst system used–more specifically, r_1 and r_2 are altered by changes in the transition metal component (Table 8-7). The nature of the Group I-III metal component usually does not affect the monomer reactivity ratios. The different effects of the two metal components corroborates the discussion in Sec. 8-4a on the greater importance of the transition metal component. The relative amounts of the two catalyst components can sometimes affect r_1 and r_2 depending on the solvent and other reaction conditions. The products from Ziegler-Natta copolymerizations vary considerably depending on the physical state of the catalyst. Atactic, amorphous copolymers are obtained when soluble catalysts are used. Amorphous ethylene-propylene copolymers have interesting elastomeric properties from the commercial viewpoint. The ability to undergo crosslinking (Sec. 9-2) is imparted to these rubbers by terpolymerizing [92] ethylene and propylene with small amounts of dienes such as dicyclopentadiene (XXXII).

Table 8-7 Monomer Reactivity Ratios in Ziegler-Natta Copolymerizations

M_1	M_2	Catalyst system[a]	r_1	r_2	Ref.
Ethylene	Propylene	$TiCl_3$-$Al(C_6H_{13})_3$	15.7	0.110	[88]
		$TiCl_4$-$Al(C_6H_{13})_3$	33.4	0.032	[88]
		VCl_3-$Al(C_6H_{13})_3$	5.61	0.145	[89]
Ethylene	1-Butene	VCl_4-$Al(C_6H_{13})_3$	29.6	0.019	[90]
		VCl_3-$Al(C_6H_{13})_3$	67.0	0.043	[90]
Propylene	1-Butene	VCl_4-$Al(C_6H_{13})_3$	4.39	0.227	[91]
		VCl_3-$Al(C_6H_{13})_3$	4.04	0.252	[91]

[a]The VCl_3 and $TiCl_3$ systems are heterogeneous; the others are colloidally dispersed.

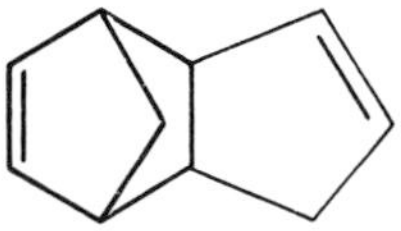

XXXII

When heterogeneous catalysts are employed, the tendency is to produce nonrandom polymers containing relatively long sequences of one or the other of the monomers due to the greater selectivity of the heterogeneous polymerization sites.

Although 1,2-disubstituted ethylenes do not undergo homopolymerization, *cis*- and *trans*-2-butenes have been copolymerized with ethylene using Ziegler-Natta catalysts [18]. The steric hindrance which prevents homopropagation of 2-butene is overcome when 2-butene monomer is added to a propagating chain which has ethylene as the terminal unit. Thus, the ethylene-2-butene system undergoes copolymerization because of a tendency toward alternation. (The alternation tendency in this case is due to decreased steric hindrance whereas in radical copolymerizations it is due to polar effects.) However, the much lower reactivity of 2-butene relative to ethylene requires special care in order to obtain copolymers with appreciable amounts of 2-butene content. The use of feeds with high 2-butene-to-ethylene ratios and soluble or colloidally-dispersed (low selectivity) catalysts allows the formation of close to a 1:1 alternating copolymer. One such copolymerization yielded a polymer fraction (by solvent extraction) which showed crystallinity. This was attributed by Natta and coworkers [93] to a structure of the *erythro*-di-isotactic type.

Block copolymers in which there are long blocks of the two monomers have been produced by adding the two monomers sequentially [94, 95]. Heterogeneous catalysts must be employed since the lifetimes of propagating chains in homogeneous polymerizations are too short (Sec. 8-4c-4) to allow the sequential addition. These block copolymers have been obtained with different degrees of isotacticity and crystallinity. The crystalline copolymers have been found to have commercial utility.

8-4e Supported Metal Oxide Catalysts

The polymerization of ethylene and several other alkenes has also been carried out using supported metal oxide catalysts [58, 96–98]. These catalysts consist of a transition metal oxide (for example,

CrO_3, MoO_3, V_2O_5 and NiO_3) physically dispersed and supported on another material referred to as the *support*. Charcoal, Al_2O_3, SiO_2, and clay are commonly used supports. The support allows the use of a catalyst with small particle size (and, therefore, large surface area) by increasing its ease of handling. The supported metal oxide is activated (i.e., converted into a catalyst for polymerization) by reduction with hydrogen at high temperatures or treatment with reducing agents such as $LiBH_4$ or NaH. The reducing agent is often referred to as a *promoter* or *activator*. The formation of the active catalyst may also involve reaction of the support material with the catalyst.

The polymerization of ethylene by supported metal oxide catalysts is of commercial significance since the product is linear polyethylene—similar to the polyethylene produced by using Ziegler-Natta catalysts. This similarity between the effects of the two types of catalysts is, no doubt, a consequence of the close relationship between their active polymerization sites and polymerization mechanisms. The activation of the supported metal oxide by reduction bears a striking resemblance to the alkylation (reduction) of the transition metal component of a Ziegler-Natta catalyst. In fact, except for the support material, most of the combinations of catalysts and reducing agents used in supported metal oxide catalysts fit the definition of a Ziegler-Natta catalyst. The supported metal oxide catalysts differ from the Ziegler-Natta catalysts in having lower activities. High polymerization temperatures (approximately 100–200°C) are used with supported metal oxide catalysts. Many monomers (e.g., styrene) which can be polymerized by Ziegler-Natta catalysts are inactive toward the supported metal oxide catalysts. The metal oxide catalysts are also very poor in their stereoregulating ability. Polypropylene can be obtained in partly crystalline form but most other α-olefins are polymerized to amorphous or only slightly crystalline polymers.

8-5 STEREOSPECIFIC POLYMERIZATION OF POLAR ALKENES

Polar monomers such as methacrylates and vinyl ethers undergo stereospecific polymerization when there is an appropriate balance between the monomer, catalyst, solvent, and temperature. Under conditions where the propagating species is free (uncoordinated), syndiotacticity is increasingly favored with decreasing polymerization temperature (Sec. 8-3). This is the case for all radical polymerizations and for those ionic polymerizations which take place in highly solvating media. Isotacticity can occur during ionic polymerizations in poorly solvating media where the propagating species is coordinated to the gegen-ion. Since polar monomers have greater coordinating powers compared to non-polar alkenes, the degree of coordination necessary for isotactic placement can be obtained with homogeneous catalysts. Heterogeneous catalysts can also be used but they are not required for isotactic polymerization as in the case of the non-polar alkenes. Many of the polymerization conditions described previously in Chap. 5 can result in isotactic polymerization. The stereospecific polymerization of some of the more common monomers will be briefly discussed with the main emphasis being on the synthesis of isotactic structures.

8-5a Methyl Methacrylate

The stereospecific polymerization of various acrylates and methacrylates has been studied. Tables 8-8 and 8-9 illustrate the effects of various reaction parameters on the stereochemical course of the anionic polymerization of methyl methacrylate [99, 100]. (Data on the corresponding radical polymerization is included in Table 8-9 for comparison purposes.) The trends shown by these data are typical of those observed in other polymerizations (including the Ziegler-Natta polymerizations of non-polar alkenes). In polar solvents, the gegen-ion is removed from the vicinity of the propagating center and cannot exert a stereochemical influence on the entry of the next monomer unit. Atacticity increases with increasing temperature while decreased temperature favors syndiotacticity.

When non-polar solvents are employed, the reaction can take place as an anionic coordination polymerization. The gegen-ion directs the isotactic placement of each entering monomer unit into the polymer chain. The extent of isotactic placement is dependent on the coordinating ability of the gegen-ion. For the various alkali metals, the order is Li > Na > K which corresponds to the order expected from the discussion in Sec. 5-3b-4. The smaller lithium ion has the greatest coordinating and stereoregulating power. At the other extreme, the large gegen-ion derived from $(C_2H_5)_2AlN\phi_2$ yields very little tendency toward isotactic placement even in a non-polar

Table 8-8 Effect of Solvent and Gegen-Ion on Tacticity of Poly(methyl methacrylate) at 0°C[a]

Solvent	% Isotactic (diad) fraction for initiation with		
	n-C_4H_9Li	n-$C_5H_{11}Na$	n-$C_8H_{17}K$
Toluene	81	72	56
Dimethylformamide	30	21	37
Pyridine	24	35	40

[a]Data from [99].

solvent. The size of the gegen-ion cannot, however, be considered independently of its identity. Thus, the polymerization of methyl methacrylate by $LiAlH_4$ at room temperature in diethyl ether yields 91 percent isotactic placement [101] due to the strong coordinating ability of lithium.

The initiator fragment from the catalyst also affects the extent of isotacticity in some polymerizations. Thus, lithium phenoxide is less

Table 8-9 Effect of Solvent, Gegen-Ion, and Temperature on Tacticity of Poly(methyl methacrylate)[a]

Polymerization system	Diad tacticity		Triad tacticity		
	i	s	I	H	S
Radical, bulk polymerization at 60°C	0.24	0.76	0.08	0.33	0.59
n-C_4H_9Li at −78°C					
% Tetrahydrofuran in toluene:					
0	0.85	0.15	0.78	0.16	0.06
2.5	0.46	0.54	0.30	0.31	0.39
5	0.41	0.59	0.24	0.34	0.42
10	0.30	0.70	0.13	0.35	0.52
$(C_2H_5)_2AlN\phi_2$ in ϕCH_3					
Temperature (°C):					
−78	0.09	0.91	0.01	0.14	0.85
−40	0.13	0.87	0.03	0.20	0.77
0	0.15	0.85	0.03	0.23	0.74

[a]Data from [100].

stereospecific than the corresponding thiophenoxide for the polymerization of methyl methacrylate [102]. The difference between the two catalysts is somewhat surprising since the propagating center is the same irrespective of the initiator. The effect is probably due to coordination of unreacted initiator with the propagating chain end and its gegen-ion. The thiophenoxide has a greater coordinating ability than the phenoxide and gives rise to a more rigid and stereoregulating chain end. The effect of temperature on isotacticity varies considerably from one polymerization system to another. Increased temperature tends to lead to decreased stereospecificity in general. However, for the highly stereoregulating catalysts, the effect of temperature is often negligible over a considerable range (up to about 50°C).

Several detailed mechanisms have been suggested to explain the isotactic placement in methyl methacrylate polymerization [6, 103]. These generally involve rigidization of the propagating chain end by coordination of the gegen-ion with both the terminal and penultimate monomer units to yield a structure such as

```
             CH3         CH3  OCH3
             |           |    |
  ~~~CH2—C—CH2—C̄——C            ←——→
             |           :    ||
     CH3O—C              :    O
              ⸌O·····G
                     +
```

XXXIIIa

```
             CH3         CH3  OCH3
             |           |    |
  ~~~CH2—C—CH2—C═══C
             |                |
     CH3O—C                   O
              ⸌O·····G·······  ̄
                     +
```

XXXIIIb

The rigid polymer chain end (XXXIII) superimposes stereospecificity on the propagation reaction in a manner analogous to that present for a Ziegler-Natta propagating species. A monomer molecule coordinates with the rigid structure XXXIII via the gegen-ion and is then stereospecifically added by insertion at the metal-carbon bond.

8-5b Vinyl Ethers

The isotactic polymerization of a vinyl ether requires a *cationic coordination* mechanism. The cationic coordination reaction is similar to that of the anionic coordination reaction except that the propagating center is a carbonium ion instead of a carbanion and the gegen-ion is an anion instead of a cation. Various catalysts, of both the homogeneous and heterogeneous types, have been observed to yield varying degrees of isotactic placement [104]. These include catalysts such as $SnCl_4$-CCl_3CO_2H, $Al(C_2H_5)Cl_2$, $Al_2(SO_4)_3 \cdot H_2SO_4$, and boron trifluoride etherate [105, 106]. The effects of solvent, temperature, and other reaction conditions on the type and extent of stereospecificity are similar to those discussed in previous sections. Both syndiotactic and isotactic vinyl ether polymers have been obtained by appropriate control of the reaction conditions.

Unlike the situation with almost all other polar monomers, catalysts of the Ziegler-Natta type can also be used for the isotactic polymerization of vinyl ethers. This usually requires an appropriate adjustment of the identity and ratio of the catalyst components so as to obtain a cationic coordination catalyst which has the proper coordinating power. Vanadium-based catalysts such as VCl_4-$(i\text{-}C_4H_9)_3Al$ have been studied in detail. The stereochemical course of the reaction is highly sensitive to the catalyst composition [107] as is the case for all Ziegler-Natta polymerizations.

8-5c Styrene

Styrene is intermediate in polarity between the non-polar and the polar alkenes. The lack of a strongly polar or reactive functional group allows styrene to be stereospecifically polymerized by Ziegler-Natta catalysts. On the other hand, the mildly polar nature of the benzene ring leads to stereospecific polymerizations with catalysts other than the Ziegler-Natta catalysts. Lithium and lithium alkyls yield stereospecific polymerizations of styrene in a manner similar to that for methyl methacrylate [108].

8-6 STEREOSPECIFIC POLYMERIZATION OF 1,3-DIENES

8-6a Radical Polymerization

The polymerization of 1,3-dienes is more complicated than that of alkenes because of the greater number of stereoisomeric possibilities

(Secs. 8-1d and 8-1e). Table 8-10 shows the polymer structures obtained in the polymerization of 1,3-butadiene and isoprene by radical initiators [109–111]. 1,4-Polymerization occurs in preference to 1,2- or 3,4-polymerization and trans-1,4-polymerization in preference to cis-1,4-polymerization. The temperature dependence of the structure of polybutadiene shows trans-1,4-addition to have a favorable enthalpy of activation of about 3 kcal/mole relative to the cis addition (although the latter has a favorable entropy of activation of about 7 eu). Trans-1,4-addition is favored over 1,2-addition by an enthalpy of activation of about 1 kcal/mole with no difference in the entropy terms for the two modes of reaction.

The polymerization of a 1,3-diene involves delocalization of the radical over carbons 2 and 4 of the terminal monomer unit (XXXIV).

$$\sim\!\sim CH_2\!-\!\overset{\cdots\cdots\cdots\cdots}{CH\!-\!CH\!-\!CH_2}$$

1 2 3 4

XXXIV

Table 8-10 Structure of Radical Polymerized Dienes[a]

Monomer	Polymerization temperature (°C)	Polymer structure (%)			
		cis-1,4-	trans-1,4-	1,2-	3,4-
1,3-Butadiene	−20	6	77	17	
	−10	9	74	17	
	5	15	68	17	
	20	22	58	20	
	100	28	51	21	
	175	37	43	20	
	233	43	39	18	
Isoprene	−20	1	90	5	4
	−5	7	82	5	5
	10	11	79	5	5
	50	18	72	5	5
	100	23	66	5	6
	203	19	69	3	9

[a]Data from [109–111].

The predominance of 1,4-propagation over 1,2-propagation is primarily a consequence of the lower degree of steric hindrance present at carbon 4 relative to carbon 2. This difference increases as the 2-position becomes substituted with the result that 1,4-polymerization is even more favored in the polymerizations of isoprene (Table 8-10) and chloroprene [16]. The occurrence of trans-1,4-polymerization in preference to cis-1,4-polymerization is a consequence of the conformation of the monomer. 1,3-Dienes exist predominantly in the s-trans conformation (XXXVa) as opposed to the s-cis conformation (XXXVb) [112].

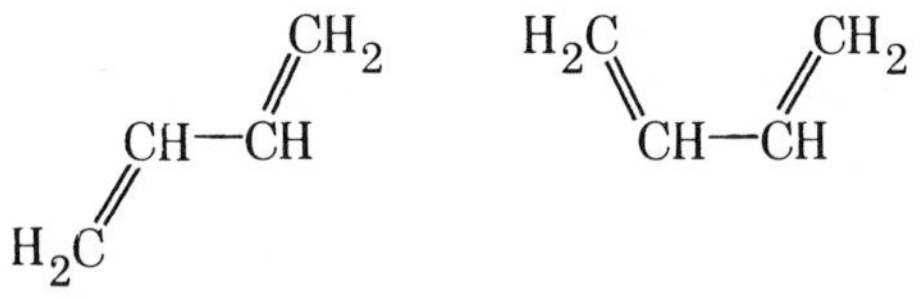

$$\underset{\text{XXXVa}}{\underset{\text{s-Trans}}{H_2C{=}CH{-}CH{=}CH_2}} \qquad \underset{\text{XXXVb}}{\underset{\text{s-Cis}}{H_2C{=}CH{-}CH{=}CH_2}}$$

The addition of a diene monomer to the propagating center proceeds by retention of the monomer conformation with the result that the polymer contains predominantly the trans configuration.

8-6b Anionic and Coordination Polymerizations

The anionic polymerization of 1,3-dienes yields different polymer structures depending on whether the propagating center is a free ion or is coordinated closely with a gegen-ion. Table 8-11 shows some typical data for butadiene polymerization [113, 114]. Polymerization via the free anion favors 1,2-polymerization over 1,4-polymerization. The anionic center at carbon 2 is not extensively delocalized onto carbon 4 as in the corresponding radical species since the alkene double bond is less of an electron-acceptor than it is an electron-donor. The same trend is found in the polymerization of isoprene (Table 8-12) [115] except that the main mode of reaction is 3,4-polymerization instead of 1,2-polymerization due to the lower electron-density on the 3,4-double bond compared to the 1,2-double bond.

Polymerization in non-polar solvents takes place with an increased tendency toward 1,4-polymerization. This effect is most pronounced

Table 8-11 Effect of Solvent and Gegen-Ion on Structure of Butadiene Polymerized at 0°C

Catalyst	Structure of polymer (%)		
	cis-1,4-	trans-1,4-	1,2-
Polymerization in pentane[a]			
Li	35	52	13
Na	10	25	65
K	15	40	45
Rb	7	31	62
Cs	6	35	59
Polymerization in tetrahydrofuran[b]			
Li-naphthalene	0	4	96
Na-naphthalene	0	9	91
K-naphthalene	0	18	82
Rb-naphthalene	0	25	75
Cs-naphthalene	0	25	75

[a]Data from [113].
[b]Data from [114].

with lithium ion which has the greatest coordinating power. Further, there is a strong tendency toward cis-1,4-polymerization with lithium even though the dienes exist predominantly in the s-trans conformation. The preference for cis-1,4-polymerization with

Table 8-12 Effect of Solvent and Gegen-Ion on Structure of Polyisoprene[a]

Catalyst	Solvent	Structure of polymer (%)			
		cis-1,4-	trans-1,4-	1,2-	3,4-
C_4H_9Li	Pentane	93			7
C_4H_9Li	90 Pentane/10 Tetrahydrofuran		26	9	66
C_4H_9Li	Tetrahydrofuran			26	74
Li	Pentane	94			6
Li	$(C_2H_5)_2O$		49	5	46
Na	Pentane		43	6	51
Na	Tetrahydrofuran			18	82
Cs	Pentane	4	51	8	37

[a]Data from [115].

lithium ion becomes overwhelming in the case of isoprene. This predominance of cis-1,4-polymerization has been attributed to the formation of a π-complex type of structure XXXVI between

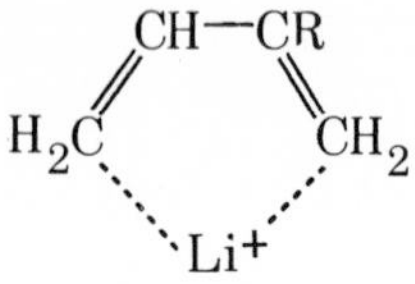

CH—CR
H_2C CH_2
Li^+

XXXVI

lithium ion and the diene to lock the diene into a cis structure before and after its addition to the propagating chain [115].

A detailed mechanism of 1,3-diene polymerization has been given by O'Driscoll and coworkers [116] who suggested that the gegen-ion is simultaneously coordinated with both the allylic carbanion propagating chain end and the entering monomer unit. The resulting species (XXXVII) yields 1,4-polymerization by bond formation

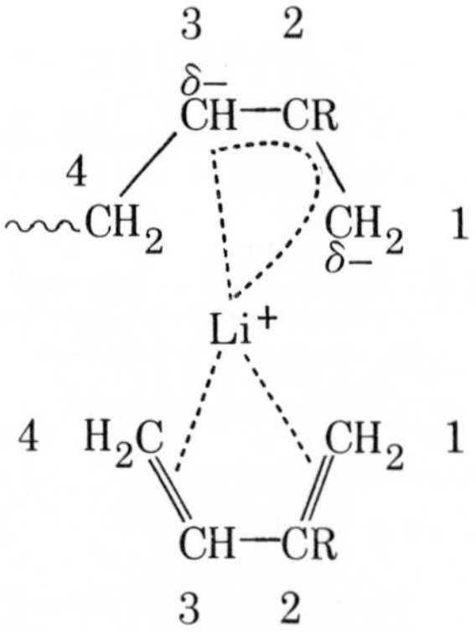

3 2
$\delta-$
CH—CR
4
~~CH_2 CH_2 1
$\delta-$
Li^+
4 H_2C CH_2 1
CH—CR
3 2

XXXVII

between carbon 1 of the allylic carbanion and carbon 4 of the monomer. If the coordination in XXXVII is strong (as it is in non-polar solvents or with lithium) rotation about the bond connecting carbons 2 and 3 of the chain end is prevented and cis-1,4-polymerization occurs. Both trans- and cis-1,4-polymerizations can occur when bond rotation is possible due to a weak coordination complex. When coordination is very weak, 3,4-polymerization occurs via bond formation between carbon 3 of the allylic carbanion and carbon 4 of the monomer.

A variety of other catalyst systems have been studied for the stereospecific polymerization of 1,3-dienes [16, 82]. One of the earliest systems is the heterogeneous *alfin catalyst*, consisting of allylsodium, sodium isopropoxide and sodium chloride, developed in 1946 by Morton [117]. The alfin catalyst increases the extent of 1,4-polymerization relative to 1,2-polymerization but it is not highly stereospecific in terms of strongly favoring either cis-1,4- or trans-1,4-polymerization. The use of Ziegler-Natta catalysts for diene polymerizations, on the other hand, has yielded truly remarkable results–even surpassing the stereospecificity exhibited by lithium catalysts. Table 8-13 shows the polymer structures obtained from butadiene using different catalyst systems [49, 118–127]. The exceptional stereospecificity of the Ziegler-Natta catalysts is even more evident in the polymerization of butadiene than in the polymerizations of alkene monomers. Four different stereospecific polymer structures (cis-1,4,trans-1,4, st-1,2 and it-1,2) are possible for butadiene. A consideration of Table 8-13 shows that each of these structures can be separately obtained to the almost total exclusion of the others by the appropriate choice of the catalyst system. The different stereospecificities of various catalysts is a consequence of the manner in which they coordinate with the propagating chain end and the incoming monomer, and the properties of the resulting intermediate (analogous to XXXVII).

In addition to the Ziegler-Natta catalysts, other catalysts based on transition metal compounds can also be used for the stereospecific polymerization of butadiene. These include various chelates and π-complexes such as bis(π-crotyl nickel iodide)

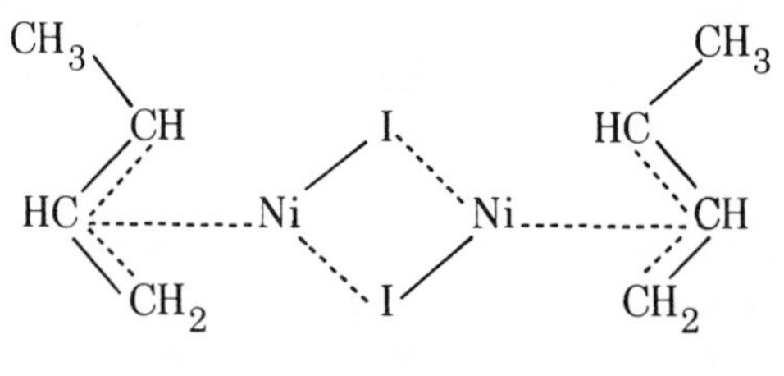

CH_3–CH, HC, CH_2 (π-crotyl) ···· Ni(–I–)$_2$Ni ···· HC, CH, CH_2 (π-crotyl) with CH_3

XXXVIII

Table 8-13 Stereospecificity in Butadiene Polymerization

Catalyst system	Polymer structure	Ref.
$TiCl_4$, AlR_3: Al/Ti = 0.5	91% trans-1,4	[118]
Al/Ti = 1	50% cis-1,4; 45% trans-1,4	[118]
TiI_4, AlR_3	95% cis-1,4	[119]
$Ti(OR)_4$, AlR_3	~100% 1,2	[118]
VCl_3, $AlEt_3$	99% trans-1,4	[118]
$VOCl_3$ or VCl_4, $AlEt_3$ or $AlEt_2Cl$	95-98% trans-1,4	[118]
V(acetylacetonate)$_3$, $AlEt_3$	~90% st-1,2	[49]
$Cr(CN\phi)_6$, $AlEt_3$: Al/Cr = 2	~100% st-1,2	[118]
Al/Cr > 10	~100% it-1,2	[118]
$Co_2(CO)_8$, $MoCl_5$	99% at-1,2	[120]
$Co(SCN)_2(P\phi_3)_2$, $(Et_2Al)_2SO_4$	~100% st-1,2	[121]
$CoCl_2$	90% cis-1,4	[122]
Co chelates, $AlEt_3$, *p*-$Cl\phi CH_2Cl$	99.5% cis-1,4	[123]
$NiCl_2$	95% cis-1,4	[122]
bis(π-crotyl NiCl)	92% cis-1,4	[124]
bis(π-crotyl NiI)	94% trans-1,4	[124]
(π-cyclooctadiene)$_2$Ni, HI	~100% trans-1,4	[125]
(π-cyclooctadiene)$_2$Ni, CF_3CO_2H: CF_3CO_2H/Ni ~ 1	~100% cis-1,4	[126]
$RhCl_3$, sodium dodecyl benzene sulfonate	96-99% trans-1,4	[127]

The various catalysts in Table 8-13 include both soluble and heterogeneous systems. Catalysts are also known which can be used in aqueous systems (usually emulsions); these include the rhodium catalyst and others based on Group VIII metals [18]. The stereospecificity of the various catalysts is highly dependent on the identity of the catalyst components and their relative amounts and on other reaction conditions such as the nature of the solvent. Thus, a change in composition of the $Cr(CN\phi)_6$-$AlEt_3$ catalyst system shifts the polymerization from exclusively syndiotactic-1,2 to exclusively isotactic-1,2-polymerization. The use of bis-cyclooctadiene nickel with HI yields trans-1,4-polymerization. When HI is replaced by CF_3CO_2H, the direction of the polymerization depends on the ratio of the two catalyst components. Cis-1,4-polymerization occurs when the two components are present in equimolar amounts. For acid-to-nickel ratios greater than one, the polymer contains equal amounts of the cis-1,4 and trans-1,4 structures in what is postulated as an alternating cis-trans arrangement [126].

The high stereospecificity of the catalysts is also apparent in the polymerizations of other 1,3-dienes such as isoprene and 1,3-pentadiene (Table 8-14) [118, 128, 129]. The latter monomer is interesting in that it itself exists as cis and trans isomers and, further, 1,4-polymerization yields structures capable of showing both optical and geometrical isomerism. The strong stereospecificity of the

Table 8-14 Stereospecificity in the Polymerizations of Isoprene and 1,3-Pentadiene

Catalyst system	Polymer structure	Ref.
I. ISOPRENE		
$TiCl_4$, $AlEt_3$: $Al/Ti > 1$	96% cis-1,4	[118]
$Al/Ti < 1$	95% trans-1,4	[118]
$Ti(OR)_4$, $AlEt_3$	95% 3,4	[118]
VCl_3, $AlEt_3$	99% trans-1,4	[118]
VO(acetylacetonate)$_3$, $AlEt_3$	90% 3,4	[128]
II. 1,3-PENTADIENE		
$TiCl_3$ or VCl_3, AlR_3	it-trans-1,4[a]	[118], [129]
$Ti(OR)_4$, $AlEt_3$	85% it-cis-1,4[a]	[118], [129]
V(acetylacetonate)$_3$, $AlEt_2Cl$	50% trans-1,4, 50% 1,2[a]	[129]
Co(acetylacetonate)$_3$, $AlEt_2Cl$:		
benzene	85-90% st-cis-1,4[b]	[129]
hexane	st-1,2[b]	[129]

[a]From both *cis*- and *trans*-1,3-pentadiene.

[b]From *trans*-1,3-pentadiene; the cis monomer does not polymerize with cobalt catalysts.

various catalysts is clearly evident since the same structures are obtained from both *cis*- and *trans*-1,3-pentadiene. The configuration of the allyl propagating chain end and the strength of the coordination forces determines polymer structure irrespective of the initial configuration of the monomer. Polymerization with cobalt catalysts are an exception in that *trans*-1,3-pentadiene polymerizes, but the cis isomer is unreactive.

Stereospecific polymerizations of 1,4-disubstituted butadienes have also been carried out. Esters of the trans-trans isomers of sorbic acid and β-styrylacrylic acid have been polymerized to tri-tactic polymers having the *erythro*-di-iso-trans-tactic structure [130], that is,

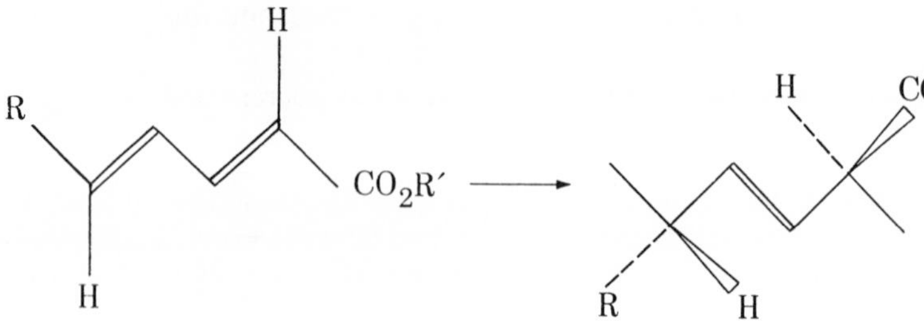

R, H, H, CO_2R' $\longrightarrow$ H, CO_2R', R, H (8-55)

where $R = CH_3$, ϕ and $R' = CH_3$, C_2H_5, C_4H_9.

8-6c Cationic Polymerization

The cationic polymerization of 1,3-dienes usually yields relatively low molecular weight polymers with cyclized structures [131]. The degree of unsaturation in the polymer based on either 1,4- or 1,2-(or 3,4-)polymerization varies considerably—from about 80 percent with conventional cationic catalysts to almost zero for complex catalysts such as $TiCl_4$-$(C_2H_5)_2AlCl$ or $TiCl_4$-$C_2H_5AlCl_2$ at high Ti/Al ratios [131, 132]. Polymerizations with the latter catalysts are not Ziegler-Natta polymerizations. Many of the usual Ziegler-Natta catalyst systems are cationic initiators when the transition metal component is in appreciable excess. Various inter- and intramolecular transfer and addition reactions have been considered to account for the cyclic structures obtained in the polymerizations of 1,3-dienes.

Gaylord and coworkers [132, 133] postulated a Diels-Alder type charge transfer mechanism to describe the almost exclusive formation of cyclopolymers when catalysts such as $C_2H_5AlCl_2$-$TiCl_4$ are used. The mechanism involves the initiation and propagation sequence

$$\text{catalyst} \longrightarrow C_2H_5AlCl^+ \tag{8-56}$$

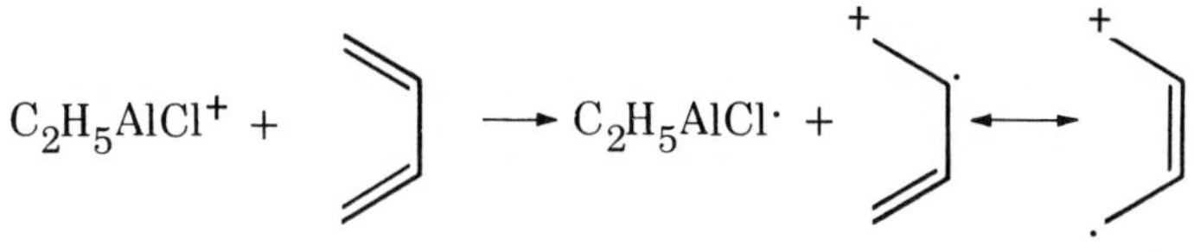

$$C_2H_5AlCl^+ + \text{[butadiene]} \longrightarrow C_2H_5AlCl\cdot + \text{[radical cation]} \longleftrightarrow \text{[radical cation]} \tag{8-57}$$

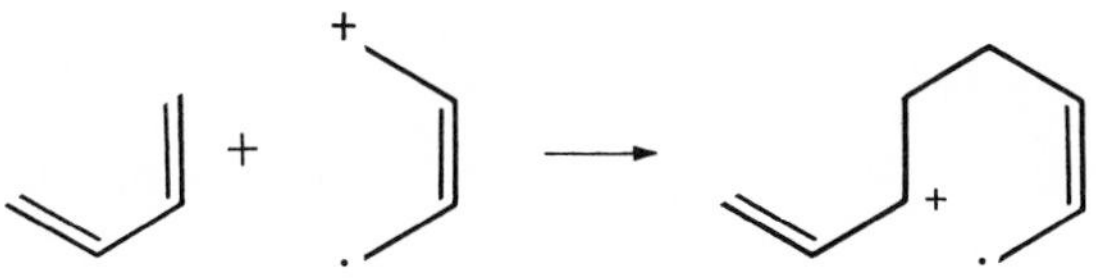

(8-58)

$$+ \; C_2H_5AlCl\cdot \longrightarrow \; + \; C_2H_5AlCl^+$$

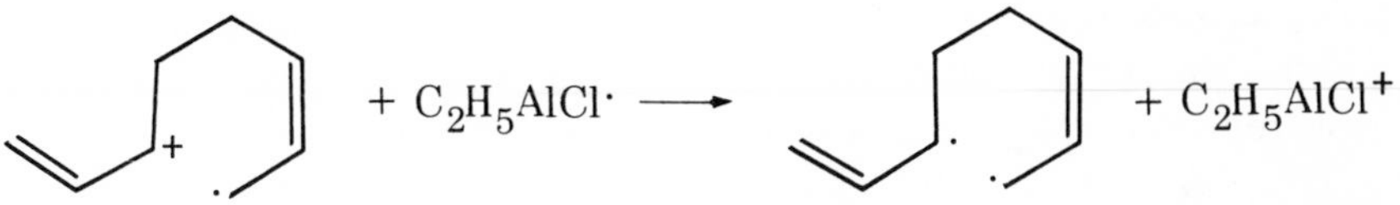

(8-59a)

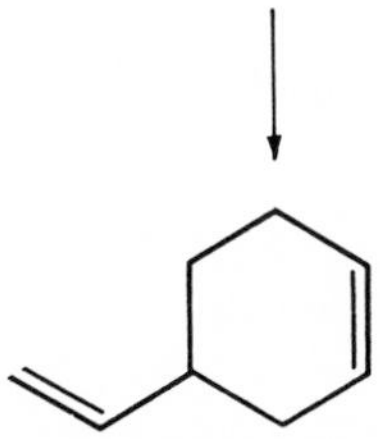

(8-59b)

The cation $C_2H_5AlCl^+$ reacts with monomer to form the activated monomer species (a radical cation) which is the species actually involved in the propagation step. Thus, the overall reaction consists of Eq. 8-57 followed by propagation which can be generalized as

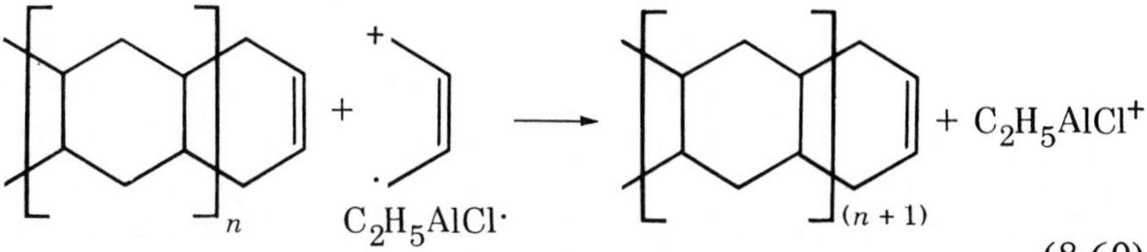

$$[\;]_n + C_2H_5AlCl\cdot \longrightarrow [\;]_{(n+1)} + C_2H_5AlCl^+ \tag{8-60}$$

Cyclopolymerization of conjugated dienes in this manner may be of interest from the viewpoint of synthesizing ladder-type polymers with high temperature stability (Sec. 2-12).

8-7 OTHER STEREOSPECIFIC POLYMERIZATIONS

Stereospecific polymerization is possible with a number of monomers other than alkenes and dienes but only epoxide and carbonyl monomers have been studied to an appreciable extent.

8-7a Epoxides

The stereochemistry of propylene oxide polymerization has been fairly extensively studied. *Isotactic* poly(propylene oxide) is obtained using catalyst systems such as zinc or aluminum alkyls in combination with water or alcohols (Sec. 7-2b-1-f) [134, 135], a $FeCl_3$-propylene oxide adduct [136], and even metal hydroxides and alkoxides under certain conditions [137]. Interestingly, the isotactic polymerization of propylene oxide by the $FeCl_3$-propylene oxide adduct was first reported [136] in 1955—the same year that Natta first reported the synthesis of *isotactic* polypropylene.

The identity of the initiating species in the various catalyst systems has been the subject of considerable conjecture. The initiator in the $FeCl_3$-propylene oxide system has been considered [138] to be

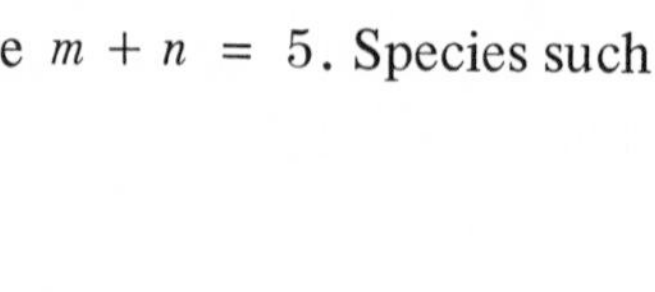

$$Cl{-}Fe\begin{cases}(OCH_2CHCH_3)_mCl\\(OCH_2CHCH_3)_nCl\end{cases}$$

XXXIX

where $m + n = 5$. Species such as

$$RZn{-}O{-}ZnR$$

XL

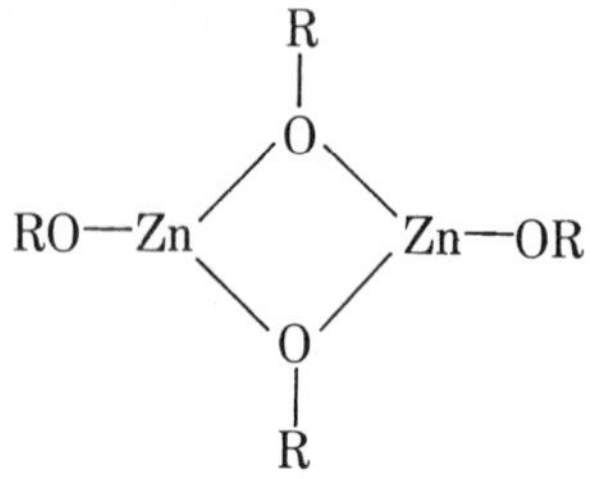

$$RO{-}Zn\langle(\mu{-}OR)_2\rangle Zn{-}OR$$

(RO–Zn and Zn–OR bridged by two O–R groups in a four-membered Zn–O–Zn–O ring)

XLI

have been postulated as the stereoregulating species in the metal alkyl-alcohol systems. None of the proposed species has been experimentally verified. The nature of the propagation reaction is also not clear—both coordinate cationic and coordinate anionic mechanisms have been considered.

8-7b Carbonyl Monomers

The stereospecific polymerization of acetaldehyde to an isotactic structure has been accomplished by a number of coordinate anionic catalyst systems [139]. These include zinc and aluminum alkyls usually in combination with water or an alcohol or other substances as well as catalyst systems based on alkali-metal alkyls, hydrides, and alkoxides [140–142]. Some analogous work has been reported on higher aldehydes such as butyraldehyde; stereoregular polymers of unsymmetrical ketones have not been synthesized as yet.

8-8 OPTICAL ACTIVITY IN POLYMERS

Optical activity is potentially possible in isotactic polymers due either to the configuration of an asymmetric atom in the main polymer chain or one in a side group on the main polymer chain. *Isotactic* polypropylene, polyacetaldehyde, and poly(propylene oxide) are examples of the former. The latter is illustrated by poly(3-methyl-1-pentene)

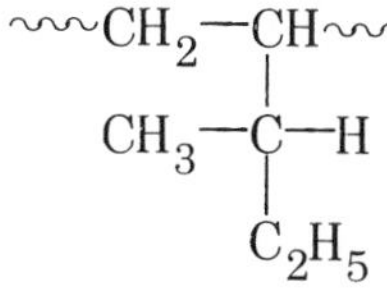

$$
\begin{array}{c}
\sim\sim CH_2-\underset{|}{C}H\sim\sim \\
CH_3-\underset{|}{\overset{|}{C}}-H \\
C_2H_5
\end{array}
$$

XLII

in which asymmetry resides in the isobutyl side group. The usual isotactic polymerization of these monomers does not lead to optically active polymers. Isotactic alkene and carbonyl polymers in which the potential optical activity resides in the main polymer chain are inactive since each polymer molecule possesses an internal plane of symmetry (Secs. 8-1a-1 and 8-1c). The isotactic polymer of an analogous epoxide such as propylene oxide is optically inactive for a different reason. The usual sample of *isotactic* poly(propylene oxide) contains equal number of polymer molecules with all *R*- and all *S*-configurations due to the random nature of starting an isotactic chain with either an *R*- or an *S*-configuration. The isotactic polymer of 3-methyl-1-pentene is inactive for the same reason—half the molecules in a sample have the *R*-configuration for the side group and the other half have the *S*-configuration. Optically active polymers can, however, be synthesized by using either optically active monomers or optically active catalysts [143-145].

8-8a Polymerization with Optically Active Catalysts

The use of a catalyst containing an optically active portion to isotactically polymerize racemic monomers such as *racemic* polypropylene oxide or 3-methyl-1-pentene often results in the preferential polymerization of one antipode over the other. The result is a polymer with optical activity due to a predominance of one isomer. Thus, optically active poly(propylene oxide) can be synthesized using diethylzinc-*d*-borneol [146] and various poly-α-olefins using the Ziegler-Natta catalyst from optically 2-methylbutyllithium and $TiCl_4$ or $TiCl_3$ [143]. Such polymerizations are referred to as *stereoselective polymerizations*. The designation of optically active polymers is usually made by using the prefixes *R*- and *S*-, for example, poly-*R*-(propylene oxide) and poly-*S*-(propylene oxide) or $[R\text{-}CH_2CH(CH_3)O—]_n$ and $[S\text{-}CH_2CH(CH_3)O—]_n$. The direction of rotation of light may be indicated by using (+)- and (−)- or *d*- and *l*- in front of the above names. Racemic polymers are designated by using the prefix *racemic*, e.g., *racemic*-poly(propylene oxide).

Stereoselective polymerizations occur by interaction of the optically active catalyst with the racemic monomer mixture so as to selectively allow the entry of only one of the antipodes into the polymer chain. The exact composition of the catalyst, the identity of its optically active portion, and its optical purity determine the course and extent of the stereoselective polymerization. The detailed mechanism by which stereoselective polymerization occurs is not known as there is little correlation between catalyst and polymer configurations.

The term *asymmetric induction* is sometimes used synonymously with stereospecific polymerization, but this is not strictly correct. Asymmetric induction specifically applies to the synthesis of an optically active polymer, from a monomer without an asymmetric center, by the influence of a nearby optically active center. This occurs in the 1,4-polymerization of 1-substituted and unsymmetrically 1,4-disubstituted 1,3-dienes by optically active catalysts. Thus, optically active *iso-trans-tactic* 1,4-poly(methyl-β-vinyl acrylate), *iso-cis-tactic* 1,4-poly-1,3-pentadiene, and *erythro-di-iso-trans-tactic* 1,4-poly(butyl sorbate) have been obtained using butyllithium-sodium-*d*-bornoxide, triethylaluminum-titanium-*l*-tetramenthoxide, and butyllithium-*l*-menthyl ethyl ether, respectively [147–149].

Another instance of asymmetric induction is the polymerization of unsymmetrical cyclic alkenes (Sec. 8-1f). Optically active polymers of benzofuran (XLIII) have

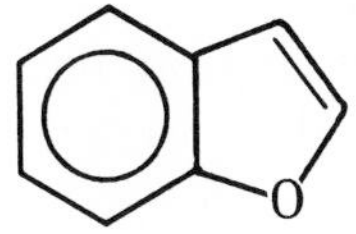

XLIII

been synthesized using cationic catalysts consisting of a Lewis acid (for example, $AlCl_3$) in combination with an optically active Lewis base (for example, β-phenylalanine and menthyl-$OSnEt_3$) [143, 144].

8-8b Polymerization of Optically Active Monomers

The polymerization of an optically active monomer is probably the most widely used method of synthesizing an optically active polymer. This method has been used with optically active α-olefins such as 3- and 4-methyl-1-pentenes, vinyl ethers such as menthyl and bornyl vinyl ethers [150], acrylic and methacrylic esters of optically active alcohols [151, 152], propylene oxide [153], aldehydes [154] and other monomers. The isotactic polymerization of an optically active monomer by a stereospecific catalyst results in placement of the asymmetric centers into the polymer chain with the same configuration.

The polymerization of optically active monomers is interesting not only because optically active polymers can be obtained but also because monomer optical activity can affect polymer tacticity. The polymerization of an optically active monomer can in some cases occur with isotactic placement even when non-stereospecific catalysts are employed. Thus, the polymerization of *racemic* propylene oxide by a non-stereospecific KOH catalyst yields an atactic polymer, while an optically active isotactic polymer is obtained from optically active monomer [155]. When a stereospecific $FeCl_3$

catalyst is used, isotactic polymers are obtained from both the racemic and optically active monomers although the latter yields an optically active polymer. The asymmetric center in the monomer, when incorporated into the polymer, directs the placement of the next monomer unit to occur with the same configuration.

An interesting case is the copolymerization of *racemic* 3,7-dimethyl-1-octene with optically active 3-methyl-1-pentene by $TiCl_4$-$Zn(i\text{-}C_4H_9)_2$ [156]. The copolymer is apparently optically active with respect to both comonomer units as the incorporated optically active 3-methyl-1-pentene units direct the preferential entry of only one of the antipodes of the racemic comonomer. The directing effect of an asymmetric center in the monomer unit has even been observed in some radical copolymerizations. The copolymerization of maleic anhydride with optically active α-methylbenzyl methacrylate by azobisisobutyronitrile yields a copolymer which is optically active even after hydrolysis (Eq. 8-61) of the optically active α-methylbenzyl group [157].

$$\left[-\underset{\text{OC—O—CO}}{\text{CH}-\text{CH}}-\text{CH}_2-\overset{\text{CH}_3}{\underset{\text{CO}-\text{O}-\text{C}^*\text{H}(\text{CH}_3)(\phi)}{\text{C}^*}}-\right]_n \longrightarrow \left[-\underset{\text{OC—O—CO}}{\text{CH}-\text{CH}}-\text{CH}_2-\overset{\text{CH}_3}{\underset{\text{CO}-\text{OH}}{\text{C}^*}}-\right]_n \quad (8\text{-}61)$$

XLIV XLV

REFERENCES

1. H. Staudinger, "Die Hochmolekularen Organischen Verbindungen," Springer-Verlag, Berlin, 1932.
2. K. Ziegler, E. Holzkamp, H. Breil, and H. Martin, *Angew. Chem.*, **67**:426, 541 (1955).
3. G. Natta, P. Pino, P. Corradini, F. Danusso, E. Mantica, G. Mazzanti, and G. Moraglio, *J. Am. Chem. Soc.*, **77**:1708 (1955).

4. G. Natta, *Makromol. Chem.*, **16**:213 (1955) and *J. Polymer Sci.*, **16**:143 (1955); **35**:94 (1960).
5. G. Natta, *Science*, **147**:261 (1965).
6. C. E. H. Bawn and A. Ledwith, *Quart. Rev. (London)*, **16**:361 (1962).
7. M. H. Lehr, Stereoregular Polymers, in A. F. Scott (ed.), "Survey of Progress in Chemistry," vol. 3, Academic Press, Inc., New York, 1966.
8. A. D. Ketley (ed.), "The Stereochemistry of Macromolecules," vols. 1 and 2, Marcel Dekker, Inc., New York, 1967.
9. L. Reich and A. Shindler, "Polymerization by Organometallic Compounds," Interscience Publishers, John Wiley & Sons, Inc., New York, 1966.
10. M. L. Miller, "The Structure of Polymers," chap. 8, Reinhold Book Corp., New York, 1966.
11. M. Goodman, Concepts of Polymer Stereochemistry, in N. L. Allinger and E. L. Eliel (eds.), "Topics in Stereochemistry," vol. 2, pp. 73–156, Interscience Publishers, John Wiley & Sons, Inc., New York, 1967.
12. J. D. Roberts and M. C. Caserio, "Modern Organic Chemistry," pp. 96–99, 129–132, 399–423, W. A. Benjamin, Inc., New York, 1967.
13. R. S. Cahn, C. K. Ingold, and V. Prelog, *Experientia*, **12**:81 (1956).
14. M. L. Huggins, G. Natta, V. Desreux, and H. Mark, *Pure and Appl. Chem.*, **12**:645 (1966).
15. G. Natta, M. Peraldo, M. Farina, and G. Bressan, *Makromol. Chem.*, **55**:139 (1962).
16. W. Cooper and G. Vaughan, Recent Developments in the Polymerization of Conjugated Dienes, in A. D. Jenkins (ed.), "Progress in Polymer Science," vol. 1, Pergamon Press Ltd., 1967.
17. P. Pino, *Fortschr. Hochpolymer.-Forsch. (Advan. Polymer Sci.)*, **4**:399 (1966).
18. G. Natta, G. Dall'Asta, G. Mazzanti, and G. Motroni, *Makromol. Chem.*, **69**:163 (1963).
19. M. Compostella, The Manufacture and Commercial Applications of Stereoregular Polymers, in A. D. Ketley, *op. cit.*, vol. 1, chap. 6 of [8].
20. E. A. Youngman and J. Boor, Jr., Syndiotactic Polypropylene, in A. Peterlin, M. Goodman, S. Okamura, B. H. Zimm, and H. F. Mark (eds.), "Macromolecular Reviews," vol. 2, pp. 33–69, Interscience Publishers, John Wiley & Sons, Inc., New York, 1967.
21. J. Brandrup and E. H. Immergut (eds.), "Polymer Handbook," chap. III-1; III-61, Interscience Publishers, John Wiley & Sons, Inc., New York, 1966.
22. A. D. Ketley (ed.), "The Stereochemistry of Macromolecules," vol. 3, Marcel Dekker, Inc., New York, 1968.
23. G. Natta, *J. Polymer Sci.*, **16**:143 (1955).
24. F. A. Bovey and G. V. D. Tiers, *ibid.*, **44**:173 (1960).
25. F. A. Bovey, *Accounts of Chem. Research*, **1(6)**:175 (1968).
26. K. Hatada, K. Ota, and H. Yuki, *J. Polymer Sci.*, **B5**:225 (1967).

27. M. L. Huggins, *J. Am. Chem. Soc.,* **66**:1991 (1944).
28. J. W. L. Fordham, *J. Polymer Sci.,* **39**:321 (1959).
29. T. G. Fox and H. W. Schnecko, *Polymer,* **3**:575 (1962).
30. F. A. Bovey, F. P. Hood, E. W. Anderson, and R. L. Kornegay, *J. Phys. Chem.,* **71**:312 (1967).
31. C. E. H. Bawn, W. H. James, and A. M. North, *J. Polymer Sci.,* **C4**:427 (1963).
32. G. Talamini and G. Vidotto, *Makromol. Chem.,* **100**:48 (1967).
33. K. Matsuzaki, T. Uryu, A. Ishida, T. Ohki, and M. Takeuchi, *J. Polymer Sci.,* **A-1(5)**:2167 (1967).
34. M. Murano and R. Yamdera, *ibid.,* **B5**:333 (1967).
35. J. Boor, Jr., *ibid.,* **C1**:237 (1963).
36. C. E. Schildknecht, A. O. Zoss, and C. McKinley, *Ind. Eng. Chem.,* **39**:180 (1947).
37. G. Natta, I. Bassi, and P. Corradini, *Makromol. Chem.,* **18-19**:455 (1956).
38. A. Zambelli, G. Natta, and I. Pasquon, *J. Polymer Sci.,* **C4**:411 (1963).
39. K. Ziegler, *Angew. Chem.,* **76**:545 (1964).
40. J. Boor, Jr., The Nature of the Active Site in the Ziegler-Type Catalyst, in A. Peterlin, M. Goodman, S. Okamura, B. H. Zimm, and H. F. Mark (eds.), "Macromolecular Reviews," pp. 117-268, Interscience Publishers, John Wiley & Sons, Inc., New York, 1967.
41. D. F. Hoeg, The Mechanism of Ziegler-Natta Catalysis. I. Experimental Foundations, in A. D. Ketley, *op. cit.*, vol. 1, chap. 2 of [8].
42. P. Cossee, "The Mechanism of Ziegler-Natta Polymerization. II. Quantum-Chemical and Crystal-Chemical Aspects," in A. D. Ketley, *op. cit.,* vol. 1, chap. 3 of [8].
43. J. P. Kennedy and A. W. Langer, Jr., *Fortschr. Hochpolymer.-Forsch. (Advan. Polymer Sci.),* **3**:508 (1964).
44. G. Natta, *J. Inorg. & Nuclear Chem.,* **8**:589 (1958).
45. F. Danusso, *Chim. Ind. (Milan),* **44**:611 (1962).
46. A. S. Matlack and D. S. Breslow, *J. Polymer Sci.,* **A3**:2853 (1965).
47. F. X. Werber, C. J. Benning, W. R. Wszolek, and G. E. Ashby, *ibid.,* **A-1(6)**:743 (1968).
48. G. L. Karapinka, J. J. Smith, and W. L. Carrick, *ibid.,* **50**:143 (1961).
49. G. Natta, *ibid.,* **48**:219 (1960).
50. F. Patat and H. Sinn, *Angew. Chem.,* **70**:496 (1958).
51. F. Eirich and H. Mark, *J. Colloid. Sci.,* **11**:748 (1956).
52. M. L. Huggins, *J. Polymer Sci.,* **48**:473 (1960).
53. J. Furukawa and T. Tsuruta, *ibid.,* **36**:275 (1959).
54. P. Cossee, *J. Catalysis,* **3**:80 (1964).
55. L. A. M. Rodriguez and H. M. van Looy, *J. Polymer Sci.,* **A-1(4)**:1951, 1971 (1966).
56. H. W. Coover, Jr., *ibid.,* **C4**:1511 (1963).

57. P. Longi, G. Mazzanti, A. Roggero, and A. M. Lache, *Makromol. Chem.*, **61**:63 (1963).
58. R. W. Lenz, "Organic Chemistry of Synthetic High Polymers," chap. 15, Interscience Publishers, John Wiley & Sons, Inc., New York, 1967.
59. L. Kollar, A. Simon, and A. Kallo, *J. Polymer Sci.*, **A-1(6)**:937 (1968).
60. E. J. Arlman and P. Cossee, *J. Catalysis*, **3**:99 (1964).
61. G. Natta, *Chim. Ind. (Milan)*, **42**:1207 (1960).
62. G. Natta, P. Corradini, and G. Allegra, *J. Polymer Sci.*, **51**:399 (1961).
63. G. Natta, I. Pasquon, and A. Zambelli, *J. Am. Chem. Soc.*, **84**:1488 (1962).
64. J. Boor, Jr. and E. A. Youngman, *J. Polymer Sci.*, **A-1(4)**:1861 (1966).
65. A. Zambelli, M. G. Giongo, and G. Natta, *Makromol. Chem.*, **112**:183 (1968).
66. L. Kollar, A. Simon, J. Osvath, *J. Polymer Sci.*, **A-1(6)**:919 (1968).
67. M. H. Lehr, *Macromolecules*, **1**:178 (1968).
68. G. Natta, P. Pino, and G. Mazzante, U.S. Patent 3,197,452 (1965).
69. H. W. Coover, Jr., R. L. McConnell, and F. B. Joyner, Relationship of Catalyst Composition to Catalyst Activity for the Polymerization of α-Olefins, in A. Peterlin, M. Goodman, S. Okamura, B. H. Zimm and H. F. Mark (eds.), "Macromolecular Reviews," vol. I, pp. 91–118, Interscience Publishers, John Wiley & Sons, Inc., New York, 1967.
70. W. Cooper, Stereospecific Polymerization, in J. C. Robb and F. W. Parker, (eds.), "Progress in High Polymers," vol. 1, pp. 279–333, Academic Press, Inc., New York, 1961.
71. A. Zambelli, J. DiPietro, and G. Gatti, *J. Polymer Sci.*, **A1**:403 (1963).
72. R. L. Combs, D. F. Slonaker, F. B. Joyner, and H. W. Coover, Jr., *ibid.*, **A-1(5)**:215 (1967).
73. P. G. Ashmore, "Catalysis and Inhibition of Chemical Reactions," chaps. 5-8, Butterworth and Co. (Publishers) Ltd., London, 1963.
74. G. Natta, *J. Polymer Sci.*, **34**:21 (1959).
75. L. Reich and S. S. Stivala, *ibid.*, **A1**:203 (1963).
76. G. Natta and I. Pasquon, The Kinetics of the Stereospecific Polymerization of α-Olefins, in D. D. Eley, P. W. Selwood, and P. B. Weisz, (eds.), "Advances in Catalysis and Related Subjects," vol. XI, pp. 2–67, Academic Press, Inc., New York, 1959.
77. C. G. Overberger, P. A. Jarovitsky and H. Mukamal, *J. Polymer Sci.*, **A-1(5)**:2487 (1967).
78. G. Lehmann and A. Gumboldt, *Makromol. Chem.*, **70**:23 (1964).
79. B. M. Grieveson, *ibid.*, **84**:93 (1965).
80. G. Bier, W. Hoffman, G. Lehmann, and G. Seydel, *ibid.*, **58**:1 (1962).
81. U. Giannini, G. Brucker, E. Pellino, and A. Cassata, *J. Polymer Sci.*, **B5**:527 (1967).
82. W. Marconi, The Polymerization of Dienes by Ziegler-Natta Catalysts, in A. D. Ketley (ed.), *op. cit.*, vol. 1, chap. 5, of [8].

83. J. Boor, Jr., E. A. Youngman, and M. Dimbat, *Makromol. Chem.*, **90**:26 (1966).
84. G. Natta, G. Dall'Asta, I. W. Bassi, and G. Carella, *ibid.*, **91**:87 (1966).
85. G. Natta, G. Dall'Asta, and G. Motroni, *J. Polymer Sci.*, **B2**:349 (1964).
86. I. Pasquon, A. Valvassori, and G. Sartori, The Copolymerization of Olefins by Ziegler-Natta Catalysts, in A. D. Ketley (ed.), *op. cit.*, vol. 1, chap. 4 of [8].
87. G. E. Ham, (ed.), "Copolymerization," chaps. IV, A-D, Interscience Publishers, John Wiley & Sons, Inc., New York, 1964.
88. G. Natta, A. Valvassori, G. Mazzanti, and G. Sartori, *Chim Ind. (Milan)*, **40**:896 (1958).
89. G. Natta, G. Mazzanti, A. Valvassori, and G. Sartori, *ibid.*, **40**:717 (1958).
90. G. Natta, G. Mazzanti, A. Valvassori, and G. Pajaro, *ibid.*, **41**:764 (1959).
91. G. Mazzanti, A. Valvassori, G. Sartori, and G. Pajaro, *ibid.*, **42**:468 (1960).
92. R. E. Cunningham, *J. Polymer Sci.*, **A-1(4)**:1203 (1966); **A-1(5)**:243, 251 (1967).
93. G. Natta, G. Allegra, I. W. Bassi, P. Corradini, and P. Ganes, *Makromol. Chem.*, **58**:242 (1962).
94. H. W. Coover, Jr., R. L. McConnell, F. B. Joyner, D. F. Slonaker, and R. L. Combs, *J. Polymer Sci.*, **A4**:2563 (1966).
95. H. J. Hagemayer and M. B. Edwards, *ibid.*, **C2**:731 (1964).
96. F. X. Werber, *Fortschr. Hochpolymer.-Forsch. (Advan. Polymer Sci.)*, **1**:180 (1959).
97. H. N. Friedlander, W. E. Smith, and R. J. Ross, *J. Polymer Sci.*, **48**:17 (1960).
98. W. E. Carrick, R. W. Klinker, E. F. Bonner, L. H. Wartman, F. M. Rugg, and J. J. Smith, *J. Am. Chem. Soc.*, **82**:3883 (1960).
99. D. Braun, M. Herner, U. Johnson, and W. Kern, *Makromol. Chem.*, **51**:15 (1962).
100. K. Hatada, K. Ota, and H. Yuki, *J. Polymer Sci.*, **B5**:225 (1967).
101. T. Fujimoto, N. Kawabata, and J. Furukawa, *ibid.*, **A-1(6)**:1209 (1968).
102. T. Hirahara, T. Nakano, and Y. Minoura, *ibid.*, **A-1(6)**:485 (1968).
103. D. J. Cram and K. R. Kopecky, *J. Am. Chem. Soc.*, **81**:2748 (1959).
104. A. D. Ketley, Stereospecific Polymerization of Vinyl Ethers, in A. D. Ketley (ed.), *op. cit.*, vol. 2, chap. 2 of [8].
105. Y. Ohsumi, T. Higashimura, and S. Okamura, *J. Polymer Sci.*, **A-1(5)**:849 (1967).
106. T. Higashimura, Y. Ohsumi, K. Kuroda, and S. Okamura, *ibid.*, **A-1(5)**:863 (1967).
107. E. J. Vandenberg, R. F. Heck, and D. S. Breslow, *ibid.*, **41**:519 (1959).
108. D. Braun, Stereospecific Polymerization of Vinyl-Type Monomers and Dienes by Alkali-Metal-Based Catalysts, in A. D. Ketley (ed.), *op. cit.*, vol. 2, chap. 1 of [8].

109. F. E. Condon, *J. Polymer Sci.,* **11**:139 (1953).
110. W. S. Richardson, *ibid.,* **13**:229 (1954).
111. D. J. Pollock, L. J. Elyash and T. W. DeWitt, *ibid.,* **15**:86 (1955).
112. D. Craig, J. J. Shipman, and R. B. Fowler, *J. Am. Chem. Soc.,* **83**:2885 (1961).
113. A. V. Tobolsky and C. E. Rogers, *J. Polymer Sci.,* **40**:73 (1959).
114. A. Rembaum, F. R. Ells, R. C. Morrow and A. V. Tobolsky, *ibid.,* **61**:155 (1962).
115. R. S. Sterns and L. E. Forman, *ibid.,* **41**:381 (1959).
116. K. F. O'Driscoll, T. Yonezawa, and T. Higashimura, *Macromol. Chem.,* **1**:1 (1966).
117. A. A. Morton and E. G. Lampher, *J. Polymer Sci.,* **44**:233 (1960).
118. G. Natta et al., *Chim. Ind. (Milan),* **40**:362 (1958); **41**:116, 398, 526, 1163 (1959); *Makromol. Chem.,* **77**:114, 126 (1964).
119. W. M. Saltman and T. H. Link, *Ind. and Eng. Chem. Prod. Res. and Dev.,* **3**:199 (1964).
120. S. Otsuka and M. Kawakami, *Angew. Chem. Intern. Ed. Engl.,* **2**:618 (1963).
121. M. Iwamoto and S. Yuguchi, *J. Polymer Sci.,* **B5**:1007 (1967).
122. W. S. Anderson, *ibid.,* **A-1(5)**:429 (1967).
123. A. Takahashi, K. Takahashi, T. Hirose, and S. Kambara, *ibid.,* **B5**:415 (1967).
124. T. Matsumoto and J. Furukawa, *ibid.,* **B5**:935 (1967).
125. J. P. Durand, F. Dawans, and P. Teyssie, *ibid.,* **B5**:785 (1967).
126. J. P. Durand and P. Teyssie, *ibid.,* **B6**:299 (1968).
127. R. E. Rinehart, H. P. Smith, H. S. Witt, and H. Romeyn, Jr., *J. Am. Chem. Soc.,* **83**:4864 (1961); **84**:4145 (1962).
128. G. Wilke, *Angew. Chem.,* **68**:306 (1956).
129. G. Natta et al., *J. Polymer Sci.,* **51**:463 (1961); **B1**:67 (1963); *Makromol. Chem.,* **51**:229 (1962); **53**:52 (1962); *European Polymer J.,* **1**:81 (1965); **5**:1 (1969).
130. G. Natta, M. Farina, M. Donati, and M. Peraldo, *Chim. Ind. (Milan),* **42**:1363 (1960).
131. W. Cooper, Polyenes, in P. H. Plesch (ed.), "The Chemistry of Cationic Polymerization," chap. 8, Pergamon Press Ltd., Oxford, 1963.
132. N. G. Gaylord et al., *J. Polymer Sci.,* **A-1(4)**:2493 (1966); **A-1(6)**; 125 (1968).
133. N. G. Gaylord and M. Svestka, *ibid.,* **B7**:55 (1969).
134. T. Tsuruta, S. Inoue, and K. Tsubaki, *Makromol. Chem.,* **111**:236 (1968).
135. T. Saegusa, H. Imai, and S. Matsumoto, *J. Polymer Sci.,* **A-1(6)**:459 (1968).
136. M. E. Pruitt and J. M. Baggett, U.S. Pat. 2,706,182 to Dow Chemical Co. (April, 1955).

137. T. Tsuruta, Stereospecific Polymerization of Epoxides, in A. D. Ketley (ed.), *op. cit*., vol. 2, chap. 4 of [8].
138. R. O. Colclough, G. Gee, W. C. E. Higginson, J. B. Jackson, and M. Litt, *J. Polymer Sci.*, **34**:171 (1959).
139. G. F. Pregaglia and M. Binaghi, in A. D. Ketley (ed.), *op. cit.*, vol. 2, chap. 3 of [8].
140. G. Natta, G. Mazzanti, P. Corradini, and I. W. Bassi, *Makromol. Chem.*, **37**:156 (1960).
141. J. Furukawa, T. Saegusa, H. Fujii, A. Kawasaki, H. Imai, and Y. Fujii, *ibid.*, **37**:149 (1960).
142. H. Tani and H. Yasuda, *J Polymer Sci.*, **B7**:17 (1969).
143. P. Pino, *Fortschr. Hochpolymer.-Forsch. (Advan. Polymer Sci.)*, **4**:393 (1965).
144. M. Farina and G. Bressan, Optically Active Stereoregular Polymers, in A. D. Ketley (ed.), *op. cit.*, vol. 3, chap. 4 of [22].
145. M. Goodman, A. Abe, and Y-L. Fan, Optically Active Polymers, in A. Peterlin, M. Goodman, S. Okamura, B. H. Zimm, and H. F. Mark (eds.), "Macromolecular Reviews," vol. 1, pp. 1–34, Interscience Publishers, John Wiley & Sons, Inc., New York, 1967.
146. Y. Kumata, J. Furukawa, and T. Saegusa, *Makromol. Chem.*, **105**:138 (1967).
147. T. Tsunetsugu, T. Fueno, and J. Furukawa, *ibid.*, **112**:220 (1968).
148. G. Natta and S. Valenti, *ibid.*, **67**:225 (1963).
149. G. Natta and M. Donati, *ibid.*, **43**:251 (1961).
150. A. M. Liquori and B. Pispisa, *J. Polymer Sci.*, **B5**:375 (1967).
151. H. Sobue, K. Matsuzaki, and S. Nakano, *ibid.*, **A2**:3339 (1964).
152. H. Yuki, K. Ohta, K. Uno, and S. Murahashi, *ibid.*, **A-1(6)**:829 (1968).
153. T. Tsuruta, S. Inoue, N. Yoshida, and Y. Yodota, *Makromol. Chem.*, **81**:258 (1965).
154. A. Abe and M. Goodman, *J. Polymer Sci.*, **A1**:2193 (1963).
155. C. C. Price and R. Spector, *J. Am. Chem. Soc.*, **87**:2069 (1965).
156. F. Ciardelli, C. Carlini, and G. Montagnoli, *Macromolecules*, 2:296 (1969).
157. N. Beredjick and C. Schuerch, *ibid.*, **80**:1933 (1958).

PROBLEMS

8-1. What is the difference between optical and geometrical isomerism? What is the origin of each in terms of molecular structure? What property differences arise in compounds due to geometrical and optical isomerism? What is the difference in the effects of stereoisomerism on polymer properties relative to the effects on small organic compounds?

8-2. What is the meaning of the term tacticity? How is tacticity measured?

8-3. Show by structural drawings the various (if any) stereoregular polymers which might possibly be obtained from each of the following:

a. $CH_2{=}CH{-}CH_3$

b. $CH_2{=}C(CH_3)_2$

c. $CH_3{-}CH{=}CH{-}CH_3$

d. $CH_2{=}C(CH_3)(C_2H_5)$

e. $CH_3{-}CH{=}CH{-}C_2H_5$

f. $CH_2{=}CH{-}CH{=}CH_2$

g. $CH_3{-}CH{=}CH{-}CH{=}CH_2$

h. $CH_2{=}C(CH_3){-}CH{=}CH_2$

i. $CH_3{-}CH{=}C(Cl){-}CH{=}CH_2$

j. $CH_3{-}CH{=}CH{-}C(CH_3){=}CH_2$

k. $CH_3{-}CH{=}CH{-}CH{=}CH{-}CH_3$

l. $CH_2{=}C(CH_3){-}C(CH_3){=}CH_2$

m. $H_2N{-}(CH_2)_6{-}NH_2 + HO_2C{-}(CH_2)_4{-}CO_2H$

n. 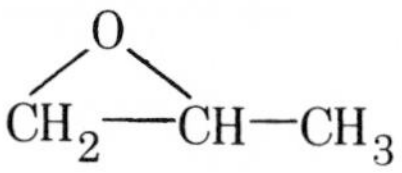 $\overset{O}{\overbrace{CH_2{-}CH}}{-}CH_3$

o. $CH_3{-}\overset{O}{\overbrace{CH{-}CH}}{-}CH_3$

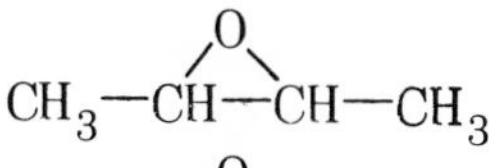

p. 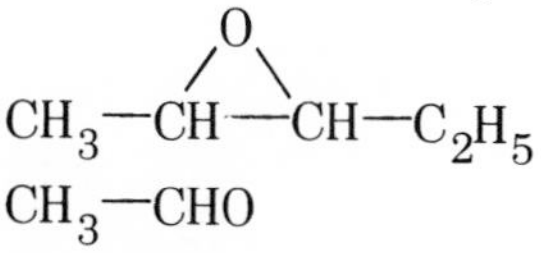 $CH_3{-}\overset{O}{\overbrace{CH{-}CH}}{-}C_2H_5$

q. $CH_3{-}CHO$

r. $(CH_3)_2CO$

s. $CH_3{-}CO{-}CCl_3$

t.

u. 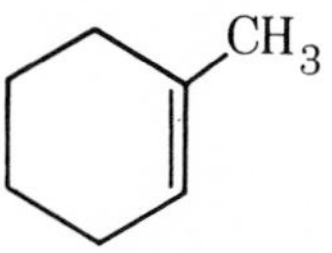 CH_3

Name the various polymer structures using the nomenclature developed in this chapter.

8-4. What are the mechanisms for syndiotactic and isotactic placements in the polymerization of propylene? Describe the reaction conditions which favor each type of stereospecific placement. Discuss the stereospecificity of radical, ionic, and coordination polymerizations.

8-5. Which reaction conditions and factors determine the relative amounts of 1,2-, cis-1,4-, and trans-1,4-polymerization in butadiene? What are the mechanisms for these three modes of polymerization?

8-6. Which of the stereoregular polymer structures in the answer to question 8-3 are capable of exhibiting optical activity? How would you synthesize optically active polymers of those structures? Explain the inability of certain of the stereoregular polymers to exhibit optical activity.

8-7. Distinguish between the terms stereoregular, stereospecific, and stereoselective.

8-8. What is meant by asymmetric induction?

8-9. Describe the monometallic and bimetallic mechanisms for Ziegler-Natta polymerization. What are the pros and cons of each mechanism?

8-10. Discuss the use of homogeneous versus heterogeneous coordination catalysts for the polymerizations of propylene, isoprene, styrene, methyl methacrylate, and butyl vinyl ether.

9
SYNTHETIC REACTIONS OF POLYMERS

The preceding chapters have dealt with the synthesis of polymers by polymerization reactions. In addition to polymerization, a variety of chemical reactions are used to synthesize new polymer structures by the modification of other polymers [1]. These include the esterification and etherification of cellulose, the hydrolysis of poly(vinyl acetate), the chlorination of polyethylene, and the crosslinking of unsaturated polyesters, 1,4-poly-1,3-dienes, and polysiloxanes. The reactions of polymers will be considered in this chapter with emphasis being on those reactions which have practical utility. Polymers also undergo a number of chemical, thermal, photolytic, and radiolytic degradation reactions but these will not be considered here.

9-1 POLYMER REACTIVITY

Polymers undergo the same reactions as their low molecular weight homologs. Acetylation of the hydroxyl groups of cellulose is basically the same reaction as the acetylation of ethanol; chlorination of polyethylene follows in the same manner as chlorination of hexane. It is usually assumed that the reactivity of a functional group in a polymer is the same as that of the same group in a small organic molecule. This is the familiar concept of functional group reactivity independent of molecular size (Sec. 2-1) which is the basis of analyzing polymerization kinetics. However, in many instances, the reaction rates and maximum conversions observed in the reactions of polymer functional groups are very significantly different than those for the corresponding low molecular weight homolog. Polymer reaction rates and conversions are often lower although higher rates are also found in some reactions.

The reactivity of a polymer functional group will differ from that of its low molecular weight homolog under several different conditions [1, 2]:

1) Crystallinity. When reactions are carried out under conditions such that portions of the polymer remain crystalline, only the functional groups in the amorphous regions are available for reaction. The functional groups in the crystalline regions will generally be inaccessible to chemical reagents and reaction will be limited to the amorphous regions. The reaction of a polymer can be exactly analogous to that of its low molecular weight homolog only when it is carried out in solution by the appropriate choice of solvent and temperature.

2) Altered Solubility. Abnormal behavior can occur in the reaction of an initially homogeneous polymer reaction system if there is a change in the physical nature of the system upon reaction of the polymer. Partial reaction may yield a polymer which is no longer soluble in the reaction medium or which forms a highly viscous system. The maximum conversion in such instances may be limited and the reaction rate may decrease with conversion. Enhanced reaction rates have also been observed in some instances of decreased polymer solubility with conversion due to the special characteristics of the reactions involved.

3) Isolation of Functional Groups. When the polymer reaction involves the reaction of a pair of neighboring functional groups, the maximum conversion is limited due to the isolation of single functional groups between reacted pairs of groups. This effect was discussed in Sec. 3-2b for reactions such as the dechlorination of poly(vinyl chloride) and the periodate oxidation of poly(vinyl alcohol). The maximum conversion for irreversible reactions has been calculated [3] as 86.5 percent, which is in good agreement with what is observed in most systems. For reversible reactions, the conversions are higher but the reaction times required for complete conversion are often impractical.

4) Neighboring Group Effect. The reactivity of a functional group can be affected by its neighboring functional group [1, 4]. In some instances, a reacted functional group alters the reactivity of its neighboring, unreacted group. The effects are due to steric and/or electrostatic interactions between neighboring groups and may lead to enhancement or inhibition of reaction rates. Thus, the saponification of many methacrylate polymers and copolymers shows an autocatalytic effect after the start of reaction. After the initial formation of some carboxylate anions, the subsequent hydrolysis of ester groups occurs not directly by hydroxide ion but by neighboring carboxylate anions [5]. The reaction proceeds by the sequence

$$\sim CH_2-C(CH_3)(CO-O^-)-CH_2-C(CH_3)(CO-OR)\sim \xrightarrow{-RO^-} \sim CH_2-C(CH_3)(CO)-CH_2-C(CH_3)(CO)\sim \;[\text{CO}-O-\text{CO ring}] \xrightarrow{OH^-}$$

$$\sim CH_2-C(CH_3)(CO-O^-)-CH_2-C(CH_3)(CO-O^-)\sim \qquad (9\text{-}1)$$

with the intermediate formation of a cyclic acid anhydride.

Rate enhancement by a neighboring group, usually referred to as *anchimeric assistance*, occurs primarily when the cyclic intermediate is the favored 5- or 6-membered ring. Such effects are also encountered in low molecular weight difunctional compounds, e.g., in succinic acid esters. Neighboring group effects of the negative type are also known. Decreased reaction rates and conversion limits less than 100 percent are observed in some instances due to repulsive electrostatic effects between the chemical reagent and the reacted functional group when both carry the same charge. The hydrolysis of polymethacrylamide in strongly basic solution is limited to about 70 percent because of the repulsion of a hydroxide ion by carboxylate anions when a methacrylamide unit has a hydrolyzed unit on each side of it [6].

Neighboring group effects are dependent not only on the functional group and reaction involved but also on the stereochemistry of the neighboring groups. Thus, *isotactic* poly(methyl methacrylate) hydrolyzes faster than either the syndiotactic or atactic polymers [7]. The isotactic structure has neighboring functional groups in the optimum position for interaction with each other to form the cyclic anhydride intermediate.

5) Conformation of Polymer Chains. Functional group reactivity can also be affected by the conformation of polymer chains. Whether the polymer chain exists in the form of a helix or coil and whether the coil is a tight or expanded one can influence the accessibility of a functional group to the chemical reagent. These factors are affected by the stereochemistry of the polymer chains as well as the solvents used to carry out the reaction.

9-2 CROSSLINKING

A number of crosslinking reactions have been previously described in Secs. 2-10a and 2-10b, e.g., the crosslinking of diol and epoxy prepolymers. The crosslinking of unsaturated polyesters, 1,4-poly-1,3-dienes, polyolefins, and polysiloxanes will be considered here. The reaction by which a polymer is converted into a crosslinked network structure is often difficult to analyze kinetically due to the insolubility of the crosslinked system. Decreased reaction rates and conversions are encountered in many instances.

9-2a Unsaturated Polyesters

9-2a-1 Copolymerization. The crosslinking of unsaturated polyesters is related to that of other prepolymers (Secs. 2-10a and 2-10b). A low molecular weight polymer (usually a viscous liquid) is poured, sprayed, or otherwise shaped into a desired form and then transformed into a thermosetting solid by crosslinking. The crosslinking of unsaturated polyesters can be accomplished by copolymerization of the alkene linkage in the polyester with a monomer such as styrene, methyl methacrylate, vinyltoluene, or diallyl phthalate [8-10]. The reaction can be depicted as

$$\sim\sim O_2C-CH=CH-CO_2\sim\sim + CH_2=CHA \longrightarrow$$

$$\begin{array}{c} \sim\sim O_2C-\underset{|}{\overset{\wr}{C}H}-\underset{|}{C}H-CO_2\sim\sim\sim\sim O_2C-\underset{|}{\overset{\wr}{C}H}-\underset{|}{C}H-CO_2\sim\sim \\ (CH_2-CHA)_n \qquad\qquad (CH_2-CHA)_n \\ \sim\sim O_2C-\underset{\wr}{\overset{|}{C}H}-\overset{|}{C}H-CO_2\sim\sim\sim\sim O_2C-\overset{|}{C}H-\underset{\wr}{C}H-CO_2\sim\sim \\ \text{I} \end{array} \tag{9-2}$$

The mechanical properties of the crosslinked polymer depend on the number of crosslinks between polyester chains and the length of the crosslinks. These factors are in turn determined by the monomer used; more specifically, by the copolymerization behavior of the polyester and monomer. Thus, for a polyester containing fumarate double bonds, crosslinking with styrene yields a harder and tougher polymer than when methyl methacrylate is used. The fumarate-styrene system shows more of an alternating copolymerization behavior than the fumarate-methyl methacrylate system ($r_1 = 2.2$, $r_2 = 0.062$ versus $r_1 = 0.50$, $r_2 = 1.05$) [9]. The result is that methyl methacrylate tends to form a small number of long crosslinks (large value of m in I), while styrene forms a larger number of short crosslinks (low value of m). Allyl monomers are also useful for producing high densities of short crosslinks due to the short chain lengths in allylic polymerization (Sec. 3-7c).

It is interesting to compare the crosslinking of maleate polyesters (formed by the use of either maleic anhydride or maleic acid) with that of the fumarates. Reactivity ratios from Table 6-2 indicate that the maleate double bond is far less reactive toward copolymerization than the fumarate double bond. Crosslinking of maleate polyesters by copolymerization would, thus, be expected to be inefficient. However, substantial isomerization (up to 90 percent) of the maleate double bond to the fumarate configuration normally occurs during the formation of the polyester [11] and crosslinking is easily achieved.

9-2a-2 Oxygen. Unsaturated polyesters in which the alkene linkage resides in a fatty acid component such as oleic acid (II) or linoleic acid (III)

$$CH_3{-}(CH_2)_7{-}CH{=}CH{-}(CH_2)_7{-}CO_2H$$

Oleic acid

II

$$CH_3{-}(CH_2)_7{-}CH{=}CH{-}CH{=}CH{-}(CH_2)_5{-}CO_2H$$

Linoleic acid

III

are termed "alkyds." Alkyds are crosslinked via oxidation by atmospheric oxygen. The process is usually referred to as *drying* or *air-drying*. Varnishes and other surface coating based on fatty acids or glycerol esters of fatty acids are crosslinked in the same manner.

The crosslinking process is different depending on whether the unsaturation is an unconjugated double bond as in oleic acid or a conjugated double bond system as in linoleic acid [8, 12]. Single double bonds undergo crosslinking via the initial formation of an allylic hydroperoxide

$$\sim\!\sim CH_2{-}CH{=}CH\sim\!\sim \xrightarrow{O_2} \sim\!\sim \underset{\displaystyle OOH}{\underset{|}{CH}}{-}CH{=}CH\sim\!\sim \tag{9-3}$$

followed by decomposition of the hydroperoxide. The reaction sequence involves

$$\sim\!\sim OOH \longrightarrow \sim\!\sim O\cdot + HO\cdot \tag{9-4}$$

$$2\sim\!\sim OOH \longrightarrow \sim\!\sim O\cdot + \sim\!\sim OO\cdot + H_2O \tag{9-5}$$

$$\sim\!\sim O\cdot + \sim\!\sim H \longrightarrow \sim\!\sim\cdot + \sim\!\sim OH \tag{9-6}$$

$$HO\cdot + \sim\!\sim H \longrightarrow \sim\!\sim\cdot + H_2O \tag{9-7}$$

$$2\sim\sim\cdot \longrightarrow \sim\sim\sim\sim \qquad (9\text{-}8)$$

$$\sim\sim O\cdot + \sim\sim\cdot \longrightarrow \sim\sim O\sim\sim \qquad (9\text{-}9)$$

$$2\sim\sim O\cdot \longrightarrow \sim\sim O{-}O\sim\sim \qquad (9\text{-}10)$$

where ~~OOH and ~~H represent the oxidized and unoxidized polymer molecules. In order to achieve practical crosslinking rates, the reaction is catalyzed by the use of metal ions (cobalt, manganese, iron, lead, zinc) in the form of carboxylic acid salts. The metal ions accelerate the decomposition of hydroperoxides in a manner analogous to the redox systems discussed in Sec. 3-4e. Their action may also involve a catalytic effect on the hydroperoxide formation. The relative amounts of carbon-carbon, ether, and peroxide crosslinks depend on the reaction conditions used.

Crosslinking of the conjugated systems usually involves the formation and decomposition of cyclic peroxides

$$\sim\sim CH{=}CH{-}CH{=}CH\sim\sim \xrightarrow{O_2} \text{(cyclic peroxide: } \sim\sim CH{-}CH{=}CH{-}CH\sim\sim \text{ bridged by } {-}O{-}O{-}\text{)}$$

$$\downarrow$$

$$\sim\sim \underset{\substack{|\\ OO\cdot}}{CH}{-}CH{=}CH{-}\dot{C}H\sim\sim \qquad (9\text{-}11)$$

to yield radicals which initiate crosslinking by 1,4-polymerization of the polymer molecules.

9-2b Elastomers Based on 1,3-Dienes

The 1,4-polymers of isoprene, butadiene, and chloroprene and some of their copolymers (butadiene-acrylonitrile, butadiene-styrene, isoprene-isobutylene) comprise the large bulk of the polymers used as elastomers. Crosslinking is an absolute requirement if elastomers are to have their essential property of rapidly and completely recovering from deformations. The term *vulcanization* is used synonymously with crosslinking in elastomer technology. Crosslinking or vulcanization of these 1,3-diene polymers and copolymers can be accomplished by using sulfur, peroxides, or ionizing radiations [13]. The commercial crosslinking of diene polymers is carried out almost exclusively by heating with sulfur.

9-2b-1 Sulfur. Although sulfur vulcanization has been extensively studied since its discovery in 1839 by Goodyear, its mechanism is very poorly understood [1, 13, 14]. Free radical mechanisms have been generally assumed in the past, but experimental evidence [15, 16] indicates that the reaction more likely proceeds by an ionic route. Radical inhibitors do not affect sulfur vulcanization and radicals have not been detected by electron spin resonance studies of crosslinking systems. On the other hand, sulfur vulcanization is accelerated by organic acids and bases as well as by solvents of high dielectric constant. The ionic crosslinking process can be depicted as a chain reaction involving the initial formation of a sulfonium ion (IV) by reaction of the polymer with polarized sulfur or a sulfur ion-pair

$$S_8 \xrightarrow{\text{Heat}} \overset{\delta+}{S}_m \cdots\cdots \overset{\delta-}{S}_n \quad \text{or} \quad S_m^+ + S_n^-$$

$$\downarrow \sim\!\sim CH_2-CH=CH-CH_2\sim\!\sim$$

$$\sim\!\sim CH_2-\underset{\underset{+S_m}{\diagdown\;\diagup}}{CH-CH}-CH_2\sim\!\sim + S_n^- \qquad (9\text{-}12)$$

IV

The sulfonium ion reacts with a polymer molecule either by hydride abstraction (Eq. 9-13a) or proton transfer (Eq. 9-13b)

$$\sim\!\sim CH_2-\underset{\underset{+S_m}{\diagdown\;\diagup}}{CH-CH}-CH_2\sim\!\sim \xrightarrow{\text{Polymer}} \sim\!\sim CH_2-CH_2-\underset{\underset{S_m}{|}}{CH}-CH_2\sim\!\sim + \sim\!\sim\overset{+}{C}H-CH=CH-CH_2\sim\!\sim \qquad (9\text{-}13a)$$

V

$$\downarrow \text{Polymer}$$

$$\sim\!\sim CH_2-\underset{\underset{S_m}{|}}{CH}-CH=CH\sim\!\sim + \sim\!\sim CH_2-CH_2-\overset{+}{C}H-CH_2\sim\!\sim \qquad (9\text{-}13b)$$

VI

The two polymeric cations V and VI undergo crosslinking by reacting first with sulfur and then by addition to a polymer double bond. A subsequent reaction with polymer by either proton (Eq. 9-15a) or hydride (Eq. 9-15b) transfer regenerates the respective polymeric cations. The sequence for polymeric cation V is

$$\sim\!\sim\overset{+}{C}HCH{=}CHCH_2\sim\!\sim \xrightarrow{S_8} \sim\!\sim \underset{\underset{+S_m}{|}}{C}HCH{=}CHCH_2\sim\!\sim \xrightarrow{\text{Polymer}} \sim\!\sim \underset{\underset{\underset{\sim\sim CH_2-CH-\underset{+}{C}HCH_2\sim\sim}{|}}{S_m}}{\overset{|}{C}}HCH{=}CHCH_2\sim\!\sim \quad \text{VII} \qquad (9\text{-}14)$$

$$\text{VII} \xrightarrow{\text{Polymer}} \sim\!\sim CHCH{=}CHCH_2\sim\!\sim \;(\text{--}S_m\text{--})\; \sim\!\sim CH_2\overset{|}{C}{=}CHCH_2\sim\!\sim \;+\; \sim\!\sim CH_2CH_2-\underset{+}{C}HCH_2\sim\!\sim \qquad (9\text{-}15a)$$

$$\text{VII} \xrightarrow{\text{Polymer}} \sim\!\sim CHCH{=}CHCH_2\sim\!\sim \;(\text{--}S_m\text{--})\; \sim\!\sim CH_2\overset{|}{C}HCH_2CH_2\sim\!\sim \;+\; \sim\!\sim\overset{+}{C}H-CH{=}CHCH_2\sim\!\sim \qquad (9\text{-}15b)$$

9-2b-2 Accelerated Sulfur Vulcanization. Vulcanization of a diene polymer by heating solely with sulfur is a very inefficient process with approximately fifty sulfur atoms incorporated into the polymer for each crosslink. Sulfur is wasted by the formation of long polysulfide crosslinks (i.e., high values of m in VII), vicinal crosslinks (VIII) which act as single crosslinks from the viewpoint of properties, and intramolecular cyclic sulfide structures (IX).

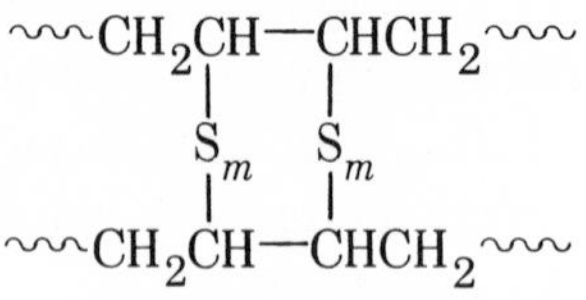

$$\begin{array}{c} \sim\!CH_2CH-CHCH_2\!\sim \\ \quad | \qquad | \\ \quad S_m \quad S_m \\ \quad | \qquad | \\ \sim\!CH_2CH-CHCH_2\!\sim \end{array}$$

VIII

$$\begin{array}{l} \qquad\qquad\; CH \\ \sim\!CH_2CH \qquad CH \\ \qquad\quad | \qquad\quad | \\ \qquad\quad S\text{------}CH-CH_2\!\sim \end{array}$$

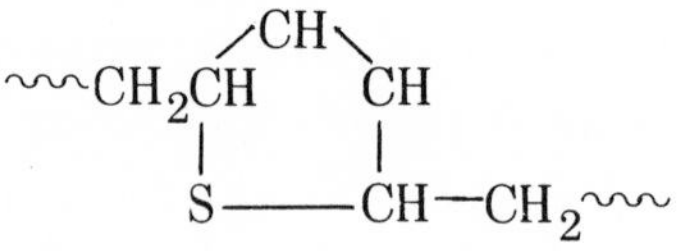

IX

Commercial sulfur vulcanizations are carried out in the presence of various additives which greatly increase the rate and efficiency of the process. These additives, referred to as *accelerators*, include various organic sulfur-containing compounds such as thiuram sulfides (X), dithiocarbamates, and benzthiazoles (XII) as well as a few

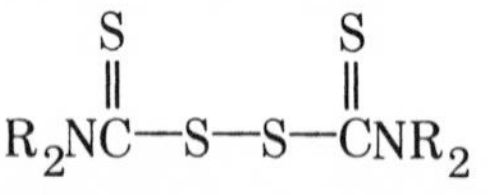

$$R_2N\overset{\overset{S}{\|}}{C}-S-S-\overset{\overset{S}{\|}}{C}NR_2$$

X

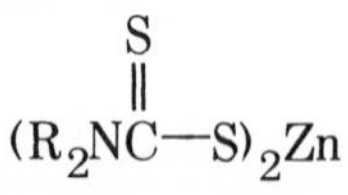

$$(R_2N\overset{\overset{S}{\|}}{C}-S)_2Zn$$

XI

$$\left[\text{(benzothiazol-2-yl)}-S\right]_2 Zn$$

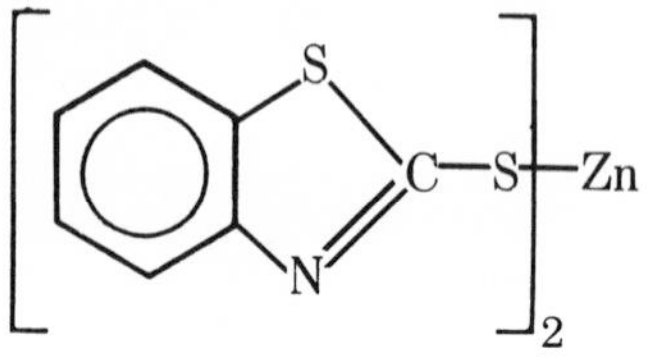

XII

non-sulfur compounds such as aryl guanidines. Actually, the use of accelerators alone usually gives only marginal increases in the efficiency of crosslinking. Maximum efficiency is obtained only when accelerators are used in conjunction with certain combinations of a metal oxide and an organic acid. The latter substances are usually referred to as *activators*. Zinc oxide and stearic acid are the most commonly used activators. Analysis of the crosslinked polymers shows that the combination of accelerators and activators greatly decreases the extent of the wastage reactions. The crosslinking efficiency in some systems is increased to slightly less than two sulfur atoms per crosslink. Most of the crosslinks are monosulfide or disulfide links with very little vicinal or cyclic sulfide units [14–18]. In spite of the great practical utility of the accelerated vulcanization process, there is a general lack of information as to its mechanism.

9-2c Polyolefins and Polysiloxanes

Polyethylene, ethylene-propylene copolymers, and polysiloxanes are crosslinked by compounding them with a peroxide such as dicumyl peroxide or di-*t*-butyl peroxide and then heating the mixture [13]. Crosslinking of polyethylene extends the upper temperature limit at which this plastic can be used—crosslinked polyethylene is a solid at temperatures at which uncrosslinked polyethylene melts and flows. For ethylene-propylene copolymers and polysiloxanes, crosslinking is essential to their use as elastomers. Peroxide crosslinking involves the formation of polymer radicals via hydrogen abstraction by the peroxy radicals formed from the decomposition of the peroxide. Crosslinking occurs by coupling of the polymer radicals

$$\mathrm{ROOR} \longrightarrow 2\mathrm{RO}\cdot \tag{9-16}$$

$$\mathrm{RO}\cdot + \sim\!\sim\mathrm{CH_2CH_2}\sim\!\sim \longrightarrow \mathrm{ROH} + \sim\!\sim\mathrm{CH_2\dot{C}H}\sim\!\sim \tag{9-17}$$

$$2\ \sim\!\sim\mathrm{CH_2\dot{C}H}\sim\!\sim \longrightarrow \begin{array}{c}\sim\!\sim\mathrm{CH_2CH}\sim\!\sim\\ |\\ \sim\!\sim\mathrm{CH_2CH}\sim\!\sim\end{array} \tag{9-18}$$

The maximum crosslinking efficiency in this process is one crosslink per molecule of peroxide decomposed—far less than that of a polymerization process where one radical converts large numbers of monomer molecules to product. Further, the actual crosslinking efficiency is often far less than one because of various side reactions of the initiator (Sec. 3-4f-2) and of the polymer radical. Thus, if a polymer radical is not formed in the close vicinity of another polymer radical, crosslinking may be impaired since the process is taking place in a highly viscous, solid system. Side reactions such as chain scission, hydrogen atom abstraction or expulsion, and combination with initiator radicals become possible. These considerations together with the high cost of peroxides limit the practical utility of the peroxide crosslinking process.

Various techniques can be used to increase the crosslinking efficiency of the peroxide process. The crosslinking efficiency for polysiloxanes can be increased by incorporating small amounts of vinyl groups into the usual polydimethylsiloxane or polyphenylmethylsiloxane structure. This is accomplished by copolymerization of small amounts of vinylmethylsilanol, for example

$$\mathrm{HO{-}\underset{CH_3}{\overset{\overset{CH_2}{\|}}{\overset{CH}{|}}}{Si}{-}OH} + \mathrm{HO{-}\underset{CH_3}{\overset{CH_3}{Si}}{-}OH} \longrightarrow \mathrm{\sim\!\sim O{-}\underset{CH_3}{\overset{\overset{CH_2}{\|}}{\overset{CH}{|}}}{Si}{-}O{-}\underset{CH_3}{\overset{CH_3}{Si}}{-}O\!\sim\!\sim} \qquad (9\text{-}19)$$

Peroxide crosslinking of the copolymer is much more efficient than that of the corresponding homopolymer of dimethylsilanol (Table 9-1) [19]. The process becomes a chain reaction involving polymerization of the pendant vinyl groups on the polysiloxane chains. The crosslinking of ethylene-propylene elastomers has been modified in a similar manner by synthesizing terpolymers containing small amounts of unconjugated dienes such as dicyclopentadiene and 1,4-hexadiene [20, 21]. The resulting terpolymers contain pendant unsaturation and can also be crosslinked by the accelerated sulfur process in the same manner as 1,4-poly-1,3-dienes.

Table 9-1 Efficiency of Crosslinking of Polydimethylsiloxane by Bis(2,4-dichlorobenzoyl)peroxide[a]

Vinyl comonomer content (mole %)	Number of crosslinks per peroxide molecule decomposed for peroxide concentration of	
	0.74%	1.47%
0.0	0.31	0.19
0.1	0.80	0.42
0.2	1.0	0.63

[a]Data from [19].

9-2d Other Crosslinking Processes

Many other crosslinking reactions are employed in the applications of polymers [1, 13, 14]. Elastomeric copolymers of vinylidene fluoride and hexafluoropropylene are crosslinked by heating with diamines and basic oxides. Crosslinking involves dehydrofluorination followed by addition of the diamine (Eq. 9-20) and/or a Diels-Alder condensation (Eq. 9-21).

$$
\sim CH_2CF_2CH_2CF_2CF_2\underset{}{\overset{CF_3}{\overset{|}{C}}}F\sim \xrightarrow{-HF} \sim CH{=}CFCH_2CF_2CF(CF_3)\sim \quad \text{XIII}
$$

$$
\text{XIII} \xrightarrow{-HF} \sim CH{=}CFCH{=}CFCF(CF_3)\sim \xrightarrow{\text{XIII}} \text{(Diels–Alder adduct: } \sim CH{-}CF{-}CH_2CF_2CF(CF_3)\sim \text{ fused cyclohexene ring bearing F, F and } CF(CF_3)\sim)
$$

$$
\text{XIII} \xrightarrow{H_2N{-}R{-}NH_2} \sim CH_2\underset{NH-R-NH}{CF}CH_2CF_2CF(CF_3)\sim \;/\; \sim CH_2CFCH_2CF_2CF(CF_3)\sim \qquad (9\text{-}20)
$$

(9-21)

Polyurethane elastomers are crosslinked by peroxides, diols, and diamines. Cellulose fibers are crosslinked, to impart crease- and wrinkle-resistance, by reaction of cellulose hydroxyl groups with dimethylolurea, dimethylolethyleneurea, urea-formaldehyde and melamine-formaldehyde prepolymers, and other reagents.

Radiation crosslinking of a variety of polymers has been studied in recent years [22]. The reaction is essentially the same as in peroxide crosslinking except that polymer radicals are formed by the interaction of ionizing radiation (e.g., electrons, gammas, and neutrons) with the polymer. (Ionic intermediates and reactions may also be involved in the crosslinking process.) Thus far, radiation crosslinking has found almost no practical application except in a few specialty applications involving polyethylene and ethylene copolymers.

9-3 REACTIONS OF CELLULOSE

The properties of cellulose, a naturally occurring polymer, are such that it cannot be used directly. It is highly crystalline, insoluble in solvents, and decomposes at high temperatures without flowing or melting—all as a consequence of the extremely strong hydrogen-bonding present. These properties of native cellulose do not allow it to be formed into useful products. However, cellulose is used in very large quantities for both fiber and plastic applications by using various chemical reactions to alter its properties [23, 24].

9-3a Solution of Cellulose

Cellulose is spun into fiber or cast into film by using a chemical reaction to convert it into a soluble derivative. This is accomplished by treating shredded cellulose (wood pulp) with concentrated aqueous alkali (usually 18 percent NaOH) at room temperature. Much of the NaOH is physically held in the swollen polymer; some of it may be in the form of cellulose alcoholates. The excess alkali is pressed out of the cellulose pulp and the mass aged to allow oxidative degradation of the polymer chains to the desired molecular weight. The alkali cellulose is then treated with carbon disulfide to form the alkali xanthate derivative of cellulose (Eq. 9-22).

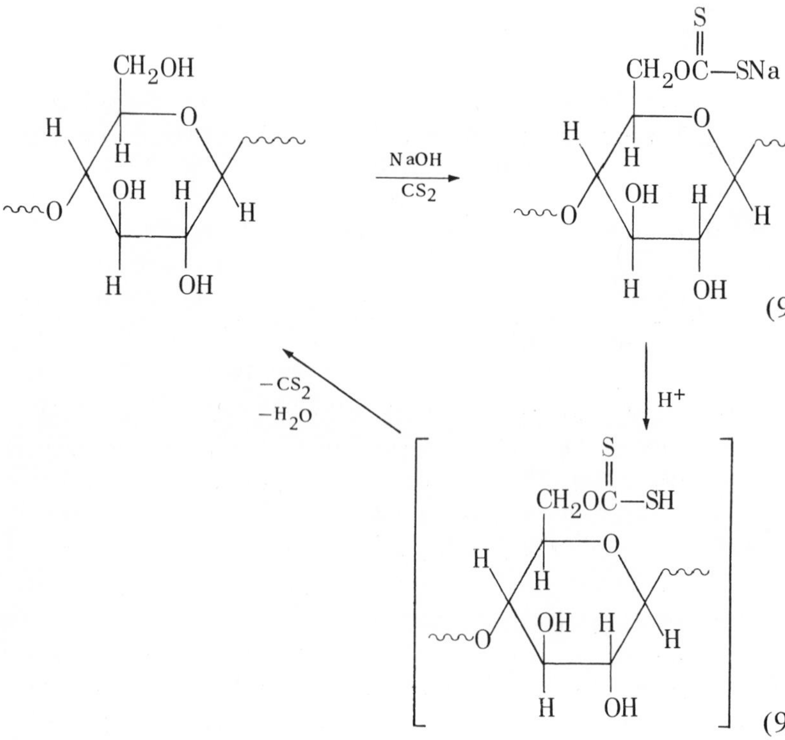

CH_2OH; H; O; H; OH H; ~O; H; H OH $\xrightarrow[CS_2]{NaOH}$ S; ‖; $CH_2OC—SNa$; H; O; H; OH H; ~O; H; H OH (9-22)

$\downarrow H^+$

$\xleftarrow[-H_2O]{-CS_2}$ [S; ‖; $CH_2OC—SH$; H; O; H; OH H; ~O; H; H OH] (9-23)

The degree of xanthation for the commercial process is relatively low—only about 0.5 xanthate groups per three hydroxyls—due to the heterogeneous nature of both steps of the reaction. However, this degree of reaction is sufficient to solubilize the cellulose. Films and fibers are produced by casting or spinning of the viscous alkali cellulose xanthate solution into a bath containing sulfuric acid. Sulfuric acid hydrolyzes the xanthate to the xanthic acid which is unstable and decomposes (without isolation) with the regeneration of cellulose (Eq. 9-23) which is insoluble in the aqueous medium [25]. The result is a solid cellulose film or fiber product. The overall process is often referred to as the *viscose* process.

An alternate procedure which is used in some instances is the *cuprammonium* process. This involves solubilization of cellulose in an ammonia solution of cupric oxide. Solubilization probably occurs by complex formation between cupric ion and the cellulose hydroxyl groups. Regeneration of cellulose, after the formation of the desired product, is accomplished by treatment with acid or alkali.

9-3b Esterification

Acetate, propionate, mixed acetate-propionate and acetate-butyrate, and nitrate esters of cellulose are produced commercially. Cellulose acetate is by far the most important ester derivative of cellulose. It is produced by the acetylation of cellulose with acetic acid

$$\text{Cell—OH} + \text{HO}\overset{\text{O}}{\overset{\|}{\text{C}}}\text{CH}_3 \rightleftharpoons \text{Cell—O}\overset{\text{O}}{\overset{\|}{\text{C}}}\text{CH}_3 + \text{H}_2\text{O} \tag{9-24}$$

in the presence of a strong acid catalyst (usually H_2SO_4 or $HClO_4$). The equilibrium in Eq. 9-24 is driven to the right by removal of water by reaction with acetic anhydride (or acetyl chloride) which is included in the reaction mixture.

From the viewpoint of polymer properties, the diacetate of cellulose is often preferred to the completely acetylated product (triacetate). Direct synthesis of the diacetate is not used since it does not yield a homogeneous product due to the heterogeneity of the reaction. Some cellulose chains might be completely acetylated while others might be completely unreacted. The diacetate is produced by controlled hydrolysis of the triacetate. The triacetate is soluble in the reaction mixture and complete solubility of the cellulose ensures the homogeneity of the final product. Hydrolysis of the triacetate is carried out by controlled reversal of the esterification reaction by the addition of water or dilute acetic acid. Although the heterogeneity of the esterification process is overcome by hydrolysis of the triacetate, the final product may not be homogeneous from the viewpoint of the distribution of acetyl groups on the three reactive positions of cellulose. Two of the three are secondary hydroxyls while the third is a primary position. The primary position is more reactive and hydrolysis of the triacetate results in a preponderance of acetylated secondary hydroxyls.

9-3c Etherification

The methyl and ethyl ethers of cellulose are produced by reacting alkali cellulose with the appropriate alkyl halide

$$\text{Cell—OH} + \text{NaOH} + \text{RCl} \longrightarrow \text{Cell—OR} + \text{NaCl} + H_2O \tag{9-25}$$

9-4 REACTIONS OF POLY(VINYL ACETATE)

In addition to its use as a plastic, poly(vinyl acetate) is used to produce two polymers which cannot be made directly since their monomers are not known [24]. Poly(vinyl alcohol) is obtained by the alcoholysis of poly(vinyl acetate) with methanol or ethanol

$$\sim\!CH_2\!-\!\underset{\substack{| \\ O \\ | \\ CO \\ | \\ CH_3}}{CH}\!\sim \xrightarrow[-CH_3CO_2CH_3]{CH_3OH} \sim\!CH_2\!-\!\underset{\substack{| \\ OH}}{CH}\!\sim \tag{9-26}$$

Both acids and bases catalyze the reaction but base catalysis is usually used because of its faster reaction rates and freedom from side reactions.

Reaction of poly(vinyl alcohol) with an aldehyde yields the poly(vinyl acetal)

$$\sim\!CH_2CH(OH)-CH_2-CH(OH)\!\sim \xrightarrow[-H_2O]{RCHO} \sim\!CH_2\overset{}{CH}-CH_2-CH\!\sim \text{ (cyclic acetal: } -O-CH(R)-O- \text{ bridging the two CH)} \qquad (9\text{-}27)$$

The reaction is usually carried out in water solution with an acid catalyst. Acetal formation does not proceed to completion due to isolation of single hydroxyl groups between pairs of acetal structures. The two most important members of this polymer class are the formal and butyral (R = —H and —C_3H_7, respectively).

9-5 HALOGENATION

9-5a Natural Rubber

The chlorination and hydrochlorination of natural rubber are commercial processes carried out homogeneously by using solutions of rubber in chlorinated or aromatic solvents [1, 14]. Hydrochlorination proceeds by an ionic mechanism to give the Markownikoff addition product with the chloride on the tertiary carbon (Eq. 9-28). Some cyclization of the protonated intermediate (XIV) also takes place (Sec. 9-7).

$$\sim\!CH_2\overset{\overset{CH_3}{|}}{C}{=}CH-CH_2\!\sim \xrightarrow{H^+} \sim\!CH_2-\underset{+}{\overset{\overset{CH_3}{|}}{C}}-CH_2-CH_2\!\sim$$

XIV

$$\downarrow Cl^-$$

$$\sim\!CH_2-\underset{\underset{Cl}{|}}{\overset{\overset{CH_3}{|}}{C}}-CH_2-CH_2\!\sim \qquad (9\text{-}28)$$

The chlorination of natural rubber involves several different reactions with the extent of each reaction depending on the process conditions. The principal reaction is substitution at the allylic position (Eq. 9-29). The evolved hydrogen chloride can bring about cyclization (Sec. 9-7) of the halogenated product (Eq. 9-30). The cyclic structure (XV) can then undergo halogen addition to the double bond or substitution of an allylic hydrogen. Some cross-linking also is reported to take place but the reaction path is unclear.

$$\sim\!\!\sim CH_2-\overset{\overset{\displaystyle CH_3}{|}}{C}=CH-CH_2-CH_2-\overset{\overset{\displaystyle CH_3}{|}}{C}=CH-CH_2\sim\!\!\sim \xrightarrow[-HCl]{Cl_2}$$

$$\sim\!\!\sim CHCl-\overset{\overset{\displaystyle CH_3}{|}}{C}=CH-CH_2-CHCl-\overset{\overset{\displaystyle CH_3}{|}}{C}=CH-CH_2\sim\!\!\sim \qquad (9\text{-}29)$$

$$\big\downarrow \text{HCl}$$

$$\text{XV} \qquad \text{cyclohexene ring bearing } CH_3 \text{ (on the double bond)}, Cl, \sim\!\!\sim \text{ and } Cl \text{ on one carbon}, CH_3 \text{ and } CH_2-CH_2\sim\!\!\sim \text{ on the adjacent carbon} \qquad (9\text{-}30)$$

9-5b Saturated Hydrocarbon Polymers

The chlorination of polyethylene, polypropylene, polyisobutylene, and various other saturated hydrocarbon polymers and copolymers has been studied [1, 26]. The reaction is a free radical chain reaction

$$\sim\!\!\sim CH_2\sim\!\!\sim + Cl\cdot \longrightarrow \sim\!\!\sim \dot{C}H\sim\!\!\sim + HCl \qquad (9\text{-}31)$$

$$\sim\!\!\sim \dot{C}H\sim\!\!\sim + Cl_2 \longrightarrow \sim\!\!\sim CHCl\sim\!\!\sim + Cl\cdot \qquad (9\text{-}32)$$

catalyzed by heat, radical initiators, and ultraviolet light. Chlorination can be carried out in solution or on the solid polymer. The heterogeneous reaction will usually be limited to the outer surface of the polymer sample for low degrees of substitution. This may be advantageous if it is desired to change the surface properties of a polymer without affecting its bulk mechanical properties.

A related reaction is the chlorosulfonation [27] of polyethylene

$$\sim\sim CH_2CH_2 \sim\sim \xrightarrow[-HCl]{Cl_2,\ SO_2} \sim\sim CH_2\underset{}{\overset{\displaystyle SO_2Cl}{\overset{|}{C}H}} \sim\sim \tag{9-33}$$

to yield a commercially useful elastomer. The chlorosulfonated product is vulcanized by the formation of either metal sulfonate or sulfonic ester linkages

$$\sim\sim CH_2\overset{\displaystyle SO_2Cl}{\overset{|}{C}H} \sim\sim \xrightarrow{PbO_2} \begin{array}{c} \sim\sim CH_2CH \sim\sim \\ | \\ SO_2 \\ | \\ O \\ | \\ Pb \\ | \\ O \\ | \\ SO_2 \\ | \\ \sim\sim CH_2CH \sim\sim \end{array} \tag{9-34}$$

$$\xrightarrow{HO-R-OH} \begin{array}{c} \sim\sim CH_2CH \sim\sim \\ | \\ SO_2 \\ | \\ O \\ | \\ R \\ | \\ O \\ | \\ SO_2 \\ | \\ \sim\sim CH_2CH \sim\sim \end{array} \tag{9-35}$$

9-6 AROMATIC SUBSTITUTION

Polystyrene undergoes all of the substitution reactions of benzene [1]. Aromatic substitution is used to produce styrene polymers with ion-exchange properties by the incorporation of sulfonic acid or quaternary ammonium groups. Crosslinked styrene-divinylbenzene copolymers are used as the starting polymer in order to obtain an insoluble final product; polystyrene would yield soluble ion-exchange products. Cationic ion-exchange polymers are obtained by sulfonation (Eq. 9-36) while anionic ion-exchange polymers are produced by chloromethylation followed by reaction with a tertiary amine (Eq. 9-37).

$$\text{polystyrene} \xrightarrow[ZnCl_2]{ClCH_2OCH_3} \text{—}C_6H_4\text{—}CH_2Cl \xrightarrow{NR_3} \text{—}C_6H_4\text{—}CH_2\overset{+}{N}R_3\ Cl^- \qquad (9\text{-}37)$$

$$\text{polystyrene} \xrightarrow{H_2SO_4} \text{—}C_6H_4\text{—}SO_3H \qquad (9\text{-}36)$$

9-7 CYCLIZATION

Intramolecular cyclization has been previously considered in Sec. 2-12 as a means of producing semi-ladder or ladder polymer structures for high temperature uses. Several other cyclization reactions are used for similar reasons. Natural rubber and other 1,4-poly-1,3-dienes are cyclized by treatment with protonic acids [1]. The reaction involves addition of a proton to the polymer double bond (Eq. 9-38) followed by cyclization via attack of the carbonium ion on the double bond of an adjacent monomer unit (Eq. 9-39). Some bicyclic and polycyclic fused ring structures are formed by propagation of the cyclization reaction through more than two repeating monomer units. However, the average number of fused rings in a sequence is only 2-4 because of the steric restrictions involved in the polymer reaction, transfer reactions which occur, and the isolation of unreacted monomer units between pairs of cyclized units [28]. Cyclization is used commercially to transform rubber into a hard plastic for specialty applications. Some cyclization of the same type also occurs in the chlorination and hydrochlorination of natural rubber since an acid is present or is formed during the reaction.

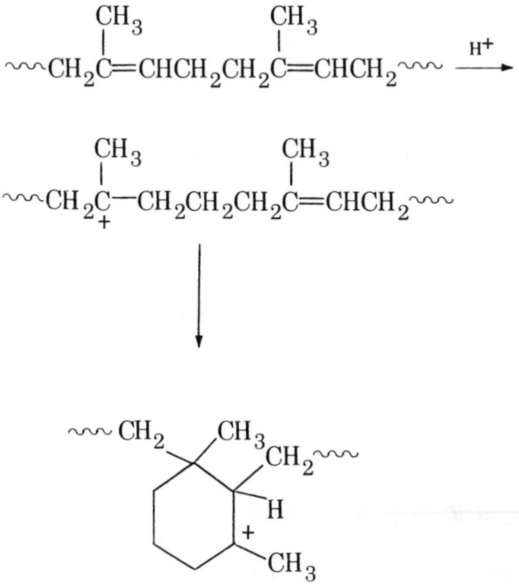

$$\sim\!\!\sim CH_2\overset{\overset{CH_3}{|}}{C}{=}CHCH_2CH_2\overset{\overset{CH_3}{|}}{C}{=}CHCH_2\sim\!\!\sim \xrightarrow{H^+}$$

$$\sim\!\!\sim CH_2\overset{\overset{CH_3}{|}}{\underset{+}{C}}{-}CH_2CH_2CH_2\overset{\overset{CH_3}{|}}{C}{=}CHCH_2\sim\!\!\sim \tag{9-38}$$

$$\downarrow$$

$$\text{cyclohexyl carbocation: ring bearing } \sim\!\!\sim CH_2,\ CH_3;\ CH_2\sim\!\!\sim,\ H;\ +,\ CH_3 \tag{9-39}$$

The pyrolysis of some polymers results in cyclization by the reactions of pendant functional groups [1]. Polyacrylonitrile undergoes polymerization through the nitrile groups to form a ladder structure (XV) [29]. Continued pyrolysis of the polymer results in

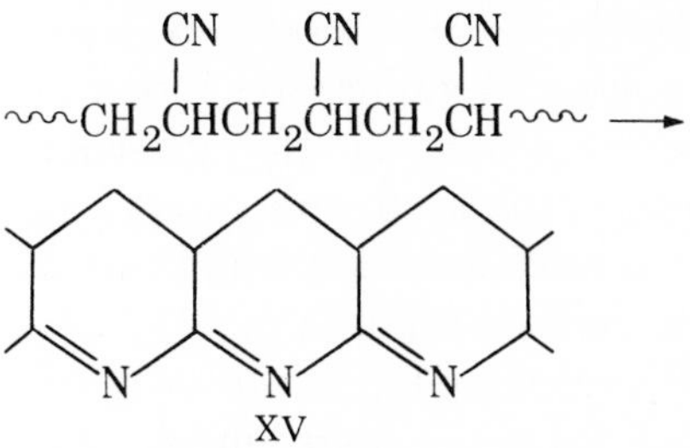

$$\sim\!\!\sim CH_2\overset{\overset{CN}{|}}{C}HCH_2\overset{\overset{CN}{|}}{C}HCH_2\overset{\overset{CN}{|}}{C}H\sim\!\!\sim \longrightarrow$$

$$\text{XV (fused ladder of rings with } {=}N{-} \text{ in each ring)} \tag{9-40}$$

XV

aromatization but probably not completely to the polyquinizarine structure (XVI); some of the rings are most likely partially hydrogenated polyquinizarine structures (XVII). The product appears to have interesting high temperature properties.

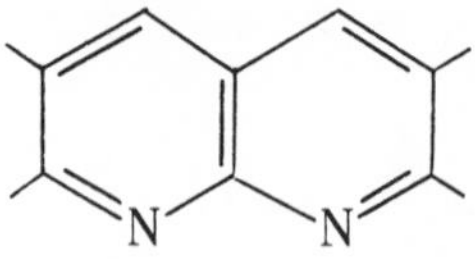

XVI

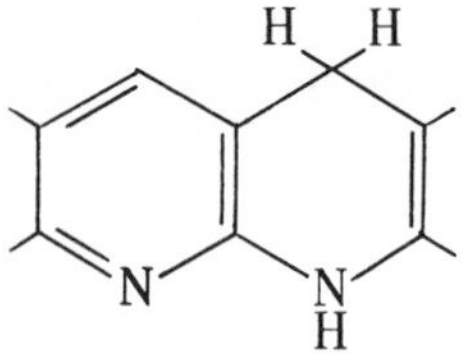

XVII

Poly(methacrylic acid) undergoes anhydride formation upon pyrolysis.

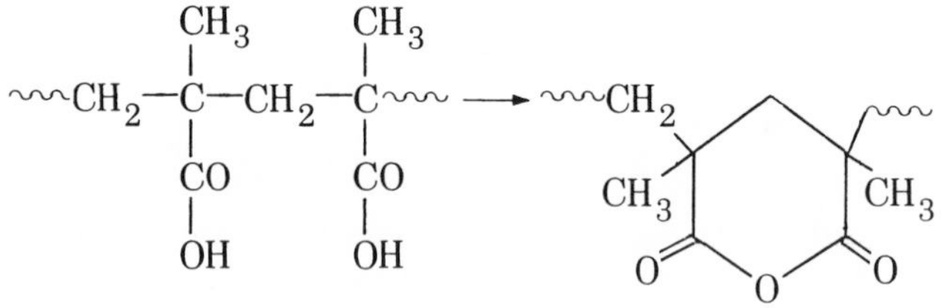

$$\sim\sim CH_2-\underset{\underset{OH}{|}}{\underset{CO}{|}}{\overset{\overset{CH_3}{|}}{C}}-CH_2-\underset{\underset{OH}{|}}{\underset{CO}{|}}{\overset{\overset{CH_3}{|}}{C}}\sim\sim \longrightarrow \sim\sim CH_2 \ \text{(cyclic anhydride ring with } CH_3, CH_3, O, O, O) \sim\sim \tag{9-41}$$

9-8 GRAFT AND BLOCK COPOLYMERS

Graft and block copolymers contain long sequences of each of two different monomers in the copolymer chain. A block copolymer contains the sequences in a linear arrangement while a graft copolymer contains a linear sequence of one monomer with a branch consisting of a sequence of a second monomer (Sec. 6-1b). A variety of techniques for synthesizing these structures has been studied [1, 30, 31]. Some of the more useful methods will be reviewed here.

9-8a Graft Copolymers

The synthesis of a graft copolymer requires the formation of a reactive center on a polymer molecule in the presence of a polymerizable monomer. Most methods of obtaining graft copolymers involve the use of radical polymerization. Ionic graft polymerizations have received much less attention.

9-8a-1 Chain Transfer. The radical polymerization of a monomer in the presence of a polymer can result in grafting due to radical formation on the polymer backbone by chain transfer from the propagating monomer. In most, but not all instances, the chain transfer reaction involves hydrogen atom abstraction, e.g., for the grafting of styrene to polybutadiene

$$\sim\sim CH_2CH{=}CHCH_2\sim\sim + \sim\sim CH_2\dot{C}H\phi \longrightarrow$$

$$\sim\sim \dot{C}HCH{=}CHCH_2\sim\sim + \sim\sim CH_2CH_2\phi \qquad (9\text{-}42)$$

$$\sim\sim \dot{C}HCH{=}CHCH_2\sim\sim + n\ CH_2{=}CH\phi \longrightarrow$$

$$\underset{\substack{|\\(CH_2CH\phi)_n}}{\sim\sim CH}CH{=}CHCH_2\sim\sim \qquad (9\text{-}43)$$

XVIII

This process is used to an extent commercially to alter the properties of polybutadiene. The graft copolymer (XVIII) is named (Sec. 6-1b) as poly(butadiene-*g*-styrene) where the first monomer inside the brackets refers to the backbone polymer and the second to the grafted monomer.

9-8a-2 Ultraviolet and Ionizing Radiation. The polymer radicals can alternately be produced by the irradiation of a polymer-monomer system with ultraviolet light (often in the presence of a photosensitizer) or ionizing radiation. Thus, the interaction of ionizing radiation with polyethylene-styrene produces radical centers on the polyethylene and these initiate the graft polymerization of styrene

$$\sim\sim CH_2CH_2\sim\sim \xrightarrow{\text{Radiation}} \sim\sim CH_2\dot{C}H\sim\sim \xrightarrow{CH_2=CH\phi} \sim\sim CH_2\underset{\substack{|\\(CH_2CH\phi)_n}}{CH}\sim\sim \qquad (9\text{-}44)$$

to produce poly(ethylene-*g*-styrene). Many graft polymerizations, especially those initiated by radiation, are heterogeneous reactions involving solid polymer swollen by and immersed in liquid monomer.

The relative rates of grafting and diffusion determine whether reaction occurs only at the polymer surface or throughout its volume [32].

Both the chain transfer and irradiation methods usually yield mixtures of products—consisting of the graft copolymer, backbone polymer, and homopolymer of the monomer. The relative amounts of the three products depend on the monomer-polymer combination and the reaction conditions. For the chain transfer method of grafting, the efficiency of the grafting reaction (i.e., the amount of graft polymerization relative to homopolymerization) is dependent on the tendency of a radical to chain transfer relative to propagation. One can make a reasonable estimate of the grafting efficiency for a particular monomer-polymer combination from the values of the propagation rate constant for the monomer and the transfer constant for the polymer. The latter is usually not available but one can refer to the corresponding transfer constant of a model compound for the polymer (e.g., ethylbenzene for polystyrene). The grafting efficiency of the irradiation method depends on the relative rates of radical formation in the polymer and monomer. This usually corresponds, at least qualitatively, to the transfer constants for the polymer and monomer (or to the bond energies for the weakest bonds in the two compounds). Thus, grafting to poly(vinyl chloride) is usually more efficient than to polyethylene because of the weaker carbon-chlorine bond. When ionizing radiations are used, the grafting efficiencies may be slightly different than expected because of the somewhat non-selective nature of radiolytic bond-breaking and the general radiolytic stability of aromatic structures.

The radiolytic method can be carried out by two variations in which the irradiation and grafting steps are separated. A polymer can be irradiated alone and then contacted with monomer. Graft polymerization is initiated by small concentrations of long-lived radicals trapped in the solid polymer. The graft copolymer is usually obtained free from homopolymer by this variation of the radiolytic method. However, the reaction rates are lower than in the case where the polymer and monomer are irradiated together. The latter process is referred to as the *mutual irradiation* process and the former as the *preirradiation* process. A variation of the preirradiation process involves irradiation of the polymer in the presence of oxygen to form peroxide and hydroperoxide groups. These are then thermally decomposed to polymer radicals in the presence of monomer.

9-8a-3 Redox. Redox initiation can be a most efficient method for carrying out graft polymerization reaction. Hydroxyl-containing polymers such as poly(vinyl alcohol) and cellulose undergo redox reaction with ceric ion or other oxidizing agents to form polymer

$$\sim\!\sim CH_2\underset{\displaystyle OH}{\underset{|}{CH}}\sim\!\sim + Ce^{4+} \longrightarrow \sim\!\sim CH_2\underset{\displaystyle OH}{\underset{|}{\dot{C}}}\sim\!\sim + H^+ + Ce^{3+} \tag{9-45}$$

radicals capable of initiating polymerization [33]. This method results in graft polymerization with no homopolymerization since most monomers are unreactive toward ceric ion. However, redox initiation is limited to the small number of polymers containing the necessary functional group.

9-8a-4 Other Grafting Systems. A variety of other graft polymerizations is to be found in the literature. Many of these involve the special preparation of polymers with functional groups which can be converted into grafting sites. Thus, mercaptan groups can be introduced into cellulose by reaction with ethylene sulfide

$$\text{Cell—OH} + \overset{\displaystyle S}{CH_2\!-\!CH_2} \longrightarrow \text{Cell—OCH}_2\text{CH}_2\text{SH} \tag{9-46}$$

The mercaptan groups can then be used for grafting via the chain transfer method. Double bonds can be introduced into cellulose for grafting purposes by reaction with acroyl chloride

$$\text{Cell—OH} + CH_2\!=\!CHCOCl \xrightarrow{-HCl} \text{Cell—OCO—CH}\!=\!CH_2 \tag{9-47}$$

Hydroperoxide groups can be formed on polystyrene containing some isopropyl groups

$$\sim\!\sim C_6H_4\text{—}CH(CH_3)_2 \longrightarrow \sim\!\sim C_6H_4\text{—}C(CH_3)_2\text{—OOH} \tag{9-48}$$

9-8b Block Copolymers

A number of methods for the synthesis of block copolymers have been described previously. Block copolymers can be obtained by the step copolymerization of polymers with functional groups which can react with each other (Sec. 2-11). Block copolymers of commercial interest are obtained in certain Ziegler-Natta copolymerization (Sec. 8-4d-2) when r_1 and r_2 are both larger than one (Sec. 6-2c-3). A versatile method is that involving anionic living polymerization (Sec. 5-3b) in which the living polymer of one monomer is used to initiate the polymerization of a second monomer

$$\sim\!\sim M_1M_1M_1M_1M_1M_1^- \xrightarrow{M_2} \sim\!\sim M_1M_1M_1M_1M_1M_1M_2M_2M_2M_2M_2M_2M_2M_2^- \tag{9-49}$$

The procedure can be repeated if desired so as to yield a copolymer with several alternating blocks of each of the two monomers. The method is applicable to the block copolymerization of alkene monomers, non-alkene monomers and cyclic monomers as well as certain combinations of these different types of monomers, e.g., styrene-formaldehyde, styrene-ethylene oxide, and δ-valerolactone-propylene oxide (Secs. 6-7b and 7-7).

9-8b-1 Mechanical Bond Scission. Block copolymers can be obtained from polymer radicals which, unlike those employed for graft polymerization, have the radical centers at their ends. This is accomplished by mechanically breaking a bond in the polymer backbone by milling or mastication of the polymer [1, 30]. Block copolymers are obtained by the mastication of either a mixture of two homopolymers

$$\left.\begin{matrix}\sim\!\sim M_1M_1\sim\!\sim \\ \\ \sim\!\sim M_2M_2\sim\!\sim\end{matrix}\right\} \xrightarrow{\text{Milling}} \left.\begin{matrix}\sim\!\sim M_1\cdot \\ \sim\!\sim M_2\cdot\end{matrix}\right\} \longrightarrow \begin{matrix}\sim\!\sim M_1M_2\sim\!\sim \\ \sim\!\sim M_1M_1\sim\!\sim \\ \sim\!\sim M_2M_2\sim\!\sim\end{matrix} \tag{9-50}$$

or a mixture of a polymer and a monomer

$$\sim\!\sim M_1M_1\sim\!\sim \xrightarrow{\text{Milling}} \sim\!\sim M_1\cdot \xrightarrow{M_2} \sim\!\sim M_1M_2\sim\!\sim \tag{9-51}$$

The former gives a mixture of the block copolymer with the two homopolymers since the polymer radicals combine randomly; the latter yields the block copolymer almost exclusively.

9-8b-2 Other Methods. Polymers with labile bonds at their ends can be used to form block copolymers. Thus, one can synthesize a polymer such as polystyrene with bromine end-groups by carrying out its synthesis in the presence of carbon tetrabromide. The carbon-bromine bond can then be broken by ultraviolet irradiation and the resulting radicals used to initiate the polymerization of a monomer

$$\mathrm{M_1} \xrightarrow{\mathrm{CBr_4}} \sim\!\sim\mathrm{M_1{-}Br} \xrightarrow{\mathrm{UV}} \sim\!\sim\mathrm{M_1}\cdot \xrightarrow{\mathrm{M_2}} \sim\!\sim\mathrm{M_1M_2}\sim\!\sim \qquad (9\text{-}52)$$

Difunctional initiators can be used to produce block copolymers if the two initiator groups can be decomposed independently, for example

$$\mathrm{HOO{-}R{-}OOH} \longrightarrow \mathrm{HOORO}\cdot \xrightarrow{\mathrm{M_1}} \mathrm{HOORO{-}M_1}\sim\!\sim \longrightarrow$$

$$\cdot\mathrm{ORO{-}M_1}\sim\!\sim \xrightarrow{\mathrm{M_2}} \sim\!\sim\mathrm{M_2{-}ORO{-}M_1}\sim\!\sim \qquad (9\text{-}53)$$

REFERENCES

1. E. M. Fettes (ed.), "Chemical Reactions of Polymers," Interscience Publishers, John Wiley & Sons, Inc., New York, 1964.
2. N. G. Gaylord, *J. Polymer Sci.,* **C24**:1 (1968).
3. P. J. Flory, *J. Am. Chem. Soc.,* **61**:1518 (1939).
4. H. Morawetz, "Macromolecules in Solution," chap. IX, Interscience Publishers, John Wiley & Sons, Inc., New York, 1965.
5. M. L. Bender and M. C. Neveu, *J. Am. Chem. Soc.,* **80**:5388 (1958).
6. J. Moens and G. Smets, *J. Polymer Sci.,* **23**:931 (1957).
7. C. B. Chapman, *ibid.,* **45**:237 (1960).
8. D. H. Solomon, "The Chemistry of Organic Film Formers," chaps. 2, 3, and 5, John Wiley & Sons, Inc., New York, 1967.
9. G. M. Burnett, *Polymer Preprints,* **8(1)**:96 (1967).
10. G. S. Learmonth, G. Pritchard, and J. Reinhardt, *J. Appl. Polymer Sci.,* **12**:619 (1968).
11. I. Vancso-Szmercsanyi, K. Maros-Greger, and E. Makay-Bodi, *ibid.,* **53**:241 (1961).
12. H. Wexler, *Chem. Rev.,* **64**:591 (1964).

13. G. Alliger and I. J. Sjothun (eds.), "Vulcanization of Elastomers," Reinhold Book Corp., New York, 1964.
14. L. Bateman (ed.), "The Chemistry and Physics of Rubber-Like Substances," John Wiley & Sons, Inc., New York, 1963.
15. L. Bateman, C. G. Moore, and M. Porter, *J. Chem. Soc.*, **1958**:2866.
16. L. Bateman, C. G. Moore, M. Porter, and B. Saville, Chemistry of Vulcanization, in L. Bateman (ed.), *op. cit.*, Chap. 15.
17. L. Bateman, R. W. Glazebrook, and C. G. Moore, *J. Appl. Polymer Sci.*, **1**:257 (1959).
18. E. C. Gregg, Jr., *J. Polymer Sci.*, **C24**:303 (1968).
19. W. J. Bobear, *Rubber Chem. Technol.*, **40**:1560 (1967).
20. L. O. Amberg and B. F. Brown, *Rubber World*, **147(3)**:52 (1963).
21. J. R. Wolfe, Jr., *J. Appl. Polymer Sci.*, **12**:1167 (1968).
22. A. Chapiro, "Radiation Chemistry of Polymeric Systems," chaps. IX, X, Interscience Publishers, John Wiley & Sons, Inc., New York, 1962.
23. E. Ott, H. M. Spurlin, and M. W. Grafflin (eds.), "Cellulose and Cellulose Derivatives," Interscience Publishers, John Wiley & Sons, Inc., New York, 1954.
24. J. A. Brydson, "Plastics Materials," Iliffee Books Ltd., London, 1966.
25. J. Dyer and L. H. Phifer, *Macromolecules*, **2(2)**:111, 118(1969).
26. R. McGuchan and I. C. McNeil, *J. Polymer Sci.*, **A-1(6)**:205(1968).
27. A. Nersasian and D. E. Anderson, *J. Appl. Polymer Sci.*, **4**:74 (1960).
28. M. A. Golub and Heller, *Can. J. Chem.*, **41**:937 (1963).
29. A. R. Monahan, *Polymer Preprints*, **7(2)**:204 (1966).
30. R. J. Ceresa, "Block and Graft Copolymers," Butterworth and Co. (Publishers) Ltd., London, 1962.
31. H. A. Battaerd and G. W. Tregear, "Graft Copolymers," Interscience Publishers, John Wiley & Sons, Inc., New York, 1967.
32. G. Odian and R. L. Kruse, *J. Polymer Sci.*, **C22**:691 (1969).
33. Y. Ogiwara and H. Kubota, *ibid.*, **A-1(6)**:1489 (1968).

PROBLEMS

9-1. Discuss the factors which may cause the reactivity of the functional group in a polymer molecule to be different from the reactivity of the same group in a low molecular weight homolog.

9-2. What reactions can be used to crosslink the following polymers:

a. polyester from ethylene glycol and maleic anhydride
b. polyester from ethylene glycol, phthalic acid, and oleic acid.
c. 1,4-polyisoprene
d. polyethylene
e. polydimethylsiloxane

Describe the crosslinking reactions by means of equations.

9-3. Show by equation the synthesis of

a. cellulose acetate
b. cellulose nitrate
c. methyl cellulose
d. poly(vinyl formal)

9-4. Show by equation the

a. chlorination of polyethylene
b. chlorination of 1,4-polyisoprene
c. chlorosulfonation of polyethylene
d. synthesis of an anionic ion-exchange polymer from polystyrene
e. cyclization of 1,4-polyisoprene by HBr

9-5. Show by formula the structure of

a. poly(propylene-*b*-styrene)
b. poly(styrene-*g*-methyl methacrylate)
c. poly(methyl methacrylate-*g*-styrene)
d. poly(methyl methacrylate-*alt*-styrene)

Describe by equations the methods of synthesizing each of these copolymers.

INDEX

Absolute rate constants:
in anionic chain polymerization, 335, 337–338
in cationic chain polymerization, 315–316, 321
in coordination polymerization, 578
in radical chain polymerization, 231–240, 316
in ring-opening polymerization, 468
in step polymerization, 44, 62, 118
Accelerator, 620
Acetylene polymerization, 358
Acidity function, 54
Acrolein polymerization, 354–355
Acrylamide polymerization, 355–356
Actinometry, 184
Activated monomer, 356, 481
Activation energies:
in anionic chain polymerization, 329, 342–344

Activation energies (*cont'd*):
in cationic chain polymerization, 323–325
in coordination polymerization, 579
in radical chain polymerization, 240–245
in ring-opening polymerization, 475–476
in step polymerization, 83
Activator, 584, 620
Activity of catalyst, 552
Addition polymers, 1–9
After-effect technique, 235
Air-drying of alkyds, 616–617
Alfin catalyst, 593
Alkyd resin, 123, 616
Allylic polymerization, 230–231
Alternating copolymer 125–126, 365
(*See also* Chain copolymerization; Copolymers)

Alternating intra-intermolecular polymerization, 436–441
Alternating tendency in copolymerization, 374–376
  (*See also* Chain copolymerization)
Amorphous polymer (*see* Crystalline-amorphous behavior)
Amylose, 537–538
Anchimeric assistance, 613
Angle strain, 65–67
Anionic chain polymerization:
  of acrolein, 354–355
  of acrylamide, 355–356
  activation parameters in, 329, 342-344
  association phenomena in, 341-342
  of carbonyl monomers, 345–349
  comparison with radical polymerization, 162–167, 302–303, 344–345
  of dimethylketene, 353–354
  effect of reaction media in, 335–344
  effect of temperature in, 329, 342–344
  initiation in, 325–327, 330–333
  of isocyanates, 356–357
  kinetics of, 327–329, 334–338
  molecular weight in, 329, 338–341
  molecular weight distribution in, 340
  non-termination in, 329–334
  rate constants in, 335, 337–338
  termination in, 328
  (*See also* Chain initiation; Chain propagation; Chain termination; Chain transfer; Stereospecific polymerization)
Anionic coordinated polymerization, 550–552
  (*See also* Stereospecific polymerization)
Anionic ring-opening polymerization:
  of *N*-carboxy-α-amino acid anhydride, 501–502
  copolymerization of, 507–513
  of cyclic amides:
    kinetics of, 483–484
    molecular weight of, 485–486
    strong base initiation of, 479–482
    use of acylating agent in, 482–483
  of cyclic esters, 497–498
  of cyclosiloxanes, 495–497
  of epoxides:
    chain transfer to monomer, 458-459
    characteristics of, 454–455
Anionic ring-opening polymerization, of epoxides (*cont'd*):
    exchange reaction in, 456–457
    kinetics of, 456–459
  of phosphonitrilic chloride, 504–506
Anion-radical, 326
A-stage polymer, 112
Asymmetric center, 521–522
Asymmetric induction, 600
Atactic polymer, 522–523, 539–541
Autoacceleration, 255-256
Autoinhibition, 230–231
Average functionality, 99–102
Azeotropic copolymerization, 375
  (*See also* Chain copolymerization)

Back-biting ring-expansion, 466, 474, 500
Back-biting self-transfer, 220–221, 267–268
Base unit, 2, 6, 56
Bimetallic mechanism for isotacticity, 557–560
Block copolymer, 125–126, 365–366
  (*See also* Chain copolymerization; Copolymers; Polymer reactions)
Branch unit, 103
Branched polymer, 16–18
Branching:
  in cationic chain polymerization, 311
  in graft polymerization, 632–635
  in radical chain polymerization, 217–221
  in ring-opening polymerization, 465, 484–486
  in step polymerization, 94–95
    molecular weight distribution in, 95–96
Branching coefficient, 103
Branching density, 219
B-stage polymer, 112
Bulk polymerization, 82–83, 268–269

Carbonyl polymerization:
  by ionic chain reaction, 345–351
  by radical chain reaction, 351
  by step reaction, 352
Carothers equation, 56–57, 99–102
  (*See also* Crosslinking)
Catalyst, 161
  (*See also* Chain initiation)
Cationic chain polymerization:
  of acrolein, 354–355
  of carbonyl monomers, 349–351
  chain transfer in, 309–310, 317–319

Cationic chain polymerization (*cont'd*):
- comparison with radical reaction, 163–167, 302–303, 316–317, 344–345
- of diazoalkanes, 357
- effect of electric field in, 322
- effect of gegen-ion in, 321–322
- effect of solvent in, 320–323
- effect of temperature in, 323–325
- inhibition in, 311
- initiation in, 303–307
- kinetics of, 312–317
- molecular weight of, 315–316
- propagation in, 307–308
- pseudocationic reaction in, 322–323
- rate constants in, 315–316, 321
- termination in, 308–311
- (*See also* Chain initiation; Chain propagation; Chain termination; Chain transfer; Stereospecific polymerization)

Cationic coordination polymerization, 588
- (*See also* Stereospecific polymerization)

Cationic ring-opening polymerization:
- copolymerization in, 507–513
- of cyclic acetals and formals, 471–475
- of cyclic amides:
  - equilibrium polymerization in, 490–492
  - initiation of, 486–489
  - molecular weight in, 490–492
  - thermodynamics of, 492–494
- of cyclic amines, 499–500
- of cyclic esters, 497–498
- of cyclic ethers:
  - back-biting ring-expansion in, 466
  - chain transfer in, 465
  - energetics of, 475–478
  - equilibrium polymerization in, 469–471
  - initiation of, 460–465
  - kinetics of, 467–471
  - rate constants in, 468
  - termination in, 465–467
- of cyclic sulfides, 500–501
- of cyclosilazanes, 506
- of cyclosiloxanes, 496–497
- of imino cyclic compounds, 503

Ceiling temperature, 252–255, 345–346

Cellulose, 3, 27, 31
- reactions of, 623–626
- structure of, 537-538

Cellulose triacetate, 31

Chain copolymerization:
- by anionic reaction, 417–418, 422–425
- of carbonyl monomers, 442–443
- by cationic reaction, 417–422
- by coordination catalysts, 582–583
- copolymerization equation in, 366–372
- crosslinking by, 614–615
- of dienes:
  - crosslinking in, 432–436
  - cyclopolymerization in, 436–441
- microstructure of copolymer, 383–385
- multi-component, 364, 385–390
- by radical reaction:
  - of miscellaneous monomers, 441–442
  - monomer and radical reactivities in, 390–411
  - rate of, 411–417
- types of behavior in:
  - alternating, 374–376
  - azeotropic, 375
  - block, 376
  - consecutive, 376
  - ideal, 372–374
  - stereoblock, 538, 541
- utility of, 364–365, 538–541
- (*See also* Copolymerization equation; Monomer reactivity ratios; Step copolymerization)

Chain initiation:
- in anionic polymerization:
  - effect of temperature on, 342–344
  - by electron transfer, 330–333
  - by metal alkyls, 333
  - by metal amides, 327
  - (*See also* Anionic ring-opening polymerization)
- in cationic polymerization:
  - effect of temperature on, 323–324
  - by Lewis acids, 304–305
  - by protonic acids, 303–304
  - (*See also* Cationic ring-opening polymerization)
- in emulsion polymerization, 290-291
- in radical polymerization:
  - activation energies for, 240–244, 264-266
  - definition of, 170–171
  - effect of autoacceleration on, 255–256
  - effect of pressure, 264–266
  - initiator efficiency in, 177, 192–201
  - by ionizing radiation, 186–187
  - kinetics of, 177–183, 185, 191–192

Chain initiation, in radical polymerization (*cont'd*):
photochemical, 181–186
purely thermal, 188–189
redox, 189–192
thermal catalyzed, 175–176
Chain polymerization (*see* Anionic chain polymerization; Cationic chain polymerization; Radical chain polymerization)
Chain propagation:
in anionic polymerization:
effects of reaction conditions on, 334–338, 341–344
rate constants for, 334–335, 337–338
in cationic polymerization:
effect of gegen-ion on, 319, 321–322
effect of solvent on, 319–321
isomerization in, 307–308
monomer reactivity in, 316–317
in emulsion polymerization, 292
in radical polymerization:
activation parameters for, 240–242, 264–266
definition of, 171
effect of substituents on, 165–167, 248–251
rate constants for, 239, 241
Chain segment, 103
Chain termination:
in anionic polymerization, 326
effect of temperature on, 342
non-termination, 329–330, 334
in cationic polymerization:
by chain transfer, 310–311
effect of temperature on, 323–325
non-termination of kinetic chain, 308–309
termination of kinetic chain, 309–311, 317–318
in emulsion polymerization, 292, 294–295
in radical chain polymerization:
activation parameters for, 240–243, 264–266
definition of, 171–172, 202–203
diffusion-control of, 257–259
effect of conversion on, 255–257
rate constants for, 239, 241
Chain transfer:
in cationic polymerization, 309-310, 317–319
Chain transfer: *(cont'd)*
in emulsion polymerization, 298
in radical polymerization:
activation parameters for, 244–245, 266–268
applications of, 216–217
back-biting self-transfer in, 220-221
branching by, 217–221
chain transfer agents, 205, 211–217
chain transfer constants, 205–221
degradative transfer, 230–231
effect on molecular weight and rate, 203–205
to initiator, 192–193, 205–211
to monomer, 205–211
to polymer, 217–221
to solvent, 203–205, 211–217
structure and reactivity in, 212–217
Chain transfer agent, 205
Chain transfer constant, 205
Cis polymer, 530
(*See also* Stereoisomerism in polymers; Stereospecific polymerization)
Classification of polymers:
by polymerization mechanism, 9–12
by structure, 2–9
Cocatalyst, 304
Collision frequency factor, 240–244, 320, 322, 343
Condensation polymer, 2–9
Conformational isomers, 520, 614
Conjunct polymerization, 311
Coordination catalysts:
components of:
Group I-III metal, 549, 552–553, 571–573
third component, 573–574
transition metal, 549, 552–553, 570–571
definition of, 549, 552–553
heterogeneous vs. homogeneous, 551–552
mechanism of stereospecificity with, 549–552
(*See also* Stereoisomerism in polymers; Stereospecific polymerization)
Coordination polymerization (*see* Coordination catalysts; Stereoisomerism in polymers; Stereospecific polymerization)
Copolymer composition equation (*see* Copolymerization equation)

Copolymerization (*see* Chain copolymerization; Ring-opening copolymerization; Step copolymerization; Stereospecific polymerization)
Copolymerization equation:
applicability of, 370–371
derivation of, 366–370
deviation from:
by depropagation, 429–432
by kinetic penultimate effect, 425–429
effect of conversion on composition, 376–381
monomer reactivity ratios, 369, 381–383, 393–395
multi-component, 385–390
types of behavior, 372–376
(*See also* Chain copolymerization; Copolymers; Monomer reactivity ratios)
Copolymers:
alternating, 125–129, 365–366, 583
block, 125–129, 365–366, 582–583
graft, 217–221, 365–366, 632–635
microstructure of, 383–385
nomenclature of, 125–126, 365–366
random, 125–129, 365–366, 582–583
stereoblock, 538, 541
(*See also* Chain copolymerization)
Coupling, 171–172, 202–203
Critical branching coefficient, 103
Critical extent of reaction, 101
Critical micelle concentration, 284
Crosslink, 97
Crosslinked polymer, 16–19, 96–98
(*See also* Crosslinking)
Crosslinking:
of polymers:
by copolymerization, 614–615
of fluoro polymers, 622–623
by oxygen, 616–617
by peroxides, 621–622
by radiation, 623
by sulfur, 617-620
in radical chain copolymerization of dienes, 432–441
in step polymerization:
Carothers equation, 99–102, 113
experimental results for, 105–107, 113
molecular weight distribution in, 107–110
Crosslinking, in step polymerization (*cont'd*):
statistical approach, 102–105, 113
technology of, 110–124
(*See also* Prepolymers)
Crossover point, 375
Crossover reaction, 368
Cross-propagation, 368
Cross-termination, 412
Crowding repulsions, 65–67
Crystalline-amorphous behavior:
crystalline melting temperature, 28–33, 129, 536
determinants of, 26–28
effect on reactivity of polymers, 612
glass transition temperature, 28–33, 129, 536
nature of, 24–26
significance of, 34–35, 534–536
Crystalline melting temperature, 28–33, 129, 536
C-stage polymer, 112
Cumulative weight fraction, 77
Cuprammonium process, 625
Cyclic acetal polymerization (*see* Cationic ring-opening polymerization)
Cyclic amide polymerization (*see* Anionic ring-opening polymerization; Cationic ring-opening polymerization)
Cyclic amine polymerization, 499–500
Cyclic ester polymerization, 497–498
Cyclic ether polymerization (*see* Cationic ring-opening polymerization)
Cyclic formal polymerization (*see* Cationic ring-opening polymerization)
Cyclic sulfide polymerization, 500–501
Cyclization:
vs. crosslinking, 106–107
vs. linear step polymerization, 63–69
Cyclopolymerization, 436–441
Cyclosilazine polymerization, 506
Cyclosiloxane polymerization (*see* Anionic ring-opening polymerization; Cationic ring-opening polymerization)

D- and *L*-configurations, 521–522
Dacron, 85
Dead-end polymerization, 199–201
Dead polymer, 172
Degradative chain transfer, 203–204
Degree of polymerization, 56, 202–203
(*See also* Molecular weight)
Depolymerization (*see* Depropagation)

Depropagation:
  in radical copolymerization, 429–432
  in radical polymerization, 251–255
Diad tacticity, 539
Diazoalkane polymerization, 357
Diels-Alder polymerization, 147–148, 596–598
Dienes:
  copolymerization of:
    crosslinking in, 614–615
    cyclopolymerization in, 436–441
  polymerization of, 271–272, 588–598
    stereoisomerism in, 528–533, 588–596
    (*See also* Stereoisomerism in polymers; Stereospecific polymerization)
Diffusion-controlled termination:
  in radical copolymerization, 415–417
  in radical polymerization, 255–260
Di-isotactic polymer, 524, 569
Dimethylketene polymerization, 353–354
Diol prepolymers, 120–121
1,3-Dipolar addition polymerization, 147–149
Disproportionation, 171–172, 202–203
Di-syndiotactic polymer, 524
Ditacticity, 524–525, 569

Elastic elongation, 34
Elastomer, 35–36, 130–131, 364–365
Electrolytic polymerization, 322
Electron transfer, 330–333
Emulsifier, 280–281, 291–292
  inhibition by, 297–298
Emulsion polymerization:
  chain transfer in, 297–298
  components of, 280–282, 290–292
  emulsifier in, 280–281, 291–292
  energetics of, 292–293
  kinetics of, 284–288
  inhibition in, 297–298
  initiation in, 290–291
  inverse emulsion system, 293–294
  Medvedev-Sheinker theory of, 295–296
  molecular weight in, 287–289
  molecular weight distribution in, 298
  number of particles in, 285, 289–290
  propagation in, 292
  Smith-Ewart behavior, 284–290
    deviations from, 294–298
Emulsion polymerization (*cont'd*):
  termination in, 292
  utility of, 279–280
End-groups, 70
Epoxide polymerization (*see* Anionic ring-opening polymerization; Stereospecific polymerization)
Epoxy prepolymers, 121–122
Equilibrium monomer concentration, 253–254, 469, 490–491
Equilibrium polymerization (*see* Reversible polymerization)
Erythro-di-isotactic polymer, 524, 569, 580–581, 583
Erythro-di-syndiotactic polymer, 524, 580–581

Fiber, 35–37, 94, 130–131
Flory distribution (*see* Most probable distribution)
Folded-chain lamella, 24–25
Fringed-micelle, 24–25
Functional group reactivity, 41–47, 60–63, 116–118, 173, 216–217
Functionality, 94

Gegen-ion, 303
Gel, 98
Gel effect, 255–257
Gel point, 98
Gelation, 98
Geometrical isomerism in polymers (*see* Stereoisomerism in polymers; Stereospecific polymerization)
Glass transition temperature, 28–33, 129, 536

Head-to-tail structure, 167–170
Heterotactic triad, 539–541
High-temperature polymers:
  by Diels-Alder reaction, 147–148
  by 1,3-dipolar addition, 147–149
  inorganic systems, 149–154, 503–506
  polyamides, 133–134
  polybenzimidazoles, 141–143
  polybenzoxazoles, 145
  polybenzthiazoles, 145
  polycarbonates, 132–133
  polyethers, 134–137
  polyimidazopyrrolones, 144–145
  polyimides, 139–141

High-temperature polymers (*cont'd*):
  polyoxadiazoles, 146–147
  polyquinoxalines, 146
  polysiloxanes, 90–91, 152–153
  polytriazoles, 146–147
  poly(*p*-xylylene), 137–139
  requirements of, 131–132, 143–144
  spiro, 148, 150
Homopolymerization, 125, 364
Hydrogen transfer polymerization, 355–356, 479–483

Ideal copolymerization, 372–374
Induced decomposition of initiator, 192–193, 205–211
Induction period, 174, 221–222
Inhibition constants, 226–229
Inhibition of radical polymerization:
  autoinhibition in, 230–231
  kinetics of, 225–230
  mechanism of, 221-225
  by oxygen, 225
Inhibitors, 221–222
Initiation (*see* Chain initiation)
Initiator, 161
  (*See also* Chain initiation)
Initiator efficiency:
  definition of, 177, 192–193
  determination of, 196–201
  mechanism of, 193–196
Inorganic polymers, 149–154, 503–506
Interchange reaction, 80
Interfacial polymerization, 91–94
  description of, 91–93
  utility of, 93–94
Intramolecular cyclization, 107
Inverse emulsion systems, 293
Ion-pair, 303
Ionizing radiation, 186–187, 633–634
Isocyanate polymerization, 356–357
Isomerization polymerization, 307–308
Isotactic polymer, 522–523, 539–541
  (*See also* Stereoisomerism in polymers; Stereospecific polymerization)

Kinetic chain length, 201–202
Kinetics:
  of anionic chain polymerization, 327–329, 334–338
  of cationic chain polymerization, 312–317
  of coordination polymerization, 574–578

Kinetics (*cont'd*):
  of radical chain polymerization, 170–178, 182–183, 185, 191–192, 225–231
  of reversible polymerization, 86–88, 252, 469–471, 490–492
  of ring-opening polymerization, 456–459, 467–471, 483–484
  of step polymerization, 47–60

Ladder polymer, 143
Ligand-monomer interaction model, 561–562
Linear polymer, 16–18
Living polymer, 330
  (*See also* Anionic chain polymerization)

Mass polymerization (*see* Bulk polymerization)
Mechanical properties:
  definition of, 33–34
  effect on polymer uses, 34–38
Medvedev-Sheinker theory, 295–296
Melamine-formaldehyde polymer, 5, 35, 38, 60, 119
Melt polymerization, 89
Micelle, 281
Microgel, 63, 118
Modifier, 216
Modulus, 33–34
Molecular weight:
  in anionic chain polymerization, 329, 339–340
  in cationic chain polymerization, 312–315
  distribution of, 22–24
    (*See also* Molecular weight distribution)
  in emulsion polymerization, 287–289
  importance of, 19–20
  in linear step polymerization:
    need for stoichiometric control, 69–71
    quantitative aspects, 71–75
  number-average, 20–21
  in radical chain polymerization:
    bimolecular termination, 201–203
    chain transfer, 203–221
  in reversible polymerization, 490–491
  in ring-opening polymerization, 456, 459, 484–485, 490–491
  viscosity-average, 21–22
  weight average, 21

Molecular weight distribution:
  in anionic polymerization, 339–340
  breadth of, 79
  definition of, 22–24
  in emulsion polymerization, 298
  number-distribution function, 76
  in radical chain polymerization:
    at high conversion, 263–264
    at low conversion, 260–263
  in ring-opening polymerization, 457, 465, 484–486
  in step polymerization:
    branching, 95–96
    linear, 75–82
    nonlinear, 107–110
  weight-distribution function, 76
Molecule-induced homolysis, 181
Monofunctional monomer, 70
Monomer, 1
Monomer-monomer interaction model, 565–568
Monomer reactivities, 392
  (*See also* Monomer reactivity ratios)
Monomer reactivity ratios:
  in anionic chain copolymerization, 422–425
    effect of solvent and gegen-ion on, 423–425
  in cationic chain copolymerization, 418–422
    effect of solvent and gegen-ion on, 420–422
    effect of temperature on, 422
  determination of, 381–383
  in radical chain copolymerization:
    alternation tendency in, 402-405
    effect of reaction conditions on, 391–392
    monomer reactivities from, 392–393
    polar effects on, 402–405
    product probability approach for, 409–411
    Q-e scheme for, 405–408
    radical reactivities from, 396–398
    resonance effects on, 395–400
    steric effects on, 400–402
Monomer unit, 56
Monometallic mechanism for isotacticity, 557–560
Most probable distribution:
  experimental verification of, 80–83
Most probable distribution (*cont'd*):
  theory of, 75–80
  (*See also* Molecular weight; Molecular weight distribution)
Multi-chain polymerization (*see* Branching; Crosslinking; Step polymerization)
Multi-component copolymerization, 364, 385–390
Mylar, 85

Natta catalysts (*see* Coordination catalysts; Stereoisomerism in polymers; Stereospecific polymerization)
Natural rubber (*see* Polyisoprene)
Neighboring group effect, 613–614
Network polymer (*see* Crosslinked polymer; Crosslinking)
Nitrile polymerization, 358
Nomenclature of polymers:
  based on source, 12–13
  based on structure, 14–15
  stereoregular structures, 522–526, 530, 532–533
  trade names, 15–16
Novolacs, 126
Number-average degree of polymerization, 56
Number-average molecular weight, 20–21
  (*See also* Molecular weight)
Nylon, 15
Nylon salt, 88

Optical activity in polymers, 599–602
Optical isomerism in polymers (*see* Stereoisomerism in polymers; Stereospecific polymerization)
Oxidative coupling, 134–139

Penultimate effect in copolymerization, 425–429
Penultimate unit, 425
Phenol-formaldehyde polymers, 4, 8, 15–16, 35, 38
  synthesis of, 60, 113–118, 123–124
Photochemical polymerization, 181–186, 231–238, 633
Photosensitizer, 185
Plastic, 35–38, 364–365
Polar effects in radical reactions, 215–216, 402–405
Polyacetaldehyde, 7, 12, 526–528, 599

Polyacetals, 5
Polyacrylonitrile, 5, 35, 545, 631–632
Poly(amic acid), 140–141
Polyamides, 2, 4, 27, 33, 35, 39
  copolymers of, 125–129
  synthesis of, 60, 88–89, 133–134
Poly(6-aminocaproic acid), 13
Polybenzimidazoles, 141–143
Polybenzothiazoles, 145
Polybenzoxazoles, 145
Poly(3,3-bis(chloromethyl)oxetane), 451
1,2-Polybutadiene, 528–529, 589
1,4-Polybutadiene, 536, 589
Poly(1-butene), 536, 579
Poly(ϵ-caprolactam), 11-12, 27 30, 450
Polycarbonates, 16, 132–133
Poly(chlorotrifluoroethylene), 12, 30
Polycyclobutene, 580–581
Polycyclohexene, 534
1,4-Poly-1,3-dienes, 272, 528–534
  crosslinking of, 617–620
Poly(2,6-dimethylphenylene oxide), 135
Polydimethylsiloxane, 30, 621–622
Polyesteramides, 129
Polyesterification, 42, 84–86
  (*See also* Step polymerization)
Polyesters, 2, 35
  linear, 84–86
  random crosslinking of, 112-113
  unsaturated, 122–123
    crosslinking by copolymerization, 614–615
    reaction with oxygen, 616–617
Polyethers, 134–137
Polyethylene, 6, 12, 27, 30, 33, 35, 37
  branching in, 217–221
  chlorination of, 628–629
  copolymers of, 365, 582–583
  crosslinking of, 621
  synthesis of, 264, 552
Poly(ethylene glycol-*co*-terephthalic acid), 14
Poly(ethylene oxide), 13, 30, 450
Poly(ethylene terephthalate), 14, 27, 30
  kinetics of formation of, 86–88
Polyformaldehyde, 7
Polyfunctional monomer, 40
Poly(hexamethylene adipamide), 13–14, 30, 32, 35–37
  molecular weight distribution of, 80–82
Poly(hexamethylene diamine-*co*-sebacic acid), 14
Poly(hexamethylene sebacamide), 14
Polyimidazopyrrolones(pyrrones), 145
Polyimides, 139–141
Polyisobutylene, 6, 30–31, 35
  chlorination of, 628–629
Polyisoprene, 7, 28, 31, 35–36
  chlorination of, 627–628
  cyclization of, 628, 630–631
  stereoisomerism in, 530, 536–537
Poly(4,4'-isopropylidene diphenylene carbonate), 16, 132–133
Polymer reactions:
  aromatic substitution, 629–630
  block copolymers, 636–637
  of cellulose, 623–626
  crosslinking:
    of fluoro polymers, 622-623
    of 1,4-poly-1,3-dienes, 617–620
    of polyolefins, 621
    of polysiloxanes, 621–622
    of unsaturated polyesters, 614–617
  cyclization, 628, 630–632
  graft polymerization, 632–635
  halogenation, 627–629
  of poly(vinyl acetate), 626–627
  reactivity of polymers, 611–614
Polymetallosiloxanes, 153–154
Poly(methacrylic acid), 632
Poly(methyl acrylate), 545
Polymethylene, 15, 357
Poly(methyl methacrylate), 6, 27, 31, 35, 38
  stereoisomerism of, 543-545, 547
Poly(3-methyl-1-pentene), 12
Poly(4-methyl-1-pentene), 536
1,4-Poly(methyl sorbate), 533
Poly(methyl vinyl ketone), 169
Polyoxadiazoles, 146–147
Polyoxymethylene, 30, 32
1,4-Poly-1,3-pentadiene, 532
Poly(2-pentene), 526
Poly(1,4-phenylene), 15
Poly(*m*-phenylene isophthalamide), 133
Polyphenylene oxide, 135
Poly(1,4-phenylenepyromellitimide), 140
Polyphenylsilsesquioxane, 152–153
Polyphosphazenes, 504–506
Poly(phosphonitrilic chloride), 504–506
Polypropylene, 30, 32, 35, 37
  chlorination of, 628–629
  stereoregular, 523, 534–536, 552, 561, 565, 599

Poly(propylene oxide), 11, 12, 450, 527–528, 598
Polyquinoxalines, 146
Polysiloxanes, 4, 28, 32, 35, 152–154
  crosslinking of, 621–622
  synthesis of, 90–91, 495–497
Polystyrene, 6, 27, 30, 32, 35, 38
  aromatic substitution in, 629–631
  copolymers of, 364–365
Polysulfide, 5, 500–501
Polysulfone, 134
Polytetrafluoroethylene, 7, 31–32, 35
Polytriazoles, 146–147
Poly(trimethylene ethylene-urethane), 14
Poly(trimethylene glycol-*co*-ethylene diisocyanate), 14
Polyurethanes, 4, 7, 35
  copolymers of, 130
  crosslinking of, 623
  synthesis of, 60, 89–90, 120
Poly(vinyl acetate), 7, 30
  branching in, 218–220
  reactions of, 626–627
Poly(vinyl alcohol), 13, 169–170, 626
Poly(vinyl chloride), 6, 12, 27, 30, 32, 35, 169
  branching in, 219
  stereoisomerism in, 544
Poly(vinyl fluoride), 30, 170
Poly(vinylidene chloride), 7, 30, 32
Poly(vinylidene fluoride), 170
Poly(*p*-xylylene), 15, 137–139
Prepolymers:
  diol, 120–121
  epoxy, 121–122
  phenol-formaldehyde, 113–118, 123–124
  polyester, 112–113
  random, 112–119
  structoset, 119–124
    structopendant, 120
    structoterminal, 120
  unsaturated polyester, 122–123
  urea-formaldehyde, 118–119
Pressure effects on radical polymerization, 264–268
Primary radical, 171, 178, 260
Process conditions, 82–84, 91–94, 268–271
Product probability approach, 409–411
Promoter, 464, 584
Propagation (*see* Chain propagation)
Pyrrones, 145

Q-e scheme, 405–408

R- and *S*-configurations, 521–522
Radical chain polymerization:
  of acrolein, 354
  activation parameters in, 240–245, 264–268
  autoacceleration in, 255–260
  of carbonyl monomers, 351
  comparison with step polymerization, 9–11, 161–162
  dead-end polymerization, 199–201
  definition of, 10
  of 1,3-dienes, 271–272
    (*See also* Dienes)
  effect of pressure in, 264–268
  effect of substituents in, 165–167, 248–251
  effect of temperature in, 240–245, 251–255
  forces of stereoregulation in, 541–545, 585
  head-to-tail placement in, 167–170
  inhibition and retardation in, 221–231
  initiation in, 175–192
  initiator efficiency in, 177, 192–193
    determination of, 196–201
    mechanism of, 193–196
  kinetic chain length, 201–202
  kinetics of, 170–178, 182–183, 185, 191–192, 225–231
  molecular weight in:
    bimolecular termination, 202–203
    chain transfer, 203–220
  molecular weight distribution in, 260–264
  non-steady-state kinetics of, 231–238
  polar effects in, 215–216
  process conditions in, 268–271
  propagation in, 171
  radical vs. ionic reaction, 163–167, 302–303
  radical scavenger in, 198–199
  termination in, 172, 202–203
  thermodynamics of, 245–251
  (*See also* Chain initiation; Chain propagation; Chain termination; Chain transfer)
Radical lifetime, 232
Radical polymerization (*see* Radical chain polymerization)
Radical reactivities (*see* Monomer reactivity ratios)

Radical scavenger, 198–199
Random copolymer, 125–129
(*See also* Chain copolymerization; Copolymers)
Rate constants (*see* Absolute rate constants)
Reactions of polymers (*see* Polymer reactions)
Reactivity:
of functional group, 41–47, 60–63, 116–118, 173, 216–217
of monomers (*see* Monomer reactivity ratios)
of polymers, 611–614
Reactivity ratios (*see* Monomer reactivity ratios)
Redox initiation, 189–192
Redox polymerization, 189–192
Regulators, 216
Repeating unit, 2, 6
Resole prepolymers, 115
Retardation (*see* Inhibition of radical polymerization)
Retarders, 221
(*See also* Inhibition of radical polymerization)
Reversible polymerization, kinetics of:
in radical chain polymerization, 252
in ring-opening polymerization, 469–471, 490–492
in step polymerization, 86–88
Ring-opening copolymerization, 507–513
Ring-opening polymerization, 11–12, 450
(*See also* Anionic ring-opening polymerization; Cationic ring-opening polymerization)
Rotating sector method, 235–239
Rubber (*see* Elastomer)

Scavenger, 198–199
s-Cis conformation, 590
Self-propagation, 368
Semi-crystalline polymer (*see* Crystalline-amorphous behavior)
Semi-ladder polymer, 143
Silk, 3
Site of steric isomerism, 611
Size distribution (*see* Molecular weight distribution)
Smith-Ewart behavior, 284–290
deviations from, 294–298
Solid-state polymerization, 270–271
Solution polymerization, 83, 269–270
Solvated electron, 333
Space network, 19
Spiro polymers, 148, 150
Starch, 3, 537–538
Statistical approach to gelation (*see* Crosslinking)
Steady-state assumption, 174
Step copolymerization, 124–125
reactants in, 126–130
types of, 125–126
utility of, 129–131
Step polymerization:
branching in, 94–96
of carbonyl monomers, 352
characteristics of, 9–11
copolymerization in, 124–131
(*See also* Step copolymerization)
crosslinking in, 96–124
(*See also* Crosslinking; Prepolymers)
cyclization in, 63–69
functional group reactivity in, 41–47, 60–63, 116–118
interfacial polymerization in, 91–94
kinetics of:
catalyzed, 57–60
reversible, 86–88
uncatalyzed, 47–56
molecular weight in, 69–75
molecular weight distribution in, 75–82, 95–96, 107–110
process conditions in, 82–84, 91–94
rate constants in, 44, 62, 118
Stereoblock polymer, 538, 541
Stereoisomerism in polymers:
absence of, in step polymerization, 528
analysis of, 538–541
in carbonyl polymerization, 526–528
in cyclopolymers, 534
from 1,3-dienes, 528–533
from disubstituted ethylenes, 523–526
from monosubstituted ethylenes, 520–523
in ring-opening polymerizations, 526–528
significance of, 534–538
types of, 520
(*See also* Coordination catalysts; Stereospecific polymerization)
Stereoregular polymers, 522
(*See also* Coordination catalysts; Stereoisomerism in polymers; Stereospecific polymerization)

Stereoregular sequence-length distribution, 545–547
Stereoselective polymerization, 600
Stereospecific polymerization:
  of carbonyl monomers, 599
  by coordination mechanism, 547–554
    activation energy in, 579
    bimetallic vs. monometallic mechanism in, 556–560
    chemical nature of, 554–556
    components of catalyst system in, 569–574
    crystal structure of catalyst in, 563–565
    direction of double bond opening in, 568–569
    kinetics of, 574–578
    model for isotacticity in, 561–563
    model for syndiotacticity in, 565–567
    molecular weight distribution in, 569
    rate constants in, 578
  copolymerization in, 582–583
  of cycloalkenes, 534, 580–581
  of 1,3-dienes:
    by anionic and coordination reaction, 590–596
    by cationic reaction, 596–598
    by radical reaction, 588–590
  of epoxides, 598–599
  factors in radical reaction, 541–545, 585
  by ionic reaction, 547–549, 584–588
  non-polar vs. polar monomers in, 551–552, 579–580, 584–588
  optical activity in polymers from, 599–602
  stereoregular sequence-length in, 545–547
  by supported metal oxide catalysts, 583–584
  (*See also* Coordination catalysts; Stereoisomerism in polymers)
Stoichiometric imbalance, 71
s-Trans conformation, 590
Stress-strain properties (*see* Mechanical properties)
Structopendant prepolymers (*see* Prepolymers)
Structoset prepolymers (*see* Prepolymers)
Structoterminal prepolymers (*see* Prepolymers)
Structural unit, 56
Supported metal oxide catalysts, 583–584
  (*See also* Coordination catalysts; Stereospecific polymerization)
Suspension polymerization, 270
Syndiotactic polymer, 522–523, 539–541
  (*See also* Stereoisomerism in polymers; Stereospecific polymerization)

Tacticity:
  analysis of, 538–539
  definition of, 522, 539–541
Telomer, 204
Tensile strength, 33
Termination (*see* Chain termination)
Terpolymerization, 364, 582, 622
Thermal polymerization, 188–189
Thermodynamics of polymerization:
  by cationic chain reaction, 323
  by radical chain reaction, 245–255
  by ring-opening reaction, 477–478, 492–494
Thermoplastics, 98
Thermosetting polymers, 98
Threo-di-isotactic polymer, 524–526
Threo-di-syndiotactic polymer, 524–526
Trans polymer, 530
  (*See also* Stereoisomerism in polymers; Stereospecific polymerization)
Transannular migration during polymerization, 581
Triad tacticity, 539–541
Trommsdorff effect, 255–256
Two-strand polymer, 143

Ultimate strength, 33
Urea-formaldehyde polymers, 5, 35, 38
  synthesis of, 60, 118–119

Viscose process, 625
Viscosity-average molecular weight, 21–22
  (*See also* Molecular weight)
Volume of activation, 264
Vulcanization of elastomers, 617–622
  (*See also* Crosslinking)

Weight-average molecular weight, 21
  (*See also* Molecular weight)
Wool, 3

Xanthation, 624–625

Ziegler catalysts (*see* Coordination catalysts; Stereoisomerism in polymers; Stereospecific polymerization)